Mt Dept —

COMPLIMENTARY   1050

HOW TO TEACH

MATHEMATICS

IN THE
SECONDARY SCHOOLS

This text is a publication in the
Saunders Science Teaching Series

Compiled under the editorship of
NATHAN S. WASHTON, *Professor of Education
and Coordinator of Sciences, Queens College of The
City University of New York*

HOW TO TEACH

MATHEMATICS

IN

SECONDARY SCHOOLS

HERBERT FREMONT

Queens College of The City University of New York

W. B. SAUNDERS COMPANY

Philadelphia · London · Toronto · 1969

W. B. Saunders Company: West Washington Square
Philadelphia, Pa. 19105

12 Dyott Street
London W.C. 1

1835 Yonge Street
Toronto 7, Ontario

How to Teach Mathematics in Secondary Schools

JUST FOR MY WIFE, MIMI

Let the relation of knowledge
to real life
be very visible to your pupils,
and let them understand
how by knowledge
the world could be transformed.

Bertrand Russell

PREFACE

An awareness of the nature and significance of mathematics, an insight into the intricate workings of the learning process, and an understanding of youngsters are all prerequisites for every teacher of mathematics. Here we have the foundation upon which any program of instruction in mathematics must be based. Here we have the basis upon which this textbook has been built.

The first section of the book explores possible answers to the question, What is mathematics? Conflicting viewpoints are encountered and considered, because this apparently simple question involves rather complex ideas. Of all the emerging ideas, one stands out: Mathematics helps us to learn more about the world in which we live. Somehow this notion must be reflected in school mathematics programs.

The second section is an investigation of some of the more interesting probes into the learning process. The different kinds of thinking engaged in by youngsters are discussed, and a pattern for instruction emerges that requires us to move from the concrete to the abstract if our students are to be able to uncover and devise mathematical concepts. In this way, thinking, rather than memorization, becomes the chief tool for learning.

The third section is the heart of the book. Here the everyday teaching strategies are developed, clearly reflecting the principles just mentioned. It is one thing to make claims that mathematics should be taught this way or that. It is quite another thing to translate general principles into specific teaching-learning activities. This is the content of Section Three, from basic arithmetic concepts through the calculus. A highlight of this section is the continuous use of important applications of mathematics in order to build the desire of the student to learn. In addition, the way in which we can create a need on the part of the student to learn runs through the development of each concept. Desire and need are two vital components of the learning process.

The text is concluded with a section on human worth. The special problems of the disadvantaged, the slow learner, and the gifted are each given careful consideration, as are particular techniques for the proper evaluation of learning. The need for and importance of individualization of instruction is presented; but what is more important, a detailed plan to enable every teacher to carry out such a program is presented.

I have always felt that mathematical ideas should be naturally accessible to the great majority of our students. The activities contained here are hopefully one step in that direction. In any case, this book should provide mathematics teachers with the beginning of a continuous program of growth and development.

ACKNOWLEDGMENTS

It takes much time and effort to become a mathematics teacher. It is a never-ending process. Each individual's progress is influenced by many, but every once in a while we study or work with someone who exerts a major influence upon the way we shall go. Dr. Gwladys Crosby of Queens College fulfilled such a role for me. In her unrelenting search for ways to provide for each and every student, she helped define the goals that have dominated and guided my development to this day. Her influence pervades the entire text.

Another important influence was Professor Morris Kline of New York University, who not only helped me to see the importance of applications in building student desire to learn, but who provided many of the applications contained herein. I offer him thanks.

To Dean Marvin Taylor of Queens College I also say thanks for reading and commenting upon a portion of the manuscript.

And finally, a special thanks is due Dr. Nathan Washton, my editor and colleague. Without his friendly prodding I might not have started this book in the first place.

EDITOR'S FOREWORD

Mathematics is responsible for much of the advancement in science and technology in recent years. Equally important are the learning of mathematics as a stimulating and scholarly discipline and the recognition of its applications in industry and contributions to human welfare. Mathematics must be taught through inquiry; teachers and students have to understand the modern content, theory, and processes of discovery in mathematics.

Professor Fremont, in writing this text, has fulfilled these needs in an outstanding manner. He begins with a sound, educational approach, develops the various mathematics courses from grades 7 through 12 in sequence, and returns to the psychological basis for learning and evaluating mathematics. Concrete illustrations are suggested for various grade levels. As the reader makes his mathematical discoveries, he is provided with effective reenforcement materials, problems, and applications. At no point does monotony occur since drill activity is both varied and interesting. Alternate approaches to and methods for solving problems are proposed. Emphasis throughout the text is placed on understanding and discovering mathematics rather than on rote methodology.

"When we think of mathematics, we have in mind a science devoted to the exploration of number, quantity, geometry, and in modern times also including investigation into yet more abstract concepts of order, and into analogous types of purely logical relations," writes Alfred North Whitehead. This is the point of view reflected throughout the text by Dr. Fremont. Each section of a unit is developed logically and systematically. Student involvement moves from the concrete to the abstract. After mathematical language is translated and applied, drill is provided for a variety of realistic situations. Excellent experiments in mathematics as well as in science are related to each other with emphasis on inquiry. Students are guided to formulate definitions as a result of these experiments.

Editor's Foreword

The author, an eminent authority on educating teachers in mathematics, has taught for many years in secondary schools and colleges. He warns the teacher about where to expect trouble spots, how to prevent them, and what to do about them. Hence, this realistic approach will prove invaluable to beginning and experienced teachers. Modern topics, such as sets and set vocabulary, including the fundamental laws, are discussed. A thorough explanation of how modern mathematics evolved in the curriculum is also given.

Dr. Fremont notes that vocabulary should be presented to the student as a result of "a variety of activities involving new concepts and words," leaving him with "a very different task—thinking." Analytical reasoning and logic are emphasized. Development of mathematical knowledge and skills is based on pupil involvement, pupil experimentation, and pupil discovery. Provisions are made for individualizing instruction as well as for special materials and procedures for the low-achieving and the gifted student. At the very beginning, Dr. Fremont indicates the importance of how attitudes toward mathematics will affect teaching and learning.

Effective principles of learning mathematics prevail throughout the book. Dr. Fremont suggests active pupil involvement with concrete objects and analysis with abstractions; freedom for the student to think and draw his own conclusions; adventurous thinking as a precedent to analytical, logical thought; pupil abstraction of mathematical principles; and presentation of visual images for understanding and using abstract mathematical concepts.

As in the other textbooks in the Saunders Science Teaching Series, Professor Fremont's *How to Teach Mathematics in Secondary Schools* is another major contribution to the improvement of the teaching of mathematics and science. Teachers of mathematics are given specific information on what and how to teach in the secondary schools in accordance with sound, up-to-date principles of learning.

NATHAN S. WASHTON

CONTENTS

Contents

SECTION FOUR   ON HUMAN WORTH

SECTION ONE

ON MATHEMATICS

1

WHAT IS MATHEMATICS?

Mathematics holds a rather unique place in our society today. On the one hand most people would accept the fact that mathematics is vital to the continued growth of our great nation, both for expanding internal advancement and for the maintenance of a leading role in the world community. On the other hand, these same people who have little doubt about the importance of mathematics usually feel completely inadequate in the subject. They seem to believe that it is a mysterious force to be understood by a chosen few.

Mathematics is assuredly not for the comprehension of every man. But do not misunderstand. No one thinks any less of himself because he cannot share in the secret world of mathematics. Quite the contrary. He sees himself as one of a great mass of people who are all the better for not having the ability to "do mathematics." Apparently he feels that it is the oddball who can successfully work with mathematics. He probably thinks of the mathematician as a person who hides from the world, as a person who does not relate well to other people, and so he looks upon the mathematician with suspicion. What manner of man can one be if he finds the complex notions of mathematics a source of pleasure? It is in this general attitude of people in society as a whole toward mathematics and mathematicians that we appear to have an interesting comment on the effect of school mathematics programs.

Of course, we may have somewhat exaggerated the situation here in order to emphasize the point, but is there not a great deal of truth in what has been stated? Can we deny the dislike and fear of mathematics that we so frequently encounter in students and parents alike? Can we deny that

3

there is a multitude of popular misconceptions about the nature of the subject itself?

If one were to assume the role of the eternal inquiring photographer and stop people at random at any street corner, how might these people respond to the question, What is mathematics? How many would describe mathematics as the science of numbers, or perhaps, the art of computation? How many would describe the subject as one of the few things in our dynamic world that always has and always will remain constant? $2 + 2 = 4$. This is a statement of fact that no one can change. It is an eternal truth. There are not too many other "facts" in our world today that can be described in this manner. This brings us directly to the subject at hand: the teaching of mathematics.

If we are to build successful programs of mathematics instruction in the schools and if we are to provide for the continuous improvement of the learning of mathematics, it would seem that such a consideration must begin with an understanding of the very nature, the very heart of mathematics itself. It would be virtually impossible to establish goals for teachers of mathematics in the secondary schools without first establishing insight into mathematics. And so, I pose again the question, What is mathematics? How would you answer? Would you be, perhaps, in agreement with the previous statements? Do you look upon mathematics in a somewhat different light? Do you feel that mathematics is the study of abstract systems? Maybe you look upon mathematics as logic; would you agree with the definition that mathematics is, actually, a way of thinking? Or would you refer to mathematics as a tool for the understanding of the world in which we live?

There appears to be an unlimited number of varying notions about the "stuff" of which mathematics is constructed. How can this be? Is mathematics to be likened to the attractive young woman who has been described as being "all things to all men"? Is it possible that mathematics at one and the same time can be different things to different people? Perhaps the time has come to look for help in the attempt to find an answer to the question about the nature of mathematics. Let us move on to the mathematician, the one who has devoted his life to working in the field of mathematics, and let us attempt to bring some order into this investigation of its innermost workings.

Bertrand Russell, the eminent English mathematician-philosopher has presented an interesting definition of mathematics. He states that mathematics ". . . may be defined as the subject in which we never know what we are talking about, nor whether what we are saying is true."[1] This is a rather striking view of the subject, but it does not aid us in our dilemma. For one thing, it would be possible to find many other areas of interest besides mathematics that might very well satisfy this same definition—politics, for example. It appears that we shall have to look further if we are to enlighten ourselves about the essence of mathematics.

Max Black, in turning his attention to this very same question about the nature of mathematics, provides a somewhat different response. To him ". . . mathematics is the study of all structures whose form can be expressed in symbols, it is the grammar of all symbolic systems . . ."[2] Now we at the least have something definite upon which to dwell: ". . . the grammar of all symbolic systems. . . ." Here we find that this entity called mathematics is viewed as a completely abstract construction. Black seems to feel that the symbols and the relationships that exist between them are the "stuff" of which mathematics is made. He makes no mention of any physical representation being of importance, and he indicates a kind of self-contained body of knowledge. Perhaps we are at last beginning to formulate some notion of mathematics.

Black's view is supported by Marshall Stone, who claims that

> a modern mathematician would prefer the positive characterization of his subject as the study of general abstract systems, each one of which is an edifice built of specified abstract elements and structured by the presence of arbitrary but unambiguously specified relations among them.[3]

This would bring us to the picture of mathematics as a completely abstract edifice, built by man and perhaps the supreme example of the capabilities of man's mind to create. This is a far cry from the "art of computation" notion that would probably be shared by many laymen. Indeed, we find that ideas of number, space, and form are mentioned nowhere in either of the two preceding definitions. Should not these concepts play some role in the definition of mathematics? Certainly, these are the ideas that come to mind when we think of work in the field. The definitions we have seen do not exclude these familiar concepts. Rather, number, space, and form would all be consequences of the structures as defined.

But what of the role mathematics has played and will continue to play in the development of mankind? How is it that we find no reference to the *use* of mathematics in the preceding descriptions? Is it that the applications of mathematics are not considered to be of consequence in discussing its intrinsic nature? Well, this would depend upon the point of view. Morris Kline, for one, describes mathematics in a completely different light. In a debate about modern mathematics and its value, he declared that

> mathematics is a creative or inventive process, deriving ideas and suggestions from real problems, idealizing and formulating the relevant concepts, posing questions, intuitively deriving a possible conclusion, and then, and only then, proving the hunch or intuitive argument deductively.[4]

This presents to us an entirely different notion about the nature of mathematics than was indicated by Black or Stone. Here the subject is seen as a process based upon intuition and construction, with the life source of this process coming from real problems. The abstractions referred to earlier would be extracted from the real problem and would have definite meaning in terms of the situation. These physical counterparts of the mathematical ideas are not recognized as being of any consequence in the earlier definitions, but Kline sees the physical world as the wellspring for the development of the abstract notions. This attitude towards mathematics is most strongly propounded by Courant and Robbins, who mince no words as they state emphatically that

> a serious threat to the very life of science is implied in the assertion that mathematics is nothing but a system of conclusions drawn from defini-tions and postulates that must be consistent but otherwise may be created by the free will of the mathematician. If this description were accurate, mathematics could not attract any intelligent person. It would be a game with definitions, rules, syllogisms, without motivation or goal.[5]

And there we have, clearly expressed, the two differing points of view in answer to the question, What is mathematics? On the one hand, we find that there is a substantial group of mathematicians who believe that mathematics is the study of abstract systems. The application of any of these systems to the problems of the physical world is of little importance to this group since these applications are not seen as mathematics. What is important is the relation-ships that exist between the elements of these systems, and between the variety of systems that make up the structure called mathematics. Expansion of knowl-edge in the field is seen as coming primarily from within as mathematicians pursue ideas developing from internal involvement with the symbolic struc-tures.

In another camp, however, we find another substantial number of mathematicians who see the close relationship between mathematics and physical reality as the very source for the continued growth and significance of mathematics. They would describe the position of those who champion the notion of "pure" mathematics as a meaningless one. They decry the fact that mathematics is a "game" and explain that such an attitude not only cuts off the subject from its life line for expanding knowledge but also reduces mathe-matics to an insignificant collection of ideas. Mathematics becomes important because it enables man to add to his understanding of his environment. It is important because of what it does. To ignore this side of mathematics is to rob it of its vigor and its significance.

These sharply divergent opinions about the essence of mathematics are extreme positions. There are many eminent practitioners in the field who sub-scribe to one or the other of these schools of thought to varying degrees. How-ever, the basic conflict in mathematical thought is clearly defined by these diverse points of view. There are those who feel that there is much of merit in each of the positions described. They do not necessarily see the answer to our original question as coming from one or the other group. As a matter of fact they would answer the question in a manner that would attempt to bind the two polarized viewpoints into one. For example, W. W. Sawyer does precisely this as he defines mathematics as follows:

> Mathematics is the classification and study of all possible patterns. Pattern is here used . . . to cover almost any kind of regularity that can be recognized by the mind. . . . Any theory of mathematics must account both for the power of mathematics, its numerous applications to natural science, and the beauty of mathematics, the fascination it has for the mind.[6]

In this same vein, a most interesting concept of mathematics is presented by J. W. N. Sullivan. In an eloquent fashion he not only connects the two ideas about the nature of mathematics but also takes us a step further by providing a most insightful observation on the role of the mathematician. He points out that

> the significance of mathematics resides precisely in the fact that it is an art; by informing us of our own minds it informs us of much that depends on our minds. It does not enable us to explore some remote region of the externally existent; it helps to show us how far what exists depends upon the way in which we exist. We are the law-givers of the universe; it is even possible that we can experience nothing but what we have created, and that the greatest of our mathematical creations is the material universe itself.[7]

This is a rather startling notion: ". . . the greatest of our mathematical creations is the material universe itself." If we accept the reasoning of Sullivan, it quickly becomes apparent that any debate about whether or not mathematics, by its nature, needs to be closely related to the physical world is totally irrelevant. Sullivan states rather pointedly that this physical universe in which we find ourselves is the greatest creation of mathematics and in effect is indistinguishable from mathematics, or mathematics from it! The implications for such a point of view are legion, bringing us to the next area of conflict regarding the essence of mathematics.

We have seen how men of recognized status in the field of mathematics have differing concepts of its true nature. Perhaps at the base of some of these differences lie incongruous notions about man and his relationship to the "real" world. Sullivan has already clearly indicated such a dilemma. Is there an eternal body of truth that makes up the entire structure of mathematics and is merely awaiting a mathematician to discover it? Or is the edifice we have come to know as mathematics a product of the creative imagination of man? In other words, to borrow from a predicament of the sciences, is mathematics an invention or a discovery? This is another vital question, worthy of consideration by each teacher of secondary school mathematics.

Once again we will find that there are opposing points of view among those who have made mathematics their life's work. On one side we shall find those who explain that all mathematics consists of eternal truths. It is the genius of the mathematician that brings forth additional information in the form of new discoveries, not inventions. As evidence of this process, an adherent of this viewpoint would cite the frequent discovery of the same mathematical ideas by two or more different mathematicians in different parts of the world almost simultaneously. The establishment of the non-Euclidean geometries by Bolyai, Gauss, and Lobachevski would be one example of this. The Newton-Leibnitz conflict over the discovery of the calculus would be another. If mathematics is the invention of the mind of man, how is it that we frequently find many men arriving at the same point in adding to our knowledge of mathematics? It would appear that Sullivan's argument that we can experience only that which we have created is sorely tested and significantly questioned, and the conclusion is drawn that the way in which we arrive at a mathematical truth affects only the extent to which it can be observed, and not the everlasting mathematical truth itself.

Sullivan is not without his supporters, however. Yes, they would admit, mathematics does have a most unusual history with respect to the recurrence of joint arrival at the same point by different mathematicians, but this does not necessarily lead to the conclusion that discovery properly describes the activity of the mathematician and not invention. Each man is a product of his time, his culture, and his civilization. Since the outcome of a mathematician's work is generally an extension of what is already developed in his time, he is actually not in full control of what he may accomplish. Therefore, when the times are right for the development of a given idea because of the progress made in the field up to that time, it is quite possible that the idea will be forthcoming from one or more members of the particular field. The act itself is, however, an act of invention and the product of the mind of the man, building upon what has already been invented prior to that moment.

Thus, we still appear to find ourselves in a dilemma that seems to increase in complexity rather than decrease as we probe deeper and deeper into the matter. But we are learning about the way in which men who have made important contributions to mathematics look upon the subject; and this is perhaps the beginning of wisdom, despite the fact that not knowing about a problem at all does provide a kind of euphoria that vanishes with enlightenment. There is still one additional place to turn in an attempt to bring order to these diverse opinions: the philosophers. How do they regard the very nature of mathematics? How might they answer the question, What is mathematics?

As might be imagined, the philosophers will reflect some of the same conflicts of opinions that we have encountered earlier. Here too, we find that there are divergent points of view. It appears that there are three main schools of philosophical thought about the nature of mathematics. They are usually designated as the logistic, formalistic, and intuitionist schools. What does each of these schools of thought involve, and who are the mathematicians generally associated with each of the separate philosophies?

Let us first turn our attention to the logistic point of view. As you might expect from the name, the followers of this school contend that all mathematical concepts can be derived by purely logical constructions. They believe that it is possible to erect the entire edifice that we know to be mathematics by the use of symbolic logic. Thus, mathematics is seen as being based upon logic; and indeed, for all intents and purposes, the two become virtually indistinguishable. The culmination of this concept of thought is found in the monumental work of Russell and Whitehead called *Principia Mathematica*.[8] This three volume work of great complexity was an attempt to show the derivation of all of mathematics, beginning with the primitive logical symbolism. In addition to Russell and Whitehead, the names of Gottlob Frege and Giuseppe Peano are generally connected with this philosophical school.

David Hilbert is recognized as one of the leading exponents of the formalistic point of view. The position taken by the formalists is that mathematics is the formal structure of the symbolism and completely independent of any meaning that may be assigned to the symbols. Mathematics may be thought of as a game played with meaningless marks. The importance of the game is to be found in the relationships these marks have to each other. It is important to understand that to the formalist there can be no truth or meaning in the symbolic systems that compose the structure called mathematics. There can only be a logically consistent system of symbols. The consistency of the symbolic systems has led to a major problem for the formalists. How shall this consistency be established? If the basic notions of the structure have no representations in the physical world, how can the formalist determine their consistency with one another? This problem may well prove to be an impassable obstacle.

The intuitionists constitute the third main philosophical school of thought. Led by L. E. J. Brouwer, this school places emphasis upon the fact that every mathematical statement must have a clear intuitive meaning. The logical rigor of the intuitionist is greater than that of either of his philosophical counterparts: the formalist or the logistic adherent. The principle of logic that every statement is either true or false with no middle possibility existing is not acceptable to the intuitionist. If propositions can be neither proved nor disproved, there can be no statement made about the truth or falsity of the given proposition. The intuitionist goes so far as to say that meaningful statements that are neither true nor false may very well be possible. Thus the proofs generally known in plane geometry classes as "indirect" proofs are not readily accepted. The intuitionist differs sharply with the logistic school in that logic is seen as a branch of mathematics rather than the reverse. In addition, it is believed that for mathematical concepts to exist they must be constructed, which necessitates a proof in a finite number of steps. Language must convey thoughts, and symbolism devoid of any meaning cannot suffice. As a matter of fact, the intuitionist sees mathematics as an ever growing process that may very well never be completely symbolized.

Thus, the apparently innocent question, What is mathematics? turns out to be not so simple after all. As a matter of fact, it is becoming a question of greater complexity as we continue to seek our answer. I do not doubt that at this point in the development you may feel very much like the poor fellow who is stranded in the middle of the Sahara Desert and is beginning to see the most exciting mirage, only to find it disappear as he approaches more closely to the spot where it seems to lie. We have sought an answer to our puzzle from mathematicians of great renown. We find that they are far from agreement. We moved on to consider the discovery-invention implications for our problem with a resulting increase in our confusion as more and more ideas are held up before us. Lastly, we turned to the mathematical philosophers to learn if their ideas could bring some clarity to the situation. Once again we find no answers—only differing points of view. Where do all these differing viewpoints really lead us? Are we not more confused now than we were at the outset? Has this exploration into the essence of mathematics led us into a maze from which we can envision no release?

There are numerous ideas of vital significance for teachers of secondary school mathematics that seem to be emerging. First, and foremost, is the understanding that there is a good deal of disagreement about the nature of mathematics. While this may not seem like an act of enlightenment, in many ways it is. How many times have people been heard to remark about mathematics that here we have one entity in our dynamic world that remains unchangeable? This is the $2 + 2 = 4$ line of reasoning, mentioned at the outset. Come what may, say the uninitiated, no one can change the fact that mathematics is completely stable. It would appear, in the light of what we have seen, that nothing could be further from the truth; for when we consider carefully the make-up of mathematics, we find that it is perhaps one of the finest products of the imagination of man. As such, its nature is constantly under scrutiny. It is continually being added to, and no one can foretell where it will eventually lead us. The disparate points of view we have encountered have dramatically attacked the myth of its being "cut and dried."

In this same vein, if teachers of mathematics are to open the eyes of their students to the wonder and beauty of mathematics, is it not imperative that these same teachers be themselves aware of the varying considerations regarding the "stuff" of which mathematics is made? Can we conceive of teachers, who are themselves ignorant of the different opinions, being able to help students come to the point of realization as to the heart of mathematics? At the least, it would seem that the probability of successfully transmitting insights into the workings of the subject are much higher with the teacher who is informed.

We must also consider the effects of these various philosophies of mathematics upon the content and methods that find their way into our classrooms. In the 1950's, a unique curriculum improvement group was formed called the School Mathematics Study Group, better known today by the initials SMSG. The uniqueness of this group was in its organization; for the first time mathematicians and school teachers sat down together to see what could be done to improve school curricula in mathematics. Now if mathematicians are going to play an important role in the development of present and future curricula, their concepts of the nature of mathematics will be directly reflected in the kinds of programs they develop. Thus, what appears on the surface to be a series of esoteric discussions on the nature of mathematics is in reality a careful analysis of the assumptions underlying the proposals for the improvement of mathematics learning in your very classroom. If you are to be able to deal intelligently with these proposals as they are presented, and if you are to be able to make some reasonable evaluation of the numerous suggestions that are being made and will continue to be made regarding the improvement of mathematics instruction, you have no choice but to become thoroughly acquainted with the basic assumptions upon which such suggestions have been formulated. This evaluative function is one that mathematics teachers are being called upon more and more to undertake. As the amount of knowledge in a given field increases, the number of administrators who can remain well informed in each area decreases rapidly. This is a classic example of the inverse law of variation. Thus administrators are relying more and more upon the experts in their schools in a chosen field for guidance in making the decision that will be of greatest advantage to the children. Mathematics teachers particularly have played and are playing a most active role in helping to revise school curricula.

The developments previously described in considering the innermost structure of mathematics are reflecting movements that are taking place throughout our society today. This may come as somewhat of a surprise to you, but think about it for a moment. How much of the art work that we see on exhibit these days is simply a kaleidoscope of color and form? How many heated arguments have you perhaps mediated between a devotee of abstract art and the fellow who prefers to see something recognizable when he looks at a painting? If we turn to the field of music, how much of what we hear today appears to be a collection of cacophonous sounds resulting from a combination of noises derived from the more familiar musical instruments, as well as from whistles, bells, and even gun shots (as opposed to those musical constructions that offer the listener the comfort of a lovely melodic theme developing within the framework of an overall recognizable structure)? Mathematics, being a vital, living, growing, and contributing force in our society is perhaps itself in a similar position. On the one hand we find those who feel that mathematics is an art form and should be appreciated as such. This beautiful creation of the mind of man need not relate to anything familiar. It should be valued

11

for its own intrinsic worth, rather than for what it can help man to accomplish. On the other hand we find those who feel that while it is true that mathematics is the finest construction of the mind of man, this construction only takes on significance when it becomes involved in the life of man and his interaction with his environment. Thus, mathematics aids man in his understanding of the world in which he lives and is in turn modified by this world and man's needs as he continues to develop. The question of which point of view is really the correct one is totally irrelevant. Those who are responsible for helping students to learn about mathematics must be aware of the differing opinions. It is in this way that each teacher begins to formulate his own ideas about the nature of things.

Another way in which these developments in mathematics reflect trends in society is a changing notion about the meaning of progress in a given discipline. At one time, man felt that as long as he continued to add to his knowledge in a field he was making progress. Man had perhaps subconsciously accepted the fact that there was no end to the possible development of additional information in a given area. Today we find that the experts in a variety of fields have turned their attention to a reexamination of the foundations upon which that particular subject is based. Thus, we are beginning to look again at assumptions—some stated, some made implicitly by the manner in which we proceeded—and as a result we are beginning to think differently about many things that have been common knowledge for some time. This examination of basic assumptions is certainly the kind of activity that has been taking place in physics and many other physical and social sciences. Once again, mathematics is demonstrating similar undertakings by the society at large.

The knowledge that the dilemmas of mathematics are perhaps not unique to this discipline may provide little solace for the teacher who finds the varying opinions rather confusing. It is much like the fellow whose toothache does not hurt him any the less because he sees that there are fellow sufferers in the dentist's office. Be that as it may, the knowledge itself is important. A valid question to pose at this stage would be, How is it that these men who have freely chosen to devote the better parts of their lives to working in the field of mathematics appear to look upon mathematics from disparate vantage points? Is it possible that they are not looking upon the same scene? Is there some error? Are they actually describing the common field in which each has been making the major effort of his life? How is it possible for such a situation to develop? What are the historical forces that have resulted in this dilemma? This will be the focal point of the next chapter.

FOOTNOTES

1. Bertrand Russell. *Mysticism and Logic*. W. W. Norton & Co., 1929.
2. Max Black. *The Nature of Mathematics*. Littlefield, Adams & Co. (paperback), 1959.

3. Marshall Stone. "The Revolution in Mathematics." *The American Mathematical Monthly.* Vol. 68 (October, 1961), pp. 715–734.
4. Morris Kline. "The Ancients Versus the Moderns, A New Battle of the Books." *The Mathematics Teacher.* Vol. 51 (October, 1958), pp. 418–427.
5. Richard Courant and Herbert Robbins. *What Is Mathematics?* Oxford University Press, 1941.
6. W. W. Sawyer. *Prelude to Mathematics.* Penguin Books, Inc. (paperback), 1955.
7. J. W. N. Sullivan. "Mathematics As An Art." *In* James R. Newman (Editor): *The World of Mathematics,* Part XVII, Vol. 3. Simon and Schuster, Inc., 1956.
8. Bertrand Russell and Alfred North Whitehead. *Principia Mathematica.* Cambridge University Press, 1910–1913, 3 vols.

FOR INVESTIGATION AND DISCUSSION

1. Ask the students in your classes to write a brief paragraph about their answers to the question, What is mathematics? Discuss what their responses indicate about their feelings toward mathematics. Compare this with their grades in the course.

2. Identify different points of view held by prominent mathematicians regarding the nature of mathematics. Give your reactions as to the reasonableness of these arguments in terms of how you envision mathematics.

3. Do you think mathematics is an active process of invention or discovery? Explain the reasons for your response.

4. What are the basic differences between the three philosophical schools of mathematical thought? What do you see as basic agreements, if any?

5. Examine the varying ideas about the nature of mathematics on the part of mathematicians and the differences in the philosophical viewpoints. Describe consistent ideas that you feel link the philosophical schools with the views of several mathematicians.

6. How does your position in the invention-discovery predicament influence the way in which you view the nature of mathematics?

7. Can you explain your own answer at present to the question, What is mathematics?

FOR FURTHER READING

Books

Stephen F. Barker. *Philosophy of Mathematics.* Foundations of Philosophy Series. Prentice-Hall, Inc. (paperback), 1964.
Max Black. *The Nature of Mathematics.* Littlefield, Adams, & Co. (paperback), 1959.
Ettore Carruccio. *Mathematics and Logic in History and in Contemporary Thought.* Aldine Publishing Co., 1964.
Richard Courant and Herbert Robbins. *What Is Mathematics?* Oxford University Press, 1941.
Nathan A. Court. *Mathematics in Fun and in Earnest.* Mentor Book (paperback), New American Library, 1961.
G. H. Hardy. *A Mathematician's Apology.* Cambridge University Press, 1940.
Philip E. B. Jourdain. "The Nature of Mathematics." *In* James R. Newman (Editor): *The World of Mathematics,* Part I, Vol. 1. Simon and Schuster, Inc., 1956.
Morris Kline. *Mathematics in Western Culture.* Oxford University Press, 1953.
Stephan Körner. *The Philosophy of Mathematics.* Harper Torchbooks (paperback), Harper & Bros., 1960.

13

What is Mathematics?

Robert W. Marks (Editor). *The Growth of Mathematics*. Bantam Books (paperback), 1964.

Bertrand Russell. *My Philosophical Development*. Simon and Schuster, Inc., 1959.

W. W. Sawyer. *Prelude to Mathematics*. Penguin Books, Inc. (paperback), 1955.

J. W. N. Sullivan. "Mathematics As An Art." *In* James R. Newman (Editor): *The World of Mathematics,* Part XVII, Vol. 3. Simon and Schuster, Inc., 1956.

Leslie A. White. "The Locus of Mathematical Reality: An Anthropological Footnote." *In* James R. Newman (Editor): *The World of Mathematics,* Part XXV, Vol. 4. Simon and Schuster, Inc., 1956.

Alfred N. Whitehead. *An Introduction to Mathematics*. Oxford University Press, 1958.

Periodicals

Elsie J. Alberty. "Mathematics in General Education." *The Mathematics Teacher*. Vol. 59 (May, 1966), pp.426–431.

Richard Courant. "Mathematics in the Modern World." *Scientific American*. Vol. 211 (September, 1964), pp. 40–49.

Preston C. Hammer. "The Role and Nature of Mathematics." *The Mathematics Teacher*. Vol. 57 (December, 1964), pp. 514–521.

Morris Kline. "The Ancients Versus the Moderns, A New Battle of the Books." *The Mathematics Teacher*. Vol. 51 (October, 1958), pp. 418–427.

Kenneth O. May. "Mathematics and Art." *The Mathematics Teacher*. Vol. 60 (October, 1967), pp. 568–572.

Mina Rees. "The Nature of Mathematics." *The Mathematics Teacher*. Vol. 55 (October, 1962), pp. 434–440.

William L. Scaaf. "How Modern is Modern Mathematics?" *The Mathematics Teacher*. Vol. 57 (February, 1964), pp. 89–97.

Marshall Stone. "The Revolution in Mathematics." *The American Mathematical Monthly*. Vol. 68 (October, 1961), pp. 715–734.

2

HISTORICAL PERSPECTIVES

We have seen that defining mathematics is no simple task. There are such extremely different and diverse opinions about the nature of mathematics that many mathematicians have suggested that mathematics be defined as that which mathematicians do. Now this may seem, on the face of it, to be an excellent pathway out of our dilemma; but once again the appearance is misleading. Such a definition adds little that will clarify the indicated differences. If we were to follow this advice, we would find that the definition we seek varied from person to person and from time to time for any given person. It would depend upon the particular mathematician under observation at the moment. Consider looking over the shoulder of a mathematician at work on a foundations problem and compare this activity with the work of the mathematician in a computer installation at a missile site, as well as with the work of the mathematician at an insurance company. The diversity is immense. It appears that we cannot minimize the difficulty inherent in attempts to define the subject. One recent heroic dictionary of mathematical terms does not even attempt a definition and fails to list "mathematics" itself among its defined terms.[1]

While we cannot minimize the difficulty, we can learn about its origin and development and perhaps begin to gain insights into the nature of mathematics by an examination of the causes for the conflicting views. To accomplish this, it is necessary for us to retrace the developments that have taken place in mathematics and to explore the early days of our subject. This attempt to shed light upon a present-day dilemma about the nature of mathematics will not become a descriptive history in any sense of the word; rather it will be a careful

and highly selective examination that focuses upon only those events of significance for our purposes. One consequence of this approach will be the omission
of particular developments and mathematicians who have played leading roles
in the making of mathematics. I trust that the references at the close of this
chapter will serve as a valuable source of additional information for the reader
who desires to close the gaps left here.

The first important historical event in the development of mathematics
for our purposes is the work of Pythagoras, the Greek philosopher-mystic-
mathematician who lived from about 570 B.C. until about 500 B.C. The exact
dates, along with much of the work of the Pythagoreans is decidedly uncertain.
This is not to say that there was little of importance done previously. Prior to
Pythagoras, we find contributions to mathematics being made by the Baby-
lonians and the Egyptians, among others; but it is in the golden days of the
Greeks that mathematics went through an era of remarkable productivity.
It was an era that caused Jane Muir to write the following in a recent collection
of biographies of mathematicians:

> Greece: Its Golden Age lasted but three centuries. Yet there have
> never been three centuries like them in the whole history of mankind.[2]

The three centuries referred to lasted from 600 B.C. to 300 B.C. The resulting influence upon mathematics was to last for more than 2000 years and is
felt today.

While there is a good deal about Pythagoras that is questionable in the
minds of historians, there is much that seems to be consistently ascribed to
him. He was born at Samos, but early in his life he began to travel, spending a
considerable amount of time in Egypt; there he learned all he could from the
Egyptian priests, who seemed to possess a good deal of practical knowledge of
mathematics, as evidenced by the construction of the pyramids. From Egypt,
Pythagoras moved on to Asia Minor and eventually returned to Samos where,
with little success, he opened his own school. The failure of his school and the
tyranny of Polycrates, the ruler of Samos, or perhaps a combination of both,
made him move once again. He came to southern Italy and opened another
school at Croton. It was here that the Pythagoreans became a society of importance as Pythagoras proceeded to teach his own brand of philosophical,
almost mystical, ideologies. When the Pythagoreans contemplated the nature
of things, they came upon some rather startling discoveries. In the field of
music, it is believed that Pythagoras himself discovered the fact that musical
harmonies depend upon numerical ratios. A 2:1 ratio in string length at the
same tension represents an octave; the musical fifth, a 3:2 ratio; and the fourth,
a ratio of 4:3. When the Pythagoreans observed the heavens they postulated
that the same harmonic proportions of music applied to the distance between
the heavenly spheres and even thought that the planets gave off harmonious
sounds, hence the present-day phrase "the music of the spheres"! Everywhere
the Pythagoreans explored, number ruled their findings. Number was the all

16

pervasive common quality that repeatedly appeared. Is it any wonder then that the Pythagoreans became convinced that *number ruled the universe?*

One by-product of the travels of Pythagoras through Egypt was the belief that there could be only one God. It was this God who was thought of as the Supreme Architect of the universe. Thus, if number ruled the universe it must also be true that God was an arithmetician! Because of the mystical nature of the society, the members readily accepted the logical conclusions to be drawn from this belief, namely that everything in the universe is expressible numerically, including the movement of the heavenly bodies, the structure of thought, and the principles of human conduct, as well as the composition of matter. The philosopher's one task was to interpret the work of the Grand Creator, and the key to the code for the comprehension of the universe was mathematics. How beautifully logical was this simple and concise presentation of the true status of things. And so began the process of determining the significance of each number and the association of each number with some object in the universe. Lest this practice be misunderstood as mere numerology, a brief word of the nature of the society is in order.

The Pythagoreans were a secret brotherhood which was popular from the time of its inception at Croton. It is said that women were accepted into the society and attended regularly despite the fact that they were forbidden by law to do so. The members of the brotherhood shared the same political and philosophical beliefs and subscribed to a rather strict discipline developed by Pythagoras that required them to eat only simple foods and to practice self-denial, temperance, purity, and obedience. The society itself was evidently divided into two groups, the Pythagoreans and the probationers. It was only the Pythagoreans who had full access to all the secrets of the society and they formed a minority when compared with the number of probationers.

Thus we find a group of people bound together in an almost mystical society, devoting their energies to the contemplation of the nature of all things. As they carried out these observations and developed their thoughts, one concept was ever recurring: *number.* And so the famous quadrivium of knowledge was established:[3]

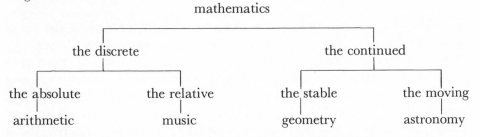

What may appear to us initially to be a belief in the occult takes on a different dimension in the light of the experiences of the Pythagoreans. As a matter of fact, were the Pythagoreans completely wrong with their concentration upon number as the code to the universe? An examination of today's

17

society provides an instant realization of the tremendous effect of number and the important role it is playing. Perhaps these Pythagoreans were merely foreseeing the future! Whatever the case, their impact upon the course of mankind cannot be overestimated. Let us examine more closely some of the more important outcomes of this society.

There are those who claim that the words "mathematics" and "philosophy" actually were coined by Pythagoras. About the word "philosopher" in particular, Dacier writes that Pythagoras was dismayed with those who called themselves "wise men" or "sages" because he believed that only God could be referred to as "wise." When asked what it was he did, Pythagoras is said to have replied that he was a "philosopher," a lover of wisdom.[4]

As they studied number and the geometric figures that filled space as they saw it, the Pythagoreans opened up the mind of man to many interesting and significant ideas. It is said that they were responsible for the first use of careful deductive demonstrations to establish the acceptance of a given proposition. The Pythagorean theorem, of course, remains the greatest monument that they left to mathematics. While it is true that the Egyptians and Orientals were undoubtedly aware of the relationships involved in this theorem, as evidenced by its apparent frequent use in these societies, it remained for the Pythagoreans to establish its certainty beyond doubt through the formulation of a deductive proof. And so it is to this day that the relationship between the sides of a right triangle, i.e., the square on the hypotenuse is equal to the sums of the squares on the other two sides, bears the name of Pythagoras. It is impossible to determine whether Pythagoras himself actually developed the proof, since all the findings of the society were ascribed to its leader, but it is doubted by only a few that this theorem was first deductively established by them.[5] The importance of this single theorem is of such magnitude that it is described by E. T. Bell as follows:

> The Pythagorean theorem is one of the enduring landmarks of all mathematical history, not only for its simplicity, generality, and intrinsic beauty, but also for what it has inspired in current mathematics, from geometry to analysis.[6]

What may be still more important was the establishment of the use of deductive logic in order to determine the acceptability of the proposition. This is no small matter for the Pythagoreans to have undertaken. What they were actually stating was that the property peculiar to the right triangle was true for all right triangles, for all time. This was quite an assumption, at that time in man's historical development. How could the Pythagoreans be sure? Could they possibly test all triangles in order to establish certainty? And if they were to examine hundreds of triangles and find verification, does this imply that somewhere there is no such triangle in existence that will not obey the law of Pythagoras? The acceptance of the deductive demonstration for establishing the truth of the proposition was an achievement of singular significance. While the theorem itself proved to be a fountainhead for the development of mathematical ideas, the use of deductive proof to establish mathematical fact altered the entire course of mankind. It was the beginning of a realization of what man could possibly accomplish on this planet when he permitted reason to replace superstition. It has been described as the beginning of the emergence of mankind from the darkness of ignorance. The establishment of this theorem was eventually to become the undoing of that great society, which in itself is no small paradox. But more of this later. For the present let us explore additional discoveries of the society.

When the Pythagoreans worked with numbers they probably used pebbles to represent them. As they arranged these pebbles on the sand, they not only became aware of various relationships between them but also became conscious of the different shapes the numbers possessed. One consequence of these observations was the identification of numbers as either odd or even. The even numbers were described as those numbers which could be divided into two equal parts, while the odd numbers could never be so divided and always yielded two unequal parts. In addition to odd and even numbers, the Pythagoreans noticed triangular numbers, or those numbers that could be arranged in the shape of a triangle when one laid out the pebbles representing the numbers (Fig. 2-1). It was probably the work with triangular numbers that resulted in the discovery that the sum of any number of consecutive natural numbers beginning with one is a triangular number itself. For example, $1 + 2 = 3$; $1 + 2 + 3 = 6$; or in general form, $1 + 2 + 3 + \cdots n = \frac{1}{2}n(n + 1)$ is a triangular number with side n.

These pebble arrangements also led to the formation of square numbers and gnomons (Fig. 2-2). A square number was considered to be one that could be represented by arranging the pebbles in a square, and the gnomons were the series of consecutive odd numbers necessary to build from one square number to the next. In order to construct the next square number after a given one, it would be necessary to add pebbles along two sides of the given square array. These L-shaped numbers of pebbles that had to be added were called *gnomons*. If you examine Figure 2-2 you will see that the gnomons illustrated are 3 $(2 \times 1 + 1)$, 5 $(2 \times 2 + 1)$, 7 $(2 \times 3 + 1)$, and 9 $(2 \times 4 + 1)$. Thus, the general expression for the gnomon is of the form $2n + 1$, the familiar representation of the odd number.

In addition to this work it appears that the Pythagoreans were also aware

Figure 2-1

19

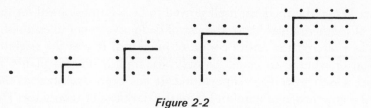

Figure 2-2

of the difference between prime and composite numbers. Try as you might, it is impossible to arrange the pebbles representing a prime number in a rectangular array. On the other hand, this arrangement can always be constructed for the composites.

A good deal of work, then, was carried out in what was to later become the study we know as number theory. But what of the mystical nature of the Pythagoreans? Has that aspect of the society weakened before the progress made with numbers? Not quite. The numbers meant a good deal more to the Pythagoreans than mere collections of pebbles. As was indicated earlier, numbers were seen to be the key to the code of the universe, and so various objects were assigned to them. It is commonly accepted that the Pythagoreans felt that 10 was the perfect number. Not only was it triangular, but it contained within its parts all that can represent the variety of objects in the universe. If 1 represented the point, 2 the line, 3 the triangle, and 4 the solids such as the pyramid and if $10 = 1 + 2 + 3 + 4$, is not 10 the true essence of all that exists? In another way of looking at numbers, 2 stood for man and 3 represented woman. What could be more obvious then for 5 (i.e., $2 + 3$) to represent marriage? And it is in precisely this way that the Pythagoreans went about the business of assigning objects to numbers and using operations upon them to add to their knowledge of the objects. Some of these have been handed down to us and are part of our present vocabulary. The symbol for justice to the Pythagoreans was 4 since this represented a square. To this day we refer to one who is just and fair as being "four-square."

The curious mixture of arithmetic and geometry on the part of the members of the society led them to compare line lengths and to describe these comparisons as ratios between the natural numbers. Since number ruled the universe, the Pythagoreans seemed to be firmly convinced at one point that any line length could be described by the natural numbers or some ratio of natural numbers. In effect, they were operating under the illusion that the rational numbers were sufficient to describe the length of any line segment, which brings us directly back to the famous theorem of Pythagoras and how this glorious achievement was in reality the undoing of the society.

The exact person who first encountered the trouble spot in the Pythagorean assumptions is unknown, but it is thought by some mathematical historians that Hippasos stumbled upon the problem as he studied the famous sign of the Pythagoreans, the pentagram (Fig. 2-3). The pentagram is a five-

Figure 2-3

pointed star that is a regular pentagon whose sides have been extended to their respective points of intersection. It is proposed that as Hippasos studied the pentagram he was attempting to describe the relationship between the line segments formed by the intersection of the lines that make up the Pythagorean star. It was this investigation that led him to conclude that the segments were not commensurable and to eventually construct a logical proof of this fact. Whether or not Hippasos originated this exploration we shall never know, but it does seem to be clear that one of the Pythagoreans had completed a deductive proof for the impossibility of expressing the diagonal of a square as a ratio between two natural numbers. Let us assume that it was the simple isosceles right triangle, with equal sides of unit length that first caught the Pythagoreans' interest. What measure shall we assign to the hypotenuse, side *AB*? (See Fig. 2-4.) If it does not seem logical that such a simple problem would not have been confronted early in the development of the Pythagorean Society, keep in mind the conviction of this group that everything was reducible to number. This overwhelming belief, coupled with the fact that the Pythagoreans did have interesting techniques for estimating the value of *AB*, left them with the feeling that sooner or later the true units would be found that would enable them to describe this particular length exactly.

Our skeptic, however, began to suspect otherwise and proceeded to use the method of reductio ad absurdum, the method of indirect proof, to demon-

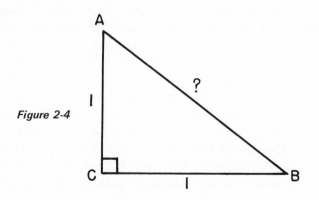

Figure 2-4

strate logically, that no such number does exist. The proof is the familiar one encountered in elementary mathematics:

Let us assume that there is a number that exactly describes the length of AB; and let us designate this number to be $\frac{a}{b}$, where both a and b are natural numbers with no common factors—that is, the fraction is in lowest terms.

Accordingly,

$$\frac{a}{b} = \sqrt{2} \qquad \text{or} \qquad a^2 = 2b^2$$

Thus it can be concluded that a^2 is an even number since it has 2 as a factor.

If a^2 is even, then a must also be an even number, so let us express a as such and write

$$a = 2k$$

Substituting this value back into the earlier equation we get

$$(2k)^2 = 2b^2 \qquad \text{or} \qquad 4k^2 = 2b^2$$

and dividing by 2 we get

$$2k^2 = b^2$$

This is a most interesting result, for this indicates that b^2 is also even and hence b is an even number too.

But wait. This cannot be true. We began with an assumption that a and b had no common factors. Our logic has led us to the conclusion that both a and b are even numbers, which indicates that they both have 2 as a common factor. This contradiction leaves us with only one conclusion: Our original assumption that line AB was expressible as a ratio between two natural numbers is a false assumption.

Consequently:

There is no number or ratio of numbers that describes this length!

What a staggering blow this must have been to the Pythagoreans. It is frequently stated that as a reward for making this discovery, the responsible Pythagorean was invited to go swimming after being handicapped somewhat by having his arms and legs bound! Whether or not this is true is immaterial. What is of importance is the question, If the universe is number and number is the universe, how could there possibly be a line segment for which there is no number? (Again, recall that "number" refers to natural number by the Pythagorean.) As a matter of fact, not only is there one such number which defies definition, the one we know as $\sqrt{2}$, but there are an infinite quantity of them: $\sqrt{3}$, $\sqrt{5}$, and $\sqrt{7}$, to list but a few. Indeed, the set of numbers known to us as the irrationals can be thought of as being more plentiful than the rationals!

The impact of this discovery upon the Pythagoreans was to shake the very foundation upon which the society had built its structure. It appears that God is not an arithmetician after all. The fact that this length which could not be described numerically could be constructed geometrically turned the attention of the Greeks to the notion that in the final analysis God must be, after all, a *geometer!* So at the same point that the Greeks turned their attention to geometry, we turn to our next milepost in the development of mathematics, emerging with the name of Euclid and a monumental work in the history of mankind and the development of mathematics called the *Elements*.

While there is some disagreement about Pythagoras and the actual role he played in the progress of mathematics, there is little controversy surrounding Euclid. It seems that very little is actually known about him. He lived during the third century B.C. and probably studied mathematics at Plato's Academy in Athens. Later he moved on to Alexandria and either at the university there or in a school of his own became one of the most famous mathematics teachers of all time. Two popular anecdotes frequently told about Euclid give us some idea of his personality.

The first concerns the response he made to King Ptolemy when he was asked if there wasn't some easier way to learn geometry. Euclid supposedly replied, "There is no royal road to geometry!"

The second anecdote claims that when a student challenged Euclid to tell him what was to be gained by learning geometry, Euclid bade his slave to give the student a coin since he must gain from what he learns.

We do not know if these anecdotes are any more accurate than the familiar tales we hear about the truthfulness of George Washington, but certainly every teacher of mathematics will agree that there is a lack of a "royal road" to geometry. And what teacher has not come face-to-face with the student who questions the worth of learning mathematics? Were we to give a coin in answer to each of these questions we would soon be unable to find the carfare to get to the school. In any case, it does seem as if the problems of teaching have not changed very much over the past 2000 years.

When the Pythagoreans were undone by the uncovering of the incommensurable line length, development in geometry was accelerated. The notion that God was a geometer gained in acceptance and the true description of the real world was seen to lie in geometric terms. In the 200 years that intervened between the time of Pythagoras and that of Euclid, the three famous problems of antiquity caught the fancy of Greek mathematicians: the construction of the trisection of the angle (by using only a straight-edge and compass), the doubling of the cube (constructing a cube twice the size of a given cube), and the squaring of the circle (constructing a square whose area is equal to that of a given circle). While the problems were not solved by the Greeks, a good deal of mathematics resulted from the attempts.

This was the mathematics Euclid learned at the Academy, and this much is known about him: He was a prolific writer who turned out books about the conic sections, astronomy, optics, music, and perhaps even mechanics. But his greatest achievement was his book on geometry called the *Elements*. It was here that Euclid started from scratch, made a few definitions, added 10 basic assumptions, and then proceeded to rigorously follow the laws of logic to establish all proofs deductively, with the resulting systematic development of the mathematics known in his time. Whether or not Euclid was undertaking a true description of the universe is not clear. This was, however, a consequence of his work—so much so that some 2000 years after Euclid lived, the philosopher Immanuel Kant was to refer to the axioms of the *Elements* as the only immutable truths known to man!

The *Elements* is a remarkable work. Its durability and widespread appeal are described as second only to the Bible. It has set a model for the school geometry textbook that has survived to this day, and for over 2000 years it was believed to be a perfect description of the space in which we live. To this day it is the basis for all construction work. Why has this work achieved virtual immortality? It was not an original title that Euclid used. Prior to his time many others had written books called the "Elements." The material contained within it was for the most part not original with Euclid. He had incorporated into the book the work of Pythagoras, Eudoxus, and Hippocrates, to name a few. Many men had previously used deductive logic to establish the theorems. In short, the *Elements* was not original in title, form, or content. What then has been responsible for the tremendous influence of this work? In a word it was *system*. Euclid had a positive genius for systematizing and organizing to the point that he was able to derive all the known mathematics of his time from a few definitions and basic assumptions, using logic as the ladder to climb to the heights. And what a majestic climb it was!

The *Elements* consists of 13 books.[7] Book I begins with definitions, postulates, and what Euclid called "common notions," which we shall examine in detail later. From this beginning Euclid carefully proved some 48 theorems that fall into three sections: triangles—constructions and congruence; the theory of parallels leading to the sum of the angles of a triangle; and parallelograms, squares, triangles—with emphasis upon area relationships.

The work of Book I is culminated in the proof of theorem 47, the Pythagorean Theorem. Book II is basically a continuation of the work of the third section of Book I. Books III and IV are devoted to the properties of the circle, while Book V is devoted to proportion, which is applied to plane geometry in Book VI. Books VII, VIII, and IX are devoted to number theory and are considered to be the first definitive work in that field. Book X has been called the most complete and most remarkable of all. It involves a development of the irrationals. Books XI, XII, and XIII are all concerned with solid geometry.

These books contain many testimonials to Euclid's genius. In the section devoted to number theory, Euclid presented a proof for the existence of an infinite number of primes that is a model of simplicity. It went somewhat like this:

> Assume there is a finite number of primes. If this is so, there must be a greatest prime, called *P*. Form the product of all these primes and add 1:
>
> $$2 \cdot 3 \cdot 5 \cdot 7 \ldots \cdot P + 1 = Q$$
>
> If we divide *Q* by each of the primes, the remainder will always be 1. Therefore *Q* is not divisible by any of these primes, which leads to 2 conclusions: it is prime itself; it is divisible by a greater prime. In either case, the initial assumption is contradicted!

Book II has been called "geometric algebra" because many of the problems of algebra are stated and solved geometrically. The crude numeration system of the Greeks made geometry an easier vehicle for this work. Among the accomplishments of Euclid in this book are the representation of a product as an area of a rectangle and the proof of the distributive and commutative laws geometrically.

But it is in his selection of basic notions that Euclid's genius really asserts itself. After his definitions he presented five common notions or axioms:

> Things equal to the same thing are equal to each other.
> If equals be added to equals, the wholes are equal.
> If equals be subtracted from equals the remainders are equal.
> Things which coincide with one another are equal.
> The whole is greater than the part.

These were considered axioms as distinct from postulates since they are statements that are true for all sciences. The postulates were thought of as "self-evident" truths for the given subject under discussion. Today this distinction between axiom and postulate is no longer made because both terms are used interchangeably. The notion of "self-evident" truths is another topic we shall discuss shortly.

Along with the common notions, Euclid listed five postulates establishing that:

> it is possible to draw a straight line from any point to any point.
> it is possible to produce a finite straight line continuously in a straight line.
> it is possible to describe a circle with any center and radius.
> all right angles are equal to one another.
> if a straight line falling on two straight lines makes the interior angles on the same side less than two right angles, the two straight lines, if produced indefinitely, meet on that side on which the angles are less than two right angles.

As you examine the list of postulates, you will probably wonder whatever happened to Euclid as he wrote the fifth one? Did he suddenly lose control of his reason? The five common notions and the first four postulates are simple, direct statements. The fifth is a world unto itself. Many mathematicians have reacted in similar manner to this postulate and were convinced that the fifth was not a postulate at all but in actuality a theorem that could be proved using the previous assumptions and definitions. And so began a 2000 year search for a proof that ended in the conclusion that a proof was not possible, something Euclid had known from the start! Thus historians refer to the fifth postulate as Euclid's greatest achievement, and George Sarton describes Euclid's undertaking in the following way: "He created a monument that is as marvelous in its symmetry, inner beauty, and clearness as the Parthenon, but incomparably more complex and more durable."[8]

And so we have moved from the Pythagorean idea of number ruling the universe to the work of Euclid. Starting with some definitions and 10 basic "self-evident" truths, Euclid constructed a model of logical thought that was to be accepted as a true description of our real world. After all, except for the fifth postulate, did not the assumptions of Euclid match our own experience? And as Euclid went on to prove theorem after theorem he also provided the world with a temple dedicated to man's endless progress and the limitless achievements that can result from his use of his power to reason, as opposed to the era of darkness that resulted from superstition and ignorance. God had become a geometer and for more than 2000 years mathematics in general and geometry in particular were to remain the true symbolic realization of the physical world.

Attempts were made to prove the fifth postulate almost as quickly as the *Elements* were widely accepted. Before exploring these attempts, let us state the postulate as it appears in textbooks today, a description from Playfair: Given a line, L, and a point P not on L, there is one and only one line that can be drawn through P parallel to L.[9] (See Fig. 2-5.)

This statement is equivalent to the longer one of Euclid, since Playfair derived it from Euclid's statement. Could there be more than one such line through P parallel to L? Examine the diagram in Figure 2-5. Does it seem possible? This looks like another of Euclid's "self-evident" truths and indeed Euclid stated it as such. Let us explore the attempts at proof.

In Euclid's own day, Ptolemy, the ruler, attempted to prove the postulate and wrote a small book about it. He thought he had developed a proof, but he had inadvertently assumed the postulate itself to be true. This fallacy was pointed out by Proclus (A.D. 410–485) as he too attempted to set down such

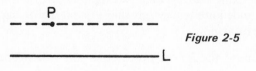

Figure 2-5

a proof. Like his predecessor, he also made an unstated assumption that proved his undoing.

In the thirteenth century Nasiraddin, a Persian, pointed out the importance of the angle-sum theorem in attempts to prove the postulate. He was the first to introduce the following figure (Fig. 2-6) which became famous in these attempts:

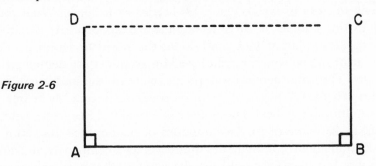

Figure 2-6

Nasiraddin was trying to establish that if *AD* and *BC* were equal perpendiculars to *AB*, then the angles at *D* and *C* would have to be right angles. However, he did not succeed. John Wallis (1616–1703) tried to construct a proof based upon Nasiraddin's work but fell prey to the fallacy of unknowingly assuming the postulate.

It took a Jesuit priest named Geralamo Saccheri (1667–1733) to introduce a fresh attack on the postulate. Saccheri decided to use the indirect method and posed what was the equivalent of three possible situations: There are no parallels possible, there is only one parallel possible, or there is more than one parallel possible.

It was Saccheri's hope to use the method of reductio ad absurdum to show that both the first and last of these situations resulted in contradictions, leaving the second one as the only possibility. Something most interesting occurred. The contradiction sought by Saccheri never appeared. What did come out of his work was a new geometry! The discovery was so startling that Saccheri believed that his results were absurd and turned back from the doorway to a new world of mathematics. Similar investigations were made by Johann Heinrich Lambert (1728–1777) and Adrien Marie Legendre (1752–1833), with no greater success.

It wasn't until the beginning of the nineteenth century that, almost simultaneously, Carl Friedrich Gauss (1777–1855), János Bolyai (1802–1860), and Nikolai Lobachevski (1793–1856) all came to the astounding conclusion that if you replace the fifth postulate with a different postulate you do not encounter a contradiction. Quite the contrary, what does evolve is simply another geometry—one that is like the geometry of Euclid in all respects except where the fifth postulate is concerned! So astonishing was this find that Gauss, the foremost mathematician of his own time and possibly of any era, realized what he had uncovered but was reluctant to publish the results lest he be the object of ridicule!

What does it mean to say that there are other geometries? If the geometry of Euclid is based upon self-evident truths, and if the resulting structure is the true description of the real world, how can there be "other geometries"? Can there be more than one correct description of the world in which we live —all contradictory to each other? This hardly seems likely. What then is the answer to this puzzle? Is there a rational explanation? As obvious as the answer appears today, it took a while for the world to accept it. The "self-evident" truths upon which Euclid based his geometry are neither self-evident nor truths! They are merely assumptions made by the mathematician as he builds his structure. What may the mathematician assume? Is he free to make any assumption he wishes? The answer is a qualified yes—yes, as long as he does not make contradictory assumptions or assumptions that may lead to future contradictions. Mathematics thus becomes a completely abstract system of ideas that has rules for employing the symbols, that uses logic as its modus operandi, and that need have no relation whatsoever to anything in the physical world! One can imagine the feeling of the mathematician as he is set free to organize any postulates he wishes and follow where they may lead, without ever having to stop along the way to determine the physical consequences of what he has invented. What a far cry from the work of Pythagoras and Euclid as they sought to explain the universe.

If mathematics is now to become a collection of abstract systems rather than a means for understanding the universe, what shall be important? It would seem that the common characteristics of all these various structures would come into focus, as well as the search to duplicate Euclid in order to perhaps find a set of postulates that will yield all these known structures. For as sure as there is more than one geometry, there must be more than one algebra and even more than one arithmetic, and such is the case. This was the charge Russell and Whitehead set for themselves as they undertook the writing of *Principia Mathematica*.

Are we ready now once again to face the question, What is Mathematics? We can see that at one time mathematics could have been defined as a means for the understanding of the environment. Since the invention of these new geometries called non-Euclidean geometries (Euclid prevailed after all) it seems that those who define mathematics as a game, a completely abstract system where "we never know what we are talking about, nor whether what we are saying is true," [10] are giving the correct definition. Especially in the light of the fact that the mathematician is free to choose any postulates he wishes, does not this attitude towards mathematics become the valid one? Not exactly. There are many restrictions upon the mathematician. He is not as free as he appears to be. First, he must satisfy the criteria for a mathematical system: It must be simple, economical, sufficient, and consistent. But is he not otherwise free to select postulates without any concern for the world around him, free to follow his idle thoughts wherever they may lead? Nathan Court asks and answers a most interesting question regarding this:

> What is the source, what is the impulse of the creative capacity of the human mind, in connection with mathematics? The answer is two-fold: observation and imitation. . . . If there is no physical picture attached to these terms [undefined terms] and the imaginative capacity of the mind is left to its own resources exclusively, progress in science is slow and laborious.[11]

As he carefully considers this relatively new found freedom of the mathematician, Court examines newly developed geometries and the different sets of postulates devised for geometry and notes a distinct similarity to those of Euclid. He asks:

> Why not these mathematicians use the freedom that is theirs . . .? The answer is very simple and at the same time of basic importance in understanding the role of mathematics in relation to epistemology and to the other sciences. The postulates of Euclid gave us a geometry which works in the world we live in, . . . a geometry which is practical, which tells us something about this world, a geometry that fits other branches of human knowledge . . . the fact that the geometry deduced from these postulates is applicable to the physical world shows that those postulates themselves have a physical basis, that they are empirical laws, refined and abstracted laws, but laws derived from experience, just as the very notions of point and line are abstracted from the physical world.[12]

Thus, we have made a complete cycle from a purely physical and empirical concept of mathematics to one completely abstract and imaginative, and back again. Are we any better for having made the journey? We should be. Perhaps we can now begin to understand some of the underlying causes for conflicting viewpoints about the nature of mathematics, viewpoints that have been reflected in conflicting curriculum improvement suggestions for schools. Where does all this leave us? It would seem that at the least we are in a better position to make up our own minds as we try to build more effective school experiences for our students. Upon which point of view shall we build, however? The next chapter will attempt to answer this question.

FOOTNOTES

1. Robert W. Marks. *The New Mathematics Dictionary and Handbook.* Bantam Books (paperback), 1964.
2. Jane Muir. *Of Men and Numbers.* Dell Publishing Co. (paperback), 1961.
3. Herbert W. Turnbull. *The Great Mathematicians,* Ed. 4. Methuen and Co. Ltd., 1951.
4. M. Dacier. *The Life of Pythagoras.* London. Printed for J. Tonson, 1707.
5. For a discussion of the possibility that it was Thales of Miletus who first proved this theorem see *The Bequest of the Greeks* by Tobias Dantzig, Charles Scribner's Sons, 1955.
6. E. T. Bell. *Mathematics, Queen and Servant of Science.* McGraw-Hill Book Co., 1951.

7. Sir Thomas L. Heath (Editor). *The Thirteen Books of Euclid's Elements*. Dover Publications, Inc. (paperback), 1956.
8. George Sarton. *A History of Science: Hellenistic Science and Culture in the Last Three Centuries B.C.* Harvard University Press, 1959, p. 39.
9. George Sarton. *A History of Science: Hellenistic Science and Culture in the Last Three Centuries B.C.* Harvard University Press, 1959, p. 40.
10. Bertrand Russell. *Mysticism and Logic*. W. W. Norton & Co., 1929.
11. Nathan A. Court. *Mathematics in Fun and in Earnest*. Mentor Book (paperback), New American Library, 1961, p. 26.
12. Nathan A. Court. *Mathematics in Fun and in Earnest*. Mentor Book (paperback), New American Library, 1961, p. 24.

FOR INVESTIGATION AND DISCUSSION

1. How do you think a Pythagorean would reply to the question, What is Mathematics?

2. What relationship exists between the Pythagorean views of mathematics and philosophy?

3. How did the Pythagoreans arrive at the conclusion that God was an arithmetician? What are the implications of this point of view?

4. Why was the proof of the irrationality of $\sqrt{2}$ a blow to the Pythagoreans?

5. Apply the Pythagorean notions about number to today's world. How well does this viewpoint stand up?

6. Investigate the three problems of antiquity: the angle trisection, the doubling of the cube, and the squaring of the circle. How have these problems been resolved?

7. What happened to direct the Greeks away from the notion of God as an arithmetician to the concept of God as a geometer?

8. How can you account for the durability of Euclid's *Elements?*

9. What prompted mathematicians to believe that they could find a proof for the fifth postulate of Euclid's *Elements?*

10. What was the outcome of the several attempts to prove the fifth postulate?

11. What is meant by the statement that the postulates are "self-evident" truths?

12. How did the Euclidean attitude toward mathematics differ from that of the Pythagoreans? How were they similar?

13. Compare the concepts of mathematics held by mathematicians before and after the invention of the non-Euclidean geometries.

14. How has the development of mathematics been influenced by the advent of the non-Euclidean geometries?

FOR FURTHER READING

Books

W. W. Rouse Ball. *A Short Account of the History of Mathematics*. MacMillan & Co. Ltd., 1935.
Nathan A. Court. *Mathematics in Fun and in Earnest*. Mentor Book (paperback), New American Library, 1961.

M. Dacier. *The Life of Pythagoras.* London. Printed for J. Tonson, 1707.

Tobias Dantzig. *The Bequest of the Greeks.* Charles Scribner's Sons, 1955.

Sir Thomas L. Heath. *A Manual of Greek Mathematics.* Oxford at Clarendon Press, 1931.

Sir Thomas L. Heath (Editor). *The Thirteen Books of Euclid's Elements.* Dover Publications, Inc. (paperback), 1956.

Morris Kline. *Mathematics in Western Culture.* Oxford University Press, 1953.

Robert W. Marks (Editor). *The Growth of Mathematics.* Bantam Books (paperback), 1964.

Jane Muir. *Of Men and Numbers.* Dell Publishing Co. (paperback), 1961.

O. Neugebauer. *The Exact Sciences in Antiquity.* Princeton University Press, 1952.

Constance Reid. *A Long Way from Euclid.* Thomas Y. Crowell Company, 1963.

George Sarton. *A History of Science: Ancient Science Through the Golden Age of Greece.* Harvard University Press, 1952.

George Sarton. *A History of Science: Hellenistic Science and Culture in the Last Three Centuries B.C.* Harvard University Press, 1959.

Sir Charles Thomas-Stafford. *Early Editions of Euclid's Elements.* London. Printed for the Bibliographical Society, 1926.

Herbert W. Turnbull. *The Great Mathematicians,* Ed. 4. Methuen & Co. Ltd., 1951.

Harold E. Wolfe. *Introduction to Non-Euclidean Geometry.* Dryden Press, 1945.

Periodicals

Paul H. Davis. "Why and How We Should Correct the Mistakes of Euclid." *The Mathematics Teacher.* Vol. 53 (November, 1960), pp. 576–581.

M. C. Gemignani. "On the Geometry of Euclid." *The Mathematics Teacher.* Vol. 60 (February, 1967), pp. 160–164.

Albert P. Shulte. "Pythagorean Mathematics in the Modern Classroom." *The Mathematics Teacher.* Vol. 57 (April, 1964), pp. 228–232.

3

AN EMERGING POINT OF VIEW

In the previous chapters, the dilemma of differing points of view about the nature of mathematics was carefully considered. This dilemma was explored in order to help develop an awareness of the differences, as well as to clarify their substance. It was pointed out that all teachers of mathematics must have a point of view upon which to base their teachings. Just as each teacher must have some overall direction to give his work purpose and meaning, so it is incumbent upon the work presented here to operate from some given base that will provide direction for the many and varied suggestions for organizing learning experiences in mathematics. In effect, this chapter is an exploration of the point of view of the suggestions presented. What attitudes towards mathematics will this treatise try to develop? Where will the emphasis be placed? What will be considered important and why? All these questions deserve answers. Some will be answered in this brief section; others will be answered over the course of several hundred pages, as the work unfolds. It is a simple matter to declare one's self to be on this particular side or that. It is a difficult task to indicate how adoption of a particular stance will be translated into day-by-day classroom activity. This chapter is concerned with the former and simpler task: a statement of goals and purposes. The latter, more difficult task is, after all, the heart of this text.

It would seem that the points made by Court at the end of the last chapter cannot be denied. Mathematics becomes important because "it works." By "working," we mean that mathematics has become an integral part of the world in which we live. If mathematics did not in some way offer something of value and importance to mankind, would it have continued to live, breathe, and grow as it has? Would it have continued to expand and extend itself if it had nothing of consequence to offer the society as a whole? Would it suffice to say that this entity is a product of human imagination and should be recognized for what it is and not for what it might help anyone to do? I, for one, think not. The influence that mathematics has had upon generation after generation and the reciprocal influence of these generations upon mathematics indicate emphatically that while mathematics is an abstract collection of ideas, it is also, at the same time, an entity that is and has been closely involved with the life of man on this planet since recorded time. This is a message of utmost importance that we, as teachers of mathematics, have not been able to successfully share with our students. This is one message that will be at the very heart of the work presented here: Mathematics is significant because it helps us to understand the world in which we live.

Mathematics Helps Us To Understand Our Environment

Our first statement of purpose or goal is that *mathematics helps us to understand our environment*. It is not an oversight that the words "control" and "master" have been omitted from the statement. There are many who firmly believe that the two go together: Understand and control nature. While our understanding of the physical world can assist us in controlling certain events, our primary purpose should be to understand nature in order that we may better learn to share the bountiful awards of nature and coexist on this planet with all living things. We have all too often seen the results of man's attempt to "master" his environment: the cutting of timber, the damming of rivers, and the poisoning of the waters with insecticides and the air with pollutants. No, it would seem that a greater understanding of nature would prevent the destruction of redwood forests and the contamination of natural resources, and so the notion of "mastery" is seriously questioned. But in understanding this world in which we live, mathematics is an invaluable tool. Imagine trying to describe and work with physical relationships without the use of the symbolic language of algebra. Imagine trying to investigate form and function in nature, and thereby in man-made objects as well, without the concepts and visual images of geometry. And how would we have advanced technologically without the power that we have to study phenomena that are offered by the calculus?

Somehow this chapter in the story of mathematics must be shared with students of the subject. This means that our students will have to participate in a great number of experiences that will enable them to one day remark to themselves, "Look what I can do with mathematics!"

Mathematics Is the Language of Science

Mathematics is the language of science, and directly related to this is the fact that mathematics is the means for communication between scientists. It is

33

the language of the scientist. The close, natural ties between mathematics and science have not been exploited in school mathematics nearly enough. By what better means could teachers of mathematics give importance and immediacy to the concepts considered in the classroom? And yet so much of the work that may be observed today appears to be totally unrelated to anything of significance outside the walls of the school building. If we emphasize the language role that mathematics is fulfilling, we not only add interest and importance to the subject but we also point up important considerations for the learning of the subject. How does one learn a "language"? If a student is conversant with the symbolism of mathematics and what it represents, he has a good head start on learning how to explore the variety of concepts that await him. Therefore, we must begin to focus upon this notion and concentrate upon helping our students to "speak the language."

Mathematics Helps Us To Do Things Otherwise Impossible

Directly related to the first two goals is the fact that mathematics will enable us to do things that would be otherwise very difficult, and perhaps impossible. Can you imagine the expression on a child's face and his innermost feelings when he is brought to the realization that by making use of mathematics he has found something that was virtually unreachable before? How simple a process it is, using calculus, to determine the speed of a falling object or the highest point reached by an object that is tossed upward. How else could we determine these easily arrived-at results? How else could we determine that the amount a spring stretches as weights are hung from it varies in the same way that the speed of a dropped object varies with the length of time it is falling? (Both are linear functions of the form $y = ax$.) How else could we determine that no matter what the lengths of the sides of a right triangle are, a square built on the hypotenuse will have an area equal to the sums of the areas of the squares built upon the other two sides? There is so much that we are able to accomplish with the use of mathematics that this should be one of the most important and one of the most easily attained mathematical goals. Yet, how many of our students complete the study of mathematics convinced that beyond elementary calculation, there is little need for mathematics?

Mathematics Is an Abstract System of Ideas

We must not be mislead by the first three goals. Emphasizing the interaction of mathematics with the culture, as well as its role as a tool for, and the language of, science does not mean that we shall mask its true identity and nature. Whatever else it may be, mathematics is still an abstract system of ideas and must be seen as such by our students if we are to present an accurate picture to them. Thus, as the students use mathematics to solve problems, we shall have to be prepared to indicate clearly how the mathematics "thing" and the physical "thing" are indeed far from being one and the same. This becomes particularly important in the study of geometry, as it is easy to confuse the visual representations of mathematical concepts with the concepts themselves. This is not to say, however, that we will in any way minimize the important use that will be served by the visual representations. But if the student of mathematics is to gain some insight into the very heart of things mathematically, we shall somehow have to organize experiences to bring out the abstract nature of mathematical systems. The role played by mathematics is of primary importance. Helping students begin to formulate concepts of the nature of mathematics is equally important. Mathematics is perhaps the finest creation of the mind of man. As such, it stands as an example of what heights man may reach when he relies upon his powers of reason. The use of deduction in mathematics provides this discipline with the unique quality of determining the certainty of propositions beyond any shadow of doubt and for all time. Certainty and permanence are not characteristic of many fields of endeavor in twentieth century society. But they are ascribable to ideas in mathematics through the use of logic. This alone would serve to establish an unusual position for mathematics among the many fields of endeavor that abound in modern society.

Mathematics Is the Study of Patterns

Finally, we must consider mathematics as the study of all possible patterns, both in the world about us and in the structure of the discipline of mathematics itself. It has already been mentioned that there are regularities and similarities in nature that would escape us entirely if it were not for the mathematical descriptions available to us. Thus $v = 32t$ and $s = 3w$, describing completely different physical situations, fit the same mathematical pattern: $y = ax$, the simple linear function. Internally, within the field of mathematics itself, this same search for and classification of patterns is always taking place. We classify all two-dimensional things, three-dimensional things, and even move into a world beyond our senses and do the same for four-, five-, and eventually n-dimensional spaces. We say that if $x^2 + y^2 = r^2$ is the equation of a two-dimensional circle, and if $x^2 + y^2 + z^2 = r^2$ is the equation of a three-dimensional sphere, we could almost expect $x^2 + y^2 + z^2 + u^2 = r^2$ to become the equation of a four-dimensional sphere—whatever that may be! Of course, the most remarkable fact about all this is that the study of problems in the real world triggers the development of new mathematics that frequently goes far beyond the problem at hand and into such areas as four-dimensional spaces. Despite the fact that new mathematics frequently has little apparent application to anything in the physical world, just as often some later use is found that assists man in his continued quest for progress. The four-dimensional geometry, for example, has become an important tool for the study of Einstein's theory of relativity. Thus, in the teaching of school mathematics we may be able to make an important beginning in helping students to realize the importance of the search for patterns through their own participation in the search.

The five principles just presented will form our intellectual goals. They will formulate the basis upon which the work in the classroom will be developed in succeeding chapters. The dilemma of differing concepts of mathematics is not hereby resolved. Far from it. This is simply a clarification of the basis upon which the work has been constructed, for the most part. The acceptance of different ideas about mathematics as being important might result in the organization of alternative learning experiences in mathematics classes. At times, some of these experiences will be mentioned and their consequences explored. But in the main, the program that follows is a direct outgrowth of the creation of experiences to develop these five principles:

> Mathematics helps us to understand our environment.
> Mathematics is the language of science.
> Mathematics helps us to do things otherwise impossible.
> Mathematics is an abstract system of ideas.
> Mathematics is the study of patterns.

These descriptive statements will guide the formulation of our mathematical goals as we work with students in our classes. If you accept these five statements, they should provide the raison d'être—the reason for being—for all the things we have our students doing. While it is postulated that the five statements shall guide classroom experiences, the final form of these experiences will have to be based upon a consideration of many other factors as well. The psychological basis upon which we must build will be the focal point of the next section.

FOR INVESTIGATION AND DISCUSSION

1. Select an incident from history to demonstrate how the test "does it work?" led to a mathematical development.

2. Give specific examples of how algebra and geometry add to our understanding of our environment.

3. In what ways may mathematics be considered a language? How might this influence classroom instruction in mathematics?

4. Give one example from each of arithmetic, algebra, and geometry to indicate how mathematics enables you to do something otherwise difficult to achieve.

5. Discuss the difference between a mathematical formulation of the area of a triangle and the physical area itself.

6. If the study of physical problems generates the development of new mathematics, how is it that this "new" mathematics is often highly abstract and has no physical counterpart?

7. Examine the list of goals on page 36. Evaluate this list, indicating whether or not you agree with each and explain why. Suggest any necessary revisions, deletions, or additions to the list with justification for your opinion.

FOR FURTHER READING

Periodical

Harold P. Fawcett. "The Reflections of a Retiring Teacher of Mathematics." *The Mathematics Teacher*. Vol. 57 (November, 1964), pp. 450–456.

SECTION TWO

ON LEARNING

LEARNING MATHEMATICS

INTRODUCTION

We have looked into the heart of mathematics in order to be clear in our minds about what we hope to achieve with our students. We have sought answers to the questions, What is mathematics? and Why is mathematics important? Sorting out these ideas so that they are clearly before us fulfills one important prerequisite for successful teaching: We must know where we are going. We now turn our attention to a second critical factor in the building of effective mathematics learning experiences: the nature of learning itself.

Training to become a teacher, filling the role of parent, working with children, and simply living in a society in which children make up the bulk of the population is bound to result in the advancement of an individual's knowledge about youngsters. Integrating into this structure the latest academic information about learning is no simple task for professional teachers. Think of the difficulty, then, involved in moving yet a step further and trying to organize this new knowledge into more effective classroom experiences for youngsters! This is a task so great as to be almost forbidding. Is it any wonder, then, that many teachers turn a deaf ear to the results of research findings? Most teachers are so pressed that they have all they can do to provide continuous improvement on the basis of what they have already come to understand about the teaching-learning process. To incorporate additional findings is almost impossible. Let us, however, try to identify some common notions shared by teachers and then explore the results of the research of some learning theorists and attempt to blend these understandings into a definite plan of attack on the problem of constructing effective learning experiences for children.

Perhaps the probability of a successful classroom experience for our students will be greatest when their needs and the requirements of mathematics are in harmony. Such a consideration poses uniquely difficult problems for the teacher of mathematics because of the highly abstract character of mathematical ideas. How can we help students to gain some insight into this fantastic structure? How do they arrive at understanding when the very substance of what they are learning may only be knowable through a few of the senses? What does the human mind do as it strives to comprehend these concepts that are beyond the senses but are nevertheless of man-made construction? In seeking the answers to these questions we begin to focus upon the nature of the learner as he joins in the pursuit of mathematics.

How much is known about how children learn mathematics? If we begin in the classroom and observe what is going on, we should expect to see in practice activities that reflect underlying assumptions about how children learn. What do we find? For one thing, we find that many teachers use a "fill up the empty bottle" notion as a way to ensure learning. The basic concept of such a theory seems to be that the teacher, knowing the content, must pour the knowledge into the student, who does not know the content. The whole process may be likened to filling a wine bottle with water. The teacher is the sender or "pourer," while the student is the "bottle" or receiver. Because of the narrow neck of the bottle, should it refuse to receive its contents (refuse to learn), the teacher must be pouring too much, too quickly. Therefore, most learning problems can be overcome by slowing down the rate of transmittal. This is coupled with a feeling that if you repeat the pouring process often enough you eventually will fill the bottle with the desired contents, which can then be poured back by the student on demand. What it all seems to amount to is this: If a teacher will only repeat what he is teaching often enough and slowly enough—with great patience and optimism—eventually all students will learn and will be able to repeat the information on request.

While this is not the only kind of learning situation observable in mathematics classes today, a good deal of teaching is carried out in this manner. How is it that such is often the case, despite the fact that we have found out a good deal about how children learn over the past two decades?

Many teachers will proceed in such a manner because it is the way in which they were taught. What is more, it is probably the only kind of classroom teaching they have ever seen, including perhaps that in their own college classrooms in mathematics and education courses. Further, there seems to be a lack of conviction that learning theorists have very much of a *practical* nature to offer the teacher faced with the realities of everyday classroom living. Not only are the results of psychological exploration believed to be impractical, but so often what is found by one psychologist is virtually contradicted by another. Therefore, the teacher reasons, no one really knows anything about how children learn since the psychologists themselves do not agree. It is, after all, not only possible to ignore these studies, but virtually necessary to do so to prevent yourself from becoming a teaching schizophrenic!

While there is much truth in this, there is also much that is completely false and misleading. Let us see how much there is of practical value for teachers to be found in the work of psychologists concerned with learning.

HILGARD

Perhaps a good point of departure is an interesting attempt made by Hilgard to discover areas of agreement among learning theorists.[1] He conducted a careful examination of a broad variety of theories regarding how children learn, and he attempted to discern whether or not there were common ideas generally accepted by psychologists regardless of their particular point of view. This study, reported in 1956, bore some interesting fruit. Hilgard felt that he could identify 14 specific points that could be considered consistent with most generally identified learning theories. Briefly these points consisted of the following:

1. The capacity of the learner varies with his age.
2. Motivation to learn makes acquisition of knowledge easier.
3. Intense motivations (fear, anxiety) detract from the task.
4. Success and reward yield more favorable outcomes than failure and punishment.
5. Learning under intrinsic motivation is preferable to learning under extrinsic motivation.
6. Tolerance for failure is built by success experiences.
7. Practice in setting one's own goals leads to realistic goal-setting.
8. Personal history may influence reaction to the teacher.
9. Active participation is preferable to passive reception in learning.
10. Meaningful tasks and responsibilities are learned more readily than nonsense.
11. To elicit automatic responses there is no substitute for practice.
12. Learning is aided by knowledge of mistakes and successes.
13. Transfer is aided by discovery and by experiencing ideas.
14. Spaced recalls help fix the materials to be retained.

Although psychologists have questioned Hilgard's 14 points and the general process of constructing lists of "principles" by inference from research studies,[2,3] evidently there are a number of important ideas that should be considered in the development of effective learning experiences for our students.

Despite the fact that Hilgard's analysis was made recently, much has been happening both prior to and since his work to add to our knowledge of the learning process. At the Rousseau Institute in Geneva, Switzerland, Jean

Piaget, the French psychologist, and his collaborators have for several decades been devising numerous ingenious experiments in attempts to develop an understanding of how children react to learning situations. This is among the most significant work done in the area to date.[4]

PIAGET

Many teachers have believed that the learning of a concept is a sudden happening, much on the order of the light bulb that flashes on over the head of a character in a comic strip. Once the bulb flashes, the child has suddenly reached a point at which he has acquired an idea in all its finality. The experiments of Piaget seem to indicate that a much different process is going on in the mind of the child. Using the techniques of observing and questioning children, making word for word records of the interview, and analyzing the data gathered, Piaget has theorized that concept formation in the mind of a child passes through several stages of development.

For example, an experiment is devised to gain information about how children learn one-to-one correspondence. As one of several situations requiring the matching of pairs of objects, Piaget and his colleagues decided to have children match eggs to eggcups since the correspondence is in closer physical proximity than the previous matching of glasses to bottles, and flowers to vases. The eggs can be placed into the cup and only one can be so placed. The cups are lined up and the child is told to take enough eggs from the stack so that he has one for each cup. The youngster selects eggs until he has a row of them that is physically as long as the row of cups. There are obviously many more eggs than cups, but the child states that they are the same in number. After being told to place the eggs into the cups, he realizes he has too many eggs. He places an egg into each eggcup and the extra eggs are taken away. Is there the same number of eggs and cups now? He replies that there is. All the eggs are removed from the cups and gathered into a pile in front of the cups. Is there the same number now? Surprisingly the child says no. There are more cups! If the eggs are spread out and the cups gathered together, the child will say that he has more eggs!

Piaget claims that this reaction is consistent among children up to the age of 4 years and he describes this period as the stage of "pre-conceptual" thought: a process based entirely upon perception, which results in global kinds of comparisons rather than attention to individual differences and characteristics. Thus the child "sees" that there are more cups than eggs if they form a longer row of objects in spite of the fact that the eggs were taken out of the cups a moment before. It seems that the perception of the child at this stage is completely unlike that of adults and older children. Piaget feels that the child's belief that the number changes when the objects are spread out or gathered together is attributable to a failure to comprehend the reversibility principle (the idea that the group can be restored to its original position), a principle Piaget describes as being fundamental to mathematical and logical thinking. Thus, at this stage, if an experimenter shows the child a cup of milk and then pours the contents into two other cups, the child will say that there is more milk in the two cups together than there was in the original container. This so-called "pre-conceptual" stage is characterized by the child's attempt to deal with his world through action. All thought is in terms of reality as the child sees it, and logical thought does not begin to appear until later.

When older children participate in the eggcup experiment they respond differently. Children in the 4 to 7 or 8 year old group characteristically will be able to select the correct number of eggs to be placed into the cups initially, but once again will deny the reversibility concept and say there is no longer a correspondence if the eggs or the cups are spread out. Piaget calls this the stage of "initiative" thought. The child can produce the correspondence but the equivalence is gone when the shape of the group changes. Thought is still closely allied with perception, although the beginning of logical thinking is stirring. Global observation of groups persists but enough comprehension of the individual characteristics of a group is present to enable the child to make the correspondence.

At the age of 7 or 8 years, children begin to demonstrate the use of intellectual powers free of immediate perception. Not only will the child select the correct number of eggs to be placed in the cups, but he will insist that the correspondence is maintained no matter how the sets of eggs or cups are arranged. He has mastered the notion of reversibility and can construct a correspondence of a purely intellectual nature: The number of eggs and eggcups are the same even though the eggs are taken from the cups and gathered in a heap. Piaget calls this the stage of "concrete operations." A child is able to take ideas and "operate" on them logically in order to formulate a conclusion, provided that the ideas concern objects that can be known through the senses, as opposed to purely abstract thought. In maintaining the equivalency of the sets, regardless of configuration, the child provides evidence that "operation" has triumphed over perception.

From 11 to 15 years the child, states Piaget, enters a period of perfected formal thought that need not relate to concrete objects. A child can now accept hypothetical ideas and try out in his mind the consequences of the assumptions. He is thereby carrying out formal logical thinking, examining intellectually the implications of possible statements.

In short, then, Piaget concludes from his studies that concept formation in the child passes through four stages of development, beginning with *global comparisons,* in which quantity, for example, may be judged by the length of a row of objects, rather than by the number of objects. This is followed by an *initiative stage* in which some relationships can be perceived but in which the reversibility of sets is still not noticed. The *concrete operations* stage ensues, during which the child grasps reversibility and can deal logically with notions drawn from objects that are known through the senses. Finally, *formal logical thought* is perfected and hypotheses can be intellectually accepted and tested.

Piaget's results seem to hold regardless of the mathematical content under consideration, from one-to-one correspondence to topological spaces. Although there is a good deal of controversy surrounding the work of Piaget and although researchers have had a difficult time trying to repeat his experiments, there is much of importance to be learned from them. It appears that students certainly look at the world about them in a manner far different from that of the adults who are instructing them. We hear a good deal about the need for "getting down to the child's level" when trying to help him learn. Piaget, in effect, helped us to do just that when he analyzed the perception of children as they pass through the stages of learning. He attempted to identify what the level of the child is at various ages and offered insights into how the child goes about the business of trying to learn.

In addition he dramatically pointed out the folly of some commonly accepted everyday teaching practices. If we were to ignore the age levels for the moment and limit our thinking to the characteristics of the stages of thought, we would find a pattern leading from action with immediately present objects to logical thinking and intellectualization without immediate presence. This may be a pattern for helping students to learn about mathematics at virtually any level. Perhaps we may call this pattern the life cycle of a mathematical idea. It is remarkably similar to the pattern of learning established by Brueckner and Grossnickle in 1947 when they postulated that learning must proceed from the concrete to the abstract.[5] Symbols are the end-product of establishing an idea—not the beginning. These are notions prominent in the thinking of most investigators of learning. What Piaget has done is to add classification to this notion by defining several levels of concrete experience based upon the maturity of the child. These patterns are fundamental to any attempt to develop learning in mathematics.

There are some vital questions that must be considered when one examines the work of Piaget. If we grant that the stages of the development of thought do in fact exist as described, do all children go through each stage of development? Is it possible that some children may never manifest the behavior described in a given stage and instead pass over that stage altogether? And what is even more pertinent to classroom experiences, is it possible that different children will spend different lengths of time in each of the developmental stages? If we are to build programs of study with the work of Piaget clearly before us, it would seem that these questions must be considered. If they are, we can take the necessary steps to provide for all our children—a continuing problem of teachers.

Another question that might be asked is still more basic. We see that mathematics is a construction of man. We know, from whatever recorded history is available to us, that various civilizations have constructed differing mathematical systems. Is it possible that the mathematical-logical fit that

Piaget has provided for the thinking of the child is a consequence of the observer rather than the child? A question is asked; the child responds. His actions are then interpreted in terms of adult descriptions of mathematics. There seems to have been an unstated building of a bridge from the child's reaction to the experimenter's conclusion. Perhaps this bridge-building process is in need of closer scrutiny and question. Because Piaget uses a mathematical term to describe the actions of a student, is it necessarily true that the child "knows" the concept in question? Piaget makes the assumption based upon observation. These are basic questions that have to be considered by Piaget.

The value of his contributions cannot be minimized, however. It seems that the thought processes of a child are indeed unlike those of an adult. The child apparently perceives the situations in a unique way that is itself modified as he matures. There also seems to be a good deal to consider in terms of student readiness for teacher-imposed tasks. For example, when a child responds that the amount of milk has increased if it is poured from its lone container into two containers, he is indicating to all teachers that they must consider the student's point of view in the classroom. The question of right and wrong takes on a new dimension under such circumstances. It seems to lose its absolute status and become relative to the situation and the observer. What we previously may have thought to be wrong responses may very well be classified as correct responses to the wrong question. How can we be sure which question the student is attempting to answer? Clearly the simple question "Which has more?" meant one thing to the experimenter and something entirely different to the student. The necessity for listening to our students becomes more important than ever before. And what is more, we must somehow try to "listen in" on what the student has failed to say but has had uppermost in his mind.

The overall pattern of thought development described by Piaget is most enlightening. It seems that logical thinking develops at the end of the cycle, a cycle that begins with thought and action almost indistinguishable. The immediately perceptible is all that is conceived. Eventually, action can be carried out in the mind without actual experience but this action still involves immediately present concrete objects, those things known to us through many of our senses. It is only later that the process of considering "what would happen if . . ." becomes a strictly logical process as the human organism becomes able to test hypotheses in the mind. This pattern must be carefully considered as we approach the learner.

BRUNER

It is almost impossible today to explore studies concerned with learning without encountering the work of Jerome Bruner, a psychologist at Harvard University. Bruner's work has moved through two broad phases: Initially he was concerned with trying to describe how learning takes place, starting from the same focal point as Piaget. Lately, however, he has turned his attention to the *improvement* of learning rather than its description.

As he examines the "act of learning," Bruner finds that three phases seem to be occurring almost simultaneously. He describes them as follows:

> First there is *acquisition* of new information—often information that runs counter to, or is a replacement for what the person has previously known . . . it is a refinement of previous knowledge. . . . A second aspect of learning may be called *transformation*—the process of manipulating knowledge to make it fit new tasks . . . the way we deal with information in order to go beyond it. A third aspect of learning is *evaluation:* checking whether the way we have manipulated information is adequate to the task.[6]

Whereas Piaget has tried to explain what the child is capable of learning at a given stage of his life, Bruner proceeds to describe the action undertaken to get there. It is conceivable that these three phases of the learning process could be carried out by children at each stage of learning described by Piaget. But there remains one serious point of disagreement. Bruner has based his analysis on the startling hypothesis that any child at any stage of development can be taught any subject in some honest form! This would seem to be a direct contradiction of Piaget's conclusion that a child in a particular learning stage cannot master certain basic concepts.

If Bruner's hypothesis is granted, the consequences for curriculum construction are legion. It would seem that it would no longer be necessary to consider whether or not the student could learn a given concept. Instead, curriculum makers only need determine what is important to include and then construct an acceptable form of the content. This would be a major change in points of emphasis. Teachers need no longer ask, "Can my students learn this?" They would, instead, focus upon, "How can I organize these ideas so that my students will find them accessible?"

The notion of "structure" is now frequently encountered as one examines suggestions for the improvement of mathematics learning. Popularity of this term is in no small way the result of the work of Bruner, who explains that "Grasping the structure of a subject is understanding it in a way that permits many other things to be related to it meaningfully. To learn structure, in short, is to learn how things are related."[7]

He views structure in this way and also considers it to be made up of the underlying principles of a given subject. He sees it as the key to transfer of what is learned beyond the immediate situation.

Turning from a description of the learning act, Bruner has centered his studies upon the improvement of learning. This he describes as a theory of instruction, rather than one of learning.[8] Such a theory must consider four major areas of importance:

Environment or predispositions to learn: Creating the desire to learn requires an environment where students are free to make mistakes.

Structure of knowledge: Knowledge should be presented in a form so that the learner can understand it.

Sequences to present material: Sequence must vary with learner, but in general should proceed from enactive, to iconic, to symbolic.

Nature and pacing of rewards and punishment: The learner must eventually take this over for himself.

Bruner emphasizes that individuals translate their experience into their own models of the world—each person's reality. He spells out three points of emphasis in this development, moving from active manipulation of objects (enactive), to perceptual organization and imagery (iconic), and then to symbolic representation using language or words. Thus, once more we have an analysis of the process by which children learn, and once again we seem to be moving from the concrete and immediately present to the abstract, symbolic representation. Except for his assumption that anyone can be taught anything in some honest form, Bruner seems to be in general agreement with Piaget. His current efforts to build methods for the improvement of learning certainly bear watching.

DIENES

Z. P. Dienes is a mathematician turned psychologist, which leaves him uniquely qualified to attempt to unravel the mysteries of how children learn mathematics. An apt student of Piaget, as well as a colleague of Bruner at Harvard, Dienes has formulated his own description of the way mathematical learning may develop. He differentiates between two kinds of thinking that are involved in the solution of mathematical problems. There is the process of logical analysis, in which the individual works systematically from one step to the next as he proceeeds from the problem to the solution in a strictly logical, analytical way. Then there is also the process that Dienes calls "adventurous thinking," in which the individual mind breaks out of the confines of a logical system and with the end clearly in mind proceeds to work toward this end in spurts and starts without being aware of the "whys" and "hows" of the construction of these ideas. Dienes refers to the former as *analytical thinking* and calls the more adventurous type of thought *constructive thinking*. He explains that different mathematical tasks require a predominance of one or the other kind of thought. He claims that the teacher must therefore very carefully select the kinds of experiences in which to involve the students. The chief reason for this is that Dienes' research has led him to conclude that children develop adventurous, constructive thinking long before they develop the analytical, logical kinds. The logical analysis of what has been learned follows later—in some cases, many years later. Dienes sees this as one of the chief causes for the fear of and distaste for mathematics so commonly found among both children and adults in our society today. He goes so far as to exclaim that ". . . our adult preoccupation with analysis has poisoned for our children what could have been a most exciting series of discoveries. . . ." [9]

Thus, he is instructing teachers to create learning situations in the mathematics class that emphasize the use of constructive thinking rather than analytical thinking. Only later, in the mathematical growth of the child, will he be able to undertake the logical analyses we all too often focus upon at the start.

Dienes goes on to evolve four principles of learning:

> *The dynamic principle:* preliminary, structured games provide experiences.
> *The constructivity principle:* adventurous thinking is emphasized in these games and precedes analysis.
> *The mathematical variability principle:* experiences involve a maximum number of variables for the situation.
> *The perceptual variability principle:* provide for differences between individuals in concept formation and help children abstract the mathematical concept by presenting this concept in a broad variety of conceptual forms.

In essence then, Dienes is pointing out how activities should evolve as children learn mathematics, as well as describing the kinds of experiences that should be provided at each level. Once again we find that the learning process begins with an active cluster of experiences involving the mathematical concept to be learned and then, much later, enters upon a logical analysis phase; and once again we see the direction of learning moving from concrete, physical experience with complete freedom to project hypotheses and test them in a given situation to the more logical, analytical abstract ordering of what has been done.

SAWYER

W. W. Sawyer is a mathematician and not a psychologist. He has been concerned with helping children to learn mathematics and has formulated some of his own ideas on the subject that are so simple and direct as to deserve brief consideration here. Sawyer describes teaching techniques in mathematics that are carried on with the pupil "outside the subject." This is the situation in which we make the learning of mathematics a memory task, rather than an "exercise in understanding and insight." If the student is to become immersed in the subject, he must be free to ask questions, make guesses, and test the consequences of these for himself as he becomes involved with the mathematics of the moment. Thus he becomes an active participant in the learning process rather than a passive one. The emphasis is transferred from memorization to inquiry and understanding. Sawyer observes that there is a widespread fallacy among teachers that memorization is easy and that understanding is difficult. He states emphatically that the opposite is true because it is very hard to remember that which you do not understand. To achieve understanding Sawyer feels that it is important for a child to have a visual image of the mathematical idea under consideration—a visual anchor, so to speak, for the abstraction. To aid the teacher in developing this, he has created an ingenious collection of visual representations.[10] Thus, he has translated the general goal of achieving understanding into the specific process of aiding visualization because he sees visualization as a key to understanding.

SUMMARY

Many other studies have been undertaken to try to expose the learning process to view. While space prevents their mention here, the reader will find a fairly complete analysis of a multitude of studies in a recent yearbook of the National Society for the Study of Education.[11]

For our purposes, the work of Piaget, Bruner, Dienes, and Sawyer will suffice. These men have arrived at differing points of view regarding the learning process but have also established common characteristics as well. The teacher who is intent upon building mathematical experiences for children cannot ignore these works if he is to help each of his students to experience the joys and satisfaction that are all too often missing in the mathematics classroom. Just exactly how the work of these learning theorists can be used to construct specific classroom experiences will be examined in detail in the next chapter.

FOOTNOTES

1. Ernest R. Hilgard. *Theories of Learning.* Appleton-Century-Crofts, 1956, pp. 485–487.
2. Robert Glaser. "Implications of Training Research for Education." *In* National Society for the Study of Education, 63rd Yearbook, Part I. *Theories of Learning and Instruction,* University of Chicago Press, 1964, pp. 167–168.
3. David P. Ausubel. *Psychology of Meaningful Verbal Learning.* Grune & Stratton, Inc., 1963, pp. 3–4.
4. Jean Piaget. *The Child's Conception of Number.* Humanities Press, Inc., 1952.
5. Leo Brueckner and Foster Grossnickle. *How to Make Arithmetic Meaningful.* The John C. Winston Co., 1947.
6. Jerome Bruner. *The Process of Education.* Harvard University Press, 1960, p. 48.
7. Jerome Bruner. *The Process of Education.* Harvard University Press, 1960, p. 7.
8. Jerome Bruner. *Towards a Theory of Instruction.* Belknap Press of Harvard University, 1966.
9. Z. P. Dienes. "On the Learning of Mathematics." *The Arithmetic Teacher.* Vol. 10 (March, 1963), p. 115.
10. W. W. Sawyer. *Vision in Elementary Mathematics.* Penguin Books, Inc. (paperback), 1964.
11. E. L. Hilgard (Editor). *Theories of Learning and Instruction,* Part I. National Society for the Study of Education, 63rd Yearbook, University of Chicago Press, 1964.

FOR INVESTIGATION AND DISCUSSION

1. Compare Piaget's stages of development with those of Bruner. Where do they agree? Where do they disagree?

2. Evaluate the general research approach used by Piaget. Point out strengths and weaknesses.

3. Discuss the implications of Piaget's work for the teacher of mathematics.

4. Examine the literature to find out about the results other research workers have had in attempting to duplicate Piaget.

5. What does Bruner mean when he claims that anything may be taught to any child in some honest form? What is your reaction to this?

6. Compare the work of Dienes with that of Piaget and Bruner.

7. Illustrate how a teacher would alter his approach depending upon whether he was a follower of Piaget, Bruner, or Dienes.

8. Reexamine the way mathematics was taught to you and compare with the ideas of Piaget, Bruner, and Dienes.

FOR FURTHER READING

Books

Jerome Bruner. *The Process of Education.* Harvard University Press, 1960.
Jerome Bruner. *Towards a Theory of Instruction.* Belknap Press of Harvard University, 1966.
Z. P. Dienes. *Building up Mathematics.* Humanities Press, Inc., 1960.
Z. P. Dienes. *An Experimental Study of Mathematics-Learning.* Humanities Press, Inc., 1963.
E. L. Hilgard (Editor). *Theories of Learning and Instruction,* Part I. National Society for the Study of Education, 63rd Yearbook, University of Chicago Press, 1964.
Kenneth Lovell. *The Growth of Basic Mathematical and Scientific Concepts in Children,* Ed. 3. University of London Press, 1964.
Jean Piaget. *Child's Conception of Number.* Humanities Press, 1952.
Jean Piaget, Barbara Inhelder, and Alina Szeminska. *Child's Conception of Geometry.* Basic Books, Inc., Publishers, 1960.
W. W. Sawyer. *Vision in Elementary Mathematics.* Penguin Books Inc. (paperback), 1964.

Periodicals

David P. Ausubel. "Some Psychological and Educational Limitations of Learning by Discovery." *The Arithmetic Teacher,* Vol. 11 (May, 1964), pp. 290–302.
Jerome Bruner. "On Learning Mathematics." *The Mathematics Teacher.* Vol. 53 (December, 1960), pp. 610–619.
Arthur F. Coxford, Jr. "Piaget—Number and Measurement." *The Arithmetic Teacher.* Vol. 10 (November, 1963), pp. 419–427.
Z. P. Dienes. "On the Learning of Mathematics." *The Arithmetic Teacher.* Vol. 10 (March, 1963), pp. 115–126.
Eleanor Duckworth. "Piaget Rediscovered." *The Arithmetic Teacher.* Vol. 11 (November, 1964), pp. 496–499.
Gertrude Hendrix. "Learning by Discovery." *The Mathematics Teacher.* Vol. 54 (May, 1961), pp. 290–299.

Bert Kersh. "Learning by Discovery: What is Learned?" *The Arithmetic Teacher.* Vol. 11 (April, 1964), pp. 226–232.

Jean Piaget. "How Children Form Mathematical Concepts." *The Scientific American.* Vol. 189 (November, 1953), pp. 74–79.

George Polya. "On Learning, Teaching, and Learning Teaching." *The American Mathematical Monthly.* Vol. 70 (June, 1963), pp. 605–619.

David Wheeler. "Dienes on the Learning of Mathematics." *Mathematics Teaching.* (Summer, 1964), pp. 40–44.

R. L. Wilder. "The Role of Intuition." *Science.* Vol. 156 (May 5, 1967), pp. 605–610.

5

PLANNING FOR LEARNING

We hear a good deal today about startling new developments in the field of education that will revolutionize the classroom as we have traditionally conceived it. We find automated programs, teaching machines, learning cubicles, closed-circuit television, single-concept teaching films, and computerized instructional sequences among some of the recent developments. It is virtually impossible to attend a conference of mathematics teachers, read a journal, or discuss mathematics learning without hearing the word "discovery" mentioned over and over again. Everyone is talking about new methods, new techniques, and new materials, to aid the learning of mathematics, but one may well question how much is actually being done about it. Moreover, it seems that it is even more important to ask how much has been done to help teachers who would like to try to do something about improving the learning of their students.

It is one thing to study the best available clues to the learning of mathematics, but it is quite another thing altogether to build classroom experiences making use of such knowledge. While there is a good deal of literature in existence about the difficulties that youngsters encounter transferring what they have learned to new situations, the notion that teachers may experience these same difficulties has not received sufficient attention. In this chapter an attempt will be made to keep clearly before us the important ideas developed previously related to learning, as well as those related to the nature and importance of mathematics, as we approach the vital task of preparing effective learning experiences for students.

Our mathematical goals, or principles, are stated in Chapter 3. As far as the principles of learning that guide the organization of classroom experiences are concerned, we will try to build upon these ideas:

1. The "life cycle" of a mathematical idea dictates that learning must proceed from active involvement with concrete objects toward analysis with abstractions.
2. Throughout this process the student must be free to think about things and draw his own conclusions.
3. Opportunities for adventurous thinking in spurts and starts should precede analytical logical thought.
4. Children can abstract a mathematical principle if presented with a broad variety of situations in which the principle is inherent.
5. Visual images are necessary for students to be able to understand and use abstract concepts.

These five statements and the five principles presented in Chapter 3 may be thought of as assumptions in the manner of the postulates of geometry. In the true sense of postulates in mathematics, let us not consider the 10 assumptions to be "self-evident" truths. They do result, however, from a good deal of observation and investigation, which also is consistent with the formulation of mathematical postulates. These 10 notions are the basis upon which we will build our plans for helping students to learn mathematics. We shall investigate the mechanics of the planning process itself on both a long- and short-term basis. Most importantly, by the term *planning* we mean the careful development of a general approach to the creation of classroom learning experiences. Thus we are striving here for a framework for the teaching of mathematics. This is a far more significant undertaking than the mechanics of making plans, although plan construction is an important part of this process and it too will be considered.

With our goals and our direction clear, we may begin. Let us select a sample topic and see in specific terms how we may proceed.

UNIT PLANNING

The introduction to linear functions and equations from elementary algebra is a good starting point. If we were to plan a 2 to 3 week unit in this area, based upon our 10 assumptions, how would we proceed? Here are some suggested headings that may enable us to keep the important ideas uppermost in our minds as we work:

I. Objectives
II. Introduction
III. Overall development and content
IV. Summary and evaluation

Using this outline as a guide, we proceed to build our unit, "An Introduction to Algebra."

OBJECTIVES

What do we want our students to know?
What understandings should they have gained?
What skills do we want them to have when this unit is completed?

Since algebra is the language of the scientist and is of greatest importance because of the power it provides for the description of relationships, the notion of function must be central in this development. Thus, we will plan experiences that will begin to help students to understand the meaning of function and the role that algebra plays as a language for the description of relationships in the physical world. Specifically, we would want students to understand what a linear function is and to be able to recognize one when they see it.

As for skill development, the solution of simple linear equations would be of primary importance, as would the beginning development of skills in translating the language of algebra. The discovery of patterns in tables of values, the drawing of accurate graphs of functions, and the use of a new vocabulary are additional skills to be achieved.

The specific content of this unit will be listed in the section on development.

INTRODUCTION

How can we actively involve our students in experiences that are interesting and germane to the mathematics concepts of this unit?

Since we have assumed that the use of concrete representations in some active process will speed the understanding of the mathematical concepts to be learned, we will attempt to find such an experience to launch the unit of work. In this instance, perhaps our requirements would be satisfied if each member of the class were to conduct some physical experiment involving a basic linear relationship. Such an experiment would yield data that could be organized in tables, and the students could seek out any patterns inherent in these tables. To add to their understanding of the relationship, graphs could be made of the particular function and predictions could then be attempted and checked. In this way, we could immerse our students in the idea of function actively and quickly.

There are many situations that involve linear relationships: the stretch of a spring, the perimeter of a square, and the velocity of a dropped object, to name a few. Let us begin with a simple machine that can be made easily and that is rather consistent in the results that it yields. W. W. Sawyer's plat-

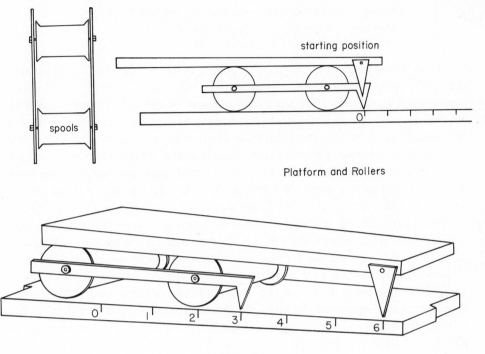

starting position

spools

Platform and Rollers

Figure 5-1

form and rollers would make a good beginning (Fig. 5-1). How far does the platform go as compared with the distance moved by the rollers?

If we provide enough platform and roller sets, we can group our students in teams of five or six and have each team conduct the experiment a number of times, collect and place the data in tables, search for patterns, and then describe the pattern using words. Later this description can be shortened to a formula, and the graph of the function can be drawn. The process of prediction enables the students to check with the apparatus. Each team of students can carry out every phase of this experience. All the important mathematical ideas are inherent in such an experience. In addition, we have made a beginning that has our students "doing" rather than "watching and listening," and at the same time we have proceeded with an activity that directly relates to our stated goals.

OVERALL DEVELOPMENT AND CONTENT

What will the students do after the introductory work?
How shall we maintain interest?
How shall we arrange the content?

What resource materials will help the students?
How can we provide a change of pace?
What are some possible trouble spots?

Once the students have become involved in conducting brief experiments that yield simple collections of data, what will they do next? How many experiments shall they do? Since the purpose of the experimentation is to involve the students in a physical process that has inherent in it the pertinent mathematical ideas, we must provide many such examples if students are to begin to focus upon the important mathematical ideas. Thus, at least two or three experiments shall be conducted as just described—two that are actually performed and a third that will perhaps be in a representational form: pictures or diagrams of a spring being stretched as weights are hung from it. At this point, instead of dealing with the concrete objects the students turn to a representation of such objects and place a ruler on the photos or diagrams in order to derive their data (Fig. 5-2). Later, diagrams of experiments will be presented to students with the data already stated on the diagram (Fig. 5-3). This will be followed by giving the students tables of data related to familiar objects and will culminate in work done with tables of numbers that do not refer to any concrete objects at all. Thus, our overall plan is to work from an active, real situation through a representation of such a situation to a final, completely abstract form.

Since our aim is to help students understand the linear function of form $y = ax$ and the ways in which such a function is described and since we also want to introduce the solution of linear equations derived from such functions, we will have to provide repetitive or drill experiences to help fix these ideas in students' minds. Regardless of the degree of abstraction, each time an experiment is considered (i.e., tables and graphs are made, followed by

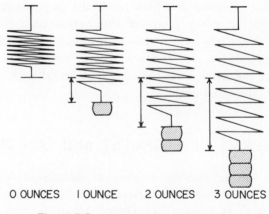

O OUNCES   I OUNCE   2 OUNCES   3 OUNCES

Figure 5-2. *An experiment in spring stretch.*

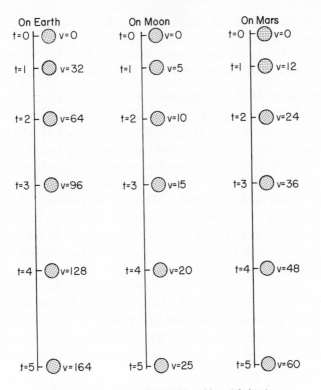

Figure 5-3. *The speed of falling objects (ft./sec.).*

predictions that are later checked and equations are solved), the student is undergoing a form of "drill," for he is repeating the work with the mathematical ideas. This would seem to be an optimum drill situation. The students work over and over again with the same mathematical concepts while the environment in which these concepts appear continually changes. Thus drill and boredom need no longer be synonymous.

In developing this unit of work, are there trouble spots that we may anticipate? Are there possible difficult areas that we may avoid or minimize by recognizing them at this stage of planning, rather than waiting for them to occur in the classroom?

We should expect to encounter student trouble with the process of translating sentences into mathematical formulas. If this should develop, a statement of the formula by the teacher, at first, will help the students over this rough spot. Because many such experiences are planned, the students will eventually devise some plan of their own for stating these formulas.

Another possible difficulty may arise in the solution of equations. It is most important to emphasize, at this time, the translation of the symbolic language of algebra, rather than to become involved in formal techniques such as application of the equality axioms and balancing. For example:

Find the amount of weight (w) necessary to stretch the spring (s) 18 inches, if the relationship is described by $s = 3w$.

Solution: $s = 18$; thus I must solve $18 = 3w$. This says that 3 times some number is 18. The number must be 6, since $3 \times 6 = 18$.

In order to avoid the pitfalls resulting from too much formal work, too soon, constant emphasis will be placed upon answering the questions, What does the equation say? and What do the symbols tell you? How to develop skill in handling more complex equations requiring the use of more formal methods will be discussed in the section devoted to algebra.

An important part of a unit is the introduction of varieties of activities in order to prevent student boredom. This will be provided for as the students move from physical experiments through pictures and diagrams to abstract collections of data. In addition, the freedom offered to the students to construct their own formulas and to make and check their predictions also builds into the unit a variety of activities.

As for the use of materials, we have already indicated that apparatus, pictures, and diagrams will all be involved in the unit as the class works in small teams as well as in whole-class groupings.

Thus the unit will evolve as described. The necessary repetition is provided, some anticipated trouble areas have been considered, and the activities of the unit carefully planned.

SUMMARY AND EVALUATION

What are the important understandings and skills to be tested for?
How shall we best determine how much has been learned?

The work of this section should reflect back upon the objectives stated at the outset. In order to provide an overview of the work of the unit, the students will be asked to conduct a complete experiment, from the collection of data to the solution of equations, in order to determine the extent to which each child has been able to master the important ideas. In addition, tables of linear relationships ($y = ax$) will be presented and students will attempt to find the patterns therein and describe their findings symbolically. Experiences will be developed to emphasize those areas in which the students have difficulty, and an examination will be administered. This test will include collections of data that relate to physical objects as well as completely abstract data. This would conclude the unit of work. If we now join these separate sections together in outline form, the finished plan for the unit looks like this:

Unit: Introduction to Algebra: The Linear Function
Length: 2 to 3 weeks
    I. Objectives

    A. Beginning of student realization of the following concepts:
      1. Algebra is the language of science
      2. Algebra describes relationships in the physical world
      3. The meaning of function in general
      4. The linear function in particular
    B. Skills
      1. Solution of simple linear equations
      2. Pattern-finding and description
      3. Drawing of graphs of the linear function
      4. Use of new mathematical words
II. Introduction
    A. Purpose: To seek out relationship between platform and rollers
    B. Procedures: Use five or six sets of platform and rollers; divide class into five or six teams to conduct experiments
      1. Perform and repeat experiment
      2. Tabulate data
      3. Search for patterns—describe verbally
      4. Reduce description to formula
      5. Draw graph
      6. Make and test predictions
III. Overall development and content
    A. Additional experimentation
      1. By doing (apparatus)
        a. Spring stretch—weights hung
        b. Perimeters of squares, given a side
      2. By measuring (pictures and diagrams)
        a. Spring stretch
        b. Number of inches in f—feet
      3. By reading from data (pictures and diagrams)
        a. Speed of falling objects—time
        b. Distance of thunder: lightning flash—time
    B. Data presented in table form
      1. Familiar situations
        a. Speed of falling objects on other planets
        b. Varieties of spring—stretch experiments
        c. Gasoline costs—gallons
      2. Abstract collections of data—In each of the preceding situations:
        a. Find a pattern
        b. Write a formula
        c. Draw the graph
        d. Compare with each other
        e. Predict results from formula and graph

        f. Check where possible against experiment or by alternate means

   3. Trouble spots

      a. Writing formulas—provide many examples; check statement and formula; compare.

      b. Solving equations—What does language mean? What do symbols tell us?

IV. Summary and evaluation

  A. Summary

    1. Weighing experiment: How many washers weigh a pound? 2 lbs.? 3 lbs.?

    2. Make a table-formula-graph. Prediction problems. How is this function like others? Unlike the others?

  B. Examination

DAY-TO-DAY PLANNING

Day-to-day planning procedures require different considerations. There are important assumptions underlying this work as well as that previously discussed. As we think in terms of a specific lesson, there are many "rules of the road" that should be kept in mind. Our first task is to create interest in what we are doing. The beginning of a lesson or a topic in general has been a sore spot in mathematics teaching for a long time. The reason for this is clear. Mathematics is a logical, sequential discipline. It begins with undefined terms, definitions, and postulates. Then, using the rules of logic, we proceed to prove propositions based upon these components, and we label as theorems those propositions with which we are successful. Thus, our mathematical structure grows. Since it does grow in this fashion, many teachers have assumed that this is also the manner in which it should be taught—and "there's the rub." How often have you been a student in a class that began like this: "The topic we will discuss today is the isosceles triangle. Now what is an isosceles triangle?" After several student responses the teacher continues, "An isosceles triangle is defined to be . . . ." This may appear to be a sound sequential development, but what of the way in which children learn? From what we know about learning, beginning with a definition of some unknown concept is deadly; for when the teacher begins in this fashion and this new entity is defined (since the students have had little or no previous experience with the isosceles triangle, let us say), what has been left for them to do? Their only choice at this point is to *remember* what the teacher or some student has said. Certainly since there has been no opportunity to work with these triangles before the stated definition, there is no opportunity to formulate one's own ideas or visual images regarding the topic. Beginning with a definition must result in rote memory work. On the other hand, if we would plan classroom activities to help children become actively involved with the pertinent ideas, *at the end* they should be able to provide us with a definition. In truth, this end product (the definition) may be somewhat different from ours, but it will usually be substantially correct and will always reflect how the student is thinking.

The same general idea would apply to the development of methods of solving varieties of mathematical problems. If the way to do something mathematically is presented to students as a model, we are asking them to memorize and copy. Despite all our protestations that we want to develop understanding, all we emphasize is the ability to remember. If, instead, we think and plan in terms of providing activities that will help a student to think and devise his own methods, we then have the greatest probability of successfully developing understanding. Thus, the point of view from which planning should proceed is to decide what to ask the students to do so that they can determine their own techniques for dealing with ideas. And the first part of this development calls for some beginning that will attract their attention, get them involved, and whet their appetites for more.

BEGINNING ACTIVITIES

How may we begin? There are many varieties of lessons. Generally, once the mathematical topic is clearly before us, we seek some interesting and meaningful activity, being careful all the while that the mathematics of concern at the moment is an integral part of that action. We are not concerned with creating interest for its own sake. Our desire is to find a setting for the mathematics to be learned that is of substance in order to help make the work meaningful. One interesting technique is to begin with a game. A game may offer an excellent opportunity, if the right one can be found. For example, we might play a "function" game with the students. In this game the teacher asks a student to say any number out loud and the teacher then responds with another number. For example,

student	7
teacher	9
another student	14
teacher	16
another student	0
teacher	2
another student	9

At this point the teacher says, "How many know what number I am going to say next?" After the students raise their hands, the teacher calls upon one and indicates that the answer is correct but suggests continuing the game to be sure that the "trick" (function) is known. He then proceeds and the making of a rule passes to the first student who guesses correctly. Such an

63

activity has all the elements of a game plus all the elements of the notion of function.

Other interesting beginnings may be made with puzzles, problems, stories, and applications. It has become customary in mathematics classes to teach skills and concepts and, once they are learned, to then present applications providing the student with an opportunity to make use of the newly learned ideas.

This progression of events is often mystifying. It seems to be moving in the reverse direction from what it should actually be. The application provides a reason for the student to learn whatever it is we want him to learn. Yet he only gets to this point *after* he has been taught the ideas. Thus, we may safely assume that he has learned whatever we have put before him without any reason other than his desire to please us. Is it any wonder that mathematics is so meaningless to so many?

"But wait," many teachers will say. "How can you possibly teach a student to work with an application if he lacks the necessary skills and understandings? He cannot carry out the desired calculations *before* he has learned how to do them." This is true, but we have lost sight of one crucial point: The teacher *knows* why the particular skills are needed because the teacher *knows* what is next on the agenda. The student, however, *does not know*. When he works to learn what we have set before him he has no purpose, no direction, and no feeling of a need to learn other than the feeling that this is what the teacher wants. He has already found out that there is a good deal in school that he is required to do that does not make sense, so one more such undertaking makes little difference! Turn the schedule around. Let us start with an application and place the student in a situation in which he is trying to find some result that has meaning to him; and if he finds himself blocked in this and in need of some new knowledge, *then and only then* let us provide what he needs.

Thus, the work that is carried out is of consequence to the student because he *needs* and, what is more important, *wants* to know. In this way what happens in the mathematics class is important *to the student* and has meaning to the student as well as to the teacher. Consequently, the teaching task, which is often thought of as preparing the student so that he may be able to deal with what is coming, may now be thought of as an act of creating situations in which the student will need and want to learn in order to be able to satisfy his desires to successfully complete the tasks before him.

It is not uncommon to find young teachers introducing a new topic in mathematics with a brief story that relates to situations of great interest to students. This is one way to gain student attention and involvement in a lesson. However, too often these situations of interest are only part of the first 5 minutes of the lesson; and as soon as the mathematical statement is derived, the remainder of the lesson is devoted to work with mathematical abstractions. Who has not heard a group of mathematics students give an audible groan of disappointment as a story of vital concern to them is eventually resolved in a symbolic mathematical statement that is the focus of the work for the day? If such a tale is to be used to create interest, it is most important to be sure that it provides a thread that continues throughout a major portion of the work that is to be done. In this way we will not be in the position of "sugar-coating" ideas for youngsters and encouraging their feelings of the uselessness of mathematics. As with games, stories involved in our lessons must have some important connection with the mathematics in question.

DEVELOPMENT

Once we have developed an activity that has the ideas we are considering as an integral part and once we have involved the students in working with ideas and have aroused their interest, we are faced with the problems of maintaining their interest and involvement and developing the lesson of the day. We then consider, What will the students be required to do as the lesson develops? We may assume that the greater the variety of activities, the greater the probability of realizing the desired learnings. Thus, we might ask the following questions and consider possible responses: Will the students have to sit still and listen? Will they be required to listen and speak in answer to questions? Will they listen, speak, and work at their desks on the tasks provided? Will they manipulate materials or observe films or film strips? Will they construct some materials of their own?

There are endless possibilities. Sitting and watching may be satisfactory part of the time, but it would seem that this is but one of the large variety of possible classroom actions. A change of pace in activity would also seem to offer a good opportunity to maintain a high level of student interest.

Whatever the topic, it would seem that it is most important for each child to have the chance to come to grips with the ideas of the day by himself before he leaves the classroom—that is to say, before he attempts such work at home. How many times have we, as students, followed the clear, logical explanations of our mathematics professors only to sit down at home later to discover that we are unable to begin to attack the first problem! How many times have we thought, "I wish the professor were here now, because *now* I know what to ask! *Now*, I know what I don't know!" Explanations and developments of ideas by teachers are clear when they are observed, but unless the student has the opportunity to try to complete the work himself, he literally does not know what questions to ask. Offering work time in class provides the student with an opportunity to find out where he may need help—at a time when you are available to provide the help required. Setting aside a portion of a class period for such work also enables the teacher to circulate around the room and get direct "feedback" from students as to how much they have been able to grasp, as well as to offer individual assistance as the need arises.

65

Encouraging students to work together during this block of time also provides aid for those in need and helps build the confidence of those offering the aid.

A work session as part of a mathematics class offers many advantages. Upon the completion of such a work session, it may be useful for the students to take a look together at some of the areas that proved difficult. Thus, a rough spot is revisited with the hope that this additional discussion may clarify concepts that were not readily understood by all.

It is conceivable that such findings may lead to the later development of additional lessons in the pertinent area.

SUMMARY AND REVIEW

The class may be concluded with an activity designed to pull together all the important ideas discussed and one that will provide the basis for the succeeding day's work. Rather than a simple restatement of ideas, such an activity might involve the presentation to the class of a problem that contains all the desired ingredients. Another such activity might be an oral or written true-false quiz that tests what has been learned and that is *not* used for grading. A game or group of puzzles that contain the mathematical ideas can also be played or replayed at this time. Moreover, it is possible that student-constructed problems could be presented for class consideration—depending upon the mathematics under consideration. Whatever is undertaken should provide something more than a simple rehashing of ideas.

How would a typical daily lesson look that had been developed along these lines? One such example follows:

Sample Daily Lesson Plan

Topic: Congruence

Aims: 1. An awareness of the corresponding parts of equal triangles that are sufficient to establish congruence
2. The importance of congruence

Method:
Beginning Activity (time—10 min.)
Problem: To find the distance across a pond, a boy put stakes at points A and B and at a convenient point, C. Walking along BC, he put another stake at D so that $BC = CD$. He did the same at E so that $AC = CE$. Will DE provide the distance wanted? (See Fig. 5-4.) Discuss to clarify what is happening. Discuss student-presented solutions.
Development (time—25 min.)
1. How can we solve the question? Make a diagram of the geometric situation, construct triangles to scale using a compass and ruler, and measure.

66

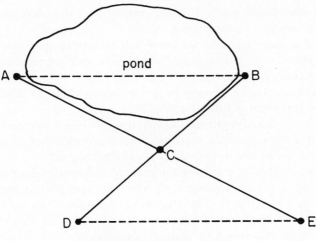

Figure 5-4. *Is* DE = AB?

2. Apply same method to new triangles—same situation but different measures. Does method still work?
3. Measure angles between equal sides. Conclusions?
4. Place a large scalene triangle on board. Ask students to make an accurate scale drawing. What measures do you want? Is one side enough? (Have student measure this.) Are two sides enough? Are two sides and an angle between enough? Conclusions?

Summary and Review (time—10 min.)

1. Will any three measures "fix" the triangle? Have students measure any desired parts of triangle and attempt to construct desired triangle.
2. Present oral true-false quiz.
   Sample questions:
   Can I construct the triangle on the board to scale if I have the following measures: Three sides? Three angles? Any two sides and any angle? Any two angles and any side? Two sides and the angle between?
3. After all questions are read and responded to, ask students to indicate question by question (by a show of hands) whether they answered true or false.

A RESTATEMENT AND THE FOUR FREEDOMS

We have considered the development of a way of life for the daily operation of our classrooms as we try to help students learn mathematics. Among the ideas emphasized were the following:

67

1. Definitions should result from experiences with the concepts, rather than becoming a starting point.
2. Instead of teaching skills we know will be needed later, we should place the student in a situation in which he feels the need and then teach to satisfy that need.
3. Applications should be used in the beginning to arouse interest, as well as at the end of a development.
4. Each lesson should begin with some attempt to create interest through the use of games, puzzles, and applications, provided that these activities have the desired mathematics as an inherent part.
5. The student should be involved in as many different kinds of activities (listening, speaking, writing, and doing, for example) as feasible to maintain a high degree of involvement and to provide for his abilities.
6. Time should be allowed for each student to work with the new ideas alone to aid him in asking intelligent questions.
7. We should develop summary activities that are more than mere restatements of ideas.

There are some additional "ground rules" that should be examined before we close this section. These considerations will not be found in lesson or unit plans, and yet they involve our daily interaction with our students. They are concerned with the climate of the room, and perhaps we may call these the four freedoms of the mathematics classroom. They are: the freedom to make mistakes, the freedom to ask questions, the freedom to think for one's self, and the freedom to choose methods of solution.

THE FREEDOM TO MAKE MISTAKES

Whenever a student makes an error in a mathematics class, he feels that he has committed some mortal sin or, at the least, that he has done something terribly wrong. His thought is that, at all costs, he must try never to make mistakes. This is a rather curious notion, for if our students did not make mistakes and in fact knew all the correct answers, there really would not seem to be any purpose in their coming to class. They are in school to learn. Not knowing is, therefore, a natural state of being and not a wrong one. It is only through student declarations of what is not understood that we as teachers gain insight into what has to be done to help. Thus, we must be fairly certain that our classroom atmosphere, above all, poses no direct threat to the student so that he is free to err and that in so doing he aids the progress of all.

In addition, we want our students to feel free to guess, to try out ideas, and in short, to use their intuition without fear of recrimination. When a student feels that every answer he gives must be a correct one, he is much too guarded in his thinking. Let us be sure to keep our classroom atmosphere ripe for the development of "adventurous" thinking. To do this we honor and accept all thoughts and, at the least, congratulate the student for sharing a feeling of his with the class. In this way there shall be a minimum of limits placed by each student in the class upon his own imagination in dealing with mathematical problems.

Another way in which to assure this freedom is to do whatever is possible to help students to see the cause of their mistakes and to unobtrusively aid them in self-correction. By whatever means, students must feel that a mistake is but one step in the process that leads to learning.

THE FREEDOM TO ASK QUESTIONS

How many times have you been witness to a classroom situation in which a student is ridiculed because of a "silly" question? How many times have you seen a student virtually destroyed verbally because he has asked a question that was just answered by the teacher the moment before? Oftentimes, the very teacher who has done the ridiculing or who has wreaked verbal destruction upon a student makes periodical pleas to his students to be sure to ask questions, or else how will he know how his students are reacting to classwork? In this instance, as in many others, we cannot walk two sides of a street at the same time. If we are genuinely convinced that it is imperative for students to feel free to ask questions, then we must maintain an atmosphere conducive to questioning, an atmosphere that will allow each child to feel completely free to ask whatever may be of concern to him. One sure way to help develop such a climate is to honor each and every question posed—no matter how often repeated and no matter how minute a point may be involved. Make the questioner feel good for having asked and everyone in your room will feel equally free to pose any question without the fear of the question being silly or holding the class back. This is a vital freedom for effective, student-teacher relationships—effective in the sense of facilitating learning.

THE FREEDOM TO THINK FOR ONE'S SELF

Earlier we discussed the effect of presenting model solutions to students with the resulting emphasis upon memorization. The student who is taught by use of these models is constantly asking himself, "How did the teacher do that one again?" rather than examining the information of the situation and trying to think through to the desired end. The unusually impossible answers that teachers find on test papers are one example of the fruits of this emphasis upon duplication. If we would, instead, devise situations in which the student is free to think for himself about the concepts contained therein, the student will then develop his own patterns of thought instead of trying to commit to memory the thinking done previously by the teacher or some textbook author. This implies a readiness on the part of the teacher to not only accept but also reward the end product of this thought, even though it may not be of the same kind, quality, or preciseness of that of the teacher. This implies that the mathematical soundness of ideas will take precedent over elegance, precision, and conciseness of thought. Teachers are understandably reluctant to permit a student to struggle through a given situation on his own when tried and true short cuts can save time and energy. Certainly, this is well intentioned; but on the other hand, if one struggles with ideas, as one thinks for himself in attempts to solve whatever problem is before him and if his efforts result in his arriving at the desired end, a degree of satisfaction is present that results in the strengthening of confidence in the ability to think through problems rather than to memorize methods of solution. Rote memorization, necessary in some areas of mathematics, may be the greatest enemy of the continued development of mathematical thought in youngsters. It certainly gives our students a completely distorted view of the nature of mathematics itself. Encourage students to think by developing classroom situations that will afford the opportunity to do so.

THE FREEDOM TO CHOOSE METHODS OF SOLUTION

Closely allied with the freedom to think is the freedom to devise and employ one's own methods of solution in attacking mathematics problems. Most problems in mathematics can be approached in a wide variety of ways; no one way is necessarily better than any other. There seems to be an unwritten law that the fewer steps one requires to achieve a solution, the more elegant is that solution. It seems that the quickest route is thought to be best. Nothing could be more detrimental to the development of sound mathematical thought in youngsters. We often see teachers who are aware of the need for children to think for themselves putting many solutions to a given problem on the blackboard, side by side. This is an excellent technique for encouraging individual thought and adventurous thinking. But all too often this same teacher will then call the attention of the class to the solution that is completed in the fewest number of statements, indicating that since this is the shortest way, this is the way everyone should proceed! What makes a short solution better than a longer one? Placing solutions on the board together provides every student with an opportunity to see varieties of sound mathematical developments. Having done this, why not permit each student to choose for himself how he will approach this particular kind of problem? In this way, he is not forced into the position of having to recall what the teacher may say, and he is free to fit the solutions to his own feelings of strength or weakness in mathematics. Just as there was "no royal road to geometry," so there is no royal road to the answering of most mathematical questions. Allow each student to select his own path and you will be helping him to realize the importance of thinking about mathematics rather than trying to remember.

Judge only the correctness of the mathematics and not the length of the demonstration. You may be rather pleasantly surprised at the quality and variety of student responses when students are free to think for themselves and devise their own appropriate solutions to problems.

Organizing classroom experiences that emphasize student originality in thought and problem solution will be developed in detail in each subject area in the next section of this book. Special problems, such as providing for individual differences and teaching the slow learner and the gifted child, will be considered in the last section.

FOR INVESTIGATION AND DISCUSSION

1. Write a lesson plan for the introduction to directed numbers to an average ninth grade class in elementary algebra.

2. Write a lesson plan for a topic in plane geometry of your own choosing.

3. Construct three ways in which a lesson for average eighth graders studying ratio and proportion may be started in order to catch student interest. Develop only the introductory part of the lesson.

4. Do the same for a topic of your own choosing from algebra or geometry.

5. Evaluate the plans just made by comparing with the general goals stated at the beginning of this chapter.

6. Discuss the use of applications and whether they should be introduced before, during, or after skills and concepts are taught.

7. Devise ways in which to develop the *need to learn* on the part of the student.

8. Discuss the "four freedoms" described in this chapter and compare with your own experiences as a student.

FOR FURTHER READING

Periodicals

Mary E. Albrecht. "A Teacher Plans Her Day." *The Arithmetic Teacher*. Vol. 3 (October, 1956), pp. 151–156.
Frank B. Allen. "Building a Mathematics Program: An Adventure in Cooperative Planning." *The Mathematics Teacher*. Vol. 49 (April, 1956), pp. 226–234.
Ethel B. Friedman and Nathan Washton. "A Teaching Unit on Graphs." *The Mathematics Teacher*. Vol. 48 (February, 1955), pp. 77–81.
Kenneth B. Henderson and James H. Rollins. "A Comparison of Three Strategems for Teaching Mathematical Concepts and Generalizations by Guided Discovery." *The Arithmetic Teacher*. Vol. 14 (November, 1967), pp. 583–588.
Paul M. Nemecek. "Stimulating Pupil Interest." *School Science and Mathematics*. Vol. 65 (January, 1965), pp. 47–48.

71

SECTION THREE

ON TEACHING

PART ONE

MATHEMATICS BEFORE ALGEBRA

6

ARITHMETIC

OVERTURE

The traditional curriculum for the seventh and eighth grade has been the weakest link in the chain of mathematics courses composing the school mathematics program. After 6 years of work with the fundamentals (basic computation with whole numbers, decimals, and common fractions) the students entered seventh grade only to be faced with an extensive review of these same computational skills. This was usually followed by the presentation of a variety of topics involving applications of arithmetic in the everyday lives of adults in our society (called *social applications*). In this way we believed that we were preparing our youngsters to meet the many different quantitative situations they would encounter as adults in our world. As a consequence, the areas of application included banking, stocks and bonds, profit and loss, insurance, and taxes—all important in the life of most adults. What then seems to be wrong

75

with a curriculum built upon this foundation? One vital consideration has been overlooked. While it is true that these applications are real and significant ones to grownups, it is equally true that young people, for the most part, couldn't be less interested in them. We have assumed that because such information would be of importance *later* to our students that they would see the need for learning *now*. This kind of borrowing against tomorrow has proved deadly from the student's point of view.

Everything we know about children and the way they develop would seem to indicate that the tasks that are laid before them must have meaning and importance now if the students are to become interested in them. We violated this cardinal principle with the expected end product of mechanical student work and confirmation of the feeling that mathematics does not relate to anything of consequence. This does not mean that there may not be topics of interest and importance included in the host of applications mentioned earlier; indeed, there are. For example, involving a 14 year old in a study of automobile insurance and financing may well attract a good deal of interest on his part. But in general, the problems that were selected and the limited experiences provided made a deadly classroom combination. Hence there was, and still is, a need for sharp revision when we face the task of defining the mathematics program for the early years of junior high school.

Along with such revision, a change in methods of teaching is also in order. We have not yet been able to successfully eliminate unwanted rote learning from our mathematics classrooms. The basic instructional pattern of explanation-question-practice that can so frequently be observed has been the generator of much rote learning. This approach must also undergo change. We have "covered" the material, it is true; but we have not uncovered the beauty and the significance of mathematics. And this is our charge. Somehow, what happens in the mathematics classroom has got to result in a feeling on the part of each student that mathematics is important, that mathematics helps us in many significant ways, that mathematics makes sense, and that it is "doable" by ordinary mortals. The entire process of "doing" must be interesting and enjoyable if it is to be satisfying. In the first section of this book, we attempted to point out what is important about the subject of mathematics itself. The second section was devoted to a consideration of the needs of the learner as he approached the study of mathematics. How these relationships are bound together to form a plan for the instruction of mathematics will now be developed in detail as we consider the variety of topics that make up the secondary school mathematics curriculum.

If the social-use approach led to the development of a good deal of meaningless applications, what shall we do instead? The answer to this question is not yet a final one. Indeed, it may be better if it never becomes final in the sense that curriculum was thought to have been finally developed prior to 1950. We are sharply aware of the fact now that change is not to be feared. But what form shall these changes take? An examination of some of the more significant mathematics curriculum improvement studies would indicate that there are certain goals common to most programs.[1] Included among these are:

1. An introduction of set vocabulary and concepts.
2. A general attempt to make vocabulary more precise.
3. A stress upon mathematical structure.
4. A general trend away from social uses.

All in all, it seems that the chief emphasis of most of the suggested changes (if they can be generalized at all) would be in the direction of including more sophisticated and rigorous mathematics cast in a more precise vocabulary and a rather elaborate symbolism. The specific topics will be examined in detail later. There is little disagreement that in the past too many of the mathematical activities of the early junior high school years were devoid of meaning and importance for most students. Will a more precise and rigorous curriculum emphasizing the structure properties of the real number system, for instance, provide an improvement in significance and understanding on the part of the student? Not automatically, if at all. Of one thing we can be sure: We will find no panaceas. There are no quick cures for the ills of mathematics education, and despite what you may read in the professional journals or in professional pamphlets, change is not synonymous with improvement. If we are to work for the continued improvement of the learning of mathematics in our schools, then it seems that we are obligated to construct methods of instruction that not only reflect what is important about mathematics but that also are based upon sound psychological principles in terms of what we know about children and how they learn. Too few programs have concentrated upon changing mathematical content without giving proper attention to the effect of student-teacher relationships. These relationships and the teaching-learning process are inextricably bound together. Unless we keep all these considerations before us, we may well negate our attempts to improve learning before they get off the ground.

With the criteria established in Chapters 3 and 5 as our guide, we turn our attention to specifics. We will focus upon three broad areas: arithmetic, informal geometry, and the newly emphasized area of statistics. A detailed examination of the important concepts of so-called "modern mathematics" programs will round out the considerations of this section.

ARITHMETIC—AN INTRODUCTION

By the time the student has completed the sixth grade, he has probably learned most of the mathematics he will be called upon to use in everyday living in our society. If we were to attempt to justify what he is taught beyond grade 6 on the basis of "social use," we would be hard put to make a strong case. There are, however, some mathematical concepts that do offer to satisfy this goal as well as the other objectives discussed previously. The key to this process is not only to teach what may some day be needed, but to include in the mathematics program those applications that are of some consequence to the student *now*. The student must feel a present need, a present importance. Why should he take our word for the fact that what he is studying today will have real significance for him tomorrow? If we want him to think for himself, he should not be asked to take our word for anything.

The learning activities to be developed may remind one of "incidental" learning that was roundly criticized in our schools not too many years ago, but there is an important difference here. Although the learning may be of an incidental nature to the students, it most certainly should not be incidental for the teacher. On the contrary, the concepts studied in this manner are those resulting from careful planning and selecting by the teacher—a far cry from "incidental" occurrence. We ought not to confuse incidental with accidental.

It is generally a good idea to resist the temptation to begin the first year of mathematics in the junior high school with an intensive review of fundamentals. When students come to us after a long summer vacation, they are actually looking forward to resuming their school work. They are eager, fresh, and hoping for something new and exciting. Nothing can ruin that fine aura of expectation quicker than a unit of work that involves "that same old stuff" of the lower grades. But what topic shall we make our starting point and how shall we go about organizing the instruction of the topic? There is no one answer for all teachers and students. There are any number of entry points into the work of the junior high school, and each teacher can make the best decision for himself and his students.

Criteria that will assist in making this choice have already been referred to. To get off to a flying start it would be to our advantage to:

1. either start with a fresh topic or introduce familiar mathematics in a new setting.
2. select a topic of potential high interest value for students.
3. introduce any topic in a way that makes the student an active rather than passive participant.
4. seek out situations that clarify the important goals of mathematics instruction, i.e., ones that demonstrate the significance of mathematics or the power of mathematics.

Let us turn to specific cases in point.

RATIO AND PROPORTION

Do you know your "rotundity index"? [2] Everyone has one and it may or may not be the same for each of us. This special statistic is a description of how tall we are as compared with how far around we are. Many years ago there was a popular song about an unusually plump fellow who measured as far around as he was high; he was called "Mr. Five-by-Five." This unfortunate gentleman has a rotundity (roundness) index of 1. Nature does not often construct creatures of this form, despite the fact that the mathematics seems nice and tidy. Most of us are a good deal taller than we are round. But how do these measurements compare?

In attempting to answer this question we have one way in which we may get our mathematics class off to an interesting beginning in their study of ratio and proportion. How shall the students proceed? To begin with, a group of volunteers might offer to be measured, with the collected data placed in a table that is made by each student. As the class discusses the relationship between the measures of height and waist, they may describe one measure as being larger or smaller than another, or they may indicate how many times one number may be larger or smaller than the other. They will soon see that working with the difference between the two figures offers little insight, and a need for the ratio comparison is present. This should simply be described as the quotient of the two numbers and should be written as a fraction in a newly added column to the table (see Table 6-1). If the indicated division is carried out for each student's data, a pattern emerges: The ratio is usually between 2 and 3. At this point each student could check this hypothesis by gathering his own measurements, using a tape measure or string and a yardstick or carpenter's rule.[3] Adding his own data to his table, each student determines his own index and observes whether or not the result is in the expected range. Examining the results from each student can lead to support or rejection of the hypothesis about the index. It is most important to be sensitive to the feelings of youngsters in the class. If any of them should be over or underweight and feel ashamed of the fact, it would be wise to avoid involving them in the public statement of results. Indeed, working with volunteers will help minimize any such undesirable happenings.

In fact, if the teacher wishes to avoid sensitive reactions entirely, it is possible to measure height and foot length and formulate another index which we might call the "balance," "knock-down," or "solidity" index, i.e., the ratio of your height to your foot length. We could think of this as an indication

Table 6-1. Rotundity Index.

Student	Height in Inches	Waist in Inches	$\dfrac{Height}{Waist}$
Tom	60	24	$\frac{60}{24} = 2\frac{1}{2}$
Ben	58	25	$\frac{58}{25} = 2\frac{8}{25}$
Marc	57	22	$\frac{57}{22} = 2\frac{13}{22}$
Teacher	71	32	$\frac{71}{32} = 2\frac{7}{32}$

Table 6-2. "Knock-Down" Index.

Student	Height in Inches	Foot Length in Inches	$\dfrac{Height}{Foot\ Length}$
Tom	60	10	$\frac{60}{10} = 6$
Ben	58	9	$\frac{58}{9} = 6\frac{4}{9}$
Marc	57	9	$\frac{57}{9} = 6\frac{1}{3}$
Teacher	71	12	$\frac{71}{12} = 5\frac{11}{12}$

of how solid the foundation is upon which you stand. The investigation of this index would proceed as described for the rotundity index. You cannot be too sensitive to the feelings of youngsters. If there is any possibility of making a student feel awkward, avoid the rotundity index entirely. There are many other interesting ratio indexes that you will probably think of for yourself. Some sample results from exploring the "knock-down" index are listed in Table 6-2.

Not only have we made an active introduction to ratio that satisfies our basic mathematical goals, but we have also involved students in measurement activities and have had a look at the workings of nature. Despite the infinite variety of humans that we see about us, it appears that nature has apparently stuck closely to an overall master plan, at least as far as the students and teacher are concerned. We may extend this beginning experience with ratio to include other living forms, such as animals and trees, depending upon student and teacher interest. Such additional experiences result in repetition of the use of ratio and measurement in a setting that is different. Interest level may remain high during these experiences designed to provide practice. This is a far cry from long lists of examples.

Does man also follow some basic order as he manufactures things for daily use? What would the rotundity index be for paper cups, for example? We have still another extension of this introduction to ratio by investigating several sizes of paper cups by the same manufacturer and comparing their height with the circumference at the widest point. Using string or tape may simplify measuring the circumference. The same experience can be extended to include various sizes of tin cans and milk containers—to name but a few of the possible objects for study. A wealth of experiences related to ratio is accumulating, requiring a good deal of measurement using varied measuring tools and involving important geometry concepts that will be discussed again later. This is a rather handsome pay-off for an apparently simple idea. In addition, many examples are encountered requiring computation with whole numbers and fractions. As students work through these examples, their needs in the important skill areas will become clear to both them and you. The necessary teaching for skill improvement may then take place. In this way the needed review is conducted in a generally favorable environment since the need is now apparent to the student. He wants to do the other work you have set before him. General reviewing at the start of the year serves the teacher's need, not the students'.

In each case we have mentioned, the investigation should be one that makes a maximum appeal to student intuition—one that makes clear what question is being considered and encourages the student to proceed in his own way. The construction of tables of results enables students to better "read" the data for any pattern of relationship. Predictions may be undertaken with objects not yet measured before as well as after it appears that a pattern has been detected. Verification or rejection results from additional measurement. The overall procedure of such an experience makes each student feel that he is undertaking his own study and, at the same time, is contributing to the class as a whole.

Similar work with ratio may be undertaken by charting the preferences of the students in an unlimited number of situations: What is your favorite TV show? Who is your favorite performer? What do you most like to do with your spare time? What do you want to be? These are but a few of the possible questions that may be considered. When student responses are tabulated, a rich source of material is available for all sorts of ratio questions. For example, Table 6-3 contains sample responses to the question about future plans. After discussion about the various occupations mentioned and their general requirements in terms of salaries, abilities, attitudes, and education, we may compare student preferences and ask such questions as: What is the ratio of would-be teachers to lawyers? How does the number of boys who want to be doctors compare with the number of girls who want to be doctors? What ratio of the total class would like to be actors?

In addition to important involvement with the concept of ratio, we are also well on our way to the study of proportion. An excellent opportunity is also present to explore significant nonmathematical ideas with students in the natural course of events. Planning for the future by gaining realistic information about job requirements is also important to students. What we do with our leisure time is becoming an increasingly important social problem as technological advancement leaves us with more and more of it. A discussion

Table 6-3. Job Preferences of Boys and Girls.

| *Job* | *Preferred by* | | *Total* |
	Number of Boys	*Number of Girls*	
Actors	3	5	8
Doctors	4	1	5
Lawyers	7	2	9
Teachers	2	4	6
Get married	0	4	4

of such problems should be carefully conducted. It may seem that we will lose valuable time for the consideration of mathematical topics, and to some extent this is true. Nevertheless, the time taken will be well spent in that it adds to the importance students will attach to mathematics as they become aware of the variety and scope of the problems which lend themselves to mathematical considerations.

A beginning may be made in tying mathematics and science together by considering the ratios involved in gears: We can arrange any number of experiences using gears of the same size, gears of varying sizes, and gear trains consisting of many gears (Fig. 6-1). There are children's toys that may be used, as well as commercial gear boards that could probably be borrowed from the school science lab. The gear teeth may be counted or the revolutions of one gear in relationship to other gears can be determined as discussions are held about the places where students have seen gears in use. Automobile transmissions, electric can openers, and bicycles are common in the background of virtually every child. If an old clock can be taken apart by students, not only would they have a good deal of fun but they would probably marvel at the gear arrangements enclosed. This could be a most fruitful area for investigation as the students consider such things as the following: How could we make a particular gear turn faster? How could we make it turn slower? How many complete turns of this gear are required to turn the other gear around once? What is the ratio of gear teeth of the larger gear to those of the smaller gear? What is the ratio of their revolutions?

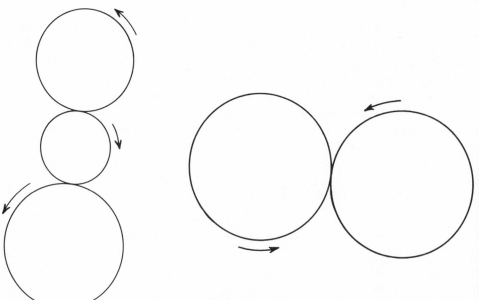

Figure 6-1

Experiences with ratio, an insight into the nature of common objects, and an opportunity to physically do things are among the advantages of such experiences. If gears are difficult to secure, cutouts of cardboard will work surprisingly well.[4] It is possible to move from concrete gears to pictures and eventually to the numbers themselves in order to provide additional experiences. This pattern of moving from the concrete and real toward the abstract is a pattern basic to the learning of mathematics. We shall follow it often.

The development of ratio concepts as just presented describes a model that will generally be followed throughout this book. We have tried to involve our students in an active program of experiences designed to introduce the desired mathematical concepts in a significant setting. Definitions have not been offered at the start as is frequently the case. Rather, it would seem that after participating in the experiences described, as well as in other related activities, each student could readily provide his own definition of ratio. Practice has been offered by introducing new experiences and situations that contain recurring mathematical content. We now extend our experience to include proportion, a comparison of two ratios.

We have many possible ways to begin the study of proportion. The job preference charts constructed earlier would provide one such point. The students might consider the way in which other classes of students of similar age and background would respond to the very same questions. Proportions could be constructed in order to enable students to attempt predictions of results. It would then be quite possible to survey the additional classes and compare predicted and actual results. (The implications for sampling will be more carefully considered in the chapter on statistics.) The students should be free to resolve the proportions in the best way that they can. Work with fractions is not new to them, and their previous experiences may suggest methods of solution. For example, in a class of 32 students containing 16 girls, there were four who responded that they wanted to be a teacher. The ratio of girls who wanted to be teachers to all the girls was 4/16 or 1/4. If the class next door has 20 girls, how many do you think will say that they hope to become teachers? The problem then is: $1/4 = N/20$. How will the students find the missing N? The ability to find equivalent fractions is one way students will solve the problem, but it is really up to them. Those who are unable to proceed may be questioned to help them think through their difficulties. This informal approach to solutions will offer the students an opportunity to think about problems for themselves. It is true that incorrect procedures may possibly result, but this is not bad. The classroom is the place in which it must be acceptable to make mistakes. The consequences of our ideas will not only help us to decide whether or not we are "on to something" but they will also enable us to grope about and eventually find our way. The "freedom to flounder" is a basic guaranteed right for all learners.

There are many other situations that may be constructed for students studying proportion, including any of those mentioned in the ratio discussion. The entire area of comparative shopping is a rich one to explore. For example:

> The $3\frac{1}{2}$ ounce toothpaste tube cost 49¢. How much should the 5 ounce size of the same brand cost if it is to be a bargain?
>
> A 2 ounce jar of instant coffee costs 43¢. The 3 ounce jar of the same brand costs 63¢. Which is the better buy?
>
> A regular 32 page Batman comic costs 12¢, while an 80 page giant issue costs 25¢. Which is the better buy?

These are but a few of the many problems that may be pursued in this area. Not only are the problems legion but the teacher has a chance to make the work as active as he dares. From the supermarket students can bring in empty cartons and cans of varying sizes of the same and different products and compare prices and sizes. Is the largest size always the best buy per unit? You may be surprised at the results yourself. Comparisons should also be made of the price and quality of similar products from different manufacturers, as well as from the same manufacturer, as the entire area of getting the most for your money comes under careful consideration.

Not only do we generate a wealth of important proportion problems, but we are also serving an important need of all consumers in our society. It is not an easy task to shop wisely in the environment of today's supermarket, with myriad products packed in all sorts of irregular sizes and elaborate packages. We have not mentioned how one attempts to determine comparative quality. An examination of advertising claims points up the difficulties here, but a start can be made—a start that helps the student to begin to become aware of his role as a consumer in society, a start that involves him in an unlimited number of proportion problems.

Other proportion experiences could result from an investigation of the following areas:

> A car-racing set has a scale of 1:32 marked upon it. Compare the lengths of the various components of the car with its real-life counterpart (i.e., length of car, distance between wheels, and width of seat). The same could be done for electric trains, model airplanes, or dolls. The H-O trains are scaled to $\frac{1}{87}$ of actual size; the scale used is always marked on the box.
>
> Through the use of oil company local-area maps, a vacation trip is planned down to the location and costs of overnight stops, meals, tolls, and entertainment. The maps may be secured in quantity by writing to the oil companies in your area. In this way each student will have one. He must use the scale of the map in order to compute distances; thus the solution of proportions is necessary.
>
> The construction of scale drawings of the classroom, the entire floor of the school, the student's room, and the floor plan of his apartment or house are a few of the possible drawings that can be made. The process of the two previous examples is reversed since the student must

determine the scale after carrying out the necessary measurements and considering the limitations of paper size.

These experiences with proportion are not the beginning and end of our study of this important area. The same concepts will be visited many times as the students work with geometry and statistics. In addition, proportion will be the basis for the introduction of the idea of percent.

The solution of proportions, as has been indicated, will probably be carried out using the idea of equivalent fractions. After many proportions have been solved, you will find students who are cross-multiplying. When this occurs (or when the need for more formal methods arises because the use of equivalent fractions is becoming tiresome and difficult), the method should be shared with the class and the question of its consistency should be considered. The teacher might say, "John seems to have found an interesting idea, but will it always work?" At this point the entire class can check the large number of proportion problems previously completed in order to test the method. After confirmation and the introduction of the names of the terms of a proportion (means-extremes) the students are left with the idea that they now have *two methods* with which to attack the problem of finding a missing term of a proportion. The choice of which one they shall use (cross-products or equivalent fractions) is best left to them. There is, after all, no one best way to solve a given problem, but there are many good ways. If we concentrate upon sound mathematical thinking rather than upon the elegant method, we may have our best opportunity to develop students of mathematics who will "think for themselves."

The solution of the simple equation resulting from multiplying the means and extremes of the proportion may well be treated in like manner. To use the example cited earlier: $1/4 = N/20$, $4N = 20$, so $N = 5$. How does the student reason his way to the last statement that $N = 5$? The choice is his. He may well focus solely upon the language of the equation directly preceding this one: $4N = 20$. What does this symbolic statement say to the student? It simply states that "4 times some number gives a product of 20." If this translation is made, the fact that 5 is the missing number becomes apparent. Here again, formal methods of solution would seem to be premature. They are certainly not necessary. Let us then postpone their introduction until such time as the need arises, and let us also be sure to plan experiences so that the need in question *will arise of necessity*.

It may well be that after completing numerous proportion problems you will find that most of the students are carrying out a process very similar to application of the division axiom (dividing equals by equals) as they find their answers. If not, examples are carefully selected to create difficulty and establish a need for more powerful methods. In the final analysis, this is the creative aspect of teaching. It is not the ability to make that wonderfully clear explanation, as we may have believed for so long, but rather it is the ability to establish the situation in which the student finds that he has a definite need to learn more in order to be able to do the task that is set before him. When his desire to know has been stimulated, the optimum teaching time is present. Creating this desire is where the imagination and ingenuity of the teacher come into play. It is a delicate balance of timing so that the past, present, and future experiences are all woven into an integrated whole.

The proportions considered thus far were direct proportions: They varied in the same direction. If we wish to keep a seesaw in balance as we increase the weight on one end (the other end unchanged), we must decrease the distance of this weight from the fulcrum—the point of support for the seesaw (see Fig. 6-2). This is an example of an inverse proportion. Other examples are: If you increase the number of men who will paint a room, you will decrease the number of hours required to do the job; if you increase the monthly payment on a debt, you decrease the number of months needed to complete payment; and if you increase the length of a wood plank (keeping other dimensions constant), you will decrease the amount of weight the plank will support.

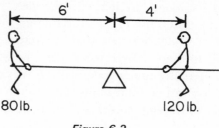

Figure 6-2

While it is not expected that inverse proportion should be a topic for extended discussion at this time, it is important to introduce one or two situations such as those just mentioned in order to prevent students from concluding that all proportions involve quantities that increase or decrease together. If a problem in inverse proportion is introduced in a series of problems without any introduction at all, it has a rather startling effect upon students. For example, consider the following problem:

A parking lot can be cleared of snow by two plows in 6 hours. How long would it take three plows working at the same rate to do the job?

The students would probably solve the problem along these lines:

2 plows take 6 hours
3 plows take h hours
$$\frac{2}{3} = \frac{6}{h}$$
$$2h = 18$$
$$h = 9$$
Therefore 3 plows take 9 hours.

There is an old proverb to the effect that too many cooks spoil the broth. Does it also hold that too many plows make the job take longer? Can you imagine the dilemma of the student as he checks and rechecks his work and is unable to find an error and yet his apparently correct mathematical result is a violation of his common sense? The resulting discussion leads to a beginning awareness of the fact that there are many types of proportions in addition to those studied earlier, the inverse proportion being one of these. Once again the student finds that he simply cannot operate with numbers without keeping track of exactly what the numbers represent.

A word about ratio and rate, and then we will extend the concept of proportion into the study of percent. It may not aid student ability to do problems involving ratios, but a clarification of the ideas of ratio and rate may aid in the formation of proportions. When we compare quantities of the same units we have a ratio: 3 men ride the train and 7 men drive cars, so the ratio of riding men to driving men is $\frac{3}{7}$. Both numbers refer to men; this is a ratio. The rates are probably most familiar to students in the form of speeds. A car travels at an average speed of 30 m.p.h. The rate may be described as $\frac{30}{1}$ where the top number is in terms of miles and the denominator is in terms of hours. Thus, in the snow problem we could have considered the rate $\frac{2}{6}$, 2 plows take 6 hours.

The prices of things are also rates. We find that we may buy 3 pencils for a dime, or perhaps 3 apples for 25¢. Although we want students to be aware of the difference between rate and ratio, we are not concerned with emphasizing differences to the point that it may interfere with the student's ability to do the work. We are interested in using correct language, but we have still greater interest in helping students develop ideas. An awareness of rates may help students to determine per unit results (2 plows take 6 hours —each plow takes 3 hours) and offer an alternative approach to the solution of problems. Otherwise the words *rate, percent,* and *ratio* may be used interchangeably.

PERCENT

I do not believe that I have ever met a student who was not able to say, "Percent means hundredths." Yet, in spite of this, I am sure that we have all encountered a great number of students who have experienced untold difficulties in working problems involving percents. How is it that students can tell you what is meant by the word and still not be able to use the idea? It seems that the words are probably spoken in parrot fashion and fail to bring any pictures or notions to mind that have meaning for the student. We will have to do a good deal more to help students than teach them to verbalize definitions with little functional comprehension.

Percent is certainly present in the student's immediate environment.

He sees the symbols used in his daily newspaper, in his local stores, on his TV set, and in almost every facet of his daily life, including the scores he achieves on his school tests. With such widespread use, the concept of percent should be perhaps one of the ideas students will master with relative ease. It is unfortunate that ease of understanding is not quite a function of the frequency of occurrence in everyday experience, and the lack of knowledge about percent is surprising in light of its constant use.

But let us not be misled by adult considerations and instead attempt to find introductory experiences of some interest to the student. Comparisons offer us one opportunity for such a start:

> The best girl basket shooter had made 12 baskets in 20 tries. The best boy was able to sink 14 baskets in 25 tries. Who was the better shot?
>
> A seventh grade class had an average of 27 students present each day, out of 30 students in the class. An eighth grade class averaged 32 students attending each day, out of a total of 36 students. Which class had better attendance?
>
> Joe put 1 ounce of chocolate syrup into an 8 ounce glass and filled it with milk. Sandy made a big batch and put 5 ounces of syrup into a 36 ounce container and filled it with milk. Which drink had the stronger chocolate flavor?

Any of these problems could serve to get the students into a situation that requires the use of percent. After time for working and thinking and time for discussion and evaluation of individual attempts at solution, writing all ratios with a common base may be offered as one way to resolve the issues. It is customary to use 100 as such a base, and so we introduce percent as the ratios written with a base of 100. The student finds that this common base makes comparisons easier. The method he uses to change the fractions into equivalent ones with 100 as a denominator should be of his own choosing. Certainly the finding of equivalent fractions in order to carry out operations with common fractions will serve as a guide. The word and symbol for percent grows naturally out of the preceding discussion. There is little need for any formal statement of what percent represents, since this is only an introduction. As we explore statistics and geometry we will find it necessary to use our knowledge of percent in order to do the tasks set before us.

Problems requiring the student to solve what has been known as the three classic cases of percent grow out of these beginning experiences. Years ago, much time was spent in mathematics classes drilling the students on memorization of how to solve each of the three cases:

Finding the percentage:	50% of 80 = □
Finding the percent (rate):	□% of 80 = 40
Finding the number:	50% of □ = 40

This kind of separation becomes totally unnecessary once the proportion idea has been considered. A percent was seen as a special case of ratio. Finding any of the missing numbers of the preceding equations can be resolved by writing them as proportions and solving for the missing member. In this way the equations may be rewritten:

$$50\% \text{ of } 80 = \square \longrightarrow \frac{50}{100} = \frac{N}{80}$$

$$\square\% \text{ of } 80 = 40 \longrightarrow \frac{N}{100} = \frac{40}{80}$$

$$50\% \text{ of } \square = 40 \longrightarrow \frac{50}{100} = \frac{40}{N}$$

4000 = 100N

N = 40

The student simply solves the proportion. He does not attempt to memorize three different methods after recognition of which particular case he has before him.

Other methods that eliminate the need for three cases are available to the students. If a good deal of equation work has been done, the use of the formula

$$b \cdot r = p, \quad \text{base} \times \text{rate} = \text{percentage}$$

is a helpful approach. The net effect is similar to that of using proportion, but the thinking is very different. In this instance, the given members of the formula are substituted into it and the resulting equation is solved for the unknown. Sometimes students may solve the equation for the unknown first and then complete the substitution process. What percent of 80 is 40? The problem may be solved by writing either

$$p = b r \qquad\qquad p = b r$$

$$40 = 80 \cdot r \qquad \text{or} \qquad r = \frac{p}{b}$$

$$\frac{40}{80} = r \qquad\qquad r = \frac{40}{80}$$

In any case, the student is making use of the fundamental relationship between base, rate, and percentage. The difficulty arises here in helping students to identify which of these three he has before him, and then applying this knowledge.

There are other methods, too; which one is best is an irrelevant question. It is not important that we teach our students *the best way*. Rather, it is important that our students learn that they can use the knowledge they have already acquired to think through to the answer in a new situation. This is what mathematics is about—not finding *the* best method. But *thinking* and *reasoning* and all such methods that take you where you want to go are indeed *best methods*. When a problem is attempted, the student thinks about how the relationships in the problem can be arranged to work for a solution, not

89

"How did we do that one in class yesterday?" Perhaps this is one way in which we may avoid the glib but empty statement that "percent means hundredths."

The methods we have described will result from the introduction of a variety of interesting problems involving percent. Here are some other situations and sample problems that may be drawn from them:

Situation

The different four-footed animals are constructed so that they carry their weight differently.[5] The table that follows indicates approximately how the weight is borne by the front and hind legs of some animals:

		Percent of Weight on:	
Animal	*Total Weight*	*Front Legs*	*Hind Legs*
Camel	1596 lbs.	67%	33%
Llama	308 lbs.	$66\frac{2}{3}\%$	$33\frac{1}{3}\%$
Elephant	4004 lbs.	58%	42%
Horse	924 lbs.	$57\frac{1}{2}\%$	$42\frac{1}{2}\%$

Problems

How much weight is on the front legs of an average horse?

How much weight is carried by the rear legs of an average elephant?

If a cow carries 60 percent of its weight on its front legs and we know it has 720 pounds on its front legs, how much does it weigh?

If a lion weighing 500 pounds is constructed so that 225 pounds is resting on its rear legs, what percent of its weight is upon the rear legs?

What percent of your weight is on your legs?

Situation

A man must eat roughly 2 percent of his weight per day in order to maintain his body heat. A mouse, on the other hand, requires food amounting to 50 percent of his weight; that is why mice seem to be continuously eating.

Problems

How much food would a boy or girl weighing 75 pounds need in order to maintain body heat?

If a 110 pound boy eats 4 pounds of food, will he have eaten enough to keep his body temperature up?

A small mouse ate $4\frac{1}{2}$ ounces of food one day. This was 50 percent of his weight. How much does he weigh?

In addition to these situations, examples may be drawn from the experiences described earlier, as well as from a consideration of sales tax (why do you have to pay pennies more than the price each time you buy something?), the percent scores on test papers, and the usual practice of having the students bring to class percent signs that appear in their newspapers and magazines. In each case time should be taken to discuss the situation itself, as this adds meaning and significance to the calculations undertaken later. For example, take time to discuss:

> Why would you expect certain animals to have most of their weight up front?
> How are warm-blooded animals different from cold-blooded ones?
> How do we keep our temperature at a fairly constant 98.6°?
> Why do we have to pay a sales tax?
> Why do banks give us interest for keeping our money safe?

In any event, don't push formal techniques in this first work with percent. The skills required in working successfully with percent problems develop gradually. A good deal of additional work with percents will result from the study of statistics. This will be explained in detail in the next chapter.

Before leaving percents, it may help student thinking about this troublesome concept if we involve them briefly in experiences in which another number is used as a common base, rather than 100. It is not unusual today to find teachers introducing students to numeration systems with bases other than 10. (This will be considered later.) Why haven't we also thought of changing the percent base and working perhaps with "persixteens"—if we found a race of people with two fingers on each hand—or "perthirty-sixes," "persixty-fours," and so on? For example, if 10 were to be our common base instead of 100 and if we called the ratios "perten," we might see a newspaper advertise 3 "perten" off on the sale of a dress. If the dress costs $60, how much would be saved in such a sale? (We will use the symbol ⅋ for perten and make it by dropping one of the zeros from the % sign—just as 10 has one zero less than 100.) In this case, 3⅋ off, our arithmetic might look like this:

$$3⅋ = \frac{3}{10} \quad \text{or} \quad .3$$

$$\frac{3}{10} = \frac{N}{60}$$

$$10N = 180$$

$$N = 18$$

The discount is $18.

Any of the examples worked before may be redone on a "perten" basis. All the shortcuts derived from percent could be explored as "perten" to examine the implications: Move a decimal point one place rather than two to change the "perten" to a decimal fraction. Equivalence charts could be drawn between "perten" and percent. This work should be brief and recreational. It is not expected that students will become proficient at using "pertens." It is merely an attempt to add to the students' understanding of percent. Some students may get caught up in the spirit of this work and begin to explore other bases and invent new symbols for them. This is an excellent experience, provided that the desire to carry it out originates with the student. It is conceivable that students would develop the ideas themselves and perhaps report back to the class, asking the class to work a variety of problems involving "perfifty" or "pereighty-one." The basic tone should be one of "puzzle-solving," although the gains lie in basic understandings.

SCIENTIFIC NOTATION

An introduction to scientific notation may be made by asking students the following questions: How fast is the speed of light? How long is a second? How many seconds make up an average life span?

If a discussion follows emphasizing the belief that man first appeared on this planet some 1,000,000 years ago and if activities are undertaken (such as finding the ratio of a single life span to the total length of time man has occupied the earth), we will have generated many interesting experiences requiring the students to compute with large numbers, and we will have offered some thought-provoking questions about nonmathematical areas of importance. For example, from Table 6-4 we see that an entire lifetime forms only $\frac{1}{5000}$ of the history of man, not to mention the number of people with whom each instance on earth is shared. What is more, such experiences give students an idea of the weariness resulting from computations with large numbers. Additional ratio questions may be constructed using other items from the table. Each time the student carries out the work, we are adding to the feeling that there must indeed be a better way to do it. At this point we may introduce the notion of scientific notation. Of course this work presupposes prior experience with exponents. A possible introduction to exponents is presented in the chapter on informal geometry.

Instead of dividing numbers in the manner we have just discussed, we may carry out division with abbreviated numbers and reconsider the ratios previously encountered. When students find that they may write 10^{13} instead

Table 6-4.   A Table of Seconds.

Unit	Number of Seconds	Rounded Off	Scientific Notation
Minute	60	60	6×10
Hour	3600	3600	3.6×10^3
Day	86,400	86,400	8.64×10^4
Month	2,592,000	2,600,000	2.6×10^6
Year	31,536,000	32,000,000	3.2×10^7
70 years	2,207,520,000	2,200,000,000	2.2×10^9
100 years	3,153,600,000	3,200,000,000	3.2×10^9
Since earliest man	—	10,000,000,000,000	10^{13}

Table 6-5. Distances in Space.

From:	*To:*	*Distance in Miles (Approx.)*	*Scientific Notation*
Earth	Moon	240,000	2.4×10^5
Earth	Sun	93,000,000	9.3×10^7
Mercury	Sun	36,000,000	3.6×10^7
Venus	Sun	67,000,000	6.7×10^7
Mars	Sun	142,000,000	1.42×10^8
Saturn	Sun	886,000,000	8.86×10^8
Pluto	Sun	3,670,000,000	3.67×10^9

of 10,000,000,000,000 and in addition are able to operate with numbers in this short form, it is not necessary for the teacher to extol the virtues of this system. The student *knows* since he has lived with the problem. There is some confusion as to the reason for writing the number in a form that requires the multiplier of some power of 10 to be between 1 and 10. For example, there are approximately 31,000,000 seconds in a year, and we may express this as 31×10^6. It is customary, however, to write the number as 3.1×10^7. All numbers written in this convenient form are in scientific notation. This was the result of using logarithms to carry out computations. Writing all numbers in this way also facilitates comparisons.

Among other situations that will yield problems involving this new notation will be those considering distances in space (Table 6-5). Travel to the moon is more than just a dream these days, and it will not be long before many of the planets will be explored by additional satellites, just as Venus has. How far away are these planets? How long would it take to journey to them at speeds approaching supersonic rates (greater than 700 m.p.h.)? What will man have to do to be able to complete such a journey? These are but a few of the many intriguing questions that may be explored in such work. Later, the comparative sizes of these heavenly bodies will be examined in the chapter on informal geometry, as the topic of planets is revisited.

In carrying out their work dividing or multiplying numbers in scientific notation, the students once again proceed in a way they deem best. We accept, for the moment, any crude or rudimentary approaches. The subtraction or addition of exponents will soon become a part of their mastered techniques because of the numerous examples provided. In this instance we have considered a beginning with these ideas, which will be discussed again. Later, if students are still struggling, we will provide the experiences necessary to add to their skill.

MEASUREMENT

The treatment, or perhaps mistreatment, of measurement concepts in the traditional program is much like that accorded problem solving. These two areas are often considered individual topics to be developed, as are all the other topics of mathematics. Problem solving is an important part of mathematical activity. It should be a part of virtually all the ideas we undertake to study in any mathematics course. Measurement concepts should follow a similar pattern. In order to do the many things that are set before us in mathematics, it is often necessary to carry out a variety of measurements. Thus, skill with measuring instruments and an understanding of measurement concepts should be a continuous development throughout the study of mathematics. In arriving at the necessary measurements and in doing the tasks already mentioned in this section, students may encounter difficulties. For example, they might ask: How do I measure my height? How shall I measure my waist? How do I use a ruler and read the measures? How can I convert inches to feet and vice versa? How many seconds are there in an hour?

As these difficulties arise they should be carefully considered. This is in line with the belief that a student in trouble is ready for instruction to enable him to overcome this particular roadblock. Measuring and using denominate numbers is not an end in itself to the student. He wants to be able to work with measures because he wants to do something else. In this way we hope to add to the desire to know.

Some activities requiring measurement have already been discussed. Others will be encountered later. Personal measurements are usually of greatest concern to an individual: How tall am I? How much do I weigh? How long is my arm? How much weight can I lift? How thick is a hair? How fast can I run?

All these questions lead to active experiences with measurement at many levels—from using a ruler, to a scale, to a micrometer. Many other suitable activities would probably occur to you. The experiences are real and refer to something of consequence to the student.

This may be an excellent opportunity to point up the differences between the numbers we have used for counting and the numbers we have used for measuring. It is not a simple task for students to begin to realize these differences, but certainly a beginning can be made. Accuracy, which is frequently so important to students, is a function of our measuring instruments. Counting, on the other hand, is an exact process. Number lines may aid student perception of the fact that we generally locate the position between two numbers when we are measuring. If our ruler is marked in eighths, we can tell that a particular reading is between perhaps $\frac{5}{8}$ and $\frac{6}{8}$. Most of the time we can

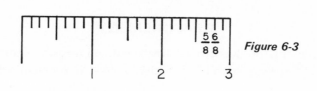

Figure 6-3

also declare which of the two measures is closer to the one we seek (Fig. 6-3); but exact measurement is a misconception, if we think about it in the sense that we know *exactly* how many books are on a desk. Stressing the margin of error as we carry out the work will help to build this awareness gradually. It is also helpful to use several rulers to measure the same line length. One ruler might be divided into quarters, another into tenths, and one even into halves (Fig. 6-4). Placing these rulers along the same line enables the students to see for themselves how the accuracy of a measurement depends upon the tool. The section on number patterns at the end of this chapter will help to build a feeling for the natural numbers, those used in counting.

The use and conversion of units of measure sometimes causes stress for both student and teacher. The physicist has a unique method of dealing with this problem that generally strikes terror in the hearts of mathematics teachers. I can to this day see the expression on the face of a colleague as he saw the physics teacher cancel units. Mind you, he thought cancellation was bad enough; but when it was done with units rather than numbers, that was too much to bear!

First, let us be clear that units, like most other concepts we have considered, are discussed as needed. There is no lesson on "units"; there need

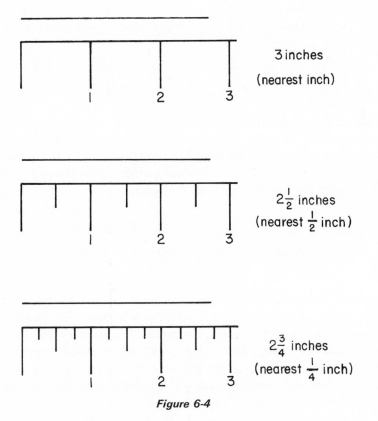

3 inches
(nearest inch)

$2\frac{1}{2}$ inches
(nearest $\frac{1}{2}$ inch)

$2\frac{3}{4}$ inches
(nearest $\frac{1}{4}$ inch)

Figure 6-4

95

not be. The activities described have resulted from ample opportunities to encounter the problem of converting units as the students were required to make and use all sorts of measures. More of such work with measures lies ahead of the student. But shall we accept the practice of

$$(5 \text{ feet}) \times (10 \text{ feet}) = 50 \text{ square feet}$$

or

$$\frac{90 \text{ ft.}}{\cancel{\text{sec.}}_1} \cdot \frac{\cancel{60}^1 \cancel{\text{sec.}}}{1 \text{ min.}} = \frac{5400 \text{ ft.}}{\text{min.}}$$

just as if we were multiplying and dividing units? The real question would seem to be, Why not? All our physicists are quick to put these symbols to work for them, so why should math teachers be reluctant? The process makes good sense to students and, most importantly, it works! Indeed, we can carry this a bit further: How far will I drive if I average 30 m.p.h. (miles/hr.) for 6 hours?

$$\frac{30 \text{ miles}}{\cancel{\text{hr.}}} \times 6 \cancel{\text{hr.}} = 180 \text{ miles}$$

The outcome is a natural one and the process should be acceptable. The conversion of units in speed-time situations may be greatly facilitated through the use of these techniques. Sixty miles per hour is equivalent to how many feet per second (ft./sec.)?

$$\frac{60 \cancel{\text{miles}}}{\cancel{\text{hr.}}} \cdot \frac{1 \cancel{\text{hr.}}}{3600 \text{ sec.}} \cdot \frac{5280 \text{ ft.}}{1 \cancel{\text{mile}}}$$

The "fractions" we have introduced can be thought of as multiplication identity elements; thus our result should have the same value that we began with. In addition, we selected the multipliers by keeping clearly before us what we wanted our answer to be. This is a typical mathematical activity—putting the symbols to work for you. In this case, the result is:

$$\frac{60 \text{ miles}}{\text{hr.}} \cdot \frac{1 \text{ hr.}}{3600 \text{ sec.}} \cdot \frac{5280 \text{ ft.}}{1 \text{ mile}} = \frac{\cancel{60}^1 \cdot \cancel{5280}^{88} \text{ ft.}}{\underset{1}{\cancel{3600}} \text{ sec.}} = \frac{88 \text{ ft.}}{\text{sec.}} = 88 \text{ ft./sec.}$$

Students who can negotiate this path are to be encouraged. Be especially careful, however, of destroying good student insight by forcing an answer about why it works. This is a most difficult question. It does work and we should in this case accept it at face value. Those who cannot master these ideas may use other techniques. We must not let words like "cancel" scare us. Our concern is with ideas, not words. If "cancel" can help students understand what is going on, let us be happy we have it to use.

Figure 6-5

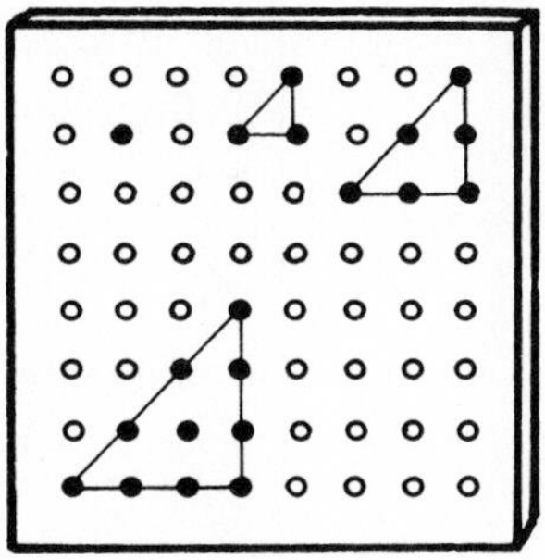

Triangular Numbers: 1, 3, 6, 10, 15, ...

PATTERNS IN NUMBERS

While we are careful to be certain that the experiences we shall develop for youngsters will involve them in meaningful activities to enable them to gain some insight into the nature and significance of mathematics, we must be equally careful not to overlook the pure joy and satisfaction that can accrue in youngsters through "playing" with numbers and number patterns. For example, using a pegboard and golf tees, geoboard and rubber bands, graph paper, or any other collection of objects, we can have some fun exploring the shapes of numbers. The Pythagoreans were great ones for this kind of work, as has been mentioned earlier; but children also get a good deal of pleasure out of noticing things about numbers.[6] We have triangular numbers (Fig. 6-5), rectangular numbers, and square numbers—all of which can be represented by the shape of an array of pegs or discs. We also have magic squares, which remarkably provide a constant sum regardless of the direction of addition (Fig. 6-6). There is the shape of the odd numbers as compared with the shape of the even ones and the shape of the composite numbers as compared with that of the primes (Fig. 6-7). And of course we have the unlimited patterns that students may find in their explorations of numbers, such as $1^2 + 1 = 2^2 - 2$, $2^2 + 2 = 3^2 - 3$, $3^2 + 3 = 4^2 - 4$, and $4^2 + 4 = 5^2 - 5$,

Figure 6-6

6	1	8
7	5	3
2	9	4

97

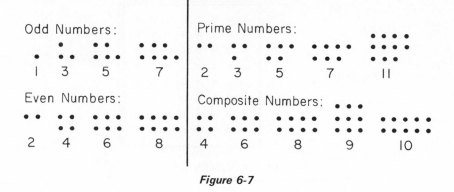

Figure 6-7

as well as the famous Fibonacci sequence in which each term is the sum of the two terms that are directly before it: 1, 1, 2, 3, 5, 8, 13, 21, ... This latter example is one of the many interesting mathematical patterns that so frequently appear in a variety of diverse environments.[7]

It is foolish not to take greater advantage of the fact that mathematics can be and ought to be fun for students. What is most remarkable is that number work lends itself to the very kind of activity that most youngsters seem to enjoy. Somewhere along the line we seem to have been sidetracked by the notion that for something to be good it has to be painful. It is time now to abandon such ideas and to try to make the mathematics class an enjoyable place for students. We could probably improve mathematics learning overnight if all teachers accepted this assumption.

FOOTNOTES

1. For a brief description of the major improvement programs in curriculum see "An Analysis of New Mathematics Programs," a report of a committee of the National Council of Teachers of Mathematics, 1963.
2. *Mathematics in Primary Schools*. Curriculum Bulletin No. 1. The Schools Council, Her Majesty's Stationery Office, London, 1965.
3. A carpenter's rule is the familiar fold-up ruler (wood or steel) that has an unlimited number of classroom uses.
4. For an excellent set of instructions for the building of gear wheels (by student or teacher) see *Designing and Making* by W. W. Sawyer and L. G. Srawley, Basil Blackwell & Mott Ltd., 1957, pp. 106–110.
5. See *On Growth and Form* by Sir D'Arcy Thompson (edited by J. T. Bonner), Cambridge University Press, 1961, p. 254.
6. See Chapter 2, pages 19 to 20.
7. For an interesting discussion of this see *The Language of Mathematics* by Frank Land, Doubleday & Company, Inc., 1963, pp. 215–219.

FOR INVESTIGATION AND DISCUSSION

1. Since most adults in our society do have to deal with situations involving insurance, taxes, and banking, why are these areas criticized as being inappropriate for junior high school mathematics classes?

2. Explain what is meant by social-use applications in mathematics. Evaluate the employment of such applications in the mathematics classroom.

3. The common goals of various improvement programs are listed in this chapter. Discuss each of these goals, emphasizing what they are and why they have been introduced. Give specific examples of content reflecting these goals.

4. Compare two seventh or eighth grade textbooks, one relatively modern and one relatively traditional (copyright before 1960), as to content, methodology, and point of view.

5. It has been suggested that review is not necessarily a good starting point for the year's work. Evaluate arguments for and against this suggestion and indicate possible alternatives.

6. Describe how an introduction to ratio and proportion may be made in an active manner, other than using the indexes described in this chapter.

7. Construct a sequence of activities for students who understand ratio in order to create the *need* to know how to solve proportions.

8. How do you explain the fact that many students can say, "Percent means hundredths" and yet cannot solve problems involved with percent?

9. Compare two methods of teaching percent ideas, emphasizing the difficulties and advantages of each.

10. Devise experiences that will involve students in the process of measuring and converting units of measure (i.e., inches to feet) and then create the way in which you will help students to develop skill with conversions.

11. Gather information about the Fibonacci sequence and the diverse areas in which it occurs. Plan a lesson for students to enable them to share your findings.

FOR FURTHER READING

Books

Irving Adler. *Magic House of Numbers*. The John Day Company, Inc., 1960.
Frank Land. *The Language of Mathematics*. Doubleday & Company, Inc., 1963.
Mathematics in Primary Schools. Curriculum Bulletin No. 1. The Schools Council, Her Majesty's Stationery Office, London, 1965.
W. W. Sawyer and L. G. Srawley. *Designing and Making*. Basil Blackwell & Mott Ltd., 1957.
Sir D'Arcy Thompson. *On Growth and Form*. (Edited by J. T. Bonner), Cambridge University Press, 1961.

Periodicals

William Giffel. "Primes and Things." *School Science and Mathematics*. Vol. 62 (December, 1962), pp. 684–687.
Lucien B. Kinney. "Teaching Percentage for Understanding and Use." *The Mathematics Teacher*. Vol. 51 (January, 1958), pp. 38–41.

Arithmetic

K. Lovell and I. B. Butterworth. "Abilities Underlying the Understanding of Proportionality." *Mathematics Teaching*. (Winter, 1966), pp. 5–9.

Herbert J. Schiff. "Let Them Measure." *School Science and Mathematics*. Vol. 57 (April, 1957), pp. 291–292.

John A. Schmid. "Arithmetic Brain Teasers for the Young." *The Arithmetic Teacher*. Vol. 14 (May, 1967), pp. 365–368.

Shelby D. Smith. "A Discussion of Powers of Whole Numbers." *The Mathematics Teacher*. Vol. 55 (November, 1962), pp. 535–537.

Arnold Wendt. "Per Cent Without Cases." *The Arithmetic Teacher*. Vol. 6 (October, 1959), pp. 209–214.

Margaret F. Willerding. "Other Number Systems—Aids to Understanding." *The Arithmetic Teacher*. Vol. 8 (November, 1961), pp. 350–356.

Pamphlets

William H. Glenn and Donovan A. Johnson. *Number Patterns*. (Exploring Mathematics on Your Own Series), Webster Publishing, 1960.

Ethel M. Turner. *Teaching Aids for Elementary Mathematics*. Holt, Rinehart & Winston, Inc., 1966.

STATISTICS

Of all the suggestions made for improving the mathematics curriculum of the junior high school, the inclusion of expanded work with statistics is one of the most important. Here is an area that is in great need by everyone in twentieth century society. All forms of communication are quick to use statistical techniques in order to convey information clearly and effectively. Tables, charts, and graphs are a common occurrence in most magazines, books, and newspapers. The entire area of statistical sampling has had such a profound effect upon our lives that it is now possible for someone in a west coast city to be informed that a candidate has been elected in a national election almost before he has gone to the polls! This is not uncommon since the advent of high-speed computers for use by television.

The local weather forecasts now will indicate that "the probability of rain is 20 percent." A government bureau tells us that "the cost of living went up 0.3 percent last month." And the insurance company states that auto insurance for men under 25 will cost a lot more than it does for women of the same age. Everywhere we turn we find our lives becoming involved one way or another with statistics. Our students need to understand statistical concepts if they are to become literate members of society.

But there is still a more compelling reason for study in this area. The techniques of statistics provide us with a powerful tool for managing collections of figures called data. They offer us an opportunity to deal with many bits of numerical information in a way that helps us to answer questions we may have about the data, answers that may help us to make decisions. The opportunity is also present to introduce the student to an important problem-solving method that has implications for areas other than mathematics.

In the process of acquiring skill and understanding with statistical techniques, students will also find that they must call into play all the basic arithmetic skills they have previously learned. Once more, we find the much needed practice being provided for in a setting of maximum utility. To the students, new ideas are being pursued, but old ideas are also being strengthened. All in all, it seems that the area of statistics is going to prove to be a rather productive one for our students—not only from the point of view of what it has to offer, as has just been considered, but also for the kind of vital, timely, and significant experiences in which it will involve students.

COLLECTING DATA AND GRAPHING

One way to be sure that the work done with statistics is to have meaning for students is to organize situations so that the numbers that students collect are of some consequence. Building on an approach that was employed in the section on ratio (see Chapter 6), we can make class surveys of characteristics of the students. How many students have green eyes? gray? or brown? How is hair color distributed? How would these data appear if we broke the class group into two subgroups, boys and girls? Carrying out the survey and gathering the data are active classroom experiences for all. What shall we do with the data once we have finished the collection process? In order to be able to examine what we have, we arrange our information in tables and then turn to graphing to make a picture that is even easier to understand.

The beginning picture in graphing can well be a physical one as the students use small discs or cardboard pieces to build what is sometimes called a column graph (Fig. 7-1). This provides the students with a wonderful physical introduction to bar graphing. When the column graph is made, everyone examines it in order to determine how the various columns compare. Specific questions such as "How many more students have brown eyes than green?" and "What is the ratio of the number of students with gray eyes to the number of students with brown eyes?" are best answered by referring to the table which contains an organized collection of the data. Questions that do not require exact numerical results but which refer to comparisons, such as "Which is there more of, green or brown eyes?" and "About how many times more students with brown than gray eyes are there?" are best answered by a quick look at the graph.

But these are not points to be dwelled upon with students. Experiences will accumulate for them to help them realize the relative uses of the different presentations of their data. If the students first survey eye color, they may then turn to hair color. Once again we have mathematical repetition: collect data, make tables, construct column graphs, and interpret, but we have a physically different situation. The only limit on the number of such investigations that the students can possibly undertake are those dictated by time and by the teacher's own power to identify a variety of circumstances. Family size, num-

102

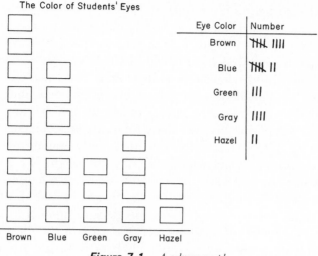

The Color of Students' Eyes

Eye Color	Number
Brown	THL IIII
Blue	THL II
Green	III
Gray	IIII
Hazel	II

Brown   Blue   Green   Gray   Hazel

Figure 7-1. *A column graph.*

bers of pets per family, shoe size, automobile makes, and even kind and number of books read (including comic books) are all possible sources for additional studies. The drawing of graphs may gradually shift from physical column graphs to paper and pencil column graphs drawn on graph paper. This enables the students to replace the physical block or disc with a filled-in square. Eventually he is simply constructing a bar graph as we know it (Fig. 7-2). The gradual movement from one to the other prevents thrusting too much upon students too soon.

For extended studies, the students might record the number of calories they consume in a day over a period of, say, a week. In addition to collecting the data, the students may now become involved in the whole question of proper diet and good eating habits and their relationship to good health. Of

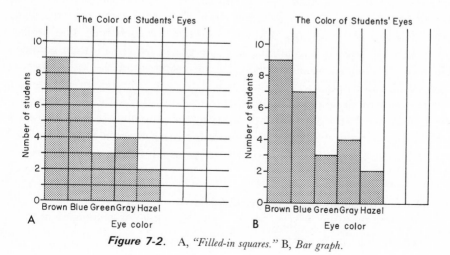

Figure 7-2. A, *"Filled-in squares."* B, *Bar graph.*

103

course the collected figures are tabulated, graphed, and then discussed much in the fashion of the earlier experiences. It may seem that we are straying rather far afield here, but it is just such discussions that add importance to the number work. It is time well spent. Good diet is as vital as an understanding of what a calorie is and why those on diets must be so acutely conscious of how many are consumed. Simple calorie charts are now inexpensive and available in five and dime stores, among others. It may be more convenient for the teacher to duplicate his own charts. In any case, such charts should be readily available. Other topics for extended study might include outside temperature readings at a given time each day, the height of a growing plant in the classroom measured daily, or the daily attendance figures.

Some of these collections may be better understood if we turned to graphs other than the bar graph. This will depend upon the nature of the data. If we were concerned with the various parts of the class that have a given hair color, we could well turn to a circle or rectangle graph (Fig. 7-3). Our purpose is served more effectively. In addition, the use of ratios and percents comes into play here, as well as the introduction of geometric concepts, as the students face the problem of subdividing the geometric figure used, circle or rectangle.

A student once inquired as to whether or not he could make a square graph or a triangle graph. This was an example of some fine thinking. In pursuing his ideas, the class attempted construction with these geometric figures (Fig. 7-4). It was startling to observe the ingenuity of students attempting to subdivide triangles. We may use what best serves our purpose, of course. There is nothing sacred about the circle or rectangle, although they may present more dramatic pictures of how an entity is subdivided.

As for line graphs, I once had the opportunity to observe a teacher demonstrate the construction of a line graph by using an overhead projector, with the picture projected upon the chalkboard. A bar graph made by a student on a piece of acetate was the subject. The teacher projected the graph onto the board, then had the students draw with chalk right over the projection, the scales of the graph, and the midpoints of each bar. The projector was turned off, leaving the points of a line graph which she then connected (Fig. 7-5). A discussion could follow this, focusing upon the values between those of the initial points. The data will determine whether or not these in-between points will be meaningful. But the relationship between bar and line graphs was made dramatically apparent to the students. It is important for them to understand that the type of graph to use is not a function of one's personal taste, but of the data and the uses to which the data will be put:

Comparing individual readings:	bar graph
Demonstrating how some entity is broken up into parts:	circle or rectangle graph
Determining rise or fall:	line graphs

The Color of Students' Hair

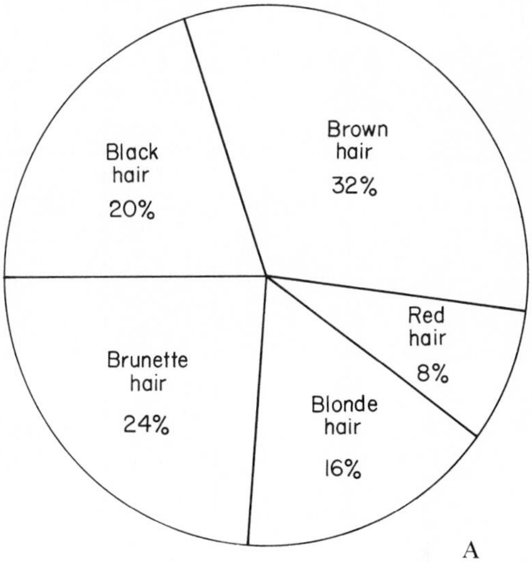

Color	No.	Part of Class	Percent of Class	No. of Degrees
Black	5	$\frac{5}{25}$	20%	72°
Brown	8	$\frac{8}{25}$	32%	115°
Brunette	6	$\frac{6}{25}$	24%	86°
Blonde	4	$\frac{4}{25}$	16%	58°
Red	2	$\frac{2}{25}$	8%	29°
Total	25	1	100%	360°

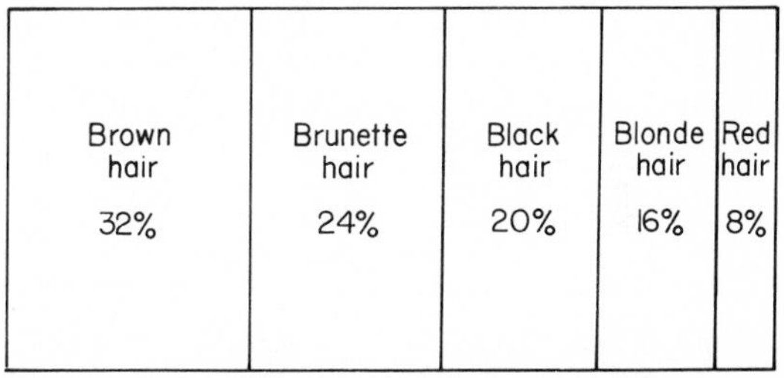

Figure 7-3. *Illustrating data by* (A) *a circle graph and* (B) *a rectangle graph.*

Of course there are many varieties of each of these standard types.

If graphs are presented to the students, or if the students are permitted to fumble and draw graphs based upon misleading practices (such as starting a bar graph at some number other than zero), when the graphs are discussed and interpreted some amazing conclusions will be drawn. Questioning these conclusions will help students to appreciate the need for care in the construction of all their graphs.

The teacher might tell the students to look at the graph (Fig. 7-6) and then ask them such questions as: "How do the numbers of boxes of cookies

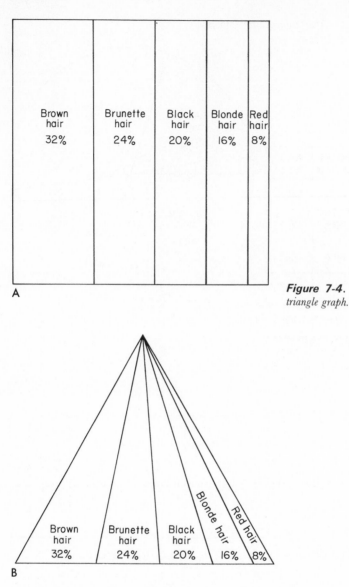

A

B

Figure 7-4. A, *A square graph.* B, *A triangle graph.*

sold by Amie and Carol compare? How many times higher is the bar representing Carol's number than that showing Amie's? How many times higher is the bar showing Ellen's sales than that showing Amie's? Did Ellen sell five times as much? Why does the graph indicate that she did? The same data are made into another bar graph (Fig. 7-7). How do the bars compare now? How is it that the graphs appear to be so different?"

As they see bar graphs distorted, as they see the curves of line graphs smoothed out or exaggerated because the scales have been tampered with, the students will soon enough come to realize that graphs can easily be misused.[1]

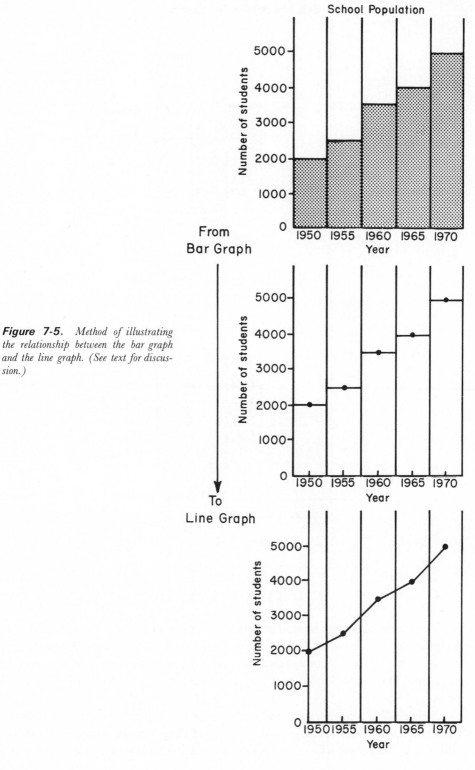

Figure 7-5. *Method of illustrating the relationship between the bar graph and the line graph. (See text for discussion.)*

107

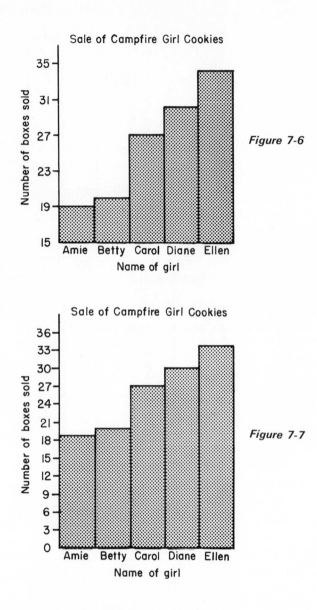

Figure 7-6

Figure 7-7

DECISION MAKING

The techniques we have just considered may also serve a most important purpose: They enable us to make the best decision in certain instances. Can we involve our students in decision-making experiences that will be meaningful to them? This would seem to be an appropriate next step in our statistical work.

Which TV shows are popular in our school? Who will win the school election? How many cars pass the school during school hours? How many children in our class will be absent next week? All these questions and many

108

more may best be answered by applying the ideas learned earlier. For example, if we were to pursue the question of how many cars pass the school in a day, we could arrange our data in table form, draw graphs, and examine these carefully in an attempt to provide an answer. Of course, there is one slight complication: How shall we go about collecting our data? It would not be possible to stand in front of the school all day and simply count. What can we do? At this point, we may introduce the notion of sampling. Since we cannot find the total for the 6-hour period (9 A.M. to 3 P.M.), why not take a count for 1 hour and multiply by 6? Perhaps we can take the count for only a quarter hour and multiply 6 × 4 or 24. Class discussion could serve to highlight many of the important considerations of sampling: How can we tell that this quarter hour is typical of all quarter hours in the 6 hour period? Don't fewer cars pass the school at certain times than at other times? Which are the busy and the quiet hours of the day? Does the day of the week influence the traffic? What effect does the weather have?

Selecting time periods at random and taking counts would serve to provide some information. Comparing results would indicate whether or not we could use any particular number as an average per quarter hour. And so we find ourselves involved not only with the notion of sampling but also with an introduction to the concept of average. At this point, the arithmetic mean could be quickly computed and the work carried out without interruption. However, should the data so warrant, it may be better to make use of the median or mode. Whatever the case, it would seem to be wise to complete the task at hand, rather than to take time for extended discussions about averages. Later, as more and more of these situations are met, the problem of deciding upon the proper average to use can be given careful attention.

When the traffic volume investigation has been completed, the students could undertake a number of similar investigations. One particularly convenient question that may be explored is the total number of words in a composition or story they have recently written. The number of words in a particular section or article of a familiar book or magazine may also be used. It is a rather tiresome task to count each and every word particularly if a selection runs more than just a few pages. Choosing a line of printing at random, the students can count the number of words in a single line. Then, as before, they select the typical number to represent each line (here is the concept of average again) and then simply multiply by the number of lines on a page and the total number of pages. In this instance, the students may check their accuracy by making an actual count of every word. If the pages are divided among the youngsters in the class, the total can be found without any undue waste of time and effort.

As we have already noted the popularity of various television shows and the prediction of success in election campaigns at the school, local, or national level, as well as student opinion on any given topic of the day, all form excellent areas for statistical investigation. Each situation enables the student to gain needed practice but always seems to introduce some new wrinkle that was not encountered before. Practice and continued learning are traveling companions. Let us briefly examine how each of these explorations might be carried out.

First, we turn to the popularity of television programs. All students have heard about the TV "ratings." Some youngsters keep track of these in much the same manner as they do the batting averages of their favorite baseball stars. What do the numbers of a rating mean and how are they arrived at? Is it possible for any company to somehow check every home and find out exactly what is or is not being watched by each family? Of course not. How then do they go about getting the figures on how many people are watching a given program? Once more the idea of sampling comes into focus. A discussion of how the sample might be selected would serve to help students identify the important characteristics of the sample if it is going to be truly representative of the population at large: Are the people surveyed old or young? What is their income bracket? What is their level of education? Where are they located? Are they male or female? These questions are some of the notions that would probably appear in the class discussion.

It can readily be seen that a good deal more than statistical concepts will come up for consideration in this work. The social aspects should not be minimized, as these are of great importance to our students. Once the sample characteristics have been considered, a decision must be made about how these people will be reached and what questions shall be asked of them. All these problems must be settled before any information gathering can even begin. A good parallel may be developed and actually carried out in class. Select a particular time period and set about the problem of trying to determine how many people of the class were watching each show. Instead of simply polling all the students, select at random a sample containing about one quarter of the class. (Use the telephone book to select numbers that correspond to class members, use a table of random numbers that may be found in most statistics books, or simply put the name of each student into a hat and draw out a few.) Poll these students. Each student should tabulate the results and convert them into percents of the sample (Table 7-1).

The students can now carry out predictions of how the entire class will respond by taking the given percents of the entire class. When everyone has made his predictions, the entire class is polled and the tabulated results are compared with the predicted results. Graphs may be drawn of the data in order to aid these comparisons. In this way we have immediate verification of the accuracy of our predictions. We can then consider why our sample did or did not provide us with enough information to enable us to predict with some reasonable accuracy. But what is still more important is that an activity such as this eliminates the need for explanations about what is going on and why specific things happen. The students will have lived the experience for themselves. The drill work with percent and proportion, as well as the con-

Table 7-1.   TV Poll.

Program	Number Watching	Part of Class	Percent of Class
Western hour	7	7/25	28%
Cartoon hour	5	5/25	20%
Comedy hour	8	8/25	32%
Mystery hour	4	4/25	16%
Did not watch	1	1/25	4%
Total	25	$25/25 = 1$	100%

struction and use of graphs, is an inherent part of this structure. We have accrued many important experiences for students of mathematics. The discussion could conclude with an examination of actual rating figures and some explanation of what they represent. Comparisons can be made between class preference and large audience preference. This gives a measure of how much like the larger group the class has been in its responses. A follow-up activity might be the prediction of how the entire grade level or school as a whole might respond to the same questions, using the class at hand as a sample itself. Polling could take place throughout the school if it is felt that such an undertaking would be of value. In any event, the work is real, immediate, and of consequence to the student. Mathematics is vital for it provides the tool with which the student may study questions of interest to him. It also offers him an opportunity to do something that might be otherwise very difficult, almost impossible. In addition, the student is making use of ideas learned previously and is extending his knowledge through encountering new ideas. It all adds up to a collection of rather productive experiences.

If we turn to exploration of student opinions and attitudes, we find that we have another extremely fertile field for investigation. By carrying out almost all the activities just described, we may seek out student attitudes in any number of socially important areas. For instance, we might attempt to assess student attitudes toward the following: How old should a youngster be before he or she is permitted to start dating? Should parents hit their children when they misbehave? Should boys be allowed in school with long hair? What should be done about Vietnam?

There is a virtually endless stream of important questions that may be placed before students and investigated in much the same manner as described for trying to determine TV popularities. Of course, the opportunity for lively discussion of the issues themselves must not be missed. This is indeed one of the significant reasons for traveling this path in the first place. Although our goals are mathematical, we must not lose sight of the human goals that are the responsibility of every teacher. What is more, it is the application of mathematical techniques to these issues of such great importance to youngsters that builds the concept of the importance of mathematics.

The very same techniques employed here can also be applied to the prediction of successful election candidates. This is another area ripe for such study today since the "poll" has become so well integrated into our daily lives. There are ample reports of polls in the newspapers that may be used as a guide for classwork in this area. In this way we also develop the opportunity to compare the results of the class with results on a larger basis. Computers have had a great influence on these practices—so much so that we find newscasters on TV predicting winners almost before the polling places are closed.

Undertaking a poll of the student body in an election for school-wide offices will offer the students an excellent chance to gain real insight into the entire process, so that the next time they see polls described in a newspaper or on a TV show they will have a much better understanding of the strengths and limitations of the results. Knowing some good questions to ask about such data is in itself a major learning goal.

The sample situations suggested here are just that: samples. Each teacher can think not only of additional situations for study but of better ones as well. As we look at the experiences described, we notice that in each case the data had to be gathered by some kind of sampling procedure. These same analytical techniques—gathering data, making tables, constructing graphs, and interpreting the results—can also be applied to situations in which the data collection process involves digging up figures that have already been organized into tables. If the class were to undertake an exploration of which drivers appear to be the safest, if any, they might want to find statistics about accidents in their local area and see if these are listed with the driver's age and sex indicated. The statistics would already have been collected by official government agencies. It would then be up to the students to organize these data and follow through with the other techniques described. Some typical questions that may fall under this kind of study are: Why are auto insurance rates higher for boys under 25 than for girls? Why do older men pay higher life insurance premiums for the same policy as younger men? Does having more education result in greater earning power?

Before leaving these investigations, a word is in order about one additional type of research that is carried out by industry—market research studies. These would involve an attempt to assess public reaction to an unknown product or a particular kind of package for a familiar one. It is quite possible for the students to carry out their simplified sampling procedures in attempting to determine whether or not most students would be interested in a make believe new product, such as a flying belt or a single-seater spaceship. Of course, the product must not be too remote from reality or else the responses would be meaningless.

This, then, is another important aspect of statistics for student experience: The failure of some well-known reliable corporations to successfully make use of new product research studies is fascinating for students. They are amazed, for example, to find out how much money the Ford Motor Company lost on its infamous Edsel. The perils of statistical sampling must be considered carefully.

Let us now turn our attention to the computation of averages.

MEAN—MEDIAN—MODE

The studies we have described will not necessarily be the first experience students will have had with averages. Certainly the school marking practices have provided many such examples. The new context, however, serves to point up a somewhat different perspective about this important statistic. For one thing, if we use the study of traffic flow as an example, we may be better off using a number that seems to occur repeatedly, rather than adding and dividing. If our quarter-hour traffic counts had been like those shown in Table 7-2, it would seem that 14 might be a better number to use, rather than the arithmetic mean—the familiar "average," which in this case would be 11. The 14 seems to be more "typical" of what is happening. This typical average, which we find by looking for the most frequently appearing number, is a newcomer to most students. It is the *mode.*

The very idea that there is more than one kind of average is somewhat surprising to students. For the most part, they have used only one and have had little inkling that any others exist. The experiences of the previous development serve as excellent generators of a need for something else. The introduction of other averages is thereby a natural process.

The *median,* or middle number of a collection of figures that have been arranged from smaller to larger, is the third average to be encountered by students in this work. While there are additional averages that may well be computed, it is usually not necessary for students to become involved any further.

Table 7-2.   Traffic Volume Survey.

Time Period	Tally	Number
9:00– 9:15	⅋⅋⅋ ⅋⅋⅋ ////	14
9:15– 9:30	⅋⅋⅋ ⅋⅋⅋ ////	14
9:30– 9:45	⅋⅋⅋ /	6
9:45–10:00	////	4
12:00–12:15	⅋⅋⅋ ⅋⅋⅋ ⅋⅋⅋	15
12:15–12:30	⅋⅋⅋ ⅋⅋⅋ ////	14
12:30–12:45	⅋⅋⅋ ⅋⅋⅋	10
3:00– 3:15	⅋⅋⅋ ⅋⅋⅋ ////	14

Statistics

How shall we know when to use which average? It is rather important to help students to understand that there are two factors that influence such a decision. First, we have the nature of the numbers themselves. If we sought to determine the average salary of workers in a paper mill, we might find the salaries listed in Table 7-3. The *mean* would be $12,000; yet we would find that out of 12 people on the payroll, nine are earning far less than $12,000. The reason for this is that the few high salaries are distorting the data. It would seem that this number is not really representative of the numbers in the set making up the payroll. What would be better? Well, if the numbers are arranged from smallest to highest we might find the *median*, or middle number, to be useful; or perhaps we might use the *mode*, the number that appears most often. In this case both of these averages are identical: $5000. This number does seem more representative of the data. So we must scrutinize the data carefully before deciding which average will be most appropriate.

Another factor to be considered is the use to which you intend to put the average. If it is typicality that is sought, then the mode seems to be the best choice. If, on the other hand, we simply do not wish to permit our average to be distorted by extremely high or low values, then we should employ the median. The freedom of choice left with the individual computing the averages should serve to help students become a bit more discriminating in dealing with averages in any case. Certainly, we should want to ask which average is being referred to. The Bureau of Labor Statistics of the United States Government computes all kinds of indexes about our society. When they say that the average family earned $4500 last year, what are they referring to? Do they use the

Table 7-3.   Annual Salaries—Jones Paper Mill.

Name	*Salary*
R. Jones	$40,000
T. Jones	40,000
Mr. A	23,000
Mr. B	5000
Mr. C	5000
Mr. D	5000
Mr. E	5000
Mr. F	5000
Mr. G	5000
Mr. H	4000
Mr. I	4000
Mr. J	3000
Total salaries	$144,000
	12 people

Mean:	$12,000	
Median:	$5000	
Mode:	$5000	

114

mean, median, or mode? Which do you think they should use? Why? Should more than one average be used?

Like the other activities described in this chapter, there is no shortage of interesting situations in which to involve our students so that they will be working and computing with meaningful problems. The entire concept of average as generally employed in society bears close examination. For example, we say in school that a youngster is an "average" student. What does

Sale of Campfire Girl Cookies

Name of Girl	Number of Boxes Sold
Amie	6
Betty	6
Carol	10
Diane	11
Ellen	12

Figure 7-8

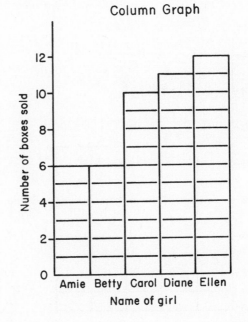

Column Graph

that tell you about him? Here are some other common averages that could lead to interesting discussions: He is an average American man; his batting average is .300; an average family has 2.4 children; she's an average teenager. I am certain you can add many more. This is another bit of evidence that some words common to both society and mathematics have rather different meanings in each place. But what is even more important, we are emphasizing the need for students to seek out the idea behind the words and to determine exactly what is being portrayed when certain words are used. In this way they are becoming more aware of the world in which they now live.

An interesting activity to aid student understanding of these three basic averages was provided for us earlier when we had students making physical column graphs prior to the paper-pencil bar graph. If you recall, the students piled up discs or cardboard pieces or perhaps made use of a pegboard. If we return to one of the situations described earlier but employ different data, we can represent the data with the physical column graph and quickly demonstrate the influence of the three different averages (Fig. 7-8). The column graph shows how many boxes of cookies each girl sold. To find the mean, simply move the pieces (e.g., pegs and discs) until all the columns are the same height (Fig. 7-9). The height of each column is the arithmetic mean. When a student carries out the physical movement of pieces and observes how all the values are spread evenly over each column he will have a better notion of the mean than you can ever supply with words. Restoring the columns to their original heights we now seek the median average number of boxes sold. To do this we simply rearrange the columns so that they are in order from lowest to highest. The one in the middle is the median (Fig. 7-10). If any one column height is repeated most often, you will have found the mode

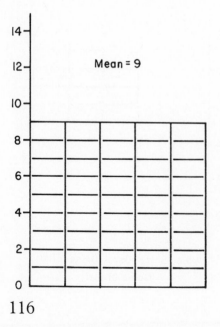

Figure 7-9. *Mean—Rearrange so that all bars have equal height.*

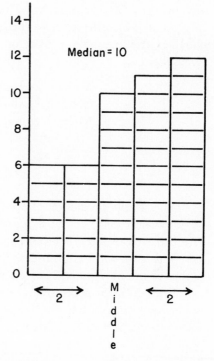

Figure 7-10. *Median—Arrange in order from lowest to highest. The middle value is the indicator.*

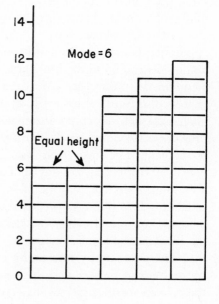

Figure 7-11. *Mode—Are any bars of equal height?*

117

(Fig. 7-11). Of course, more than a single experience is necessary for students to fully see what is happening; but as they move the pieces, it is expected that any mystery that surrounds a given average will gradually be dispelled.

Finally, in order to help students remain clear about just which average is which, they can concentrate on these words and probably find it easier to remember:

> Mean   = the old friend always used
> Median = middle
> Mode   = most

PROBABILITY

The simple prediction of events carried out when we used our knowledge of proportion and percent is a good beginning for extending prediction work into the area of some equally rudimentary work with probability.

This can well be a most intriguing area for students since it involves the realm of taking chances, considering the odds, and looking into the future.

Probability is a relatively new topic in the junior high school, but it is an important one that is also playing a greater role in our daily lives than we are perhaps aware of. Most students know that the local weatherman now reports the chances of rain in terms of probability. What does he mean when he says that there is a 30 percent chance of rain today? What is he telling us about his prediction of the weather? Will it rain? Will it be fair? Should we take an umbrella? How can we tell from the 30 percent that he reports to us? Well, prior to the use of probabilities, in the same situation the weatherman might have said, "There's a chance of some rain tomorrow." Is it a good chance? Is it a slight chance? With the use of probabilities, one thing seems apparent: These questions are now set in more specific terms—30 percent. Shall I plan to go to the ball game on this basis? Shall I cancel my plans for a picnic in the park? Just what does the 30 percent represent? Perhaps we can express this most simply by assuming that given the weather conditions observed (such as temperature, wind velocity and direction, and barometric pressure) rain would result 30 times out of every 100 such situations, hence the 30 percent. The answers to our questions may then be a function of each person's "risk-taking" quotient. The weatherman has supplied the best available information. It may be of interest to students to keep long-range charts indicating how often the weatherman's given probability for rain was actually followed by rain. In this way the varying percents reported in forecasts and the incidence of rainfall could be related.

There are many interesting experiments that may easily be carried out by students as they extend their study of probability. Here is a list of some of these: coin tossing, die tossing, tack tossing, drawing cards, drawing colored

118

balls (marbles) from urns, and using varieties of spinners. In each case the study begins with a discussion of what one would expect to happen. This is followed by the construction of a plan for testing hypotheses or guesses. The experiments are completed, the results tabulated and charted, and conclusions drawn as the hypotheses are reexamined in light of the experimental evidence. Each student is able to conduct his own experiment or is part of a small group carrying out an experiment. In this manner each student becomes personally involved. For example, if the students were testing the hypothesis that half the time a tossed coin should turn up heads ($P = 50$ percent), each student could toss and tally or the students could work in small teams. In this way, large numbers of trials may be accumulated by adding all the separate experiments—assuming that the coins are enough alike, of course. Whereas it might be tiresome for a single student to carry out 1000 tosses, to a class of 30 it means only some 35 tosses each. The same approach could be applied to tossing dice, tacks, and other such items in similar experiments.

Marbles of different colors in a box or bag serve to provide experiences in selecting balls at random. Spinners, too, offer many interesting possibilities, as was indicated in a British curriculum improvement program, the Midlands Mathematical Experiment.[2] These people had their students cut out two kinds of octagonal cards and stick short pencil stubs through the center of each to make spinning tops. One card is a regular octagon, but the second one is made with two different central angles, causing it to be somewhat distorted (Fig. 7-12). The resulting effect should form an interesting experiment for students. There is no reason why the cards must be only octagons. They could also be made of an assortment of polygonal shapes. In addition, arrow spinners can be constructed (Fig. 7-13). Geometry would become an important part of this work, as would percents and proportions, if the angles were to be varied a bit. The theoretical probabilities may be calculated by taking the ratio of the area of the triangle to the area of the entire figure. This is a lively way to involve students with probability concepts and determination of odds by experimentation. The formal language and symbolism can be introduced as the need arises to be able to communicate easily.

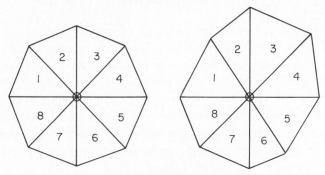

Figure 7-12

119

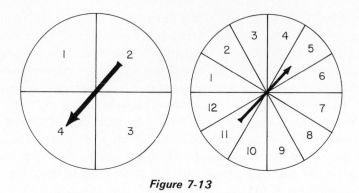

Figure 7-13

The classic definition of

$$\text{probability} = \frac{\text{favorable number of outcomes}}{\text{total number of outcomes}}$$

will grow naturally out of the experiments. There are six events that are possible results on a toss of a single die. I am interested in the appearance of a 2. This may happen in only one way; the probability is $\frac{1}{6}$. Determining the proper number of possible arrangements may not be easy to do, but at this stage it would seem unnecessary to dwell upon it. The important thing is to involve the students in the entire process of formulating and testing hypotheses through actual experimentation. In this way they will become aware of the importance of mathematics.

Tossing two dice, using two spinners at a time, and extending the work to include any number of coins or cards also adds spice and complication to the work. Just how far to take this work is a decision to be made by the teacher after observing the way in which the students react to these experiences.

CONCLUSION

We have considered a development of beginning ideas in the area of statistics. It is a vitally important area for many reasons. A literate member of modern society must feel comfortable with and understand statistics, rather than fear them. I had a friend who used to win all his arguments by making up statistics on the spot, such as: "Yes, but did you know that 71 percent of the people are afraid to fly?" He confessed one day that when he offered his "instant statistics" people never questioned his source and readily accepted them as correct. Number concepts strike fear into the hearts of brave men. Perhaps developments like those suggested here will help to eliminate negative feelings about numbers in our students.

Another reason for the study of statistics lies in the discussion in the first two chapters, where the significance of mathematics is considered. What better way is there to offer students evidence for the power of mathematics to enable us to learn more about the world in which we live, as well as the power of mathematics to help us find out that which would otherwise be most difficult to obtain? And we did this by organizing active experiences for all students, a prerequisite of sound learning procedures. The area of statistics is an unusually fruitful one on many accounts.

One advantage that has not yet been mentioned for such study is the ability statistical techniques offer us to explore wide assortments of problems. Those who are concerned about integrating school mathematics with any other school subject have the key to such integration in statistics. Problems from the social studies would most certainly lend themselves to the kind of investigation employed here, as would those of foreign languages and the several science areas.

We have emphasized basic techniques of investigation. Frequency distributions and the computation of averages in such a situation, histograms, and even measures of dispersion such as the standard deviation, although not uncommon to some junior high school mathematics texts, were not discussed here. The goal of this discussion was to present important concepts from a particular point of view. Certainly if class interest is high and you decide that the time will be well spent, these additional topics can be introduced in much the same manner as the earlier ones. The important thing to keep in mind is that a pattern has been established that may easily be extended. A particular development is but a single piece in the entire set of pieces that make up the student's junior high school mathematics experiences.

FOOTNOTES

1. See *How to Lie With Statistics* by Darrell Huff. W. W. Norton & Co., 1954, for a collection of the ways in which graphs may be tampered with.
2. *The Midlands Mathematical Experiment*, "O" Level, Book II. George G. Harrap & Co. Ltd., 1964, p. 152.

FOR INVESTIGATION AND DISCUSSION

1. Discuss reasons for and against adding work with statistics to the school program.

2. List suitable topics for graphing, including the comparison of meaningful factors in the lives of the students.

3. Consider the uses of the various types of graphs and give an example of a situation that would lend itself to each.

4. Devise a plan for the development of a study requiring students to make use of random sampling in an area that will be of some consequence to them.

5. Establish criteria to enable the students to carry out and evaluate the sampling procedure employed in the previous problem.

6. Compare the mean, the median, and the mode. Give specific examples to indicate the relative uses of each.

7. Construct a lesson plan that aids student understanding of averages through the use of physical bar graphing as indicated in this chapter.

8. Compile a list of common uses of probability found in today's society. You may draw examples from a variety of sources, including television, radio, and newspapers.

9. Develop a plan for the experimental determination of the probabilities for tossing a thumbtack so that it lands with its point facing upward as compared to facing downward.

10. Construct a unit that would provide experiences to enable students to learn about the decision-making power of statistics.

FOR FURTHER READING

Books

Darrell Huff. *How to Lie With Statistics.* W. W. Norton & Co., 1954.
Mathematics in Primary Schools. Curriculum Bulletin No. 1. The Schools Council, Her Majesty's Stationery Office, London, 1965, Chapter 6.
The Midlands Mathematical Experiment, "O" Level, Book II. George G. Harrap & Co. Ltd., 1964, pp. 150–156.
Richard S. Pieters and John J. Kinsella. "Statistics." *In* National Council of Teachers of Mathematics, 24th Yearbook: *The Growth of Mathematical Ideas, Grades K–12.* The National Council of Teachers of Mathematics, 1959, Chapter 7.
School Mathematics Study Group. *Introduction to Secondary School Mathematics,* Vol. 2, Part I. A. C. Vroman, 1962, Chapter 16.

Periodicals

Ruth A. Girard. "Development of Critical Interpretations of Statistics and Graphs." *The Arithmetic Teacher.* Vol. 14 (April, 1967), pp. 272–277.
Benjamin A. Grass. "Statistics Made Simple." *The Arithmetic Teacher.* Vol. 12 (March, 1965), pp. 196–198.
R. D. Harrison. "An Activity Approach to the Teaching of Statistics and Probability." *Mathematics Teaching.* (Spring, 1966), pp. 31–38.
Jack D. Wilkinson and Owen Nelson. "Probability and Statistics—Trial Teaching in Sixth Grade." *The Arithmetic Teacher.* Vol. 13 (February, 1966), pp. 100–106.

Pamphlet

Donovan A. Johnson and William H. Glenn. *The World of Statistics.* (Exploring Mathematics on Your Own Series), Webster Publishing, 1961.

Film Strip

Using Statistics: Making the Best Decision. (Modern Junior High School Mathematics Series, Set II), McGraw-Hill Book Co., 1966.

8

INFORMAL GEOMETRY

GEOMETRY—AN INTRODUCTION

Although we begin our discussion of geometry at this point, we have already considered many experiences that were to one degree or another involved with geometric concepts. Constructing circle or bar graphs requires the use and knowledge of geometric figures. In the beginning work with ratio, suggestions about using circumferences of a variety of objects were made. We might certainly expect that our students will have had numerous experiences with geometric concepts simply through the process of living. The moon and sun appear to be circles; the houses they see have very definite shapes; the common objects found around the home all have identifiable geometric shapes of one sort or another. It is sometimes difficult for us to believe that our students could have learned things outside of school, but of course they do. It is these experiences that help us to focus upon the importance of geometry in the school curriculum.

While the reasons for teaching school geometry are considered in detail in Chapter 15, justification is worthy of brief presentation here. If we ask the question, Why study geometry in the junior high school? we do not find the answers to be what we might expect. It is quite possible for a person to live his life without knowing any of these concepts, as far as his earning power is concerned. But that is a bit like saying that it is also possible to conduct your life without ever reading a newspaper or having any knowledge at all about what is going on in the world around you. If you would better understand this world in which you live, you will gain from a study of geometry. There are two important ways in which this happens.

123

First, all that we know we have learned through our senses: taste, touch, sight, smell, and hearing. It is believed that perhaps as much as 70 percent of what we perceive is sensed visually. But being able to see means not only what our eyes pick up and flash to the brain, but that which requires more than casual observation. If you look at a field, you may see lots of green grass with occasional colorful tufts of flowers here and there. But do you also see the variety of grasses that are probably growing, the varieties of plants with flower petals, pollen, and long graceful stems and leaves? Do you get any picture at all of the teeming insects that undoubtedly dwell in the field both above and below the soil? There is a way to see that enables some people to look upon the same scene as others and yet "see" a great deal more. When you look at a bridge, what do you see? Do you see lots of steel in the form of girders and cables supporting concrete roadways to enable autos to cross over some body of water, or do you see triangles in the girders to add strength to them and borings that had to be made deep into the river bed in order to anchor the supporting columns, which may be steel resting on poured concrete footings? Miles of cable appear like an endless cylindrical surface holding up the rectangular solid block of concrete that forms the roadway.

Geometry can help us to see more in man's constructions and in the constructions of nature as well. For we are not concerned with form alone. Form has a function. In common objects that are thoroughly familiar, we lose sight of this important relationship because we take the thing for granted. A teapot is round, an oil tank is cylindrical, and a honeycomb made by bees is hexagonal. These and the myriad of objects around us have purpose in their forms. It is the study of geometry that can help all students begin to gain some insights into the nature of their environment, both natural and man-made. We have as a goal, then, the sharpening of our senses to be better able to understand our world.

Geometry also offers us the opportunity to cast mathematical ideas in a visual form. This is a point more fully developed in the later chapter on geometry, but let us briefly point out here that most of us must have some mental picture of concepts if we are to be able to deal with them. So much of our school mathematics concerns abstract ideas that unfortunately have brought little visual imagery to the minds of our mathematics students; hence these students find mathematics an exceptionally difficult subject to grasp, and they resort to a good deal of memorization. How unnecessary! As Hadamard, among others, has pointed out, when he does his own creative work he translates the mathematics into its geometric counterparts and then deals with these.[1] He draws conclusions and sees relationships and then translates the geometric forms back into the mathematical setting from which they came. In order to think about mathematics, it would seem that most people have to think in terms of some kinds of images. Geometry is the "stuff" from which these visualizations are made. Our students attacking ideas for the first time have the same need for visual imagery as the creative mathematician. Few

124

of our students will be able to work with the abstract symbols without this truly "visual aid" that we call geometry.

Not only is it necessary that the learning and creating process be built on visual images, but the communication of ideas is also assisted by this role of geometry. The Ontario Mathematics Commission committee on geometry states emphatically that geometry is the language of science—so much so, that scientists would be illiterate without a knowledge of geometry, as the general public would be in attempting to understand scientific theories. The committee goes on to say that "the ability to visualize geometrically is a basic part of the scientist's mental equipment. Every scientific theory, or abstract model, will involve this ability to a greater or lesser extent."[2]

Another significant contribution of geometry to the development of mankind has been the example it offers of the ability of the mind of man to create when he relies upon logic and reasoning, instead of being ruled by prejudice and emotion. This lesson is, unfortunately, still being learned; for we have not yet been able to fully use logical thinking in order to improve the lot of us all. More detailed discussion of this area will also be presented in Chapter 15.

We have considered some arguments that help us to establish a reason for the teaching of geometry to youngsters. In so doing we have also established the desirable mathematical outcomes to result from such a study: a better understanding of environment, a better understanding of mathematics in general and geometry in particular, and of course the interest and desire to go further into mathematics. Let us now turn to the development of geometry itself.

VOLUME AND AREA

One good way to catch student interest is to pose a challenging problem. Bring to class a collection of some four or five differently shaped boxes, all rectangular with the identical volume of, say, 24 cubic inches, and ask the students to arrange these boxes in order of size from the smallest to the largest (Fig. 8-1). If five or six collections of such boxes are provided (perhaps the students might be asked to construct these boxes as a way of beginning this investigation), it would then be more suitable to cluster the youngsters in small groups and permit each group to attempt to arrange the boxes in order of size without assistance. However the activities develop, the problem of determining which of the arrangements are correct will soon be before the class and with it the companion problem of how we can determine who is right and who is wrong.

There are at least two viewpoints that might result from student discussion of this problem: Some students may wish to focus upon how much

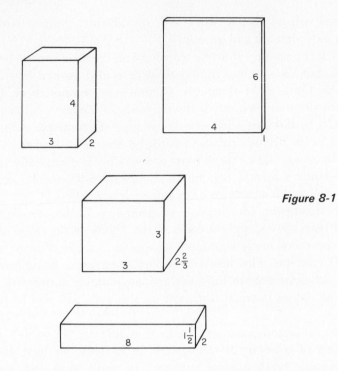

Figure 8-1

the box contains, while others may wish to determine how much cardboard was needed in order to make the box in the first place. One approach is as legitimate as the other, but for the time being we could direct our attention to an attempt to see how much each box might hold. If there is a supply of 1 inch cubes available, the students can fill the boxes with them and determine for themselves the comparable sizes. Of course, sand or water, if you have the courage, are also excellent for this. It may well be little short of surprising to many students to find that such differently shaped objects do indeed hold the same number of 1 inch cubes.

Rather than attempting to generalize on the process at this time, it would be best to follow up this initial experience with additional boxes for the students to arrange in order of size. It is feasible to provide boxes of equal volume, as before, or perhaps boxes of different sizes; either practice seems suitable. We could then move to presenting pictures or diagrams of boxes with their dimensions clearly marked upon them. As the students may still have the 1 inch cubes available, they may wish to construct solids by accumulating and stacking the cubes in order to test for the contents of a given figure. Eventually we will present the dimensions without pictures and ask the same kind of question, Which is larger or smaller?

Let us pause a moment and take a close look at what has happened.

First of all, a problem was presented to the students which referred to available physical objects. In attempting to find a solution to the problem of which object was larger, the students were not told how to proceed. They had to decide how to go about finding an answer by themselves. They had to create their own plan of action. So often, when we try to help our students get off on the right foot with some simple instruction about what to do, we have most effectively blocked any attempt on their part to think for themselves about a given situation. In the case described here, the students had the boxes; the rest was up to them. After discussion of possible solutions, and evaluation of these, we arrived at the point at which the cubes were suggested to help resolve difficulties. (If the idea of surface area was brought up, it was temporarily held in abeyance. It is a good and valid concept, and the student suggesting it is not wrong. It is simply that we must turn our attention to one concept at a time.) When the boxes were finally checked for their capacity to contain the 1 inch cubes, it became apparent that they held the same number. In fact, the students would most likely speak about the results in just that way: "This box contains 24 cubes." When the problem was resolved, we presented yet another to the class and then turned to problems that involved pictures, eventually getting to the point at which the students worked simply with the measurements and had no picture at all before them (other than the ones that previous experiences had built in their minds).

It would be expected that many of the students would simply multiply the dimensions in order to determine capacity in terms of the cubes. After continued experiences like these, virtually all will probably no longer need the actual cubes. In any event, we have provided experiences that should give the students an excellent feeling for volume, a feeling that is built upon visual images resulting from genuine experiences of interest and challenge. The vocabulary usually employed in working with volume is introduced naturally as part of the overall experience. We eventually call capacity by name—*volume*—and speak of the specific quantity as *cubic inches*. By this time these units should hold no mystery for the students at all. We have, all in all, another example of how to help students work from the concrete toward the abstract.

EXPONENTS

Our work with cubes has resulted in the writing of repeated multiplications as students calculated volumes. *After* they have had many experiences like this, a new symbolism may be introduced to shorten student work—exponential notation:

Instead of writing $5 \times 5 \times 5$, let us put a small 3 at the upper right-hand corner of the 5. Whenever we see this small number we will recognize it to be the repeated multiplication. Instead of $5 \times 5 \times 5$, then, we will write 5^3.

If this is done casually each time the volume of a cube must be determined, it will soon become a part of the student's vocabulary. Extended to the later work with squares, we expand on the idea a bit more. Eventually (after many experiences) we may wish to take time to focus upon the idea of exponents itself.

The introduction as described will have been founded on the physical cube. A sharp mental image of a cube should be present whenever the student sees the abstract symbols. Indeed, the words we use to read the symbols reinforce this image: (5^3) "five cube." The same is true of the later work with squares—an image of a square should accompany 7^2 as the words "seven-square" clearly indicate. It is the extensive use of physical cubes, and drawings and cutouts of squares, *before* introducing the notation that helps make the visual representations clear to the students. Reversing this order may well result in the many difficulties students frequently encounter with exponents.

Operations with numbers in this form will also stem from the experiences of finding volumes and areas. Asking students to sum volumes and areas of collections of geometric figures would be one way to introduce such problems.

You may be wondering why volume was introduced before any discussion of area. This is an interesting question. First, let us be clear about the fact that the order of events in mathematics, which is by its nature a highly sequential subject, is not as rigidly defined as we might believe. We know quite well that the order must make sense to the student. But no one can say with any degree of certainty what the best order of events should be for all children. So we may begin with volume, just as well as we may begin with area.

On the basis of common experience we have a factor in favor of presenting volume first. All the child's experiences are taking place in a three-dimensional world, not in the two-dimensional world of "Flatland."[3] It would then seem more natural to begin the geometric experiences of the student with those objects that come out of his own experience. This does not mean that all such work must start with volume. All that is being stated here is that it is as natural to start with volume as it is to begin with a consideration of area. The final choice is the teacher's, but the teacher must first be aware of the fact that he indeed does have a choice. While this freedom to choose may sound like an unimportant point, it is anything but unimportant. Many times we find that we cannot make the most of student interest because we must satisfy the needs of an apparent sequential development of the subject. However, this need does not have to be a deterrent. The chapter on individualized instruction will expand the discussion relative to choice. Suffice it to say that we have more freedom here than we might have suspected.

Earlier, we had temporarily postponed consideration of one way of

128

placing the original group of boxes in order by size: finding out how much "stuff" each box required in order to be constructed. We have examined the implications of determining the amount that the boxes could hold, i.e., volume. The same basic approach could be applied to the amount of "stuff" needed to make the box—surface area. How can we find out how much cardboard is required to make each of these boxes? After guessing about the required amount, one suggestion might be to cut the box along its edges so that we could "flatten" it out. Then by laying all the "flattened-out" boxes side by side we might be able to arrange them by observation (Fig. 8-2). Another procedure might require that we attempt to cover the sides of the box with colored drawing paper. In this way we could compare the amount of paper necessary to cover each box.

Still other students might want to work with the individual faces of the box and try to make some calculation of its size by summing all the faces. As before, suggested methods are judged by whether or not they do the intended job. Those that do and do so correctly are good methods. Those that do not are incorrect. Soon, however, we would want a quantitative measure of the boxes. How much bigger is one than the other? If two have about the same amount of "stuff," how can we be sure which is larger? In working with volume we used a cube as a standard for measuring. What might we use here? Cutout paper or thin cardboard squares could be supplied to the students (or can be cut out by them) and they could carry out this study in much the same fashion as the earlier volume explorations. If the teacher prefers that the students not handle so many pieces of paper, the faces of the rectangular solids could be traced onto graph paper with 1 inch squares, although other squared paper could be adapted for such use. In this way each student calculates the number of squares required to cover all the space of either each face or the entire "flattened-out" solid (Fig. 8-3). They compare their results and check their earlier guesses.

Since it turned out that the volumes of the initial collection of solids were equal, some students may feel that their surface areas are also equal. The results will prove quite surprising to them. In any case, we have thrown the students into a situation in which they are experimentally computing areas,

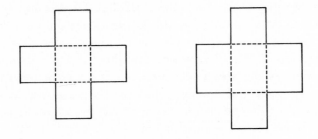

Figure 8-2

129

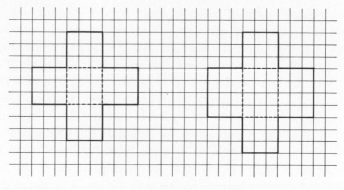

Figure 8-3

and they are doing this with the very same set of boxes we employed earlier in our introduction to volume concepts. Like volume, this introduction to area stresses an intuitive understanding of the concept, with as little formalization of the work as possible. Words and symbols are introduced as needed in order to save time and aid communication. The students move from saying, "That rectangle needs six inch-squares to cover it" to "That rectangle has an area of six square inches." We want the students to think of the physical square inches when they think of area, just as we tried to develop a situation in which they would see cubes in their mind's eye when they thought about volume. Multiplying lengths and widths could be gradually brought into the picture by working toward more abstract situations in virtually the same manner as we did earlier: first boxes, then pictures of boxes, then pictures of faces of boxes separately, and finally measurements of lengths of faces without any representations at all. By this time it is expected that most of the students will have forsaken the squares or the squared paper and will have invented pencil and paper techniques for computing the area.

The use of graph paper makes it possible for students to attempt to find the area of irregularly shaped objects as well. How much area is contained in the surface of your hand or your foot? The students could trace an outline of the body parts directly onto graph paper and then approximate the areas in question by counting squares. They could build a series of such experiences by using any number of familiar objects. If they are encouraged to estimate beforehand, something extra is added to their quest for results. The more experiences the students have of this nature, the greater will be their comprehension of what is meant by area. In addition, we have provided a foundation for the study of the area under a curve. This will be considered shortly.

In both the area and volume work, the shapes of the figures involved should be varied, although in the study of volume it would be wise to use solids that may be closely approximated as to content by use of the cubes. Larger cubes, rectangular solids, and pyramids having squares and rectangles as bases are best for now. Our chief aim is a feeling for volume, a feeling for area. We will soon extend these learnings to many different figures of both two and three dimensions.

There are many pathways that may be followed at this point. It is possible to devise activities to consider different polygons, their areas and perimeters. We could also turn to the volume-area concepts just explored, seek out relationships between them, and at the same time employ ratio concepts once more: What is the ratio of the volume of a solid to its surface area? It is also an opportune time to introduce a multitude of growth problems that involve these concepts and have some most interesting applications that will add to our understanding of nature in no uncertain terms: What happens to the volume of a cube if I double the dimensions? What happens if we triple the dimensions? What effect does this have upon the surface area?

Let us take a brief look at each of these possible courses and see where they lead. In so doing let us also be aware that the order in which these activities develop is simply for the ease of discussion and is by no means a model for classroom sequences.

POLYGONS

Why do bees and wasps build their honeycombs so that a cross section of the hive discloses that the cells are hexagonal in shape (Fig. 8-4)? A British publication describes how this question was investigated by an 11 year old in an English school.[4] It is a fascinating question that has many implications. For example, why don't the bees use square cells? A square is simpler than a hexagon. We immediately open up two areas of investigation: comparisons of squares and hexagons with equal perimeters and attempts to create patterns by fitting together a variety of shapes using one polygon at a time. (We assume the use of regular polygons for the sake of this discussion.)

Placing hexagons on graph paper or using the squares employed earlier would simplify comparisons of area. Once the area of the hexagon of a given

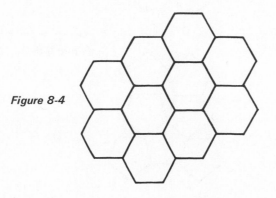

Figure 8-4

perimeter has been determined, the area of a square of equal perimeter may easily be considered. Table 8-1 gives some experimental results. It soon becomes apparent that given a hexagon and a square of fixed perimeter, the hexagon will enclose greater area within its sides than does the square. Many questions may result from such an investigation: Does a triangle enclose greater area than a hexagon of equal perimeter? Does an octagon of equal perimeter with a hexagon enclose greater area? How do the other polygons relate to those studied in this respect?

If the area seems to increase with an increase in the number of sides of a regular polygon (the perimeters fixed), why doesn't the bee construct the hive cells in an octagonal or decagonal shape, rather than hexagonal? Now we may invite students to attempt to fit together octagons, and other polygons, and to construct sample hives. (Cutting out such pieces may be most instructional, as students must figure out how to first make the various polygons.) As they try to make patterns using a given polygon, the students will become sharply aware of the difficulty of building patterns that do not leave any spaces (Fig. 8-5). We have the solution to our problem. The bee constructs his beehive cells in hexagonal form and they fit together and leave no spaces because, in the words of the 11 year old mentioned at the start, "with the same length of wall and the same amount of material the bee gets more area and therefore more volume in building a hexagonal honeycomb than if it builds a square one . . ."[4]

We have now had students exploring areas and perimeters of a broad

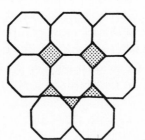

Figure 8-5

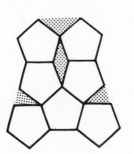

Table 8-1. Comparison of the Areas of Hexagons
and Squares with Equal Perimeters.

Perimeter	Hexagon		Square	
	Side	*A (Approx.)*	*Side*	*A*
6	1	2⅗	1½	2¼
12	2	10⅖	3	9
18	3	23⅖	4½	20¼
24	4	41⅗	6	36

assortment of polygons. After discussion of places other than hives where they may have seen this hexagonal cell construction (e.g., floor tiles, packaging, and large telescope lenses), additional examples could be presented comparing areas and perimeters, with the eventual introduction of triangular areas through the use of graph paper. If we begin with right-angled triangles, the students quickly see that the area is half the completed rectangle or square (Fig. 8-6). Other triangles then require careful consideration, as does the parallelogram resulting from the placing of two such triangles together. But use of the experimental approach will enable the students to build their own methods for finding area (eventually without the graph paper or squares) and will result in the invention of their own formulas. Symbols may be introduced to simplify their presentation. These activities may be followed by the exploration of circles—areas with a given perimeter—and the comparison of these with polygons. This work may then be extended to three dimensions, questioning why given shapes are used for various containers brought in from the supermarket. Finally, solids can be constructed using two-dimensional figures to focus upon the number of faces, number of edges, number of vertices, and so on.

In addition to graph paper and squares, the student may be assisted by making use of pegboards, Tinkertoys, Erector sets, and fold-up carpenters' rules as he works with the various figures. It is possible to construct solids out of Tinkertoys and a set of rods and connectors called D-Stix.[5] There seems to be an endless supply of interesting, active experiences available here that can aid student development of concepts and skills in a meaningful way.

Teachers will often say, "I'm teaching the area formula today." The statement in itself points up a rote kind of teaching activity. We do not

Figure 8-6

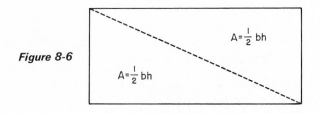

$$A = \frac{1}{2} bh$$

$$A = \frac{1}{2} bh$$

133

"teach" formulas. We organize experiences for children that 'will result in their invention of formulas. This does not imply that it is any easy task to develop experiences that enable students to invent their own ideas about things. On the contrary, it is a most difficult undertaking, but we cannot avoid facing the fact that as teachers this is exactly what we are here to do. This is our charge.

Before we leave this development, let us be clear about its implications: If a circle gives greatest area for a fixed perimeter (or circumference) and a sphere gives greatest volume for a fixed surface area, we have an explanation for the shape of many manufactured products, as well as for the conditions under which many living things exist. We will deal with this in detail as we consider how perimeters, areas, and volumes grow.

THE GROWTH OF AREA AND VOLUME

Many years ago a book was written about a man named Gulliver who traveled to distant and strange lands.[6] On one of his voyages, Gulliver encountered a civilization of giants who were built just like him except that they were 12 times each of his dimensions. Gulliver was about 6 feet tall; the giants were 72 feet tall. On another voyage Gulliver encountered a nation of tiny people who were constructed much as he was but who were one-twelfth as large. The book goes on to describe Gulliver's adventures with these strange people and becomes a fascinating tale that has been read for years.

Let us take a brief but careful look at Gulliver's giants, for the idea of a race of giants has been with man ever since he has been able to dream. If a giant existed who was like us in every way, except 10 times larger (let's use 10 rather than 12 to simplify the work a bit), could he run as fast as we do? What do you think? It is known that the strength of a part of a structure (e.g., a girder of a bridge or a section of thigh bone) depends upon the area of a cross section. A cross section of thigh bone of a man is less than that of the giant; hence the giant's thigh can support more weight. But how much more weight can it support? To be able to answer this question we will have to investigate how areas and volumes (we will use this as an indicator of weight, since weight depends upon how much stuff makes up the body) change as the dimensions change. Let us do some simple experiments:

Area: As we double the dimensions of a two-dimensional object, what have we done to the area? Triple it? Quadruple it?

Volume: What happens to the volume as we double all the dimensions of a solid? Does it triple?

Using any materials that they feel are necessary, or simply applying formulas, the students can tabulate the length of a side and the area of squares

134

Figure 8-7

Square			Cube	
s	A		e	V
l	l		l	l
2	4		2	8
4	16		4	64
8	64		8	512

and the length of a side and the volume of cubes (Fig. 8-7). To add to their understanding of these relationships, line graphs may be drawn to present a picture of them (Fig. 8-8). The area grows with the square of the side, whereas the volume grows as its cube. Hence a surprising result becomes apparent: Double the length of a side of a square and you have increased the area by four times! Not only that, but you have increased a cube eight times in volume by doubling its side!

Volume grows a good deal more rapidly than area, which itself grows at a faster rate than the length of a side. This is shown rather dramatically by the graphs: We see the sharp upward climb of the line on the volume graph, as compared with that of the line on the area graph. Additional situations could be explored by constructing tables and graphs of the growth of particular rectangles, rectangular solids, and other figures. Among other advantages, we have some interesting practice with graphing.

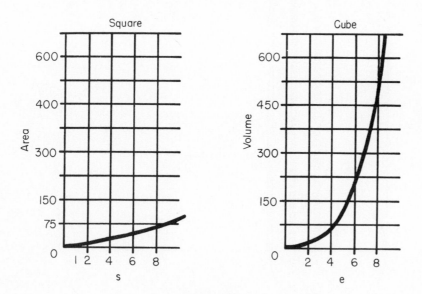

Figure 8-8

The circle may be explored in a rather effective way by involving students in an experiment suggested in the British curriculum bulletin mentioned before.[7] The students may bring a variety of tin cans, or jars, to class and use these to determine the famous diameter-circumference ratio, π. Masking tape and a large sheet of graph paper are needed in addition to the cans. After guessing diameters, tape is fitted around each can and cut to fit as closely as possible. The open end of the can is then placed upon the axes of the graph so that the diameter begins at the origin and coincides with the horizontal axis (Fig. 8-9). Mark the horizontal axis at the right-hand edge of the diameter and remove the masking tape and stick it on the graph perpendicular to the axis at that point. We have the length of the diameter marked off on the horizontal axis and the length of the circumference represented by a vertical strip of tape. The students measure each and record the circumference and diameter in a table and repeat the work for larger cans. Table 8-2 contains this information. After several measurements are completed, the students

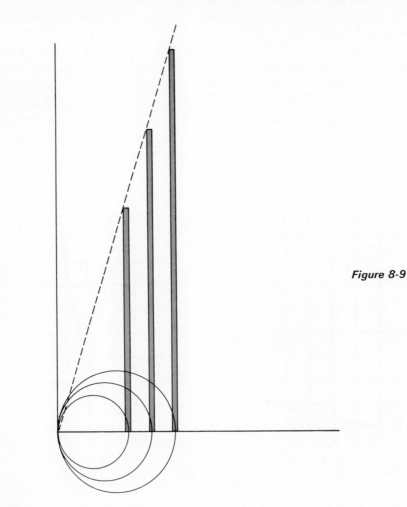

Figure 8-9

136

Table 8-2. A Comparison of Diameter and Circumference.

D (inches)	C (inches)	C/D
1	3¼	
2		
3		
4		
5		
.		
.		
.		

notice that the tops of the vertical tape strips (bars) will lie in a straight line and be a little more than three times the distance from its foot to the origin. The table will show the ratio of $\frac{C}{D}$ as computed. In terms of growth, doubling the diameter results in doubling the circumference. If we add the area to our consideration, we would find that here too doubling a diameter increases the radius four times, just as we saw before.

After experimentation we return well equipped to probe for answers to our problem of the giant. Since the strength of the thigh bone depends upon the area of its cross section, if we increase all dimensions 10 times, how will the area of the cross section be affected? Its strength will go up as the square of 10, i.e., increase 100 times! That bone will certainly be stronger than its counterpart in man. But how much more weight will it have to support? Well, since we are using volume measures to indicate weight, we must find out how much volume increases if all dimensions are increased 10 times. Our experimentation showed us that volume grows as the cube of the linear dimension; hence volume will increase 1000 times! Our big, strong giant is a most unfortunate fellow! He has 100 times more strength in his thigh bones but must lift with it 1000 times more weight! Each time he gets to his feet we can expect him to proceed to break both of his legs! Gravity has become a violent enemy. The implications of such a discussion are numerous. All kinds of changes in strength of arms and legs, as well as lifting ability, may be considered. But most important of all is the role of these physical and mathematical laws and their effect upon the shape of all living things.[8] There are many animals larger than man, such as the elephant and the rhinoceros, but their limbs are not proportional to those of man. Their thigh bones would be much thicker in order to compensate for the added weight. Haldane points out in a classic article on this subject that as we move from a gazelle to a rhino, the thickening of a leg becomes quite pronounced. Gravity, a mortal enemy of our mythical giant, has very little effect upon the smaller animals. It is quite common for a mouse to survive a fall from a 10 story building. Thompson and Haldane have made available to us the basic information necessary to carry out numerous fascinating and significant investigations involving the mathematical concepts of perimeter, area, volume, ratio and proportion, and percent, to list a few. The kinds of questions that may lead to investigations would include:

1. If tiny people who were like man in every way but were 10 times smaller in each dimension actually existed, what would they be like?
2. If a man coming out of a swimming pool carries about 2 percent of his weight in water drops upon him, what do you think happens to a fly which lands in the pool?
3. If you require a pound of meat a day and a quart of milk, how much would we need to feed to the giant who is 10 times us in every way? How much would be needed to feed the tiny man who is one tenth of us?
4. If we were to build an exact scale model of a miniature bridge and make it 100 times as large in all its dimensions, what is the ratio of the weights each could support?
5. If a rope with a 2 inch diameter was able to support 200 pounds before breaking, how much would be the maximum lifting power of a 4 inch diameter rope?
6. If 5000 mice weigh as much as one man, how would their combined surface area compare with that of the man?

There is one further consideration to be mentioned before leaving this discussion. We lose our body heat through our skin. The more skin surface we have, the more heat we will lose in a given time period of similar activity. (Exercising would result in greater heat loss than resting.) In order to maintain our constant body temperature we need certain amounts of food, as do all living things. The needs vary with the surface area: A man requires one fiftieth of his weight in daily food, while a mouse must consume half his weight. The smaller animals produce more heat (per unit of body substance) than the larger ones in order to replace heat loss. They get caught in the cycle of more heat—more energy used—more food needed—more work done. A shrew must eat constantly to be able to get all the necessary food into his small digestive track. That is why it is impossible to find a warm-blooded animal smaller than a shrew. Such an animal would be unable to keep up with his food needs in time to survive! Nature is an unusually skillful architect. Man, too, makes use of these concepts in his constructions.

This notion of heat loss also underlies the design of tea and coffee pots, home heating equipment, and indeed any area that is concerned with dispensing or conserving heat. And this completes our circle and brings us back to the beehive discussion in which we found that a circle offers maximum area for a given perimeter and that the sphere offers maximum volume for a given amount of surface area. We may now attempt to answer the simple question, Why is a teapot made round? Since heat is lost through surface area, we must minimize this area if the water in the pot is to stay hot. Furthermore, a manufacturer would like to minimize surface area because it means less material per pot and lower cost. What shape will maintain a volume of a quart and still satisfy these two objectives? A sphere will: Flatten the bottom, add a handle, and you have a tea pot. This will be explored further in a later chapter on geometry.

The applications considered thus far are excellent situations to employ as they satisfy all our basic criteria for the informal geometry program. What better way to help students realize the role of mathematics in understanding the environment?

AREA-VOLUME RATIO

To add to student understanding of why a shrew must consume a comparatively enormous quantity of food, an experiment forming area-volume ratios is suggested. If a chart is made containing the necessary information, conclusions may easily be drawn (Fig. 8-10*A*). In computing surface areas, we must include all six faces unless there is some particular reason to exclude the top. It becomes easy to see how the ratio of area to volume declines as the size increases, which means that the larger objects have proportionally less surface area than the smaller ones. A graph of the data could also be drawn by the students (Fig. 8-10*B*). This brings us near the close of the discussion of area and volume, the study of which made us call into play so much of our earlier mathematics. In this way we move forward and at the same time strengthen what has already been learned. Extending these experiments to figures other than the cube would provide additional experiences. It may be of great interest to students to determine surface areas and volumes of a variety of solids (cylinders, cones, and pyramids) and to check their area-volume ratios. Additional problems of physical significance may be drawn from the following relationships:

1. The density of materials is found by finding the ratio of weight to volume

$$\left(D = \frac{W}{V}\right).$$

2. The specific gravity of a material is the ratio of its weight in air to its weight in air less its weight in water

$$\left(\text{S.G.} = \frac{A}{A - W}\right).$$

3. The volume of water collected from a dripping tap depends upon the length of time the water is dripping.
4. The lifting force of a balloon is proportional to the cube of its diameter.

A final word is in order about another interesting application—the com-

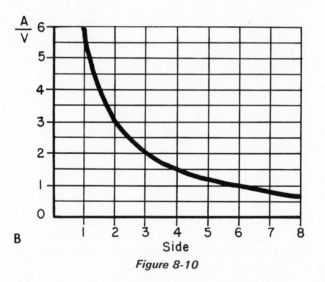

Cube

Side	Area of Face	(A) Surface Area	(V) Volume	$\frac{A}{V}$
1	1	6	1	6
2	4	24	8	3
3	9	54	27	2
4	16	96	64	1.5
5	25	150	125	1.2
6	36	216	216	1
7	49	294	343	.86

A

B

Figure 8-10

parative sizes and volumes of the planets in our solar system. Table 8-3 gives the radius of various planets, as well as of the sun and moon. A series of interesting problems may be developed from this information involving the computation of volume, surface area, ratio, and proportion; the use of scientific notation; and the conversion of units. It also helps one to gain some perspective about the size of our universe and to see how the earth fits into the larger scheme of things.

140

Table 8-3. Table of Radii.

Planet	Radius in Meters	Circumference at Equator	Volume	Surface Area
Mercury	2.6×10^6			
Venus	6.31×10^6			
Earth	6.38×10^6			
Mars	3.4×10^6			
Jupiter	7.2×10^7			
Saturn	6.0×10^7			
Uranus	2.7×10^7			
Neptune	2.5×10^7			
Pluto	uncertain	?	?	?
Sun	7.0×10^8			
Moon	1.7×10^6			

CONSTRUCTIONS: CONGRUENT AND SIMILAR TRIANGLES

There are many interesting and challenging experiences that are not concerned with application but with the concepts of geometry itself. Puzzle value alone makes such explorations well worth while for students. If a triangle is placed upon the board and the students are asked to make a scale drawing of the triangle at their seats using whatever tools they wish (compass, ruler, protractor), how shall they proceed? Such a problem is suggested in the report of the Ontario Commission referred to before.[9] It is an interesting challenge since it permits students to think for themselves and yet combine their efforts in an attempt to meet the demands of the problem. They are free to measure whatever lengths they wish of the triangle that was presented for copying. In addition, after one such exercise is completed, it is a simple matter to extend the challenge to another and still another, providing interesting repetition and a variety of experiences at the same time.

This is one way to begin the informal study of congruence. To focus upon the parts necessary for congruence, the constructions may be varied by limiting the number of allowable measurements to three or possibly two and eventually eliminating use of the protractor altogether. In this way the students become aware of the conditions under which it is impossible to construct the triangle, as well as the conditions under which they can succeed. There are many side issues that grow out of this type of work. The classification of angles and triangles (acute, obtuse, right, isosceles, equilateral, and scalene) occur naturally as we consider each triangle to be duplicated in turn. If these terms are used for purposes of description rather than rote exercises, a later full-fledged discussion of these ideas has some basis in student experience. Discussions based upon a rich variety of experiences are necessarily of greater significance to the students.

141

In addition to duplicating given figures, cutout triangles can form a pool of triangles to be copied by construction. As this work is carried out, the students will have to learn how to copy given line segments and given angles and how to bisect angles and line segments, all resulting from their desire to complete another task—the duplication of the triangle. Thus, to them the constructions are serving a definite purpose.

Many of the properties to be studied later as geometric theorems can be developed on an intuitive basis through construction exercises. Bentley and Potts have written a fine little book containing an interesting collection of just such construction exercises.[10] Although the constructions are carried out with compass and straightedge, the ruler and protractor will be used extensively as the students gather data about the figures under consideration through measurement. This is excellent practice, for it offers the chance for verification of hunches as well as the opportunity to explore a wide range of relationships.

The angle-sum theorem is one that can be considered through experimentation. Using the cutout triangles mentioned before, or simply asking each student to draw his own triangle, then measuring the three angles and recording these results in table form will provide the students with a large number of instances in which the angle sums will collect about 180°. Indeed, if the averaging techniques of the previous chapter are employed, the difference from 180° will be diminished. Tearing off the vertices of a paper triangle and fitting the angles together at a common vertex will provide additional acceptance of the fact that the sum is a straight angle.

Construction of the three angles using a common vertex is another activity that may be developed (Fig. 8-11). Whatever is done we must be sure to

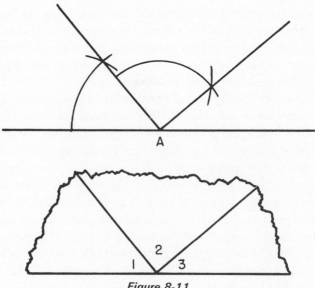

Figure 8-11

emphasize the remarkable quality of this property of triangles. No matter how small or how large a triangle may be, the angle sum is always the same! It certainly defies our powers of observation, because the concept of angle is a difficult one to visualize for us all. How many students feel deep down inside, no matter what anyone says, that the angle with longer arms is the larger angle? Arriving at a formal definition of angle is no simple task.[11] Perhaps the best way to help students gain insight into the meaning of an angle is to use the notion of rotation. A board compass, two pieces of an Erector set with a common joint, the hands of a clock, and indeed even the arms of a student may be employed in an attempt to indicate that the size of the angle is a function of the amount of rotation of one side about the other, with the two sides sharing a common connection point (Fig. 8-12). (Later, we can introduce the notion of an angle as two rays with a common end point.) This work can be supported, and the introduction of similarity can be accomplished in a single exercise involving the extension of the sides of a triangle (Fig. 8-13). If the students draw a right triangle and extend its sides *AB* and *AC* to form a new right triangle, *AB'C'*, there are many questions that may be asked about this situation involving some surprising ideas:

> Has ∠*A* changed in size?
> What is the relationship between ∠*B* and ∠*B'*? ∠*C* and ∠*C'*?
> Are segments *BC* and *B'C'* related in any way?

In addition to these questions, we may explore the various ratios that exist between corresponding sides of the two triangles. Such experiences offer the opportunity to use ratio concepts once more at the same time that they lay the groundwork for triangles that have the same shape but not the same size,

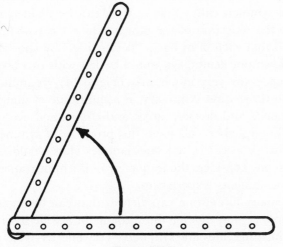

Figure 8-12

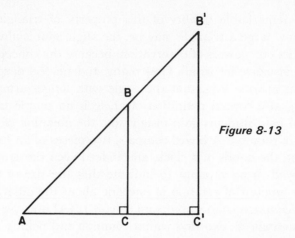

Figure 8-13

i.e., similar triangles. Further extension of the sides, together with tabulations of the resulting ratios, helps students find out for themselves what some of these relationships are. When they think that they have found something, they can draw additional figures to test their findings. We add the vocabulary to the situation as it is needed. This simple investigation has offered experiences with angle measurement, similarity, and even parallel lines, not to mention the basic understandings involved in the trigonometric ratios.

SYMMETRY

One of nature's trademarks is the symmetrical development ·of so many of her creatures. The exteriors of virtually all insects, animals, and plants are constructed symmetrically; that is, they can be divided into two halves, one of which is the reflection of the other. While it is true (as any actor will quickly tell you) that each of us has a "better side," by and large, if a vertical line is drawn down our center, we would be left with two body halves whose outside appearances are very much alike (Fig. 8-14). In addition to the many creatures of nature, we find symmetry in a multitude of man's constructions: an automobile, suits and dresses, tables and chairs, and even the very letters used to form the alphabet—all have the property of symmetry (Fig. 8-15). The study of this property in the mathematics class would seem to be most important when one considers the frequency of the appearance of symmetrical objects in all the students' experiences.

There are many interesting experiences that can be organized about the concept of symmetry that involve the students in a wide assortment of activities. Paper folding illustrates line symmetry very effectively, as does the cutting of designs into the paper after folding. The number of folds may vary to show varieties of types of symmetry that may be present. Ink blots, made by

144

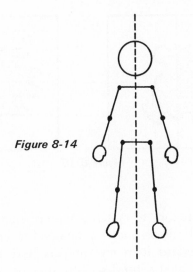

Figure 8-14

dropping a spot of ink on the center of a page and folding the paper upon it, form surprising symmetrical designs. The same is true of paint blots that may be created in the same manner (Fig. 8-16). Wallpaper designs may also contain symmetrical figures and, if necessary, students may be permitted to cut out designs thought to contain symmetry along the suspected axis. They may then place one part upon the other in order to check for likeness. Of course this kind of work is facilitated through the use of see-through paper or sheets of acetate. Tissue and wax paper may be held up to the light to check the superposition of markings.

An interesting discussion of the use of mirrors to carry out activities involving symmetry appeared in an article by Walter.[12] She has constructed what she calls mirror cards that require the students to place a mirror on a

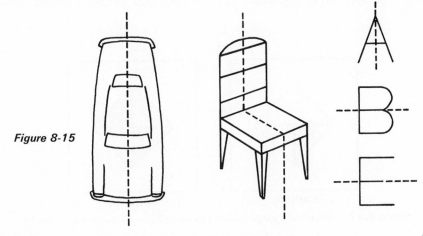

Figure 8-15

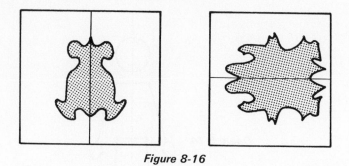

Figure 8-16

diagram in order to attempt to match a pattern shown in another diagram (Fig. 8-17). Safe metal mirrors may be obtained in any camping equipment store; they are a standard item for campers and are inexpensive. These mirrors, in addition to the use just described, may be employed in other ways. Mirrors offer us an interesting way to experiment with the reflection of light and to experimentally check the reflection law: The angle of incidence is equal to the angle of reflection.[13] Draw a solid line on a sheet of paper and intersect it at any angle with a broken line (Fig. 8-18). Place a mirror vertically on the point of intersection so that the solid line and its reflection form a straight line. Use any straightedge to draw a continuation on the paper of the reflected dotted line. Compare angle measures with a protractor. You will undoubtedly be able to think of many other uses for the mirrors.

The different geometric figures just studied may also become subjects for the symmetry test. In fact, careful observation of these figures enables the students to find different axes of symmetry (Fig. 8-19). After many experiences we may well consider what the mathematical description of symmetry might be. The students should be encouraged to devise some mathematical way of explaining this reflection property. Their result may also form a test for the presence or absence of symmetry. Whatever they finally do derive from these experiences, one thing is certain: To discover this property called *symmetry*

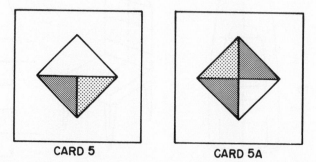

CARD 5 CARD 5A

Figure 8-17. *Where must you place the mirror on card 5 to see the pattern of card 5A?*

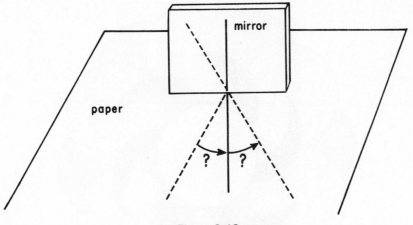

Figure 8-18

present in so many of nature's creations, from the tiniest insect to the leaves and branches of trees and the largest animals known, gives one some significant insight into the apparent order in nature, order that has become more understandable to us through mathematics.

Design making combines the elements of construction and symmetry and has always been a fascination for students. How often have you seen a student condemned for having a "short interest span" sit for hours with a compass creating all sorts of intricate patterns and patiently coloring them so as to make them attractive. Offer designs to students and ask if the designs can be duplicated (Fig. 8-20). Students will need little encouragement to try this and to move on to the invention of their own designs. The symmetric qualities of the designs are considered and tested to add to the mathematical side of these experiences.

One final word about symmetry that may be of interest. In England the schools are much more concerned about teaching a motion geometry, involving all kinds of transformations, than are the American counterparts.

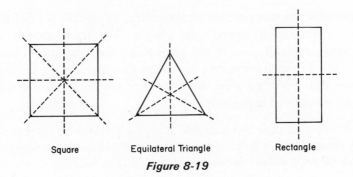

Square   Equilateral Triangle   Rectangle

Figure 8-19

147

Figure 8-20

This is usually begun in the lower grades in England. In such an approach, symmetry is seen to be but one of the many transformations that may be made to a figure. Some other kinds of transformations would involve *rotating figures,* in which properties that remain constant, as well as those that change, are observed; *translation of figures,* in which a figure is moved in a particular direction without turning; and *reflection,* in which symmetry is a special case that results when the figure as a whole remains unchanged. For an interesting discussion of these concepts, see Book T of the British School Mathematics Project.[14]

SPEED-TIME GRAPHS

Before we leave this chapter on geometry, let us take a brief look at one additional consideration, speed-time graphs. We have already seen how graphing grew naturally out of the geometric concepts under consideration. We have one more such instance to examine that involves the familiar motion relationship and offers us a very nice way to tie together many of the different concepts we considered separately.

> You get on your bike and ride at a steady rate of 12 miles per hour for 4 hours. Draw a graph showing the relationship between speed and time and use it to find the distance traveled (Fig. 8-21).

148

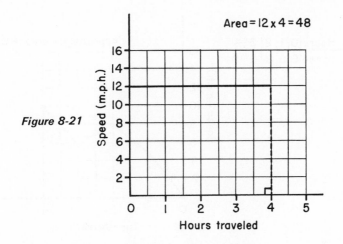

Figure 8-21

The graph turns out to be a horizontal line since the time is changing but the speed is not. If we were to drop a perpendicular from its right end point down to the time axis, we will have drawn a rectangle. But where is the distance in all of this? We have here the kind of visual representation that we will find most useful throughout our mathematics work, for we have a geometric model of a physical event. This model also constitutes a picture of multiplication. Distance (under constant rates of speed) is found by the familiar $D = RT$. Hence, it is the product of the speed and the time. The rectangle we have drawn has an area defined to be the product of its length and width. If we look at the graph, we find that the length and width of the rectangle are representations of speed and time. In this instance the ideas are interchangeable. Therefore, the area of the rectangle—the area under the curve—will indicate the distance, 48 miles.

Let us alter the situation slightly. You get on your bike and ride, increasing your speed at a steady rate so that the chart in Figure 8-22 describes your

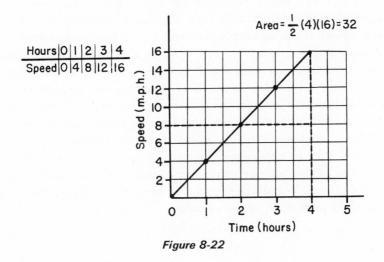

Hours	0	1	2	3	4
Speed	0	4	8	12	16

Figure 8-22

149

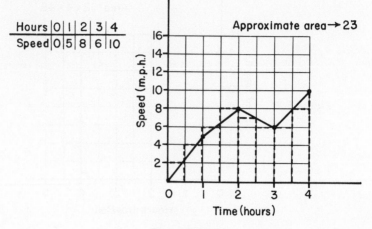

Hours	0	1	2	3	4
Speed	0	5	8	6	10

Figure 8-23

speed. What distance have you gone after 4 hours? After the students draw the graph, they may want to discuss ways to use the graph to find the answer. They may also wish to consider alternative methods. These become valuable as checks. The graph is now a straight line that moves upward as it moves to the right. This time if we drop a perpendicular from the right end point, we find we have enclosed a triangular area under the curve. Using our knowledge of triangle area, we may compute it and thus determine the distance, 32 miles. Is there a rectangle that would be involved with our graph that has this same area? We see that a horizontal line through the midpoint of the curve of our graph would have created a rectangle equal in area to the triangle: 8 × 4 or 32 miles. Once again, we have found distance to be the area under the curve.

Finally, you get on the bike and take readings each half hour of a 4 hour ride and record the values found in the chart in Figure 8-23. Find the distance traveled in 4 hours. Here is a fine puzzle for the students. If they are encouraged to work together, they may offer some ingenious methods of solution. Even though this is no simple problem, it is an important one that has the seeds of the calculus planted within it. How shall we proceed? Earlier we found the areas of many irregular figures by counting squares. This is an excellent method to employ here. After counting the squares we find the desired area. We may also construct rectangles of equal bases with heights varying in accord with the curve and then approximate the area in this fashion. Many problems involving a wide range of motions can be presented for additional student experience. We are using our methods for graphing, our knowledge of motion, our geometric concepts of area, and untold arithmetic computations. We are preparing the ground for the upcoming study of algebra and the later study of the calculus.

150

FOOTNOTES

1. Jacques Hadamard. *The Psychology of Invention in the Mathematical Field*. Dover Publications, Inc., 1954, pp. 76–77.
2. *Geometry, Kindergarten to Grade Thirteen*. Report of the (K–13) Geometry Committee. The Ontario Institute for Studies in Education, 1967, p. 4.
3. Edwin A. Abbott. *Flatland*. Dover Publications, Inc., 1952.
4. *Mathematics in Primary Schools*. Curriculum Bulletin No. 1. The Schools Council, Her Majesty's Stationery Office, 1965, pp. 55–56.
5. "D-Stix." Manufactured by Geodestix, Spokane, Washington.
6. Jonathan Swift. *Gulliver's Travels*. W. W. Norton & Co., 1961.
7. *Mathematics in Primary Schools*. Curriculum Bulletin No. 1. The Schools Council, Her Majesty's Stationery Office, 1965, p. 154.
8. For interesting descriptions see "On Being the Right Size" by J. B. S. Haldane. *In* James R. Newman (Editor): *The World of Mathematics*. Simon and Schuster, Inc., 1956, pp. 952–957; also see *On Growth and Form* by Sir D'Arcy Thompson (edited by J. T. Bonner), Cambridge University Press, 1961.
9. *Geometry, Kindergarten to Grade Thirteen*. Report of the (K–13) Geometry Committee. The Ontario Institute for Studies in Education, 1967, p. 65.
10. W. H. E. Bentley and E. W. Maynard Potts. *Geometry, Part One*. Ginn and Co., Ltd., 1937.
11. Harry Sitomer and Howard F. Fehr. "How Shall We Define Angle?" *The Mathematics Teacher*. Vol. 60 (January, 1967), pp. 18–19.
12. Marion Walter. "An Example of Informal Geometry: Mirror Cards." *The Arithmetic Teacher*. Vol. 13 (October, 1966), pp. 448–452.
13. Richard F. Thaw and John E. Morlan. *Experiences and Demonstrations in Elementary Physical Science*. William C. Brown Company, 1964, p. 3.
14. *School Mathematics Project, Book T*. Cambridge University Press, 1964, p. 45. See also "Geometry and Transformations" by Daniel E. Sensiba. *In* National Council of Teachers of Mathematics, 27th Yearbook: *Enrichment Mathematics for the Grades*. The National Council of Teachers of Mathematics, 1963, pp. 302–311.

FOR INVESTIGATION AND DISCUSSION

1. Discuss the geometric knowledge of students before they begin to study the informal geometry of this chapter.

2. Among the purposes for the study of geometry are (a) a better understanding of environment, (b) a visual representation of abstractions, and (c) an aid to scientific thinking. Discuss the significance of each of these purposes.

3. Describe how you would begin the study of geometry with an activity other than that presented here, but one that recognizes the need to work from the concrete toward the abstract.

4. Compare the advantages and disadvantages of studying volume before or after area.

5. List objects that are common to students that could be used for initial volume and area experiences. Select one concerned with area and one concerned with volume and explain in detail how each may be integrated into a classroom lesson.

6. Develop a plan of activities that will involve students in experiences designed to aid student invention of a method for calculation of the area of parallelograms.

151

7. Develop a lesson plan that asks students to explore the growth of the area of a particular rectangle and the volume of the prism (rectangular solid) formed with the given rectangle as a base.

8. Read Chapter II, "On Magnitude" in *On Growth and Form* (listed in references) by Sir D'Arcy Thompson. Describe how the ideas therein may be used in geometry classes.

9. Use Table 8-3 to develop a lesson comparing the volumes of planets in our solar system.

10. Describe a sequence of activities designed to help students become aware of the fact that the sum of the angles of a triangle is fixed.

11. Describe common objects that contain examples of symmetry of one form or another. Devise a lesson to teach students about symmetry using the objects.

FOR FURTHER READING

Books

W. H. E. Bentley and E. W. Maynard Potts. *Geometry, Part One.* Ginn and Co., Ltd., 1937.

Irvin H. Brune. "Geometry in the Grades." *In* National Council of Teachers of Mathematics, 27th Yearbook: *Enrichment Mathematics for the Grades.* The National Council of Teachers of Mathematics, 1963, pp. 134–147.

Geometry, Kindergarten to Grade Thirteen. Report of the (K–13) Geometry Committee. The Ontario Institute for Studies in Education, 1967.

Frank Land. *The Language of Mathematics.* Doubleday & Company, Inc., 1963, pp. 160–178.

Mathematics in Primary Schools. Curriculum Bulletin No. 1. The Schools Council, Her Majesty's Stationery Office, London, 1965.

School Mathematics Project, Book T. Cambridge University Press, 1964.

School Mathematics Study Group. *Introduction to Secondary School Mathematics,* Vol. 2, Part I. A. C. Vroman, 1962.

Sir D'Arcy Thompson. *On Growth and Form.* (Edited by J. T. Bonner), Cambridge University Press, 1961.

Periodicals

Irvin H. Brune. "Some Geometric Ideas for Junior High School." *The Mathematics Teacher.* Vol. 53 (December, 1960), pp. 620–626.

Denis Crawforth. "What is a Quadrilateral?" *Mathematics Teaching.* (Summer, 1967), pp. 18–20.

Peter Dunn-Rankin and Raymond Sweet. "Enrichment: A Geometry Laboratory." *The Mathematics Teacher.* Vol. 56 (March, 1963), pp. 134–140.

Thomas P. Hillman. "Colors, Geometric Forms, Art and Mathematics." *The Arithmetic Teacher.* Vol. 14 (October, 1967), pp. 448–452.

D. T. Moore. "Secondary Modern School Mathematics—IX Geometry." *Mathematics Teaching.* (Summer, 1962), pp. 54–58.

Pauline L. Richards. "Tinkertoy Geometry." *The Arithmetic Teacher.* Vol. 14 (October, 1967), pp. 468–469.

David F. Siemens, Jr. "Of Bees and Mathematicians." *The Mathematics Teacher.* Vol. 60 (November, 1967), pp. 758–760.

Lewis B. Smith. "Geometry, Yes—But How?" *The Arithmetic Teacher.* Vol. 14 (February, 1967), pp. 84–89.

Marion Walter. "Some Mathematical Ideas Involved in the Mirror Cards." *The Arithmetic Teacher.* Vol. 14 (February, 1967), pp. 115–125.

9

MODERN TOPICS

The decade of the 1950's was marked by the organization of numerous groups whose sole purpose was the improvement of mathematics curricula.[1] Despite popular belief to the contrary, many of these groups began their work in the pre-Sputnik days, although it is true that the sudden appearance of a Russian satellite in the sky had a remarkable effect upon the availability of funds for the improvement of mathematics education. Although each improvement study group was organized and proceeded to develop in its own way, there were somewhat similar goals that were entertained by these groups that led to the emergence of suggestions for curricula improvement. Certain common threads emerged from the programs in general, but first a word is in order about the makeup of these groups, which was revolutionary in itself.

For the first time professional mathematicians, mathematics educators, and school teachers sat down together to consider the improvement of mathematics education. For the first time the several parties concerned with these problems attempted to jointly consider the ways and means of making the learning of mathematics a more effective experience. New topics were suggested for the curriculum in order to try to reflect some of the changes that were known to have taken place in the field of mathematics in the last 60 years but that had been completely ignored by the traditional school curricula. Among these topics we find the notion and vocabulary of sets as the central theme. *Set* became the catchword of the new programs. In addition, attention was directed for the first time to the study of finite arithmetics. The fundamental laws were emphasized, and work with numeration systems to a variety of bases was also included. These four topics were generally found in most programs bearing the name "modern."

Modern Topics

In an attempt to make mathematical language more precise and to emphasize the logical structure of mathematics, those working on curriculum improvement projects introduced new vocabulary and new symbolism, as well as new curriculum topics. Some were equally concerned about the methodology of instruction in mathematics, the University of Illinois Committee on School Mathematics[2] being perhaps the one group most responsible for the new-found emphasis upon discovery ideas—that is, creating a classroom environment in which the students are able to devise their own methods, rather than placing them in a situation in which memorization becomes their chief learning technique. Other groups later stressed these same ideas.

But the excitement of the years mentioned was a result of the fact that the mathematics curriculum was undergoing basic and fundamental changes for the first time in half a century. Nothing on this earth seemed more static, more everlasting than the school mathematics curriculum. Not only that, but if you entered school classrooms in the 1940's and 1950's, you felt right at home; for little had changed about school instruction in the lifetime of most adults alive then. This is no small feat because the educational system was emerging from a tidal wave of change brought on by the progressive education movement.[3] Although there were a good deal of new and significant changes made in the way children were taught mathematics in the elementary school (due in no small part to the fine book by Brueckner and Grossnickle called *How To Make Arithmetic Meaningful,* first published in 1947 by The John C. Winston Company), very little effect was felt in the junior high school and still less in the high school. I can still recall my own student teaching days in a junior high school in New York City in 1949. My cooperating teacher was teaching percent to a class of eighth graders and she had the class memorize *the* method for dealing with each of the infamous three cases by repeating aloud after her and in unison exactly how to handle each case! Of course there were many fine teachers of mathematics functioning at that time, helping the students to look upon mathematics as something exciting and important. But by and large rote learning was the order of the day and repetition was the key to learning. There was little doubt that change was long overdue. When it finally began to become a reality under the leadership of men like Max Beberman, Dean Albert Meder, and John R. Mayor, mathematics education embarked upon a new area.

When a new product has to be sold in our society, a slogan or catchy name is often employed to make people more receptive. Mathematics education is no exception. Somewhere along the line this profession got its share of catchwords. "Modern mathematics," the name generally applied to virtually all curriculum change, is one example of this. Just what is modern mathematics? Like so many things in life, these words are almost meaningless since they mean different things to different people. If the purpose of language is communication, then these words fail the test. But the words had a most instrumental role in how improvement suggestions were received, because much more than a name for these suggestions was involved. It became a virtual war cry on the order of "Remember Pearl Harbor" since it quickly established two armed mathematical camps that were in direct conflict: It became the "modern, new math" against the "old, traditional math." The lines were clearly drawn in the historic fashion of a movie or TV western. In this way, the name attached to the changes became a device for helping both school teachers and the public to easily separate the "good guys" from the "bad guys." Everyone knew instantly how to get on the side of right. Unfortunately, in this process the two sides as envisioned simply did not, and indeed, *do not* exist. Once again we were in the position of having to assign our loyalties to this or that side when the situation actually called for a careful examination of improvement suggestions to be certain that they offered us progress in overcoming the long-standing and well-entrenched enemies of effective mathematics learning experiences for youngsters: learning based upon memorization, the manipulation of symbols without understanding, and the lack of meaning and importance of so many mathematics classroom activities.

It appears to this observer that the enthusiasm generated by the prospect of long-awaited change has now settled down somewhat so that a more rational appraisal of where we are and where we wish to go is now underway. There was a time when suggested changes met with little critical discussion in public and with equally little resistance. There were a few men who voiced their concerns in no uncertain terms about the directions of suggested changes, led perhaps by Morris Kline as the chief antagonist.[4] But for the most part the academic community seemed to be so thankful for the opportunities for improvement that it seemed to fear that undue criticism might foreshorten the chance to bring about changes. But the role played by Kline was an important one. It is not enough to simply say that what we have is bad and that therefore we will discard it and introduce the first suggested change that appears. Rather, we will have to build upon what we have that is of value, trying to alter, revise, eliminate, and add in order to minimize those practices and topics that have not helped us move toward our goals and to introduce those subjects and methods that will. Kline's objections have helped us to explore this process. Of course, we have to be clear about our aims and objectives. The first two sections of this book were devoted to just that. Improvement can best be brought about through alteration of content and methodology, since the two are completely interdependent. So we are left with the important task of attempting to evaluate improvement suggestions against our aims and objectives and the way in which we will try to achieve these. Hence, we must ask basic questions of those who would alter our practices: Why should we teach children set ideas and use set vocabulary? Why must we stress the fundamental laws? Why does a student have to become involved with adding numbers using a base 5 numeration system?

These are important questions for all teachers and administrators to ask. It is not enough that these topics are now found in textbooks and curriculum guides, since meaningful and effective teaching of these ideas will result from those who know what they are about and why. And if the answers to these and similar questions should be rather difficult to find, we may also have to be prepared to reject the ideas as not helping us to go where we must travel as teachers of mathematics. The suggested changes encountered to date are not the end of it. They are hopefully only the beginning of a situation of continuous improvement in our profession as we strive manfully to develop what W. W. Sawyer has called the "Model T Ford" of mathematics: the program that will provide meaningful and significant mathematics experiences for everyone.

Let us now take a closer look at some of the major topics suggested for the improvement of curricula.

SETS AND SET VOCABULARY

At the very heart of improvement suggestions has been the recommendation that sets and set vocabulary be employed in school as early as possible. It is not uncommon today to examine a series of textbooks published, say, for grades one to eight and find that virtually each book in the series begins with a chapter on sets. Why is it so important that this concept be a central one in the teaching of mathematics? It seems that set theory has been a powerful tool of the research mathematician who is basically concerned with the unification of all mathematical ideas. Sets are therefore seen to be an important unifying agent that also simplifies the concepts under consideration. These are admirable qualities that are desirable for any school program. In one of the many paperbacks on the "new" mathematics, Johnson and Rahtz state that "there are two aspects of sets that concern mathematicians—one, the way sets are useful in the study of all branches of mathematics; and, second, the study of sets as a mathematical phenomenon in their own right."[5] Johnson and Rahtz go on to explain that failure to understand these two aspects has led to confusion and criticism, since it is the former purpose that has application in the schools, and new programs were being criticized for the latter. "Most often we mean simply that youngsters should become acquainted with the idea of sets and see how useful it is in all of their work in mathematics."[5] Specific examples are presented to clarify the point. One-to-one correspondence and set operations involving collections of objects generally familiar to the children are two of the topics discussed. No one concerned about mathematics education can reject the stated goals for the teaching of sets. For children to see the usefulness of the topics of the curriculum has been one of the sad omissions in the past; that is why so much has been made of usefulness in the developments described in this book. But we are speaking of usefulness in terms of the student's perception here and not "usefulness" as interpreted by an adult. Can students gain an appreciation of the usefulness of set ideas and operations in their mathematics work? If they can, let us by all means be sure to teach such ideas. If they cannot, perhaps we may offer more valuable experiences.

If we turn to the examples usually employed to demonstrate how sets may be purposely developed with youngsters, we find examples like the following:

1. Bob, Joe, and David are teachers. Sam, Charles, and David are scoutmasters. Who is both a teacher and a scoutmaster? (This is an example of intersection.)
2. We have two sets: (1) cup, saucer and (2) dinner plate, soup plate. Is there some way to combine these sets into a single set of dishes? (This is an example of union, which is said to be very much like addition.)

Of course it is generally suggested that the proper sets be expressed symbolically with braces and perhaps represented pictorially with Venn diagrams (Fig. 9-1). In addition to these examples we can often find mention of the importance of sets in algebra through computer circuitry, in logic, and in geometry as well. The role of sets in algebra will be considered in the algebra section of this book. As for the examples presented, perhaps it is a matter for personal judgment, but it is difficult to determine just how these are seen to be useful in the study of mathematics for students. When such examples are completed, what exactly has the student accomplished? In considering the use of sets in the elementary school, Howard Fehr states rather emphatically that

> Set notation and symbolism, and any *theory* of operations on sets have no genuine significance for the learning of elementary school mathematics. There is nothing magical or necessary in the use of the word "set" . . . But the theory of sets is nonessential in learning school mathematics; recognition of collections of things is essential.[6]

Fehr does go on to illustrate later in the same article how the *idea* of a collection of things can be used to build number concepts and counting,

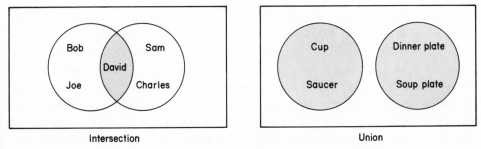

Figure 9-1. *Pictorial representation of sets with Venn diagrams.*

157

among other things; but he stresses that language is unimportant, as is set symbolism. Fehr's objections appear to be directed at words, rather than at the set concepts themselves—although he too does not clarify why this set concept and operations are preferable to what has gone before.

In the study of algebra, as we become involved in the consideration of inequalities and their graphs and the solution of inequalities and systems of inequalities, we will make use of set ideas to enable students to do things that would otherwise prove more difficult. It is at this point that set ideas will be utilized. To use them at any other time would seem to be serving the notion of sets at the expense of the student. Granted that the ideas are most important ones, but unless we can provide experiences to help students gain insight into these significant uses, we would be better disposed to teach something else and hold the set ideas for a more opportune time. It is quite possible to introduce set as an experience in mathematics that is presented for its own interest value. We have already done this several times here. This is certainly a legitimate undertaking that requires only challenging, puzzling, and interesting problems. But to imply that students will find set useful in all mathematics and that they will thereby gain appreciation of the unification of mathematics is not quite acceptable. As for the unifying idea, it is virtually impossible for a youngster to gain insight into the ability of sets to unify that which he has not yet studied. If he does not have the parts, how is he expected to wonder at how these same parts have been strung together to form a single entity called mathematics?

We can, however, begin to build this important notion. Not in the fashion that was described in the set examples presented earlier and not at one specific point in the student's experience with mathematics, but when he has studied arithmetic, algebra, and some geometry ideas it can be pointed out how these seemingly diverse topics may be thought of in terms of a common element called set:

> Addition in arithmetic involved the combining of sets of objects; in algebra we draw graphs of sets of points; in geometry we saw that a circle was a set of points, each a given distance from a fixed point.

At this stage these concepts are mentioned virtually in passing. Each time another situation presents itself—the study of locus, the definition of the conics—we point this property out again and again. Eventually, at a later time, we may well dig in to study more about the set idea itself. It then has a reason for existing, a reason that has built up slowly over a long period of time. To throw all the early mathematics experience of our students onto a "set economy" from the start may well establish the kind of climate that has the greatest possible opportunity for creating just those meaningless experiences we wish to eliminate.

158

THE FUNDAMENTAL LAWS—
STRUCTURE PROPERTIES

Another comparative newcomer to the mathematics classroom is the collection of structure properties that underlie the real number system. These include the fundamental commutative, associative, and distributive laws, as well as the identity elements, inverse elements, and closure property. Here it appears that teachers have misunderstood the intent of suggested improvement ideas; otherwise how can we explain lessons devoted to the teaching of these properties through countless numbers of examples that are so reminiscent of the drill work of the "traditional" program, the raison d'être for improvements? While no one will deny that the ideas are important ones for students to know, this does not mean that formal instruction in these concepts is necessary. When the ideas are encountered they should be referred to; for example: "Some of you checked your adding by adding down rather than up. Isn't it convenient that we get the same answer both ways!"

The very names of the basic laws need not be mentioned until later. When there is a large accumulation of incidents over a period of time, the student begins to become aware of the fact that they are of some consequence. He begins to think of the number 1 as a special number: "When you multiply by it you don't change anything." He regroups his numerals to simplify additions: "If I make combinations of 10, I can get the correct answer easier." He realizes that some operations are not reversible: "In subtracting I must be careful about which number is on top." Altogether, he works with these basic properties not for their own sake, but rather as recurring important characteristics of the number activities with which he is involved.

There is one caution we must be careful to observe. It is often indicated that a basic law, such as the commutative law, helps the student to understand why, let us say, he may add up as well as down. This is misleading. Knowing the commutative law does not explain *why* this happens. It merely indicates that it does happen. The numbers contain this property. It is there. When we talk of helping students to understand *why* something happens, we are speaking of cause and effect. In the case of the fundamental laws, we do not have a cause and effect relationship. These are properties contained in the system. As a matter of fact, people were aware that numbers can be added in reverse without changing the sum long before the fact that this is possible was given a name. The question "Why?" is not an easy one to answer to the satisfaction of the student. It's much the same thing as attempting to explain why things that go up must come down (within certain limits). Gravity tells us *what* is happening—not *why*.

FINITE ARITHMETICS

In order to emphasize the aforementioned structure, it has also been suggested that the students become involved in working with tidy little finite arithmetics. The simple finite arithmetics contain all the properties of our system. In this way students can focus upon structure properties in a setting that does not contain the complications of our familiar arithmetic.

If we do not overemphasize the structure properties, we may have in these arithmetics some interesting pattern activities that offer us an opportunity to bring rather startling results before our students. But if we are to get the most from them, the emphasis is best placed upon the puzzle value and not on the abstract qualities. Let us look at a sample in order to be clear about what is intended:

When is $10 + 4 = 2$?
How could it be that $2 - 3 = 11$?
When is $3 \times 5 = 3$?

Indeed, these may sound like rather strange results to our students, and it is of interest to permit them to discuss these examples and consider when

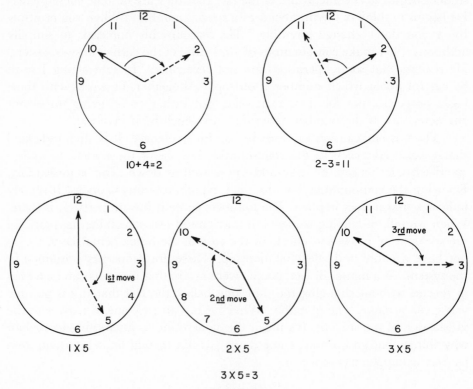

Figure 9-2

they may be correct. The examples, of course, are not as far-fetched as they may appear. They explain what happens when you perform operations with the familiar numbers of the clock. For instance, 4 hours added to 10 will result in 2 on the clock. The same is true of the other examples: Three hours before 2 o'clock is 11 o'clock, and if we begin on the numeral 12 and make three moves of 5 hours each, we will end up on the 3; thus $3 \times 5 = 3$. (See Fig. 9-2.) These examples would undoubtedly lead the students into immediate construction of problems of their own, always a good source of interesting exercises for students.

After spending some time trying to determine answers, we might pose the question of using a "clock" with fewer than 12 numerals on it. The students could make a clock based upon any number they wished, using zero as one of their numerals to simplify the work. Keeping the numerals smaller than, say, 5 or 6 will also help. In this way all the addition results and multiplication results may be tabulated (Tables 9-1 and 9-2).

This is an interesting kind of mathematics investigation since students have the freedom to make a clock of their own choosing and then explore the resulting addition and multiplication combinations. The totality of such facts may be recorded in a table, an impossibility with our familiar system because we have an infinite number of possible combinations. It is also possible for each student or group of students to become expert on a given clock arithmetic and devise a collection of problems involving the two operations and their reverse operations (inverses). These problems can be shared with the class as patterns develop with regard to the results. These unusual systems can also shed some light on our own system, although as pointed out earlier this is not the only reason for working with them. In our arithmetic, we may reverse addition and multiplication. Can you do that with these new systems? Does it matter if we do an example like $2 (4 + 1)$ by multiplying first instead of adding first? Students will generally find this work fascinating. While it may grow out of discussions of the familiar clock, it soon spins off into a purely mathematical consideration; and yet it involves carrying out familiar operations altered somewhat for the clock. We do not dwell on the abstract structure properties, but we do refer to them in passing. The freedom students have in developing their own clock systems adds to their pleasure in using mathematics. It is not surprising to find students coming to school with all sorts of tables worked out involving clocks with a variety of numerals.

If class interest is high enough, this kind of recreational mathematics can be extended to include modular systems, which are very similar to the clock arithmetics. Here again, the modulus may be any number and so the students have an opportunity to work at things of their own choosing. All the comments about clock systems apply here, except that we do not have the clock as a familiar object to help build the concept. If the modular sys-

Table 9-1. Addition Table.

+	0	1	2	3
0	0	1	2	3
1	1	2	3	0
2	2	3	0	1
3	3	0	1	2

Table 9-2. Multiplication Table.

×	0	1	2	3
0	0	0	0	0
1	0	1	2	3
2	0	2	0	2
3	0	3	2	1

tems are constructed by the tallying of remainder classes (see Table 9-3), perhaps the students will be better able to see what is going on. Like clock arithmetic, it is important to maintain one's sense of what is important about these investigations and not delve too much into the abstractions.

Perhaps one great benefit from this work is the slow awareness on the part of the student that his arithmetic system is not the only one there is. Prior to this exploration of clock and modular systems if we were to use arithmetics (the plural form), the students would have been convinced that we had made a mistake. Now they know that there are other arithmetics. They have had fun with numbers and have had a chance to broaden their mathematical horizons.

Table 9-3. Mod 4 System.

When we divide by 4, the **remainders** *may be 0, 1, 2, 3:*

$\dfrac{0 \text{ R}0}{4\overline{)0}}$	place zero in 0 class
$\dfrac{0 \text{ R}1}{4\overline{)1}}$	place 1 in 1 class
$\dfrac{0 \text{ R}2}{4\overline{)2}}$	place 2 in 2 class
$\dfrac{0 \text{ R}3}{4\overline{)3}}$	place 3 in 3 class
$\dfrac{1 \text{ R}0}{4\overline{)4}}$	place 4 in 0 class

Remainder Class			
0	1	2	3
0	1	2	3
4	5	6	7
8	9	10	11
12	13	14	15
.	.	.	.
.	.	.	.

Before we turn to different base numeration systems, let us consider the number-numeral controversy. Strictly speaking, we frequently misuse these words, using *number* when indeed we are referring to *numeral*. The symbols on a clock face are numerals; we do written work on paper with numerals. In fact, when we compute we are working with the names of numbers and symbols representing numbers, rather than with the numbers themselves. Number is a complete abstraction. This has caused a good deal of confusion unnecessarily. As a matter of fact, the technical misuse and interchanging of these two words have resulted in a good deal less confusion than has appeared since the careful separation of the two. It is therefore suggested that we forget this differentiation unless it is truly going to aid our mode of expression. For example, if I would like to explain in words what the symbols $\frac{1}{2}$, $\frac{3}{6}$, $\frac{4}{8}$, and $\frac{5}{10}$ indicate, it may be easiest to simply describe them as numerals for the same number. Otherwise, let us accept both words from students interchangeably. Professor Calandra, at Washington University in St. Louis, describes the behavior of those who insist on the number-numeral differentiation as much like that of the teacher who asked a student who he was. "I am John," replied the student. "You must never say that!" admonished

163

the teacher. "You must say that 'I am the boy whose *name* is John.'" This eloquent example seems to say it all.

NUMERATION SYSTEMS OF BASES OTHER THAN 10

The study of numeration systems to bases other than 10 is one of those "new" topics that is not really new. Many teachers taught the idea to their students long before it found its way into the improvement programs. Why shall we bother students with these numeration systems when all their lives they will probably only have to compute with decimal numbers? Is this another of the esoteric concepts that is best postponed for another time? The question is not as easily answered as it may appear. A great deal will depend upon the way in which the concepts are developed in class. The reasons for wanting to introduce these concepts at all relate to the important characteristics of our decimal system: It is a place-value system utilizing only nine figures and zero. The base, of course, is 10. How can we help our students appreciate the place-value system they have taken for granted for so long? They simply are too close to it and work with it without thinking.

In order to sharpen their awareness, let us take them out of their familiar system and thrust them into a strange system, but one that has all the important qualities of the decimal system. Where shall we find such a parallel system? All we have to do is change the base. Everything will be as it is with the decimal system except that the base will be different—and correspondingly, the number of figures used will diminish or increase; i.e., if we decide upon base 5, we shall only need the numerals 1, 2, 3, 4, and zero. This is the rationale for including the concepts in the school program. There is also the concomitant aim of helping students learn a bit about the numeration system used in many computers, the binary system. Fehr considered this goal in the article mentioned previously and concluded that ". . . to educate elementary school children as though everyone would become a computer programmer is nonsense."[6] This condition would not seem to have suddenly changed at the junior high school level.

Does this mean that we are better off forgetting about introducing such concepts? Not entirely. Earlier it was mentioned that much would depend upon the way in which the concepts are taught to students. This is the crucial point. In the section related to the learner we took some time to explore the work of Z. P. Dienes, the English mathematician and psychologist. Among the many achievements of this talented gentleman has been the development of what he refers to as "multibase blocks."[7] These are wooden blocks made up in a variety of bases. They consist of cubes that are scored in accord with the base: A base 9 cube would be scored so that it demonstrates nine squares on every face. Smaller pieces complete the set for each base and are constructed so that students may build up the larger cube with the pieces. The point of it all is that the students have concrete representations of the different numeration systems, and these together with the games devised by Dienes provide the student with experiences that are important to the understanding of the significant ideas of the base system. He has children begin using these different systems early enough and in a way that helps them to naturally learn about each of them. Later they turn their attention to the one system that is used throughout society. From this point on they concentrate on becoming proficient with the decimal system.

This kind of experience seems to make a good deal of sense. It involves the sorely needed concrete experiences and works gradually toward the abstractions. Shall we teach different base numeration systems? If it is taught in this manner and at the early elementary grades, the answer is yes.[8] Otherwise, it would be advisable to limit the work to some simple translations from one base to another and let it go at that, with the possible inclusion of some simple addition and multiplication examples. The chief purpose would be to clarify the decimal system.

The binary numbers hold special appeal to some students; in light of the extended role of computers in society today, it may be of value to devote some time to this numeration system in the manner of the recreations described earlier. The reason for using binary numbers in digital computers (i.e., computers used for counting, like your fingers—as opposed to analogue computers used for measuring, like a slide rule) is the use of electrical current. Either there is a current or there is not; the light is either on or off. To represent numbers with these lights and currents we must use but two figures to match the two states of the computers. We could use a large number of bulbs to set up as many different columns as we feel we may need, but each light can be either on or off; hence, it can represent only two possible figures. Our familiar decimal system is a place-value system, and that is good. But the base is 10, which requires the use of nine figures and zero, and that is bad. Is there a system that is a place-value system that requires the use of only two symbols? The

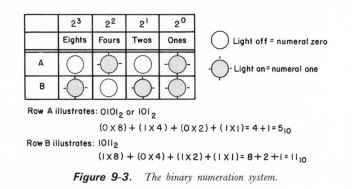

Row A illustrates: 0101_2 or 101_2
$$(0 \times 8) + (1 \times 4) + (0 \times 2) + (1 \times 1) = 4 + 1 = 5_{10}$$
Row B illustrates: 1011_2
$$(1 \times 8) + (0 \times 4) + (1 \times 2) + (1 \times 1) = 8 + 2 + 1 = 11_{10}$$

Figure 9-3. *The binary numeration system.*

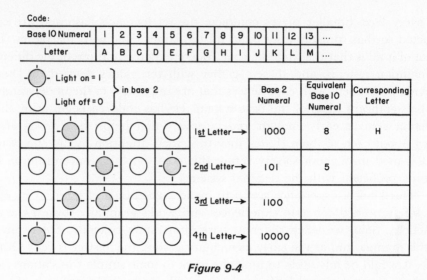

Code:

Base 10 Numeral	1	2	3	4	5	6	7	8	9	10	11	12	13	...
Letter	A	B	C	D	E	F	G	H	I	J	K	L	M	...

	Base 2 Numeral	Equivalent Base 10 Numeral	Corresponding Letter
1st Letter →	1000	8	H
2nd Letter →	101	5	
3rd Letter →	1100		
4th Letter →	10000		

Figure 9-4

binary system fills the bill perfectly. It is a place-value system employing only the numerals 1 and 0 to write all possible numbers (Fig. 9-3). This is the key to the high-speed electronic computer. It is possible for the students to send word messages through the binary computer by assigning numbers to the letters and then translating these numbers into binary notation. When the computer responses are recorded and translated into binary numbers, the students then must decipher the number code back into letters (Fig. 9-4). In this way a good deal of interesting practice is painlessly carried out at the same time that the students gain insight into the role played by the binary system in computer operation. If interest warrants, the instructions given to a computer, "the program," can also be attempted in some very simple situations. The sharply detailed instructions required by a program offer the student an excellent opportunity to test his understanding of basic processes

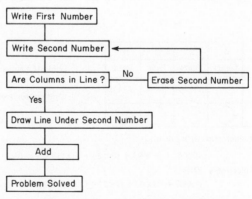

Figure 9-5. A program for addition.

(Fig. 9-5). As he attempts to write a program for the addition of whole numbers, or perhaps the division of two decimal fractions, he must call upon all his understandings of the particular process. There is no stigma attached to this work, no matter what the level, since it is the instructions for a computer. In fact, it may well be of value to pair a student with a lower-grade student who is attempting to learn the very process for which the upper grader has constructed a program. One way to learn is to teach.

CONCLUSION

We have asked some important questions about the inclusion of specific topics in the school program. The answers to these questions as considered here may help you to formulate your own responses. This is the intention of this section. We must not accept suggestions blindly from just any source—including, of course, this very book—as many did in the early stages of the so-called "modern" programs. Our initial excitement about change has calmed somewhat, but the situation can never be the same again; for once we were able to see the opportunities offered by change, we could no longer settle for the status quo. We will no longer offer to teachers the solace of a fixed program that will be *the* program for many years to come. The dynamic nature of our society has obviated any such position. We have moved from stagnation and will continue to move. Our chief concern should now be with the direction of all this movement. Perhaps the pages to follow will clarify one such course.

FOOTNOTES

1. For interesting descriptions and analyses of these programs see the following:
   National Council of Teachers of Mathematics. *The Revolution in Mathematics*. 1961.
   National Council of Teachers of Mathematics. *An Analysis of New Mathematics Programs*. 1963.
   Donovan A. Johnson and Robert Rahtz. *The New Mathematics in Our Schools*. The Macmillan Company, 1966.
   Studies in Mathematics Education. Scott, Foresman and Company, 1960.
   Edwina Deans. *Elementary School Mathematics—New Directions*. United States Department of Health, Education and Welfare, Bulletin 1963, No. 13, U. S. Government Printing Office, 1963.
2. University of Illinois Committee on School Mathematics. Champaign, Illinois.
3. Lawrence A. Cremin. *The Transformation of the Schools*. Alfred A. Knopf, Inc., 1961.
4. Morris Kline. "The Ancients Versus the Moderns, A New Battle of the Books." *The Mathematics Teacher*. Vol. 51 (October, 1958), pp. 418–427.
5. Donovan A. Johnson and Robert Rahtz. *The New Mathematics in Our Schools*. The Macmillan Company, 1966, p. 36.
6. Howard F. Fehr. "Sense and Nonsense in a Modern School Mathematics Program." *The Arithmetic Teacher*. Vol. 13 (February, 1966), p. 84.
7. See description in *Building Up Mathematics* by Z. P. Dienes, Hutchinson & Co. Ltd., 1960, pp. 55–74.

8. Other concrete materials may serve as well as those of Dienes, such as The Cuisenaire Rods, Cuisenaire Company of America, Inc., 9 Elm Avenue, Mount Vernon, N.Y.

FOR INVESTIGATION AND DISCUSSION

1. Read the two articles appearing in the October, 1958 issue of *The Mathematics Teacher* entitled "The Ancients Versus the Moderns, A New Battle of the Books" by Morris Kline (pp. 418–427) and "The Ancients Versus the Moderns—A Reply" by Albert E. Meder, Jr. (pp. 428–433). Compare the arguments of the two authors. Explain which one you are in agreement with and why.

2. Why have suggestions been made for the inclusion of "modern mathematics" in school programs?

3. What are some of the major problems facing those concerned with the teaching of mathematics?

4. Why are set vocabulary and set ideas becoming a part of school mathematics programs today?

5. Discuss some arguments for and against the teaching of sets to children in grades seven to 12.

6. Devise a problem, drawing on student experience, to illustrate the meaning of intersection and union of sets. Use Venn diagrams.

7. What are "structure properties"? What are some of the reasons for and against the teaching of these to children in grades seven to 12?

8. Construct a lesson to help students realize the importance of the fundamental laws and other structure properties through work with a finite arithmetic.

9. Our students will only find it necessary to compute with a base 10 system when they leave school. Why shall we teach systems with bases other than 10?

10. Make a lesson plan for a 45 minute lesson for average eighth grade students to demonstrate the purpose(s) outlined in question 9.

11. Plan a lesson to clarify why a binary numeration system is important to high-speed electronic computers.

12. Select one of the recently developed mathematics improvement programs and analyze it as to your evaluation of how effectively it achieves its purpose.

FOR FURTHER READING

Books

Z. P. Dienes. *Building Up Mathematics*. Hutchinson & Co. Ltd., 1960.
Donovan A. Johnson and Robert Rahtz. *The New Mathematics in Our Schools*. The Macmillan Company, 1966.
J. David Lockard (Editor). *Report of the International Clearinghouse on Science and Mathematics Curricular Developments, 1967*. A joint project of the American Association for the Advancement of Science and the Science Teaching Center, University of Maryland, 1967.

National Council of Teachers of Mathematics, 23rd Yearbook: *Insight Into Modern Mathematics*. The National Council of Teachers of Mathematics, 1957.
National Council of Teachers of Mathematics, 24th Yearbook: *The Growth of Mathematical Ideas, Grades K–12*. The National Council of Teachers of Mathematics, 1959.
National Council of Teachers of Mathematics, 29th Yearbook: *Topics in Mathematics*. The National Council of Teachers of Mathematics, 1964.

Periodicals

Irving Adler. "The Cambridge Conference Report: Blueprint or Fantasy?" *The Mathematics Teacher*. Vol. 59 (March, 1966), pp. 210–217.
Howard F. Fehr. "Sense and Nonsense in a Modern School Mathematics Program." *The Arithmetic Teacher*. Vol. 13 (February, 1966), pp. 83–91.
Eugene Ferguson. "Current Reforms in Mathematics Curricula—A Passing Phase or Progress?" *The Mathematics Teacher*. Vol. 57 (March, 1964), pp. 143–148.
Herbert Fremont. "New Mathematics and Old Dilemmas." *The Mathematics Teacher*. Vol. 60 (November, 1967), pp. 715–719.
Margaret Haines. "Modular Arithmetic." *The Arithmetic Teacher*. Vol. 9 (March, 1962), pp. 127–129.
E. W. Hamilton. "Number Systems, Fad or Foundation?" *The Arithmetic Teacher*. Vol. 8 (May, 1961), pp. 242–247.
Charles Hudson. "Some remarks on Teaching Different Bases." *School Science and Mathematics*. Vol. 63 (November, 1963), pp. 649–652.
J. V. Hudson. "A Binary Teaching Aid." *Mathematics Teaching*. (Winter, 1966), pp. 40–41.
Donovan Johnson. "Next Steps in School Mathematics." *The Arithmetic Teacher*. Vol. 14 (March, 1967), pp. 185–189.
Burton W. Jones. "Miniature Number Systems." *The Mathematics Teacher*. Vol. 51 (April, 1958), pp. 226–231.
Morris Kline. "The Ancients Versus the Moderns, A New Battle of the Books." *The Mathematics Teacher*. Vol. 51 (October, 1958), pp. 418–427.
Albert E. Meder, Jr. "The Ancients Versus the Moderns—A Reply." *The Mathematics Teacher*. Vol. 51 (October, 1958), pp. 428–433.
Francis J. Mueller. "The Revolution at Sputnik-Plus-Ten." *The Mathematics Teacher*. Vol. 60 (November, 1967), pp. 696–706.
Francis Scheid. "Clock Arithmetic and Nuclear Energy." *The Mathematics Teacher*. Vol. 52 (December, 1959), pp. 604–607.
Margaret F. Willerding. "A Teaching Unit in Modular Arithmetic." *School Science and Mathematics*. Vol. 60 (October, 1960), pp. 511–518.

Pamphlets

Robert B. Davis. *The Changing Curriculum: Mathematics*. Association for Supervision and Curriculum Development, National Education Association, 1967.
Edwina Deans. *Elementary School Mathematics—New Directions*. United States Department of Health, Education and Welfare, Bulletin 1963, No. 13. U. S. Government Printing Office, 1963.
National Council of Teachers of Mathematics. *An Analysis of New Mathematics Programs*. The National Council of Teachers of Mathematics, 1963.
Studies in Mathematics Education. Scott, Foresman and Company, 1960.

169

PART TWO

ALGEBRA

10

THE LINEAR FUNCTION

OVERTURE

Algebra is one of the most important areas of mathematics studied by students. For many it is the beginning of their work with "higher" mathematics on a comprehensive level, since most of the work previously undertaken focused primarily upon arithmetic. The student of algebra is about to take a giant step forward in his mathematical growth and development. Algebra may well prove to be a turning point in the budding mathematical careers of some. The attitudes and understandings that are shaped in this course may influence the way in which the student always perceives mathematics and may determine his ultimate relationship with it. The development of an elaborate symbolic language that becomes a powerful tool, the introduction of an important extension of our number system (the negatives), and the search for patterns of relationship in a broad variety of situations all pose formidable problems for the student of algebra. Add to this the frequently encountered fear and dislike of mathematics and we begin to get a glimpse of the task ahead for both teacher and student.

In recent years many curriculum changes have been recommended and the algebra curriculum has undergone more than its share of careful analysis. Numerous recommendations have been made with an eye toward its improvement—suggestions which have been translated into new textbook materials and changing classroom activities.[1] Not only has the content of algebra been altered and the symbolism refined, but there has been an evolution of different points of view upon which to base the entire course. Is algebra a generalized arithmetic? Is it the study of the real number system? Is it the study of relationships? It is possible today to find textbooks for student use that are based upon each of these ideas and some, perhaps, that are devoted to more than one of these underlying assumptions. Whatever pathway a teacher decides to follow, it is quite clear that he must know where he is headed. He must have some overall guide if the work of his classroom is to have direction and purpose.

In the previous chapter it was pointed out that a change in the content of mathematics courses will not necessarily result in improved learning of mathematics. The chronic problem, for example, of undue emphasis upon memorization is seen to be more a function of method than of content. While many of the newer programs have attempted to solve "method" problems with "content" solutions, two programs are notable exceptions: the University of Illinois Committee on School Mathematics (UICSM) and the Madison Project.[2] The Illinois program has brought discovery techniques into focus and more than any other group is responsible for the widespread acceptance of such an approach to the learning of mathematics. The Madison Project, originally a supplement to the regular curriculum, has altered both content and methodology in an attempt to improve interest in and the quality of the learning of mathematics. In the main, however, it seems that a basic faulty assumption has been made that improving mathematics curricula alone would result in improving mathematics learning. To think for a single moment that changing content will develop understanding is to strengthen the very weakness we are trying to eliminate, for not only will you fail to rid the mathematics classroom of unwanted rote learning, but in addition improved content will be rendered ineffective.

As you read about improvements designed to aid mathematics learning, you will notice how methodology and content are frequently confused. This is not to say, of course, that it is entirely possible to divorce one from the other. On the contrary, we must consider content and methods together. This is precisely why an attempt to improve one by focusing only upon the other is doomed to failure. Thus, we will continue to find teachers who taught "traditional" mathematics in a rigid fashion now teaching "modern" mathematics in a rigid, rote fashion. The content-methods paradox reminds one of the well-known song about love and marriage, "You can't have one without the other."

How then shall we approach the task of improving the learning of algebra? In earlier chapters we explored the important considerations to be kept uppermost in mind as we approach students of mathematics. The basic program has to be a primarily active one—one that emphasizes ideas rather than words and one that involves analytical thinking only after many experiences with the ideas have first been realized. As for our mathematical goals, it should be stressed that mathematics is an abstract system of ideas—perhaps the most fantastic product to come from the mind of man. While it is abstract, it still provides the scientist, in particular, with a powerful tool for the study of the world in which we live. It enables him to describe and explore patterns that are everywhere in the world around us. These are our general goals and under-standings as we seek ways of teaching mathematics to all children effectively.[3] But what of algebra, specifically? Are there objectives that are peculiarly the property of the algebra?

Algebra is the language of the scientist. It not only aids in the under-standing of our environment but also provides the language with which scien-tists communicate. If you study algebra, you learn the language of mathe-matics. Algebra adds to our ability to understand and describe relationships between objects in the physical world, as well as between the algebraic symbols themselves. Thus, if there is any single theme that runs through all of algebra, it is the mathematical notion of *function*. This appears to be the central idea, the idea upon which the experiences in algebra should be based. This also appears to be consistent with the current emphasis upon structure in the im-provement of mathematics curricula. While it may seem odd that emphasis upon the notion of function is a result of placing the stress upon structure, we have only to recall the definition of "structure" by the man who has probably been singularly responsible for its popularity, Jerome Bruner:

> Grasping the structure of a subject is understanding it in a way that permits many other things to be related to it meaningfully. To learn structure, in short, is to learn how things are related.[4]

What clearer case can be made for using the function concept as the basis for building an algebra curriculum? Function is a description of "how things are related," and in its broadest sense this is structure, as distinct from the concept of structure usually encountered, such as the structure of the real number system or the structure of a group.

At times, in this chapter, the development of algebra concepts based upon different assumptions will be explored and their consequences considered, but for the most part, the work here will proceed with the function concept upper-most.

INTRODUCTION TO ALGEBRA

At the start of any new term it is important to begin with a clear indica-tion to the students that the work to be undertaken this year is interesting, challenging, and yet within their ability to work with successfully. In algebra this is probably more necessary than in any other branch of mathematics because many students approach the study of algebra with fear and apprehension. The student grapevine is a most effective means of communication, albeit at times inaccurate. Thus, when students begin the study of algebra, many of them are prepared for the worst. It is crucial to quickly and effectively dispel these unfounded fears. With this in mind, as well as the purposes emphasized earlier, the beginning work in algebra should consist of a brief active overview of the work in an attempt to whet the student's appetite for the main course itself.

One possible way to start is to begin with a simple experiment. It should be one that will provide fairly consistent results and one that is comparatively easy to perform: How much will a spring stretch as different weights are hung from it? While any variety of springs that are flexible enough to give meaningful results can be used, it is perhaps most convenient to make use of small fishing scales. In this way we have a ready indication of the amount of weight added, as well as the ability to easily measure the resulting extension of the spring. If ounce weights are not readily available, the washers, nuts, or bolts of any hardware store will suffice. Before the students actually carry out the experiment, it would seem necessary to discuss briefly the process of experimentation. It might be well for the teacher to inform the class that each student will take the role of "scientist" in the lesson. Consideration might be given to these questions: What do scientists do? What is an experiment? How are experiments conducted? What is scientific observation?

It may then be announced that the students themselves will do an experiment this very day, an experiment involving the way in which the length of a spring changes as weights are hung from it.

What do you suppose will happen to the spring under these conditions? This is a most important question to put to the class before the experiment is done. The answers the students give, together with their explanations, serve to stimulate thinking about the situation and create interest in *wanting* to do the experiment. Everyone will be anxious to see if the results were anticipated with any degree of correctness. Guessing builds the desire to do the task.

How shall the students proceed? Let us hang the weights from the spring one at a time (or 1 ounce at a time, if your equipment permits), measure the resulting stretch, and record the results in a table of information such as this:

When we hang:	The spring stretches:
(weight in ounces)	(stretch in inches)

The physical arrangement of the room will depend upon the amount of equipment the teacher has available. For the best possible results, five or six setups of springs and weights could be located in different areas of the room so that the children could cluster about these in small groups. If only a single experiment is available, the experiment could be undertaken at the front of the room with several students coming up and doing the work—one student to record the results on the chalkboard while the others do the same at their seats, another student to actually place the weights on the spring, and perhaps a third student to read off the results after carrying out the measuring process. When the experiment is completed and the data collected, each child will have a table of data before him. If multiple sets of equipment are used, we have the results of five or six experiments readily available. If only one set was employed, the teacher might emphasize the need for repeating the experiment in order to be sure that the recorded results are the product of the weights and the springs rather than the experimenter. In any case, we are now ready to examine the data. First, did things come out as you had expected? Compare your guesses with the results. Second, is there any pattern in the numbers of the table? The various patterns found by the students should be written out in sentence form on the chalkboard as the class explores each one in an attempt to determine if it actually does fit the data. If we assume that the spring in question yielded results that showed a stretch of 3 inches for each ounce of weight added, the statements given by the students might include:

> The stretch is three times the weight.
> The weight is always one third of the stretch.
> You add three to the last stretch to find the new one.

Whatever the description, at this point the only relevant question to be asked is "Does the description fit the data in the table?" It is most important to refrain from trying to correct student statements here despite the fact that it is necessary to differentiate, for example, between the thing and the number of units of the "thing." While no attempt is made to play down these important concepts, they are not considered at this time since they may detract from our main purpose, which is a general study of functions by working with mathematics in action. Precision will come later as needed, when precision is important.

After the sentences have been written on the chalkboard and checked against the tables, we look for some way of shortening the statement so that it may be more manageable. At this point in the development, the teacher may select the one statement that he feels will be the description that will lead to a linear function of form $y = ax$, i.e., in the example cited in which the stretch was 3 inches per ounce, $s = 3w$. To arrive at this we select a statement such as:

> The amount of stretch is three times the amount of weight.

Crossing out the unnecessary words leaves:

> ~~The~~ amount ~~of~~ stretch is three times ~~the~~ amount ~~of~~ weight.
>
> or
>
> stretch is three times weight.

174

And lastly, changing to symbols yields:

$$s = 3 \times w$$

This final symbolic short form is called a formula. A brief discussion of formulas may follow, offering students an opportunity to recall familiar formulas they have met earlier, such as:

$$A = s^2 \qquad C = 2\pi r \qquad I = PRT$$

Knowing the formula gives us an understanding of the relationships involved in the given situation. Look at the formula $s = 3w$. Whenever a symbol is written in a mathematical sentence, it has a definite purpose for being there:

> What does the s represent?
> What does the w represent?
> What does the 3 represent?

The last question may puzzle students. They should consider the question, Would the 3 appear if we used a different spring? Here, the teacher might want to repeat the experiment with a variety of springs to indicate that the constant will change; hence, it has something to do with the nature of the spring iself—perhaps its thickness, the strength and elasticity of the metal of which it is made, or the number of coils it contains. This might be a fruitful area for further study. In any case, each symbol in the formula has an important reason for being there, an idea we shall emphasize again and again so that there is little mystery in the use of the symbols.

We can add still more to our understanding by looking at a picture of the relationship, a graph. The graphing of the particular function at this stage should proceed in the same manner as did graphing in the lower grades. The students will make a two-dimensional graph, setting up vertical and horizontal axes that will constitute only the first quadrant of the Cartesian plane. Since in this instance the stretch depends upon the amount of weight, we identify the horizontal axis as the w-axis and the vertical as the s-axis. This is justified solely on the basis of tradition. When the points are plotted and the line drawn, we have a picture of the relationship (Fig. 10-1). The students might consider the following:

> Examine the graph. What kind of curve is it? Does it go through the origin? Must the graph extend only as far as the points we have in the table?

With the completion of the graph, we will have developed four alternate ways of describing a relationship: with words, with a formula, with a table, and with a graph.

When we know the relationship and have described it mathematically, we have gained some power to predict events. We turn now to this process of prediction and ask the students to determine how much the spring will

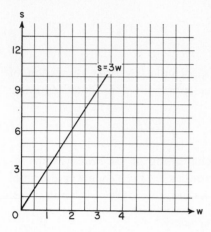

Figure 10-1. *Graph showing the relationship of stretch to weight.*

stretch if we hang 5 ounces of weight upon it? If we hang 6 ounces? What about 7 ounces? The students are encouraged to figure out the answers in any way they wish (trial and error, formula, or graph) and then to check these results with the springs themselves. Thus, the equipment first used to generate data is now used as a means for checking.

This elementary beginning to the study of the linear function and the solution of linear equations is carried out at this time in a completely unstructured and informal manner. For the most part we limit ourselves to finding the dependent variable when given the independent variable (if $s = 3w$ and you are given w, find s). It should not be minimized, however, that in predicting through the use of mathematics we are completing a rather fantastic process. The information contained within the table was a result of observation. Now we are indicating what will happen without doing the experiment at all. Using paper and pencil, we are offering a description of what would take place in the physical situation, and lo and behold *it works!* This is a rudimentary beginning of the development of insight into the wonder of mathematics.

Let us reexamine what we have done if we begin as indicated. The start we have made is an active one that poses a definite challenge to the student, yet does not rely to any marked degree on his previous work with mathematical concepts. He starts fresh. Psychologically, we seem to be building upon a firm base. By deriving mathematical expressions from a physical experiment and using the symbolism to describe the inherent relationship, we are helping youngsters to learn the language of mathematics based upon concrete experiences, with the emphasis upon the notion of function. The informal nature of the work done provides maximum opportunity for success for students, with the hoped-for result that they will begin to conclude that this "algebra" is not going to be a formidable enemy after all and, perhaps, may even be a good friend.

But it was stated earlier that this introduction was to be a kind of over-view of things to come; so we do not at this point exploit all the possibilities in the situation from an algebraic point of view. Instead, we go on to study other interesting relationships, remaining for the time being with the same type of linear function.

A slight digression is in order, however, before we continue. Should the proper equipment become a problem, the teacher might want to use drawings or diagrams of springs in series, illustrating how a spring is extended under a given amount of weight (Fig. 10-2). The only equipment necessary is a ruler, in order that the students may be able to measure on the diagrams to deter-mine for themselves the amount of stretch in each case. Thus, while they are not active participants in the sense of carrying out the experiment, they are only one step removed because they *are* gathering their own data. Of course, the first-hand experience of working the experiment is preferable, but the conditions of classroom life frequently limit the quality of the experience. The process of using representations is an important one in the total development since our goal will be to begin with the physical, concrete experience and work gradually toward abstraction. Thus, the business of gathering data from draw-ings is the first step away from the concrete toward the abstraction and the eventual presentation of tables of data involving only x and y with no concrete counterpart.

Once the spring experiment is completed, we then offer a new experi-ment, remaining for the moment with the linear relationship $y = ax$. The use of W. W. Sawyer's platform and rollers is one possibility (Fig. 10-3). In this situation the students will be exploring the distance traveled by the platform as compared with that traveled by the rollers, a relationship that is described by $P = 2R$. The teacher proceeds in the manner established with the first experiment:

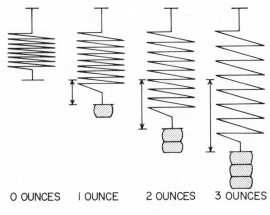

0 OUNCES   I OUNCE   2 OUNCES   3 OUNCES

Figure 10-2

The Linear Function

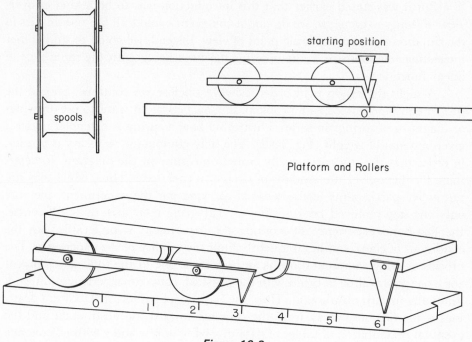

Figure 10-3

1. What do you think will happen? Guess.
2. How shall we do the experiment?
3. How shall we keep a record of what occurs?
4. Do the experiment. Verify the data. Record the results.
5. Look for a pattern.
6. Write a sentence and reduce it to formula.
7. Draw the graph.
8. Attempt predictions and check with apparatus.

In addition to the treatment of the ideas described as the first experiment was discussed, we have added another important factor: By doing another experiment, the students are given repetitive experience regarding the mathematical ideas. Despite a completely different setting they are getting practice looking for patterns, solving simple equations, describing physical situations with mathematical symbols, and drawing and using graphs, to name but some of the more important notions. This is somewhat different from long lists of examples with little purpose.

To extend this introduction and continue to build student confidence and experience with the important mathematical ideas, we introduce a third experiment. This time, perhaps, we develop a situation resulting in a relation-

178

ship of the form $y = ax + b$. Such a formula would result from any of the following:

If we add weights to a spring and record its total
length each time and if the spring is 4 inches
long at the start: $\qquad\qquad s = 3w + 4$
If a school population of 100 is increasing at the
rate of 40 students per year: $\qquad\qquad P = 100 + 40t.$

After examining the various ways in which a function may be described and attempting some simple predictions, the introductory unit is concluded with a presentation of a nonlinear function, a simple quadratic. Such a relationship could be derived from each of these situations:

How does the area of a square change as we
change the length of a side? $\qquad\qquad A = s^2$
How does changing the diameter of a rope effect
the amount of weight it will lift? $\qquad\qquad w = d^2$

When the same activities that were described earlier are developed in this case, the students will have completed an introduction to the work of the year. They will have investigated relationships through experimentation, for the most part gathering their own data. These data are graphed, and the relationship between the variables is described by a formula. Using their knowledge of the pattern of the relationship and mathematics, the students predict results. All this work is carried out in an informal manner with the emphasis upon understanding the language of algebra. If a student were attempting to predict the resulting stretch of a spring obeying the law $s = 3w$, he would answer the question "How much would the spring stretch if 7 ounces were hung from it?" by simply stating that $3 \times 7 = 21$; therefore, the stretch would be 21 inches. If he were asked to find the necessary weight to extend the spring 15 inches, he would probably respond by answering the question "Three times what number will give 15?" This would be an interpretation of the mathematical statement $15 = 3w$.

Thus, the introduction would provide experience with a broad variety of functions. The graphs of some of these functions are straight lines, but others are not. Some graphs go through the origin and some do not. The vocabulary introduced will be determined by the needs of the moment. The words *variable, constant,* and *unknown* would be among the first to be used because of the nature of the work. They would not be presented as formal definitions; but after the students have worked with tables of data and have written formulas to describe the inherent relationships, these words would naturally appear. It is one thing to describe a variable as something that varies. It is quite another thing altogether to talk about variables as a result of having seen several collections of data in which some value was seen to change. The formal definition

179

in this instance will probably be forthcoming from the student as one outcome of the work, rather than having been introduced by the teacher at the start. There is nothing magical about the student saying something rather than the teacher, but there is an important difference between being told what the definition of a term is and working with the thing and formulating one's own definition on the basis of experience. The former requires only memorization; the latter emphasizes thinking.

FUNCTIONS OF FORM $y = ax$

We turn now to the important ideas of algebra and undertake their study in greater depth. While each topic will be treated more carefully and in greater detail, the overall approach will vary only slightly from that of the introductory work. Although we will continue to explore familiar relationships as before, we will now travel little side roads wherever necessary in order to focus upon concepts and skills that require careful attention and practice. The overall approach is still primarily informal. One may wonder, "Informal work is fine but won't the student be stranded when he attempts more complicated problems?" This is quite correct. The only change advocated here is one of timing. Instead of requiring the premature use of formal techniques on the grounds that they will most certainly be needed later (as we have all at some time proclaimed, leaving the students to place their trust in our infinite wisdom), the formal techniques will be withheld until a situation has been created in which the students find it impossible to proceed with what they already know, until they have a need for more powerful techniques. At this point, we undertake to teach them. The learning of new techniques proceeds with the need for what is to be learned clear in the minds of the students, offering, perhaps, a situation of greatest willingness to learn. It is most important to understand that the teacher in this operation does not stand by and hope that the "need" will arrive. Quite the contrary. What the teacher does is to create this very situation by the nature of the problems he has selected for the students to complete. This is the primary function of teaching: to create the situation in which the student needs to and wants to learn.

The work proceeds as before. Perhaps a new spring experiment is undertaken, either by doing the experiment, measuring on diagrams of an experiment, or looking at pictures and diagrams and reading off values. The data are gathered, the graphs are drawn, and the formula is found describing the relationship. Perhaps this experiment yields $s = \frac{1}{2}w$. The verification procedure of checking the formula against the original data is carried out and we begin the prediction process. Wherever possible, the results are checked against the actual experiment itself. At this time the emphasis is upon solving this simple form of the linear equation; that is, given values of the dependent variable (s or stretch values), the student is challenged to find the resulting value of the independent variable (w or weight values). Thus he begins the solution of linear equations. Once more, the student is free to solve the equation as best he can:

$$6 = \tfrac{1}{2}w$$

"One half of what number gives 6? Half of 12, so $w = 12$."

$$7 = \tfrac{1}{2}w$$

"Seven is half of what number? 14, so $w = 14$."

Students should also be directed to check their findings with the graphs they have drawn. If 12 ounces of weight is necessary to extend the spring 6 inches, let us check the graph and see whether or not (12,6) is a point on it (Fig. 10-4). As the graphs are used, the vocabulary necessary to describe what you are doing will be introduced as it comes up in the natural course of events. The words

ordered pairs	x-axis	origin
variable	y-axis	coordinates
coefficient	coordinate axes	plotting

will all be in common use, as well as the necessary symbolism for the points (x,y).

The ready-made results involving other spring experiments may be presented to students, using many different coefficients for w in order to provide a variety of practice situations (Fig. 10-5). This should be limited to a few cases since the spring law is but one example of the linear function.

An interesting alternative relationship to explore at this time would be that involving the speed of a dropped object on or near the surface of the earth. The experiment of Galileo from the leaning tower should be mentioned. Since this is a rather difficult experiment to perform, the use of pictures or

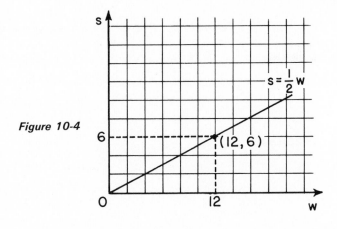

Figure 10-4

Spring A			Spring B			Spring C	
w	s		w	s		w	s
0	0		0	0		0	0
1	4		1	$1\frac{1}{2}$		1	$2\frac{1}{2}$
2	8		2	3		2	5
3	12		3	$4\frac{1}{2}$		3	$7\frac{1}{2}$
4	16		4	6		4	10

Figure 10-5. *Results of experiments with three different springs.*

diagrams would be advisable in order to help the students to gather their data (Fig. 10-6). Repeating the process of graphing and constructing a formula results in a statement:

$$v = 32t$$

It is important to discuss the necessary qualifications for the results of each of these "experiments" with the students in order that they do not get a misleading impression of what is being done. The formula for the speed of a dropped object is an excellent case in point. As stated, the formula assumes

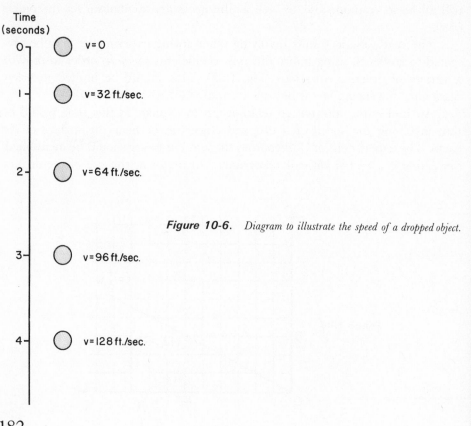

Time
(seconds)

0 — v = 0

1 — v = 32 ft./sec.

2 — v = 64 ft./sec.

Figure 10-6. *Diagram to illustrate the speed of a dropped object.*

3 — v = 96 ft./sec.

4 — v = 128 ft./sec.

that the object is falling in a vacuum, which is really an idealized situation. The mathematical description itself is always an idealized description, and it is important for the teacher to remind the students about this as the work develops. For example, in our previous discussion of the stretched spring, it may very well be that continued experimentation would cause the spring to lose some of its elasticity over a period of time. But with these limitations clearly before us, we can go ahead with our development and our work will be meaningful.

The motion experiment is an important one since it concerns one of the basic laws of nature on our planet. It also involves numbers that are larger and somewhat more difficult for computation, and thus, it begins to build student dissatisfaction with this informal equation solution. In the act of considering this relationship, some time should be devoted to a discussion of what the formula means, what is actually happening, and why the various symbols appear as they do. This should be true of any situation explored. As a new situation is considered and graphed and as linear equations are presented for solution, the teacher is providing built-in practice work for his students. The motion formula is particularly fruitful for practice since all one has to do is change the locale and the same problems that were considered on earth now take on a new face. For example, on earth the acceleration due to gravity is approximately 32 ft./sec. for each second of motion, hence the formula $v = 32t$. On the planet Mars, the formula for the speed of a dropped object would be $v = 12t$, since the pull of gravity is approximately 12 ft./sec. for each second of motion. Table 10-1 gives the various gravity figures for some of the better-known heavenly bodies. The teacher can build his own experiences using this information to assure a wealth of interesting material and meaningful practice experiences. For example:

1. If on earth a boy drops a ball from the top of a building, how fast is the ball falling after 3 seconds? If the same motion is carried out on the moon, how fast is the ball falling? (Answers: 96 ft./sec.; 15 ft./sec.)
2. On earth a high school broad jumper can jump 17 feet. If he makes the identical jump on the moon, about how far would he jump? (Answer: about six times as far)

Table 10-1. Acceleration Due to Gravity.

Heavenly Body	*Acceleration Due to Gravity, in ft./sec.*^{2}
Sun	900
Moon	5
Mars	12
Mercury	9
Venus	27
Saturn	35
Jupiter	80

The Linear Function

Other problems of a similar nature can be constructed as the need arises. How much practice is necessary is a judgment only the teacher can make.

Before investigating additional linear relationships, we may ask a curious question about the motion formula $v = 32t$: "If a ball of wood and a ball of steel were dropped from the top of a tall building, which would strike the ground first?"

After discussion about this question and its consequences, the following tables of data, which indicate the results of actually dropping the two balls in question, should be offered to the students:

Wooden Ball			Steel Ball	
t	v		t	v
0	0		0	0
1	32		1	32
2	64		2	64
3	96		3	96

Is there some mistake? The tables are identical. No, there is no mistake. The mathematical formula includes everything important in the relationship and in this case the velocity of the drop depends only upon the time. Whether the balls were made of light or heavy substances has no effect on its fall. Thus we lend importance to the use of the symbols of the formula.

Additional experience with the linear function of the form $y = ax$, as well as the solution of additional equations resulting from these functions, can be derived from the following situations:

The perimeter of a square:	$p = 4s$
The distance traveled at fixed speed:	$D = 30t$
The height of water filling a pool at the end of t hours:	$h = 2t$
The distance of lightning based upon the time between the flash and the sound of thunder:	$D = \frac{1}{5}t$
The amount of food needed to maintain man's body temperature based upon his weight:	$F = \frac{1}{50}W$

These formulas are examples of linear functions of the form $y = ax$, and as such they provide the teacher with a collection of experiences that may be used. The general approach has been described, as well as the direction of working from the concrete situation toward the abstract, so that although actual experiments may be done with springs, pictures might be used with the motion relationship, and tables of values might be used with the relationships just described. How much time should be devoted to any given stage of the representation will be a decision of the teacher, a decision that will be based upon the way in which the students react to the work being done.

No mention has been made of finding the means for the formal solution

184

of these equations, except by interpreting the language of the expression. Don't the students ever learn to solve equations in a more formal way? The answer, of course, is yes. Formal methods do not have to be taught at this point since most of the students will be able to work through to the correct answer without such techniques. Why introduce techniques that are unnecessary? It is also important that each student have a clear understanding of the meanings of the symbols used. The symbols should hold very little mystery for students. This understanding is fundamental to all the work that follows. It provides us with a firm foundation upon which to build all our mathematical ideas. Emphasis upon the language will be one step toward the elimination of rote learning.

Formal techniques are important, however, and must be a part of any effective mathematics program. Creating the need to learn such techniques before attempting to teach them may make for better quality learning in the long run.

After extensive work solving these simple linear equations, the work can be complicated by introducing numbers that cannot be dealt with easily. For example, how much weight must we add to the spring in our experiment, to cause a stretch of 6.42 inches? This would lead to the students examining the equation $6.42 = 3w$.

If we had first provided a large number of experiences involving the equations that do not require formal solutions, we would probably find that the students would, by themselves, arrive at the conclusion that the missing member of the equation can be found by dividing by the coefficient of the unknown. In this case many students would simply proceed to do just that: divide 6.42 by 3 and thereby solve the equation. The others who may not be able to see the pattern of the work so easily can be referred back to the equations that were solved previously. Upon examination they too would probably see that division is necessary. Finally, those that are still unable to complete the work may be assisted by pointing out that our task is to find which number multiplied by 3 gives a product of 6.42. Having this clearly before you, let us see how we would find the result in a similar fashion with small numbers that enable us to see what should be done almost immediately, i.e., which number multiplied by 3 gives a product of 6? How did you find it? Which number multiplied by 3 gives a product of 12? How did you find that one? Let us try the same technique with the difficult problem and we should, if our calculations are correct, arrive at the solution of the equation. Checking the equation by substitution is now introduced as a means of verifying the result obtained.

In addition to the gradual introduction of the need for more formal approaches to the solution of equations, the teacher may provide a good deal of practice with the basic computational skills by simply selecting those numbers that are of concern. Thus we begin to move slowly away from the informal solution, but we have not yet introduced the idea of applying the equality axioms in order to solve the equations. This is a goal to be accomplished later, after a need to use such ideas will have first been established.

The beginning work with the linear function has been developed in detail because the basic approach employed is the one that will underlie the introduction of all the mathematics to be considered throughout this section of the book. This work sets the pattern, and there will be frequent references to the activities described here in detail.

VOCABULARY

Before looking at the next topic, it may be well to take a moment to discuss vocabulary. All too often in mathematics classes, we find a lesson beginning with a definition of the new concept of the day. A definition is presented to students who have little, if any, idea about what the definition really means. It is the premise here that definitions, rather than being the starting point of a development, are actually its end product. In this way, if we develop the kinds of classroom experiences that are effective, we may assume that in the end the students will each be able to write a fairly accurate definition by themselves. While the organization of a mathematical system may begin with definitions, the teaching of mathematics is another thing altogether. Presenting a definition at the start leaves the student with but one task: remembering. Presenting him with a variety of activities involving new concepts and words leaves him with a very different task: thinking.

In the exploration of the linear function just completed, the concept of variable was an important notion. In the equation $s = 3w$, we may speak of s and w as variables. The students, having collected the data from the spring experiments, have ample physical evidence of the varying nature of these quantities. The meaning of variable is observed in action, as was described earlier. Each time a new experiment is undertaken, additional situations involving varying quantities are introduced. Little by little, bit by bit, the student begins to formulate his own concept of variable at this stage in terms of the dependency relationship. Later, it is expected that this idea will become a more abstract and generalized notion. It is intended that the experiences described here will lay the foundation for the abstraction.

OPEN SENTENCES

The notion of variable contains some difficulty since its substance seems to change when the student transforms the equation to work toward a solution:

$$s = 3w$$
$$15 = 3w$$

May we consider the w in the second equation a variable? When we fix the value of s have we not also fixed w? Does this alter its status as a variable? And if it is not a variable, what is it?

Recently there has been a tendency to avoid this difficulty altogether by referring to equations containing variables as open sentences, and by referring to variables as placeholders for members of a replacement set.

When we admit this concept instead of the variable and indicate that the placeholder may be replaced by any member of the replacement or universal set, we have changed the situation markedly. Let us look at a specific example:

Examine: $\{n \varepsilon N | n + 6 = 10\}$ with N the replacement set, the set of natural numbers $\{1, 2, 3, 4, \ldots\}$

> The discussion would proceed somewhat like this: $n + 6 = 10$ is an open sentence, since we cannot determine whether it is true or false as it stands. When we replace n by a member of the replacement set, we may then decide whether it is a true or false statement. Therefore, n is a placeholder for elements of the replacement set, some of which make the statement true, some of which make the statement false. Those replacements for n making the statement true are called elements of the truth or solution set. Th others are elements of the false set.

While this approach does serve as a beginning for the student in the study of mathematics as logic, as well as an introduction to the important concept of sets, the accompanying expense in unnecessary vocabulary, symbolism, and elaborate ideas would appear to inhibit rather than expedite the task at hand. For when we boil it all down to its essentials from the student point of view, why is there all this talk about true and false statements in the first place? What are we trying to do? As far as the student is concerned he is trying to find (in the equation $n + 6 = 10$) which number added to 6 will yield 10. He knows this to be 4; hence, all the discussion about replacement sets is excess baggage to him.

It is therefore suggested that, despite the difficulties, we work only with the language that we need in order to make sense out of what is before us at the moment. As we add to these experiences and continue to build upon this solid foundation, we will extend the knowledge of the student and prepare him perhaps most effectively for the work to follow. For if what he does today is interesting, makes sense, and is "doable," we will be building the kind of positive attitudes and confidence that will make for future continued growth. The needs of the future must be prepared for today, true. In so doing, however, it is not intended that we sacrifice today, thereby losing the student altogether. And so it is suggested that the notion of variable be used as described here in this stage of the algebra work.

Before concluding our work with linear functions, we re

functions developed earlier. First we look at $v = 32t$ and ask, If a ball is dropped from a building 128 feet high, how fast is the ball falling after 6 seconds? When the answer 192 ft./sec. is offered, we have to point out that after 4 seconds the ball struck the ground! Its speed after 6 seconds is therefore 0. How is it that mathematics provides an apparently incorrect answer? Is our mathematics wrong? Have we miscalculated? It is important at this point to stress the difference between mathematics and the physical world. The mathematics world is a world of abstract ideas, whereas the physical world is a three-dimensional reality. Our answer of 192 ft./sec. is mathematically correct but does not fit the physical situation which has meaning only up to $t = 4$. Thus, we begin to intuitively develop the idea that mathematics is a model which matches reality remarkably well—albeit far from perfectly. As such, mathematics provides much information, but we must check our results in the physical situation to be sure they "work."

This important concept is reinforced by exploring the pool-filling situation. If a pool 8 feet deep is filled with water at the rate of 2 feet per hour, how deep will the water be after 2 hours? 3 hours? 4? 5? Of course, it is the 5 hour mark that interests us here. Mathematically the situation is described by $h = 2t$, and if $t = 5$, then $h = 10$; thus the water in the pool is 10 feet deep. But the pool is only 8 feet deep. After we run the water for 5 hours there may be a good deal of water in the area but the depth of water in the pool will only be 8 feet. Once again we discuss the necessary restrictions on the variables ($0 \leq h \leq 4$) and the difference between mathematical "things" and physical "things." Once more we point out that mathematics is a model of the "real" world and it is remarkable that it fits the environment as well as it does. The spring law may offer yet another example of this since the spring may well break if too much weight is hung from it. It will not stretch indefinitely. This vital notion about mathematics must be explored each time the occasion arises in order to help the students grasp these subtle but basic differences.

In summarizing the work done with linear functions and equations, we list each of the formulas explored and try to determine if any pattern is consistently found among them. Some description, such as "there is a variable equal to some constant times another variable," would lead to the symbolic representation of all these formulas with $y = ax$, where x and y are variables and a is a constant.

We represent these functions by a general mathematical description and offer the name *linear function*. All the graphs of these functions were straight lines, which explains why the word *line* appears in the name linear. We also recall that the solution of linear equations for x was found by division expressed symbolically as

$$y = ax$$

$$x = \frac{y}{a}$$

Thus, we have generalized a step further in our search for patterns and have used the mathematical language to describe our findings. We have therefore created a new formula—one that enables us to solve any equation of the form $y = ax$.

At this point sets of practice exercises with equations of form $y = ax$ may be presented. These lists of exercises involve many different letters and contain abstract equations that may or may not relate to any physical counterpart. We now turn to more complicated linear functions.

FUNCTIONS OF FORM $y = ax + b$

How shall we begin to extend the notion of functions to include those of form $y = ax + b$? The life cycle of a mathematical idea has been described as developing from the concrete to the abstract, and this is the pattern we try to follow. Returning to actual experimentation, one possible starting point would be the spring experiment investigated earlier but with one change—we seek the answer to a different question. What is the total length of the spring as we hang weights from it? (Earlier we were concerned with the amount of stretch.) The resulting formula will be of form $L = 2w + 4$. The formula should be discussed so that everything that appears in it is understandable to the student, i.e.,

> L and w represent the variables in the experiment, while 4 is the original length of the spring. The coefficient of w, 2, is a product of the properties of the spring itself, as was discussed in the first spring experiments.

The solution of equations will grow out of trying to determine the amount of weight necessary to extend the spring until it has a given length. The procedures to be used will follow the pattern of the previous work based upon the understanding of the language. If the question to be answered were how long the spring would be if we hung 5, 6, or 7 ounces of weight from it, the students would work along these general lines:

$$L = 2w + 4; \text{ if } w = 5,$$
$$L = 2(5) + 4 \text{ (substitution of 5 for } w)$$
$$L = 10 + 4$$
$$L = 14$$

Finding the desired value of L does not involve any new techniques but calls only for substitution and arithmetical calculations or translation of algebraic symbolism.

ORDER OF OPERATIONS

An important side road may be traveled here. After substitution in the equation just presented, the right-hand member becomes $2 \times 5 + 4$. It may well be that several students, by carrying out the indicated addition first, will calculate this expression to equal 18. The question then arises as to which is correct, 18 or 14? Both answers are the result of what appears to be correct calculation. Can there be two different correct values for this expression?

$$2 \times 5 + 4 = 10 + 4 = 14$$

and

$$2 \times 5 + 4 = 2 \times 9 = 18$$

An excellent way to resolve this dilemma would be to return to the experiment, if possible, and see what actually would happen. An examination of the graph would be another way to determine the expected result. Certainly only one of the two values can be considered correct. Which one? Well, it is most important that the mathematics we use "works"; hence, 14 must be correct. If we are to be consistent, we must be sure that all such problems will be dealt with in the same manner; so the first method (multiplying and dividing first before doing addition and subtraction) becomes the method we must agree to follow whenever such a situation develops. Briefly then, we shall multiply and divide, in order from left to right, before doing any adding or subtracting. The reason for this decision is that in this way our mathematics matches the physical situation; i.e., it "works." Rather than long lists of practice examples involving the order of operations, for the time being we simply call attention to this whenever it occurs. After several such experiences, lists of exercises for practice will be in order, as will the introduction of parentheses in order to indicate that the second value is desired.

GRAPHING

Let us take a close look at the graph of the function $L = 2w + 4$ and compare it with the graphs already drawn. How does this graph differ from those we made earlier? Use the earlier spring-stretch data as a comparison (Fig. 10-7). All of our earlier graphs went through the origin. They all contained the point (0,0). The graph of this new function, however, does not go through the origin. When the weight is zero, the spring length is 4 inches; hence the point is (0,4). Notice that there is a 4 in the equation. Is there any connection between the two (the 4 in the equation and the spring length)? The curve itself is a straight line, however; therefore this function is also an example of a linear function. The equation contains a constant that was not present before. Is this true of other linear functions as well? Let us explore further and see. The ideas just presented are only conjectures based upon this single comparison. The questions are not yet ready to be solved.

The introduction of another relationship of form $y = ax + b$ follows in

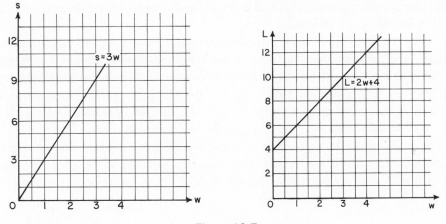

Figure 10-7

order to offer additional experiences with relationships of like form. Any of the following are suitable:

A regular increase in the temperature of a laboratory ($+2°$ each hour): $\qquad\qquad T = 10 + 2h$
The speed of an object thrown downward: $\qquad\quad v = 16 + 32t$
The population growth of a town: $\qquad\qquad\quad P = 200 + 20t$
The perimeter of a rectangle with a length of 6 inches: $\qquad\qquad\qquad\qquad\qquad\qquad\quad P = 2w + 12$

Each of these relationships may be introduced through experiments, pictures, diagrams, or tables of accumulated data. The best form is up to the teacher and will be dictated by the students' needs and the situation itself. Once the tables are derived, a pattern is sought, the formula found, and the graph drawn. Values of the dependent variables are required: How fast the ball is falling after 6 seconds (find v), what the town population would be after 4 years (find P), what the perimeter of a rectangle with a width of 6 inches is (find P). (Since finding values of the independent variable requires solving the equation, we hold these for later.) The calculations to be done require observance of the agreement with respect to the order of operations. These new instances of using this notion are examined carefully to be sure that we are consistent and are finding correct results. In this way we continue to reinforce the notion.

The graphs are drawn, examined, and compared to those done previously. Once again we notice that all are straight lines that do not go through the origin, and once again we check to see if the constant term and the intercept on the y-axis have anything in common. This last item may not be mentioned by the teacher at all, but yet he may wish to simply call attention to this. The number of examples worked will undoubtedly speed the recognition of this fact by many students.

The students have now experienced work with a variety of functions whose form is somewhat different from the simple ones explored initially. What do these several functions have in common? Before too long students will be quick to conclude that they are linear, their graphs being straight lines, and that their general form is that of a simple linear function with a constant term added on. We come upon the complete linear function with the general form $y = ax + b$. The groundwork has been laid for the determination of b as the y-intercept, with the role of a yet to be explored. But we are now ready to attempt the solution of linear equations of any form.

SOLVING EQUATIONS OF FORM $y = ax + b$

Let us take another look at the spring function $L = 2w + 4$. How much weight must be hung from the spring if it is to be extended until it is 14 inches long? Can we predict the answer to this question using our knowledge of mathematics and this function as expressed by the formula? The students are free to proceed in any way they wish. Once an answer has been determined, they may use any other means to check themselves. In general, it is expected that most students will try to substitute in the formula and solve, this time solving for the independent variable. Some, however, may make use of the graph or extend the table of values. If the equipment is available, it may be used later to test the accuracy of the prediction. In any case, it is the use of the formula with which we are interested here; so no matter how the answer is found, the formula should be one method employed—if not for the prediction, then certainly for verification. This work is still of an informal nature and would probably proceed somewhat like this:

> $L = 2w + 4$. If $L = 14$, our formula is transformed to $14 = 2w + 4$. This says that twice a number with 4 added is 14. Since 4 added to 10 is 14, the "twice a number" must be 10; hence, $2w = 10$. If twice a number is 10, then the number must be 5, i.e., $w = 5$. Therefore, 5 ounces of weight will stretch the spring to 14 inches of length.

Some students may want to use division after arriving at the equation $2w = 10$. Whatever the method, the important thing at this stage is that the method used should employ sound mathematics and allow the student to arrive at the correct answer.

CHECKING EQUATIONS

It is possible to verify our answer as being mathematically correct by introducing a technique known as "checking" the equation. Is 5 really a root

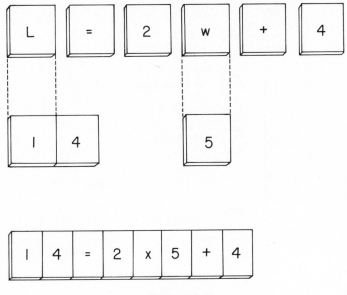

Figure 10-8

of the equation? If it is and we substitute it into the equation, what value should the right-hand member attain? In seeking the answer to this question we introduce checking. We may even phrase the question a bit differently by asking if both sides of the equation are actually numerals for the same number. A brief clarification of a numeral as merely a name for a number would suffice here. The checking process is a good way to verify whether or not a root has been found. To help students see clearly what is being done, a simple but effective device to use is a modified Scrabble set. Instead of the letters, the wooden or cardboard squares of such a set may be marked with the letters, numerals, and signs of mathematics. Then each equation may be represented with the squares and when substitution is employed to check a result, the piece with the numeral upon it can physically replace the letter variable (Fig. 10-8). Instead of providing lists of practice exercises for checking, we simply check each equation as it is encountered. Later, after additional experiences, this technique can be dealt with as a practice exercise.

THE EQUALITY AXIOMS

Solving equations using a knowledge of the meaning of the symbols is an important way to begin. The students must begin to "speak" the language of algebra. This is crucial. However, the ability to use the language will not always help the student to work toward a solution. Working on the assump-

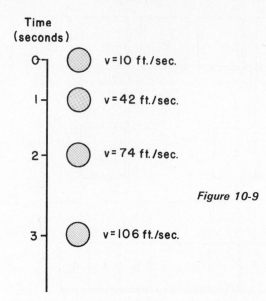

Figure 10-9

tion that it is unwise to teach a student formal methods before he sees the need, we now attempt to put him into the position of "needing" to learn such methods. There are many ways to introduce such a situation. Virtually any of the complete linear relationships would suffice, but the motion formula is a particularly good example. Here we may well begin with pictures of the data (Fig. 10-9) or the tables themselves:

t	v		t	v
0	10		0	32
1	18		1	64
2	26		2	96
3	34		3	128
4	42		4	160

In any case, it is important that the students fully understand what is happening in the situation.

Example: A baseball is thrown downward from the roof of the Yankee Stadium and here is the speed of the ball for each second it is falling:

Time (sec.) t	Speed (ft./sec.) v
0	16
1	48
2	80
3	112

194

When the students have been able to describe the relationship with a formula, the information is graphed and the resulting curve once again compared with the earlier graphs. By this time most of the students should have developed their own techniques for finding formulas; however, the larger numbers here may cause some difficulties. In general, the students will probably note that

> . . . it goes up by 32, and since the zero is 16 the formula should be $v = 32t + 16$. The coefficient of t appears to indicate the constant difference while the zero of t gives the constant.

This is not an outcome to be demanded of all students at this point, since it is expected that continued experience with this form will eventually result in such learning for all. Of course, the teacher may have to aid some of the children in coming to such a realization.

Having found the formula and graphed it, the students should have no doubts as to its meaning. Some attention must be given to questions such as:

> Why are the two terms in the formula ($32t$ and 16) added?
> How is it that we have a value of $v = 16$ when $t = 0$?
> What does this mean?

The ensuing discussion, albeit on a very simple physical level, serves to reinforce the importance of mathematics and its uses and adds meaning to the entire situation.

After predictions are made, determining the velocity at various instances in time, we ask the question, How many seconds will it take the baseball to reach a speed of 176 ft./sec.? This question would require a solution of the equation

$$176 = 32t + 16$$

The size of the numbers here may result in student uncertainty as to how to proceed. It may be quickly noticed that "some quantity added to 16 yields 176; hence, that quantity must be 160." This fact is written as $32t = 160$, and the division process employed earlier may suffice. If the students are able to proceed in this manner, they should most assuredly be permitted to do so. Others may need additional instruction, however, and this should be provided along the lines established previously, without any overconcentration on the development.

The question to be asked next would be, How many seconds will it take the ball to reach of speed of 224 ft./sec.? These numbers should cause concern. If not, larger numbers or fractions can be employed. Eventually a discussion must follow of some more effective method of operation. At this juncture we introduce the equality axioms and along with these axioms a simple balance scale to aid student understanding (Fig. 10-10).

195

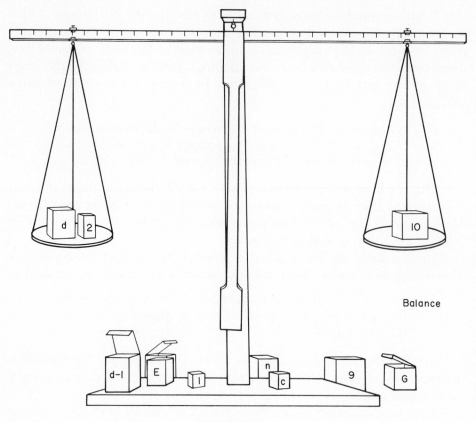

Figure 10-10

The balance scales serve to provide a physical representation to students that the process of "doing the same thing to both sides" does indeed maintain the equality. While the immediate needs of the situation require the use of subtraction and division only, after the problem of a particular equation has been resolved, the question may well be asked, Would the equality be maintained if we added or multiplied both sides of it by equal quantities? In this way we are not only extending the "balancing" to include all four basic operations, but we are also building an understanding of how mathematical knowledge is extended. Often, a mathematician becomes interested in a physical problem and in trying to find a solution he develops many ideas and follows many hunches that go far beyond the immediate need. In this simple instance of "balancing" we have an opportunity to plant a seed of this important understanding and to offer some insight into how mathematics is built.

Thus, the students are now in possession of two basic approaches to the solution of equations: using the language and "balancing" or using the equality axioms; i.e.,

If $a = b$ and $c = d$, then $a + c = b + d$.

If $a = b$ and $c = d$, then $a - c = b - d$.

If $a = b$ and $c = d$, then $ac = bd$.

If $a = b$ and $c = d \neq 0$, then $\dfrac{a}{c} = \dfrac{b}{d}$.

It is important to understand that the fact that the axioms have been learned and are now available to the students does not mean that henceforth each student will solve equations using only these axioms. Not by any means. It must remain up to the student to decide how to solve any of the equations he meets, in the way best suited to himself. Only the student can make this decision, but it is up to the teacher to be sure that the approach a student uses in the solution of an equation involves the correct use of sound mathematical thinking. The important question is not, Which method did you use? but rather, Is your thinking mathematically sound and is the answer correct?

There has been a tendency lately to declare that the answer is unimportant and that it is the way the student works that is important. He must understand. This is not entirely true. We must not forget that to the student the answer is of vital importance because this is his indicator for correct or incorrect work. We should not try to deemphasize answers, but rather we should try to put this emphasis to work for us as we try to help students understand mathematics. The student has a desired end in the mathematics class: getting the right answer. This is where he derives a good deal of his satisfaction. We, as teachers, should share this goal: Students should be able to arrive at the right answers. The route that they take to get there should be an outgrowth of their own thinking. We should judge the mathematical correctness and not insist on one method in preference to another. Hence, it may well be that a student will solve an equation in this way:

$224 = 32t + 16$
Since 16 and 208 give a sum of 224, we may write $32t = 208$.
Applying the division axiom, dividing by 32, gives $t = 6.5$.
The answer is 6.5 seconds.

Here we have a mixture of methods: The language is used and the axiom is used. This is just as effective from the student point of view as any other method. It has correctly helped the student to get where he wanted to go. Independent thinking is thereby encouraged. The number of steps required to get somewhere is of far less importance than using correct mathematical thinking, no matter how inelegant by someone else's standards. Freedom to think is in the spirit of mathematics.

A variety of relationships involving the complete linear function should then be explored in order to provide practice in equation solution without tiresome repetition. Among these we may find:

197

Motion problems applied to other planets—
for example, on Mars the problem just
described would be: $\qquad$ $v = 12t + 16$

Finding the Fahrenheit temperature from
the speed of an ant: $\qquad$ $T = 11s + 39$

The amount of money deducted from income tax by a married couple for de-
pendents: $\qquad$ $D = 1200 + 600n$

The number of diagonals in a polygon of s
sides that can be drawn from any one
vertex: $\qquad$ $d = s - 3$

The length of a steel rod at given centigrade temperatures: $\qquad$ $L = 10 - .00012C$

These situations can provide a good deal of practice in solving equations, as well as in basic arithmetic operations with all kinds of numbers. In this way we offer repetitive experiences with the desired mathematical concepts, while the changing environment in which we find the mathematics enables us to maintain interest in the work. When these problems have been completed, abstract lists of equations involving x and y are in order.

PARENTHESES

Another relationship of the form $y = ax + b$ that provides interest is one commonly used by architects in the construction of stairways. This formula could be presented directly to the students rather than having them examine tables of data. Within certain clearly defined limits, the relation between the rise and tread of the steps in a stairway is

$$R = \tfrac{1}{2}(24 - T)$$

(R varies from 6.0 to 7.5, while T varies from 9 to 12.) It may be of interest to the students to measure the rise and tread of the steps at school, in their homes, or at the library to see how closely the formula approximates actual stairways.

The use of parentheses provides the first opportunity to work with these symbols. Why are they used? How would the formula look without them?

$$R = \tfrac{1}{2} \times 24 - T$$
$$\text{If } T = 10,$$
$$R = \tfrac{1}{2} \times 24 - 10$$

Once again we encounter a situation in which we could conceivably come up with two different values for this expression despite correct calculations. Earlier we saw that in order for the mathematics to "work" a definition was made that we multiply and divide in order from left to right before doing any adding or subtracting. Without the parentheses, then, the expression is evaluated as follows:

$$R = \tfrac{1}{2} \times 24 - 10$$
$$R = 12 - 10$$
$$R = 2$$

In this case, however, two is not the answer we need to fit the situation. In light of our earlier agreement, and in order to conserve the proper meaning, we make use of parentheses, a symbol for grouping. Thus we write:

$$R = \tfrac{1}{2} (24 - 10)$$

What the parentheses have done is to unite the 24 and the 10 and indicate that the subtraction, in this case, is to be performed first, before carrying out the multiplication. The desired value is:

$$R = \tfrac{1}{2} (24 - 10)$$
$$R = \tfrac{1}{2} (14)$$
$$R = 7$$

Thus, a 10-inch tread would require a 7-inch rise.

For a second time, then, we have revisited the notion of the order of operations and we have added a new dimension through the introduction of parentheses when it is necessary to group the numbers differently. Notice that the solution of equations (solving for T, given R values) was not undertaken at this time. Initially it is well to point out how parentheses affect the order of operations. Later, we may explore how to eliminate parentheses in equations such as

$$7 = \tfrac{1}{2} (24 - T)$$

as well as to introduce the distributive law for multiplication over addition. Suffice it to say that in this instance (the rise-tread relationship) the students can form a table of values from the formula by selecting values for T and finding the corresponding values of R, within the given range of values. At this point it would be helpful to provide the student with practice exercises involving the value of expressions both with and without parentheses, such as $7 + 3 \times 2 - 1$, $5 - (2 \times 1) + 4$, and $30 \times 6 - 4 \times 5$.

This would also be an excellent time to introduce the game of "Identities."[5] Briefly, it is the object of this game to use the four basic operations and parentheses and equality signs to form statements called *identities* with any given set of three to six numbers. If the student were given, for example, 7, 1, 6, he might write $7 = 1 + 6$ as one such identity; or he might write $7 - 1 = 6$. He must use the numbers in the order given. Other examples are:

$$1, 2, 3, 7 \qquad\qquad 1 + 2 \times 3 = 7$$
$$8, 2, 4, 0 \qquad\qquad 8 - 2 \times 4 = 0$$
$$6, 3, 1, 9 \qquad\qquad (6 + 3) \, 1 = 9$$

This is a game that has greater use as we extend the number system, add to our list of operations, and introduce inequalities. It is a good source of interesting practice work.

FOOTNOTES

1. See these references, among others:
   Report of the Commission on Mathematics. *Program for College Preparatory Mathematics.* College Entrance Examination Board, 1959.
   School Mathematics Study Group. *First Course in Algebra, Parts I and II.* A. C. Vroman, 1960.
2. University of Illinois Committee on School Mathematics. Champaign, Illinois. Madison Project of Syracuse University and Webster College, 8356 Big Bend Blvd., St. Louis, Mo.
3. For a more complete statement of goals see Chapter 3.
4. Jerome Bruner. *The Process of Education.* Harvard University Press, 1960, p. 7.
5. See "License Plates and Mathematics" by William L. Schaaf. In *Mathematics Student Journal.* Vol. 9 (March, 1962), p. 3.

FOR INVESTIGATION AND DISCUSSION

1. Identify and compare different points of view about the purposes of learning algebra.

2. Compare two algebra textbooks—one with an original copyright prior to 1957, the other with a copyright after 1963—with regard to author's point of view, topics covered, basis for introduction, and vocabulary and symbolism.

3. Compare the School Mathematics Study Group publication *First Course in Algebra, Parts I and II* with the two texts used for question number 2.

4. Make a lesson plan for a first lesson in algebra for average youngsters in ninth grade based upon the idea that algebra is the study of relationships.

5. Construct another lesson plan for a first lesson in algebra based upon the idea that algebra is a generalized arithmetic.

6. How would the beginning lesson in algebra be modified if we were to base the lesson on the idea that algebra is the study of the real number system?

7. Devise physical experiments that may be carried out by students involving the linear function of form $y = ax$.

8. Describe how a situation may be created that would require students to solve simple linear equations of form $y = ax + b$.

9. Create a situation in which students find themselves unable to solve equations using their knowledge of the language of algebra and are in need of the axioms of equality.

10. Show how the axioms would be introduced to students emphasizing student participation in this process.

FOR FURTHER READING

Books

Charles H. Butler and F. Lynwood Wren. *The Teaching of Secondary Mathematics,* Ed. 4. McGraw-Hill Book Company, 1965, Chapter 15.

Hollis Cooley, David Gans, Morris Kline, and Howard Wahlert. *Introduction to Mathematics,* Ed. 2. Houghton-Mifflin Company, 1949, Chapters 4 and 5.

Robert S. Fouch and Eugene D. Nichols. "Language and Symbolism in Mathematics." *In* National Council of Teachers of Mathematics, 24th Yearbook: *The Growth of Mathematical Ideas, Grades K–12.* The National Council of Teachers of Mathematics, 1959.

Lancelot Hogben. *Mathematics for the Million.* W. W. Norton & Co., 1937, Chapter 7.

Donovan A. Johnson and Gerald R. Rising. *Guidelines for Teaching Mathematics.* Wadsworth Publishing Co. Inc., 1967, Chapter 12.

Morris Kline. *Mathematics and the Physical World.* Thomas Y. Crowell Company, 1959, Chapters 5 and 6.

Mathematics in Primary Schools. Curriculum Bulletin No. 1. The School Council, Her Majesty's Stationery Office, London, 1965, Chapter 6.

Report of the Commission on Mathematics. *Appendices.* College Entrance Examination Board, 1959, Chapter I.

W. W. Sawyer. *Vision in Elementary Mathematics.* Penguin Books, Inc., 1964, Introduction and Chapter 3.

Periodicals

Jackson B. Adkins. "Goals in Algebra." *The Mathematics Teacher.* Vol. 47 (May, 1954), pp. 368–370.

John J. Bowen. "Mathematics and the Teaching of Science." *The Mathematics Teacher.* Vol. 59 (October, 1966), pp. 536–542.

J. F. Clark. "A Concrete Approach to Elementary Algebra." *The Mathematics Teacher.* Vol. 53 (April, 1960), pp. 285–287.

Susanne K. Langer. "Algebra and the Development of Reason." *The Mathematics Teacher.* Vol. 59 (February, 1966) (reprinted from same journal May, 1931), pp. 158–166.

Bruce E. Meserve. "New Trends in Algebra and Geometry." *The Mathematics Teacher.* Vol. 55 (October, 1962), pp. 452–461.

Barnett Rich. "The Place of the Variable in the Teaching of Mathematics." *The Mathematics Teacher.* Vol. 48 (December, 1955), pp. 538–541.

Pamphlets

W. W. Sawyer. *Math Patterns in Science.* American Education Publications, 1960.

Teaching Mathematics in Secondary Schools. Ministry of Education Pamphlet 36. Her Majesty's Stationery Office, London, 1958, pp. 56–64.

Filmstrip

Introduction to Algebra. (Modern Junior High School Mathematics Series, Set I), McGraw-Hill Book Co., 1965.

The Linear Function

Sample Textbooks for Comparison

Max Beberman and Herbert E. Vaughan. *High School Mathematics, Course I*. D. C. Heath Company, 1965.

Mary Dolciani, Simon Berman, and Julius Freilich. *Modern Algebra: Structure and Method, Book 1*. Houghton Mifflin Company, 1962.

Howard Fehr, Walter Carnahan, and Max Beberman. *Algebra I*. D. C. Heath & Company, 1955.

E. H. Lockwood and D. K. Down. *Algebra*. University of London Press, 1954.

School Mathematics Study Group. *First Course in Algebra, Part I*. A. C. Vroman, 1960.

11

DIRECTED NUMBERS

INTRODUCING DIRECTED NUMBERS

One of the crucial points in the study of elementary algebra is the mastery of directed numbers. It may be likened to the pons asinorum of plane geometry.[1] Most teachers of algebra classes can usually predict which students will be in danger of failing the entire course after completion of the unit of this extension of our number system, for those who fare poorly here are doomed to difficulty throughout the remainder of the course. Everything that is done in any future work in algebra will involve using these new numbers and using them with ease. Our start in this area should be unhurried and as meaningful as we can make it.

Negative numbers will certainly not be new to most students at this grade level. They will have had experience with these numbers as part of daily living. Temperatures below zero, gains and losses on the stock market, scoring for games, and indications of land below sea level are but a few of the more obvious instances in which negative numbers are used. Many students may have been introduced to these numbers in the lower grades, so we must not proceed as if total ignorance of negatives were the case. Because of its familiarity, the temperature scale offers a possible place to begin.

Consider a scientist doing an experiment in the laboratory, carefully controlling the temperature, and examining the change in a particular metal. This table gives the temperature readings for the experiment for each hour:

Directed Numbers

After h hours	Temperature T is
0	10
1	8
2	6
3	4

The students examine the table as before and look for a pattern, write a formula, and draw the graph. In a discussion of the situation it is brought out that at the start of the experiment the temperature was 10°; thus we see that $T = 10$ when $h = 0$. The temperature is decreasing at a steady rate of 2° per hour. When the formula $T = 10 - 2h$ is checked against the table, all the ordered pairs seem to fit. We begin to discuss predictions:

What would the temperature be after 4 hours? 5 hours? Substitutions are made and the desired values of T are computed and then checked by alternate methods, i.e., from the graph and by extending the table. We arrive at the question, What will the temperature be after 6 hours? Substitution yields:

$$T = 10 - 2h$$
$$T = 10 - 2 \times 6$$
$$T = 10 - 12$$

This is an interesting problem since it requires that we subtract 12 from 10, a process we have generally said cannot be done in the work with arithmetic. How can we take away 12 from 10? On the other hand, it is also apparent that there will be some temperature reading in the room after 6 hours have elapsed. Therefore, if our mathematics is to work, there must be an answer to the 10 minus 12 question, and by reasoning we also know what this answer should be! If the temperature is at zero and falls two degrees, it will be at $-2°$. Thus, to keep our mathematical ideas "working" we find that if

$$T = 10 - 2h \text{ and } h = 6, \text{ then}$$
$$T = 10 - 2 \times 6$$
$$T = 10 - 12$$
$$T = -2$$

which in this case translates to a temperature of $-2°$.

We have taken a significant step forward in our development. Among other things, we are now able to do an example that was previously impossible: We are able to take a larger number from a smaller one, at least in the problem before us. We extend our work by exploring the T-values corresponding to h-values of 7, 8, 9, and higher; and we encounter additional examples similar to the one just discussed. Each time an answer is determined, the students should be encouraged to use the temperature scale either as a check or as a means for finding the correct response. In this way we build up a reservoir of acceptable answers to the examples that we find we are now able to do. Additional experiences with these "new" numbers may be provided by examining the changing height above sea level as we descend a mountainside into Death Valley, the lowest point in the United States. If we start recording these heights when we are 250 feet above sea level and if we are descending at the rate of 50 ft./hour, then our height will be described by the formula

$$H = 250 - 50t$$

In this case, since we are able to reason what the formula should be and can begin with the formula, the students can construct the table of values by substituting values for t and calculating the corresponding values of H. Of course after 5 hours we begin to reach land levels below sea level and once again encounter negative numbers.

Additional examples can be introduced by examining the profit and loss record of a business that made $20,000 but has since been declining in profits steadily at the rate of $5000 per year. After 4 years, a loss is encountered and once again negative numbers appear ($P = 20,000 - 5000y$).

We have begun to extend our number system. The introduction of negative numbers, through the use of these familiar relationships, not only places these numbers in a meaningful context but also parallels the introduction of such numbers historically—recording profits and losses in commerce. While the context is somewhat different, the basic process is mathematically the same, or as students frequently describe it, "We're taking away more than we have." Although the mathematical elegance of this statement leaves much to be desired, the idea of subtraction as "take away" is a sound notion to build upon. Later, we may emphasize that subtraction is the inverse operation of addition and that "take-away" is meaningless with numbers. But for now, it provides a sharp visual image of what is happening, something all too often lacking when one considers mathematical operations. It is also a notion we shall build upon when developing skill in calculating with directed numbers. And so we have introduced directed numbers with the process of subtraction, rather than with the familiar procedure of using addition as a starting point. Long lists of examples are not necessary at this introductory stage. There is much more to be done before attempting practice exercises.

GRAPHING

One interesting offshoot of this work occurs in graphing. Earlier when the students encountered a new relationship and made a table of ordered pairs, they constructed a graph of the function. The function described by $T = 10 - 2h$ would also have been graphed (Fig. 11-1). However, we have

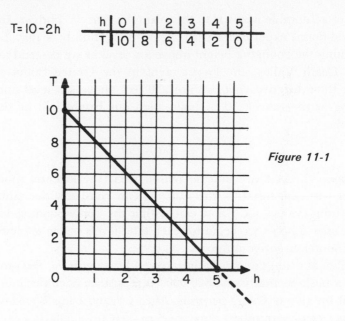

$T = 10 - 2h$

h	0	1	2	3	4	5
T	10	8	6	4	2	0

Figure 11-1

extended the number of hours to include 6, 7, and greater numbers, and we found that the corresponding temperatures are negative numbers. Where do these appear on our graphs? Are they present? If not, where should they be? Since the temperature values involve numbers above and below zero on the number scale, we must provide for these numbers on our graph. We therefore extend the T-scale to include negative values and simply extend our line. The entire process is as natural a consequence of our work as one could want. The temperature graph now looks like that shown in Figure 11-2, as do the graphs for the sea level relationship and the profit-loss situation.

Some discussion might be devoted to the question, Can the h-values also be negative? What would it mean? If we look at the temperature graph once again we see that it would become necessary to extend the h-axis to the left and extend the line that is the curve of our graph upward to the left. Thus, mathematically we have the graph shown in Figure 11-3.

What value of T corresponds to an h-value of -1? Does $h = -1$ have any meaning? Well, if the temperature is descending at a steady rate, $h = -1$ would be 1 hour *before* we began our observations, and at that point the graph indicates that the temperature would have been 12°. Thus, it is possible to interpret negative values of h into meaningful information about the physical situation. Whether or not these values would accurately describe the situation would require checking. It is not unlikely, then, that both axes can be extended to include negative values; and indeed in practice this is precisely what we do. Consequently, in the future we should construct all our graphs on an extended set of intersecting axes to include four parts or quadrants. Before arriving at this conclusion, however, it would be well to

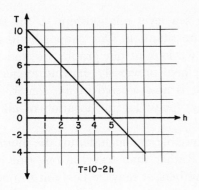

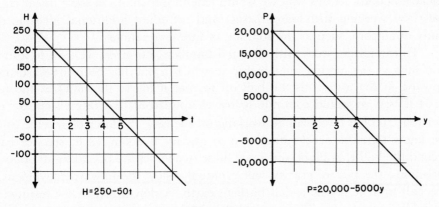

Figure 11-2

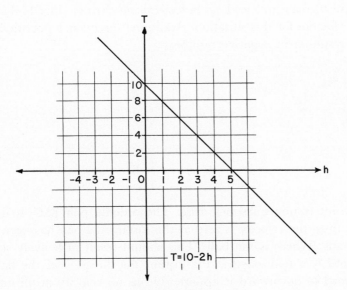

Figure 11-3

subject the profit-loss and above-below sea level relationships to the same discussion undertaken for the temperature situation. One cannot build generalizations upon a single example. As we look at our graphs we find that zero is taking on a different role than it held previously. It is no longer the starting point of our scale, but rather it is now located in the center. It is still, however, a very necessary reference point for the location of all our number pairs.

With this discussion it would be advisable to conclude, for the moment, our consideration of negative numbers. Rather than travel a long side road to explore how to operate with these numbers, it may be best not to undertake too much at once and to return to consideration of some more complicated linear functions. In this way we would extend the ability to solve linear equations (by working with parentheses) and introduce additional ideas in our study of algebra, such as the solution of literal equations.

To extend the work with directed numbers, however, we turn to a function such as the motion relationship in which a ball has been tossed straight upward. If the toss sends the ball off so that it leaves the hand at the rate of 64 ft./sec., it would continue to travel upward at that rate except for the fact that another force will be working on the ball, the force of gravity. Since we know that the acceleration due to gravity is about 32 ft./sec. for each second the ball is in flight and since these two forces are operating in opposite directions, the pull of gravity will eventually slow the upward movement of the ball until it begins to fall back to earth. A downward throw resulted in an addition of forces. The upward thrust, therefore, results in their subtraction, and the formula for this situation becomes $v = 64 - 32t$. Each second the ball is in the air its upward motion is retarded 32 ft./sec. Eventually the motion will increase in speed *but in a downward direction* (Fig. 11-4). We tabulate the velocities for this situation. Additional practice is provided with subtractions resulting in negative numbers:

t	v
0	64
1	32
2	0
3	-32
4	-64

Some interesting questions arise. The ordered pair (2,0) is included in the table; thus, the velocity is zero at the instant the ball has been in the air for 2 seconds. Where is the ball? This should result in a lively student discussion until it is realized that the instant the direction of the ball changes from upward to downward it apparently has no velocity at all and may be thought of as being suspended in space. At any rate, directly after that instant

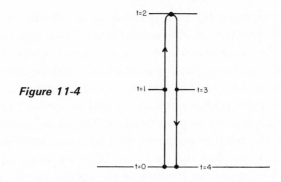

Figure 11-4

the ball begins to pick up speed again, this time in a downward direction, and the mathematics we are using tells us precisely that, since these values are negative! This mathematics is a powerful tool. A graph of the situation may be constructed; in this way a good deal of help is provided to give students a "feel" for negative numbers.

Look at the motion of the ball. (See Fig. 11-4.) How is the speed at 1 second different from that at 3 seconds? Both have the same magnitude (32) but they are different in direction (one positive, one negative). This is exactly the concept of opposites that we wish to emphasize with regard to negative numbers: The sign −, which we already know as an operation sign (subtraction), is now being used for another purpose, i.e., to indicate an opposite direction from the positive number of equal magnitude. (It should be read as "negative" to minimize confusion.) What better way to emphasize the notion of opposites than to see positive used for upward motion and negative for downward? This is what the motion formula enables the teacher to do. The formulas examined earlier may now be revisited with the notion of opposites in mind: Above sea level is positive, below sea level is negative; profit is positive, losses are negative; temperature above zero is represented by positive numbers and that below zero is shown using negative numbers.

The number scale may well be employed here to add emphasis to this relationship of opposites. While it is confusing to students to see a familiar symbol of operation take on a new role, after a while the interchangeability of uses for the subtraction sign will add to the student's power to use mathematics. Many textbooks and improvement programs in mathematics have advocated a separation of operation and direction by changing the use of the symbol. One technique that has been used is to place a small addition or subtraction sign at the upper left-hand edge of the number; for example, $^{+}5$ or $^{-}8$; it is common to see examples such as $^{+}3 + {^{+}9} =$. While this does eliminate the problem of two functions for a single sign, it provides the additional problem of letting go of this crutch since this is not standard symbolism. But what is even more important, this technique would seem to inhibit the

209

student's ability to make his own decision as to whether he shall consider the sign to be an operation or direction as he analyzes a given problem.

The use of the number line at this point can emphasize what a momentous step has been taken by the introduction of these negative numbers. We have now extended our number system and in so doing have added again as many points on the number line as we had previously; that is, there are as many negative numbers as positive ones. All our arithmetic numbers are now also called the positive numbers, with the two sets (the positives and negatives) and zero forming the set of numbers we shall call integers. It is most important for the present to think of the arithmetic numbers as a subset of the integers, rather than to think of these positive numbers as a completely different set. In this way we are better able to build upon what the student already knows as we help him to develop the skill necessary for correct use of these numbers.

OPERATIONS WITH DIRECTED NUMBERS

Now that a good deal of experience with the "new" numbers has been provided, we can turn our attention to the basic operations. Building upon the established pattern we make use of an appropriate relationship. The following table illustrates how the age of a student, Joe, is related to that of his teacher:

Joe's age (s)	Teacher's age (T)
12	30
13	31
14	32
15	33
16	34

A formula is found for the relationship and the graph is drawn. Working with $T = 18 + s$, we consider these questions: How old will the teacher be when Joe is 20? 25? How old was the teacher when Joe was 10? 5? 1? If we set $s = 0$, find the T-value. What does this mean?

Having considered the teacher's age at the time Joe was born, we may well ask how old the teacher was the year before Joe's birth. While the answer is simple enough to determine without algebra, let us see what this means algebraically:

$$T = 18 + s$$

How may we show our substitution for s? In light of the discussion about opposites and the development here, and since a year from now appears as 1

210

or $+1$ on the new scale, a year ago can be shown as -1. This conclusion should be a natural one here. Thus, the formula becomes $T = 18 + s$; if $s = -1$, then $T = 18 + (-1)$. What is the value of T? Since the students have reasoned that the result must be 17, this same result must be the correct answer. Hence, $17 = 18 + (-1)$.

We have completed our first example in addition of directed numbers. Additional examples finding the results for $s = -2, -3, -4$, and so on will follow. We have found the answer because it was a natural consequence of the conditions established; i.e., the teacher was 16 years old 2 years before Joe was born. Additional experiences can be developed by selecting other student-teacher age relationships, all of which offer the student an introduction to addition with integers. These experiences, coupled with the work done before carrying out subtractions that result in negative differences, have provided the background necessary to formalize the work with addition and subtraction. One important fact to focus upon before beginning this work is exemplified by the situation used previously, $T = 18 + s$, in finding the teacher's age 18 years before Joe was born. By substitution the statement appears like this:

$$T = 18 + (-18)$$
$$T = 0$$

In additional situations with other student-teacher comparisons, the fact gradually emerges that in general $x + (-x) = 0$. This relationship should be highlighted and perhaps visualized by using the number scale (Fig. 11-5).

ADDITION AND SUBTRACTION

The students have completed many examples requiring the addition of numbers, one of which was negative. They have also subtracted to find a negative outcome. How will addition and subtraction be carried out with these new numbers? We turn away from physical situations and undertake a mathematical exploration.

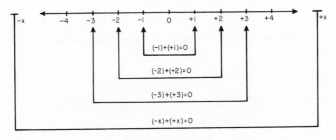

Figure 11-5

Directed Numbers

The Number Line

The number line most often plays a central role in textbook developments of operations with directed numbers. Addition is usually referred to as placing vectors end-to-end as indicated by sign and length, and then subtraction is developed by thinking of the additive concept of subtraction. For example, to demonstrate the addition process on the number line we proceed as indicated in Figure 11-6. The vectors are placed end-to-end as shown.

Subtraction is approached in a similar manner, maintaining the idea of addition. For example, in the case of 5 − 3, the student asks, "What must I add to 3 to give 5?" In the case of 9 − 4 he asks, "What must I add to 4 to give 9?" Students may be reminded that this was the way in which the subtraction examples were checked in their work in arithmetic. Figure 11-7 demonstrates how this work would appear on the number line.

The reasoning in the case of (+5) − (+2) would be: How much must be added to +2 to get +5? Since it is necessary to move three units to the right, the answer is +3.

Thus the student is able to determine the correct answer to any subtraction example involving integers. By examining many different combinations of numbers and the correct results, it is expected that each student will be able to formulate his own methods for dealing with these examples. In this way, the learning of rules is hopefully eliminated and replaced by student formulated methods.

Loops and Pipe Cleaners

Perhaps the most difficult of all operations with directed numbers is the process of subtraction. For the most part, the student has been accustomed to think of subtraction in terms of "take away." Now he comes upon negative numbers and the "take away" procedure is no longer applicable. One way to take advantage of the physical idea of "take away" and to help students visualize what is happening when adding and subtracting integers is presented here.[2] In order to enable students to represent examples visually, the following

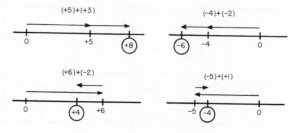

Figure 11-6

212

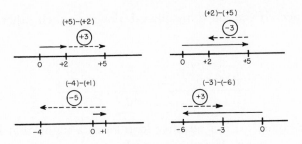

Figure 11-7

scheme has been devised: We shall use the letter "P" for positive, with one "P" standing for one positive unit. However, in the interest of brevity we shall write only the upper portion of the "P," just ⊃. Thus, +3 will be represented by ⊃ ⊃ ⊃ and other positive numbers may be visualized as shown:

$$+4 \quad ⊃ ⊃ ⊃ ⊃$$
$$+2 \quad ⊃ ⊃$$
$$+6 \quad ⊃ ⊃ ⊃ ⊃ ⊃ ⊃$$

Since the negative numbers are the opposites of the positives, we can illustrate negative numbers by reversing the symbol:

$$-2 \quad ⊂ ⊂$$
$$-3 \quad ⊂ ⊂ ⊂$$
$$-4 \quad ⊂ ⊂ ⊂ ⊂$$

If we keep in mind the notion of the additive inverse, $x + (-x) = 0$, we are ready to operate with these numbers. We begin with addition. Problems involving only the positive integers are not in need of discussion. The students should complete the problems as they have been doing for years in arithmetic. These should not be treated as new examples and the use of aids is unwarranted. However, one problem is demonstrated here simply to illustrate the use of symbols.

(+5) We represent this as ⊃ ⊃ ⊃ ⊃ ⊃
+ (+3) We represent this as ⊃ ⊃ ⊃
Thus we have in all ⊃ ⊃ ⊃ ⊃ ⊃ ⊃ ⊃ ⊃ or +8.

Now we turn to an addition involving negative numbers, $(+4) + (-3)$, and use the loops.

(+4) ⊃ ⊃ ⊃ ⊃
+ (-3) ⊂ ⊂ ⊂

Since we are adding, we combine sets and in so doing we come upon an inter-

213

esting occurrence: If the loops are placed alongside each other, they appear like this:

$$
\begin{array}{ll}
(+4) & \supset \quad \supset \quad \supset \quad \supset \\
+ (-3) & \subset \quad \subset \quad \subset \\
\hline
& \bigcirc \quad \bigcirc \quad \bigcirc \quad \supset
\end{array}
$$

A positive loop joined with a negative loop forms a figure that looks remarkably like a zero, $\bigcirc$, and in fact we consider it to be zero for we have already established that $(+1) + (-1) = 0$. Thus, the result of the example just given is the single positive loop $\supset$, or $+1$. Other examples follow this pattern:

$$
\begin{array}{ll}
(+2) & \supset \quad \supset \\
+ (-3) & \subset \quad \subset \quad \subset \\
\hline
& \bigcirc \quad \bigcirc \quad \subset \text{ or } -1
\end{array}
\qquad
\begin{array}{ll}
(-4) & \subset \ \subset \ \subset \ \subset \\
+ (-1) & \subset \\
\hline
& \subset \ \subset \ \subset \ \subset \ \subset \text{ or } -5
\end{array}
$$

The students now have a way of determining the correct answer to all addition problems. These same loops may be made from the common variety of pipe cleaners. They are easily shaped and just as easily joined and separated again. In this way the students can actually do these problems physically on their desks to find the correct answer. The three-dimensional representation is important to many youngsters.

As for subtraction, the approach is exactly the same except for the fact that we think of subtraction as "taking away" part of a single set and determining how many are left, rather than combining two sets to form a new third set, as in addition. With the loops or pipe cleaners, we are now physically able to employ the concept of "take away." Those examples involving only the positive integers with the larger magnitude at the top do need the use of loops. We turn to the following example as a demonstration of the method:

$$
\begin{array}{ll}
(+4) & \supset \ \supset \ \supset \ \supset \\
- (+2) & \\
\hline
\end{array}
$$

We may now physically take away two positive units:

$$
\begin{array}{ll}
(+4) & \not\supset \ \not\supset \ \supset \ \supset \\
- (+2) & \\
\hline
\end{array}
$$

and thus we are left with $+2$, the correct result.

The problem of a larger subtrahend is most interesting. Let us reverse the position of the numbers and work with the newly formulated example:

$$
\begin{array}{ll}
(+2) & \supset \ \supset \\
- (+4) & \\
\hline
\end{array}
$$

Here we seem to encounter a difficulty since at most we can take away only two positive units, yet our example requires that we remove four such units. But we have a way out. We again make use of the additive-identity property of zero. Since adding zero does not alter the example, we do so twice:

$$(+2) \quad \supset \supset \; \bigcirc \; \bigcirc$$
$$- \, (+4)$$

Now we find that we *are* able to take away four positive units. Doing just this results in the following:

$$(+2) \quad \not\supset \not\supset \; \not\bigcirc \; \not\bigcirc$$
$$- \, (+4)$$
$$\text{leaving} \qquad \subset \quad \subset \quad \text{or} -2, \text{ the correct answer.}$$

This work can now be applied to any subtraction example, simply adding zeros wherever it is necessary to do so in order that we may be able to "take away." Some additional examples follow:

$$(-3) \quad \not\subset \not\subset \not\subset \not\bigcirc \qquad\qquad (-2) \quad \subset \subset \not\bigcirc$$
$$- \, (-4) \qquad\qquad\qquad\qquad\qquad\qquad - \, (+1)$$
$$\qquad\qquad\qquad \supset \text{ or } +1 \qquad\qquad\qquad\qquad\qquad \subset \subset \subset \quad \text{or} -3$$

The loops or pipe cleaners, whichever are used, may then be employed by the students in doing a wide variety of addition and subtraction examples. Larger numbers will discourage the use of this device and move students to examine the results of their work with an eye toward creating their own methods without the use of loops. The ingenuity of students in creating methods for solving examples is surprising indeed. But they first need the freedom to be able to develop such methods. We now turn to multiplication and division.

MULTIPLICATION AND DIVISION

The area of greatest concern for both teachers and textbook authors alike, as they consider directed numbers, seems to be the way in which to treat the fact that the multiplication of two negative numbers results in a positive one. Many ingenious rationales have been built to help students to accept the result. Let us be quite clear about the gains resulting from these ingenious creations: They only serve to add to the plausibility of the result in order that students will more readily accept it. These devices are questionable aids to student understanding in the sense of gaining insights into the process. They

215

do help students to believe that the answer is correct. The correct outcome is a consequence, however, of things too far removed from the scene. We will examine the attempts to make $(-1)(-1) = (+1)$ more readily acceptable as we develop the multiplication of integers. We start here by returning to the functional relationships that have become such an integral part of all our algebra work. A function similar to the temperature function used before is one starting point. This time the experiment involves raising the temperature 3° per hour, with the temperature 10° at the start of our observations. (This is another situation in which the students may well gather the data from pictures or diagrams of thermometers (Fig. 11-8). The table of data will look like this:

Hours of observation, h	Temperature in degrees, T
0	10
1	13
2	16
3	19
4	22

The students fit a formula to the data and draw the graph. We now examine the formula $T = 10 + 3h$ and discuss finding temperatures after 5 hours and more. Then we turn our attention to the question, What was the temperature 1 hour ago (assuming a constant rate of increase)? The pattern in the table indicates that the temperature at this time was 7°, a value that

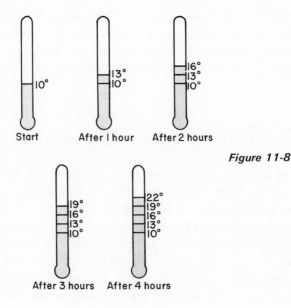

Start   After 1 hour   After 2 hours

Figure 11-8

After 3 hours   After 4 hours

216

may also be determined from the graph. Substitution into the formula results in $T = 10 + 3(-1)$.

We have encountered our first need to carry out a multiplication with directed numbers. What does the expression $3(-1)$ mean? Recalling the meaning of multiplication from the work in arithmetic would indicate that multiplication is a repeated addition. Thus the students may interpret $3(-1)$ to be another way of writing $(-1) + (-1) + (-1)$. Both expressions are numerals for the same number. Since addition of integers has already been developed, it becomes apparent that $3(-1) = -3$, and the formula becomes $T = 10 + (-3)$. Once again, using the knowledge of addition, we find that the result is 7° and we can verify it since this is the same answer that was arrived at by reasoning from the table. Additional examples result from exploring what the temperature was 2, 3, or even more hours ago. These may be carried out to the point where T itself becomes the negative value. Before attempting generalizations involving multiplication, we need additional experiences.

One way to introduce similar experiences is to make use of the population-increase formula mentioned earlier. Although the graph of $P = 200 + 20y$ is questionable (connecting the points admits to fractions of a person), the town with a population of 200 and steady growth rate of 20 persons per year offers some interest. Again we ask questions much the same as we did with the temperature problem: What was the population a year ago? 2 years ago? and so on. Completing these problems seems to build the idea that multiplication is carried out in much the same fashion as it was in arithmetic. Only the proper sign seems to pose a problem. The multiplication of two positive numbers is the familiar problem from arithmetic. The numerical value of the product is easily arrived at, and it seems that the sign of the product is dependent upon the signs of the factors. The only situation remaining to be considered is the product of two negative numbers. How shall we determine the sign of this product?

In the situation of a constant decrease in temperature we have a formula that may prove fruitful. If our observations began when the temperature was 0° and if the decrease was a constant 3° per hour, the formula would be $T = 0 - 3h$. If we omit the zero, we now have the formula $T = -3h$. To determine what the temperature was for a number of hours prior to the start of our observations, we encounter the product of two negative numbers. Before the situation is formalized, reasoning will help the students determine the correct answer. A graph will also aid this process as it is extended to include the negatives (Fig. 11-9).

At any rate, given a steady decrease in temperature of 3° per hour, and with our observations beginning at zero temperature, 1 hour before the temperature must have been +3° or 3° above zero; hence this is the value that must be given to $T = -3(-1)$. Therefore, (-3) multiplied by (-1) somehow

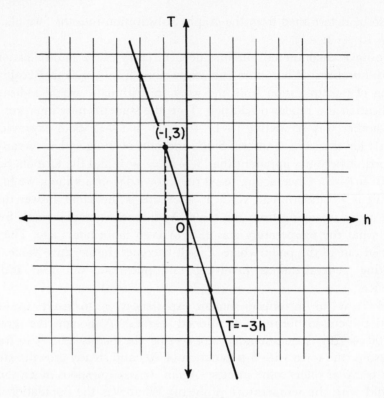

Figure 11-9

gives a product of $+3$, a surprising but nevertheless correct result! Many more examples should follow this beginning, and then all the completed multiplications should be reexamined as the students attempt to formulate their own ideas for the multiplication of directed numbers. What we have tried to do here is to make the result a necessary consequence of the given situation if mathematics is to be of use in these situations. In this way, it is hoped that the plausibility of the result is readily acceptable to the student.

Division is then thought of as the opposite or inverse of multiplication; and just as an additive approach was discussed for subtraction, one emphasizing multiplication aids the investigation of division. For example, $(+8) \div (+2)$ is an example of ordinary arithmetic numbers. When a negative number appears, $(+12) \div (-3)$, we ask the question, What number multiplied by (-3) gives a product of $(+12)$? In this way an approach to the division of integers is made.

Further Explanations for the Product of $(-1)(-1)$

Earlier it was mentioned that many elaborate schemes have been devised in order to make the product of $(-1)(-1)$ seem reasonable. One interesting

218

idea involves the study of patterns. After having developed the ability to multiply a negative and a positive number, the students are asked to find the following products:

$$(-3)(+3) =$$
$$(-3)(+2) =$$
$$(-3)(+1) =$$
$$(-3)(0)\ \ =$$
$$(-3)(-1) =$$
$$(-3)(-2) =$$

As they record the answers, they find the first four to be -9, -6, -3, and 0, in that order. Following this pattern it becomes natural to expect that the very next answer will be $+3$. This idea of developing a pattern can be employed with any of the operations involving integers. If enough of these patterned exercises are completed by the students, they have an opportunity to devise their own methods for dealing with the numbers.

Another way to establish the necessity of $(-1)(-1) = +1$ is to make use of the distributive law, $a(x + y) = ax + ay$. Using the skills learned earlier, students are asked to evaluate the expression $-3\,[(+2) + (-2)]$. The result is zero since $(+2) + (-2)$ gives zero, and multiplication by zero is always zero. However, if we apply the distributive law, we get the following result:

$$-3\,[(+2) + (-2)] = (-3)(+2) + (-3)(-2)$$

Since $(-3)(+2) = -6$, if the sum must be zero it must also follow that $(-3)(-2) = +6$.

The use of a pump and camera and the delivery of bills and checks by a postman have also been suggested to help with the problem of multiplying two negative numbers. The camera photographs water being pumped out of a well (negative); water going into the well is considered positive. The camera's film projected forward is positive direction, while running the film in reverse is considered to be negative direction. Thus, if we project on a screen in reverse (negative) water being pumped out of a well (negative), the resulting pictures will show water flowing into the well—a positive result. Of course, this development requires a good deal of careful work with students in order that they may understand the proceedings.

The same is true for the postman approach. Here we think in terms of financial gains or losses for the receiving family. The delivery of a bill is termed a bad thing for the family (negative); the paying out of a check is also a negative transaction. These two negative transactions, however, leave the family with less debts—a positive result.

Finally, a gear board may also be used to illustrate this troublesome result (Fig. 11-10). Each gear is thought of as an operator performing multiplication by (-1). When the marked slides are moved, the product is read

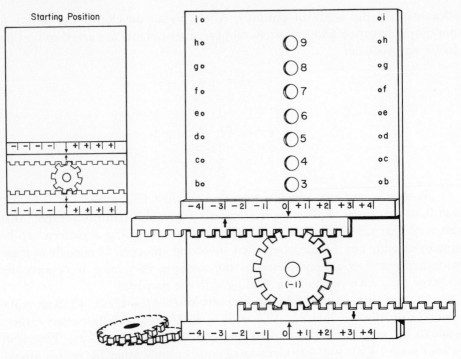

Figure 11-10. *Gear board illustrating* $(-3)(-1) = +3$.

from the board. Thus, if a single gear is used, all numbers are multiplied by negative one and the slides move in the opposite direction. When two gears are employed, $(-1)(-1)$, the slides move in the same direction, giving the effect of multiplication by $(+1)$. (See Fig. 11-11.)

In summary, there are a variety of ways to help students to see that $(-1)(-1) = (+1)$ is a reasonable answer. These techniques are not to be misconstrued as proofs. They do not really aid understanding, but they do make the result acceptable. It would probably be advisable for a teacher to use as many or as few of these different presentations as necessary to help students learn.

POLYNOMIALS

A rancher has 100 feet of fencing and wishes to fence off a rectangularly shaped corral that will provide him with the greatest possible area. What dimensions should the corral be? This challenging little problem offers us an introduction to the study of polynomials.

After permitting a good deal of student free experimentation in attempting a solution, we try to organize the thinking in a mathematical way. Discussion will result in the recognition of the fact that the perimeter is fixed;

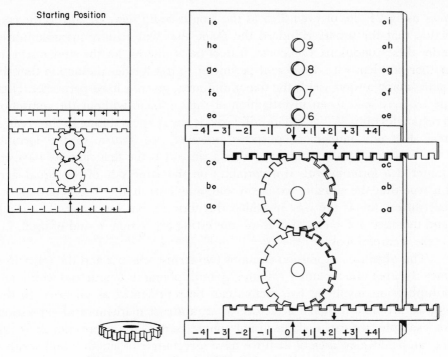

Figure 11-11. *Gear board illustrating (+2)(+1) = +2.*

and if x and y are used to represent the length and width of the rectangle in question, we may write a formula for all possible rectangles whose perimeter is 100:

$$2x + 2y = 100$$

Substituting arbitrary values for the length (x) would result in fixing values for the width (y). The students could tabulate these results and then add a third column with the heading *Area* to their table:

x	y	*Area*
5	45	225
10	40	400
15	35	525
20	30	600
25	25	625
30	20	600
35	15	525
40	10	400

The information demonstrates that the peak seems to be around 25 feet for both length and width. This is the shape of the square. Computations of

221

areas using 24, 26, or even 25.5 as the length could serve to add to the conviction that the square is indeed the shape that will achieve maximum area under these conditions. Of course, it may be of interest for the students to try another problem with a different perimeter to test further the notion that the square shape always yields the maximum area, given a fixed perimeter. High interest may lead to an investigation of this problem without the restriction to rectangles only. Will a square still provide the shape resulting in the greatest area? For our immediate purpose, however, we return to the formula $P = 2x + 2y$. This is a unique formula since it is the first time we have encountered a formula with two variables on the same side of the equal sign. It is true that the equality axioms would enable us to alter this situation, but nevertheless this is the way in which this formula has been met. The right-hand member of the equation is an interesting expression in and of itself. Let us take a careful look at $2x + 2y$.

This algebraic expression contains two terms, one in x and the other in y. Since the area of a rectangle is found by multiplying its length and width, any multiplication involving two factors can be represented as an area. In this way we are able to make a picture of an abstract mathematical expression. For example, we can make a visual counterpart of the expression $2x + 2y$. We can achieve an area of $2x$ if we have a rectangle of length 2 and width x. In like fashion we can represent an area $2y$ (Fig. 11-12). Since we are adding these two terms, all we need do is place the rectangles alongside each other and we have an illustration of the expression $2x + 2y$ (Fig. 11-13). A close examination of the picture points up an item of interest. If we look at the large rectangle, which is the sum of the two smaller ones, it appears that $2x + 2y = 2(x + y)$. This is a fact worthy of further investigation. After the students draw the visual representation of many expressions of the form

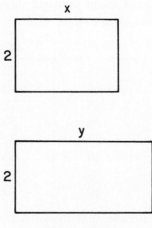

Figure 11-12

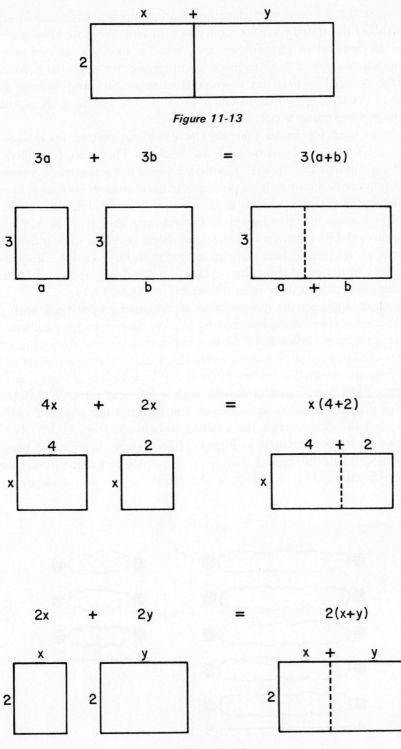

Figure 11-13

$$3a \quad + \quad 3b \quad = \quad 3(a+b)$$

$$4x \quad + \quad 2x \quad = \quad x(4+2)$$

$$2x \quad + \quad 2y \quad = \quad 2(x+y)$$

Figure 11-14

$a(x + y)$, it may be indicated that this relationship is a basic one in mathematics called the distributive, or do-it-to-each, law. We now have a method for the elimination of parentheses and, what is more, a way of picturing polynomials. *Polynomial* is introduced as the name we apply to a collection of terms. We use *monomial* for a single-term expression and *binomial* for an expression containing two terms (such as $2x + 2y$), but all such expressions have the general name of polynomial.

Just as we have found that we can carry out certain operations with numbers, we may do the same with polynomials. They may be added, subtracted, multiplied, and divided. Consistent use of the geometrical representations of polynomials may help to prevent the usual student confusion in carrying out these operations, as well as in attempting to combine like terms. For example, we made use of rectangles to demonstrate how $2x + 2y = 2(x + y)$. The pictures vividly illustrate why the sum cannot be $4xy$ or some other curious statement we frequently find students assigning to this example. This process seems more to the point than the explanation of adding apples and oranges. Some sample problems have been illustrated in Figure 11-14.

Another approach to the problem of visualizing operations with polynomials is most effectively presented by W. W. Sawyer in his excellent book *Vision in Elementary Mathematics*.[3] Sawyer represents the variables as unknown numbers of objects, and he demonstrates this visually through the use of little clouds over the array. For example, $5a$ is five equal rows of objects while $3b$ represents three equal rows of objects with a different number of objects in each row than is indicated by b. We see the first and last object of each row (circles) but the cloud covers the amount in between (Fig. 11-15). The sum of $5a$ and $3b$ is then pictured in Figure 11-16. Sawyer is trying to present a clear demonstration of the fact that $5a + 3b$ cannot be written in any shorter way. He is attempting to eliminate the tendency of some students to add

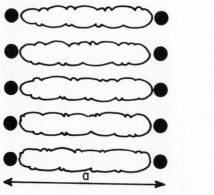

Figure 11-15

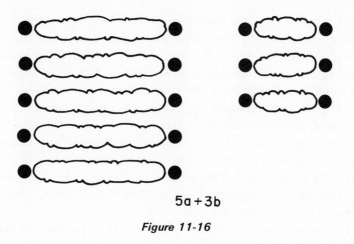

5a + 3b

Figure 11-16

$5a$ and $3b$ and arrive at some incorrect response such as $15ab$. The visual representation seems to be most effective.

Addition of like terms—in fact, the general process of addition of polynomials—may be neatly developed using Sawyer's illustration technique. The sum of $(2x + 3y)$ and $(4x + 2y)$ is shown in Figure 11-17. Subtraction may be demonstrated with equal effectiveness, as the "take-away" idea is once more

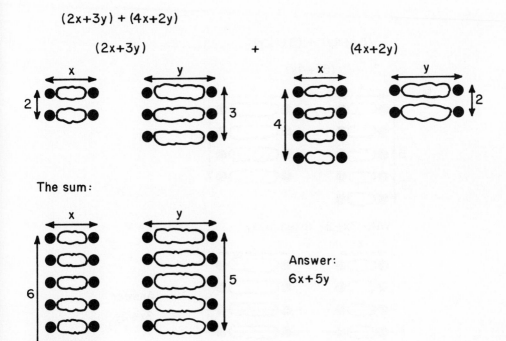

Figure 11-17

225

employed. Figure 11-18 shows how the example $(5x + 4y) - (3x + 2y)$ would appear using these visuals. The implications for removal of parentheses in carrying out subtraction are clear. A variety of examples completed using these visualizations would enable most students to formulate their own rules for such techniques. At the least, the student has a picture in his mind upon which to hang the mathematical abstraction. Similar "pictures" may aid the consideration of multiplication and division.

Still other representations may be made of these difficult manipulations. A pegboard or geoboard may be used to illustrate the meaning of carrying out operations with polynomials. The result is very much like Sawyer's pictures, with the additional advantage of being three-dimensional. The pegs (golf tees are most effective) form the end points, and the clouds are replaced by rubber bands looped around the end pegs. It is then possible for the students to proceed as before. Figure 11-19 is a picture of how the addition example that was worked before would look on the pegboard. Rubber bands looped over the nails of a geoboard would appear much the same as they did with the pegs.

Contrary to popular belief, there is no shortage of ideas for the concrete and visual representation of many of the abstractions of algebra. Extended experiences with these materials would help students to formulate their own

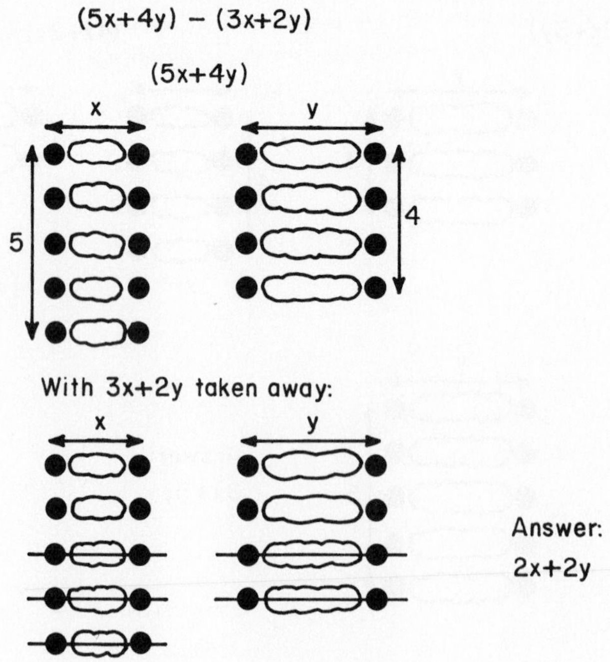

Figure 11-18

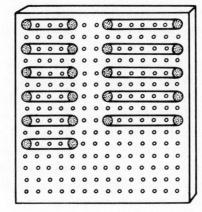

Figure 11-19

methods for operating with polynomials and perhaps help them to avoid the common mistakes so frequently encountered in this work. But most importantly, visual representation enables the teacher to make the study of these manipulations an interesting investigation into the world of algebra.

INVERTING THE LINEAR FUNCTION

It has been common practice in algebra classes to test how well the procedures of equation solving have been learned by asking students to work lists of literal equations, abstract equations that are solved for a given letter or variable. In this way, many teachers feel that a good estimate of mastery of techniques can be made. While there is a good deal of truth in this, there is also some question as to its effectiveness. Students are asked to solve for this variable or that without any purpose other than the mechanical practice provided. Perhaps this work can be made more challenging in the following manner:

> Two kinds of thermometers are used in scientific work to measure temperatures, the Fahrenheit and centigrade thermometers. The Fahrenheit thermometer is arranged so that it reads 32° when water freezes and 212° when water is at the boiling point. The centigrade scale, however, is arranged so that the freezing point of water is at zero degrees, while the boiling point is at 100°. The formula which relates to these two scales is $C = \frac{5}{9}(F - 32)$. If an experiment resulted in a temperature on the centigrade scale of 20°, what would be the equivalent temperature on the Fahrenheit thermometer? Find the equivalent Fahrenheit temperatures for the following centigrade readings: 30°, 50°, 75°, and 110°.

As each different centigrade reading is substituted into the formula, a

227

lengthy process is undertaken in order to solve the equation for F. Is there any way in which this work can be accomplished with less effort? At this point we may suggest solving the equation for F first and then simply substituting values for C and solving. Thus, we have "inverted" or changed the subject of the formula. When we have many values of the independent variable to calculate, it is time saving to invert the formula and then carry out the substitution process. It would now seem to be conceivable to return to any of the formulas introduced earlier, invert them, and evaluate them for the newly formed dependent variable. In this way we not only provide a good deal of interesting practice with the skills developed earlier but we also point out that the designation dependent-independent as applied to variables is not a hard and fast assignment, but rather a product of the way in which one chooses to look at the situation. It is a product of the most convenient manner of carrying out the work to be done. In those situations which require work with abstract expressions devoid of physical counterparts, an arbitrary designation is made of independent and dependent variables, although in this case the terms are less meaningful.

It would probably be of interest to students to draw the graphs of these newly formed relationships. An examination of the effect of inverting the function upon the graph is one that surprises students. The curve does not change, but its location in the plane does because the variables have exchanged scales.

Once the students have completed several problems inverting familiar formulas, they are ready to attempt to solve any linear equation for a given variable. They are also prepared to work on lists of equations in order to fix the learnings developed thus far.

THE GENERAL LINEAR EQUATION: IN CONCLUSION

An overview of all the work undertaken as the linear function and the linear equation have come under study can be provided; but at the same time student interest may be maintained through the use of more complicated linear relationships. As the students become involved with these relationships they are called upon to use virtually all the skills they have previously learned. Once again, the environment is new, but the mathematics is familiar.

Scientists are busy trying to determine how, if at all, insects communicate with each other. Although insects give off sounds and probably can hear them, scientists have been unable to determine how insects hear. The noises they make prove to be most interesting. Surprising as it may seem, insect sounds have been found to be a function of the temperature.[4] Scientists have determined the following formulas for these insects:

T represents the Fahrenheit temperature.

N represents the number of chirps per minute.

228

House cricket: $$T = 50 + \frac{N - 40}{4}$$

Katydid: $$T = 60 + \frac{N - 19}{3}$$

Tree cricket: $$T = 50 + \frac{N - 92}{4.7}$$

These formulas can provide a rich variety of experiences for students that will enable them to call into play all the skills they have already learned. Posing problems where the temperature is provided and the expected number of chirps per minute is to be determined would require the use of equation solving skills. Finding the temperatures that correspond to many different N-values would require inverting the formula. Drawing the graphs after formulating tables of ordered pairs should be of interest. These are but a few of the possible problems resulting from these relationships.

Another relationship of interest is that of the proper height for the chalkboard in a room for a given grade level. Most students will have noticed that the boards are lower in the elementary school than they are in the rooms of the junior and senior high schools. An approximate formula for chalkboard height is

$$H = 25 + \tfrac{3}{2}(G - 4)$$

This is a particularly interesting formula as it concerns something in every student's experience and yet offers an opportunity to explore many different skills. It may be well to actually measure the chalkboards in several school classrooms to test the accuracy of the formula. At any rate, from graphing to equation solution to work with parentheses, a rich fund of problems may be devised.

In addition, a discussion of admissable values for H and G would be well taken here. How large or small may G become? What is the resulting effect upon H? Can H take on any value? Compare the results of this discussion with the graph that is drawn. In this way we begin to help the students to see the importance of knowing the range and domain of variables, as well as providing another example of the important difference between the mathematics and its physical counterpart. Formulas discussed earlier may be recalled and examined in the light of these new ideas.

There are many such relationships that may provide the teacher with a storehouse of problem situations that help to build the idea of the importance of mathematics, as well as to offer interesting practice work. Several are briefly listed here:

"Normal" adult weight (W) as a function of the height (h): $$W = 1\tfrac{1}{2}(h - 40)$$

229

The height (h) of an 8-inch candle depends
upon the length of the time it burns (t): $\quad h = 8 - 1\frac{1}{2}t$

The membership of a school club (M) with 10
charter members and constant growth of
three members per year (y): $\quad M = 10 + 3y$

The weight (W) of a 150 pound man who is
on a diet resulting in a 2 pound loss each
week (t): $\quad W = 150 - 2t$

Finally, let us emphasize the form of all the formulas under exploration and arrive at the general linear equation $y = ax + b$. An examination of the graphs in an attempt to determine how the numbers of the formula influence the graphs could lead to the important slope-intercept technique for graphing. A particularly good formula to reexamine for this purpose involves the tread and rise of steps. This physical picture is a good one to use when helping students keep clear in their minds that the slope ratio, $\triangle y / \triangle x$, is actually rise/tread. Many teachers have used rise over run, which is also a good way to clarify the changes in which we have an interest. Working with the familiar formulas by changing them into the slope-intercept form $y = mx + b$ and then graphing using the slope and y-intercept form could be followed by lists of equations involving only x and y. We now turn our attention to systems of linear equations.

FOOTNOTES

1. See Chapter 15, page 311.
2. Herbert Fremont. "Pipe Cleaners and Loops—Discovering How to Add and Subtract Directed Numbers." *The Arithmetic Teacher*. Vol. 13 (November, 1966), pp. 568–72.
3. W. W. Sawyer. *Vision in Elementary Mathematics*. Penguin Books, Inc., 1964.
4. Rudolph Haffner. "Insects of Note." *Science and Math Weekly*. Vol. 2 (January 17, 1962), pp. 174–175.

FOR INVESTIGATION AND DISCUSSION

1. Describe instances in which most people would become involved with negative numbers.

2. Devise a situation that results in the need to carry out computations with negative numbers.

3. Demonstrate two different ways to introduce the addition and subtraction of directed numbers. Compare one with the other.

4. Make a lesson plan for the introduction of multiplication of directed numbers.

5. Describe and compare two methods of building acceptance for the fact that $(-1)(-1) = +1$.

6. Show how the concept of a product represented as an area may aid the understanding of the distributive law.

7. Make a lesson plan for the learning of multiplication of polynomials using geometric representations.

8. Choose a situation from those listed near the end of this chapter and build a lesson designed to provide practice for students in solving linear equations.

FOR FURTHER READING

Books

Frank Land. *The Language of Mathematics*. Doubleday & Company, Inc., 1963, Chapter 4.
E. H. Lockwood and O. K. Down. *Algebra*. University of London Press, 1954, Chapter 7.
David Page. *Number Lines, Functions and Fundamental Topics*. The Macmillan Company, 1964.
W. W. Sawyer. *Vision in Elementary Mathematics*. Penguin Books, Inc., 1964, Chapters 9 and 12.

Periodicals

Robert B. Ashlock and Tommie A. West. "Physical Representations for Signed-Number Operations." *The Arithmetic Teacher*. Vol. 14 (November, 1967), pp. 549–554.
H. C. Christofferson. "Positive and Negative Numbers." *School Science and Mathematics*. Vol. 25 (May, 1925), pp. 507–514.
Louis Cohen. "A Rationale in Working With Signed Numbers—Revisited." *The Arithmetic Teacher*. Vol. 13 (November, 1966), pp. 564–567.

$$12$$

SYSTEMS OF EQUATIONS

BEGINNING WITH THE LEVER

The solution of systems of simultaneous linear equations provides a good deal of practice for students in using many of the concepts and skills learned earlier. In addition, an important relationship in science can provide the setting in which to develop these ideas.

The use of the lever offers an interesting physical base for the introduction of systems of equations. Because the lever is a machine which has many important uses for man, it is a machine that is familiar to most students. What child has not spent an afternoon enjoying the up-and-down ride provided by a seesaw? How many have never seen a crowbar used to raise an object or force open some stubborn cover? Like all machines, the lever helps man to do work. It is an important and fruitful concept for students because it helps to demonstrate the use of mathematics.

The properties of the lever may well be explored through experimentation. In addition to the many commercial levers that are available,[1] homemade variations of the lever will do rather nicely for the mathematics classroom (Fig. 12-1). The students can carry out experiments with the lever, gathering data about the balancing relationships of weights at varying distances from the fulcrum. If the lever itself is a ruler, the distances are readily available. The use of common hardware for weights (e.g., nuts and washers) works out well. Whatever the equipment, the children could record the results of experimentation in a table similar to the following:

232

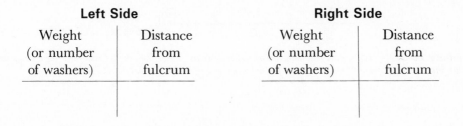

Left Side		Right Side	
Weight (or number of washers)	Distance from fulcrum	Weight (or number of washers)	Distance from fulcrum

The completion of such a table for three to five trials may well result in the discovery by students of a relationship described by the following formula:

$$WD = wd$$

where W is the amount of weight at one end of the lever, D is the distance of W from the fulcrum, w is the amount of weight at the other end of the lever, and d is the distance of w from the fulcrum.

In this way, the students may encounter many problems that involve the linear function (Figs. 12-2 and 12-3) and the use of parentheses (Fig. 12-4). Eventually we may pose problems that require the use of two equations in order to find a solution (Fig. 12-5). There are many different ways to approach

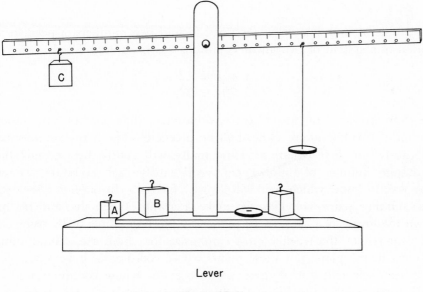

Lever

Figure 12-1

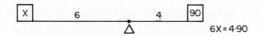

$$6X = 4 \cdot 90$$

Figure 12-2. *How much weight must be placed on one end of a 10-foot lever if it is to balance a weight of 90 pounds, which is 4 feet from the fulcrum, at the other end?*

233

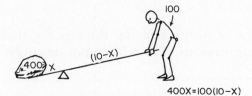

Figure 12-3. *If a 50-pound child sits at one end of a seesaw 5 feet from the fulcrum, how far away from the fulcrum would another child weighing 30 pounds have to sit in order to balance the seesaw?*

Figure 12-4. *Bob, who weighs 100 pounds, is trying to raise a 400-pound boulder off the ground. He has a 10-foot pole that he can use. How far from the stone should he place the fulcrum in order to be able to lift it?*

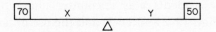

Figure 12-5. *Joe and Dan want to balance each other on a 12-foot seesaw. If Joe weighs 70 pounds and Dan weighs 50, how far should each boy be from the fulcrum?*

such problems; but since it is necessary to find two numbers, a need for the solution of a system of two linear equations has been established:

$$x + y = 12$$
$$70x = 50y$$

Here the student encounters a situation calling for the simultaneous solution of two equations. How shall he proceed? How many number pairs will satisfy the first equation? How many will satisfy the second? Since an infinite number of number pairs will satisfy each equation, we need some way to know which pair will "work" for both. In order to "see" what these number pairs look like, we make a graph. When the students have drawn the graph of $x + y = 12$ (either by plotting points or by using slope and y-intercept), the teacher must emphasize that from the infinite number of points in the plane just those points whose coordinates have a sum of 12 have been selected; and if there are any points whose coordinates add up to 12, those points must be on the line. A remarkable process! Some points should be selected both on and off the line to demonstrate this. But the line consists of many, many points. How can we possibly find the one whose co-ordinates will satisfy both equations? Isn't this tantamount to trying to find the needle in the haystack? Let us now place the second line on this same set of coordinate axes by drawing the graph of $70x = 50y$. This line contains all the number pairs that satisfy the condition that the first coordinate multiplied by 70 is equal to 50 times the second coordinate. All such number pairs must lie on that line.

Thus we have a second set of points that satisfy the second condition. Is this graph of any help in solving our problem? Take a close look at it (Fig. 12-6). The lines intersect each other. If all the points on the first line satisfy the first condition and if all the points on the second line satisfy the second condition, what can be said of the point of intersection of the two lines? In this way we try to help the students understand what is happening as we use the graphs to work toward our solution. The wonder of this process must not be underestimated. By the simple placement of the two lines upon the Cartesian plane we have forced our needle out of the haystack! The result must be checked in the situation to which we apply it, of course, before it is accepted.

Similar problems that lend themselves to graphic solution should follow, and then a turn toward algebraic methods can be made. The introduction of similar problems that involve balancing a lever may be employed—but with one modification: This time the answer should contain fractions. In this way the student can clearly see that the use of the graph is questionable since it requires some degree of guessing about the true values needed. As graphing becomes unsatisfactory, the time is right for the introduction of new techniques; and we then turn to the methods of substitution, addition-subtraction, and comparing.

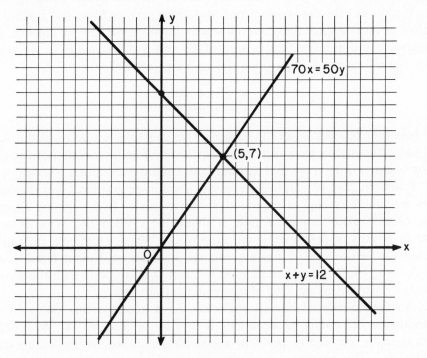

Figure 12-6

235

OTHER BEGINNINGS

It is quite possible to generate a good deal of interest in situations involving simultaneous equations by posing problems that have some puzzle value:

> I am thinking of two numbers. I will not tell you what they are, but I will give you their sum and their difference. Can you find the two numbers I am thinking of?

Many students will immediately begin to try number pairs until they are able to find the ones that satisfy the conditions of the problem. It is a mistake to discourage this kind of solution. A very real part of creative work involves the use of trial and error. While it may not appear to be an economical way to approach a problem, it frequently provides many insights into what is happening, with the net result that unsuccessful trials offer enough information to help us work toward a solution. As a matter of fact, many students have been so discouraged by teachers from using any but formal algebraic techniques that they find themselves at the complete mercy of these techniques. As a consequence they bring this rigid approach to all mathematical problems; and instead of trying to see relationships in problems, they work with complete faith that the power of algebra will see them through. Often it does, but just as often it does not. Most important, they have lost the adventurous spirit that is a prerequisite for mathematical thinking.

We do not discourage the trial and error process here, but instead we explore several approaches, one of which involves the use of algebra. For example, if the numbers had a sum of 12 and a difference of 2, we would write this information down using the language of algebra:

$$x + y = 12$$
$$x - y = 2$$

We may now proceed as we did earlier by turning to a picture of all the number pairs that satisfy each of the two equations. The intersection of the lines is the one and only point that satisfies both conditions simultaneously.

Fractions may be employed again to discourage graphing, but the equations are simple enough to suggest algebraic solutions. In developing substitution, or any of the other methods, it should be stressed that what is being done is typical of how mathematicians work: When a difficult, unfamiliar problem is before you, if you can change it to an equivalent familiar and simpler one, you will find the solution to the first by working with the second. This is a most important kind of mathematical strategy.

Another puzzle of interest that may be a good starting point for the introduction of systems of equations is one introduced by W. W. Sawyer, who actually sees in this problem a possible beginning for the entire study of algebra.[2] The problem concerns a man and his two sons who are twins. The height of the man and a single son is 10 feet; the height of a man and

236

his two sons is 14 feet. The reader is asked to find the height of the man and each of his two sons. Of course, the problem yields two equations:

$$m + s = 10$$
$$m + 2s = 14$$

More important, however, is the clever way in which Sawyer goes from pictures of the situation to lines representing the same relationships, as the students find that reasoning alone will enable them to find the missing heights (Fig. 12-7). Sawyer also develops the solution of simultaneous equations by addition and subtraction in a remarkably visual manner, basing all the work on simple reasoning. Presenting a system,

$$m + s = 10$$
$$3m + 5s = 36$$

he proceeds to build the first equation until he has a statement comparable to the second, i.e.,

1 man and 1 son take up 10 feet
2 men and 2 sons take up 20 feet
3 men and 3 sons take up 30 feet

Thus he arrives at

$$3m + 3s = 30$$

which is placed together with

$$3m + 5s = 36.$$

Therefore, the students can readily see that 2 sons must take up 6 feet:

$$2s = 6$$
$$s = 3$$

This is a most interesting and creative development.

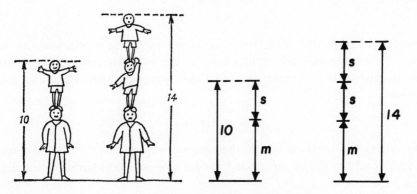

Figure 12-7. *(From W. W. Sawyer:* Vision in Elementary Mathematics. *Penguin Books Ltd., 1964.)*

Systems of Equations

Finally, it is possible to move into the area of systems of equations through the use of familiar relationships that the students encountered earlier. For example, the formula describing all the possible rectangles that had a perimeter of 100 is $2x + 2y = 100$. Suppose we now ask that the rectangle whose perimeter is 100 be found, but we add the condition that the length and width must be equal. Thus, we now have two conditions:

$$2x + 2y = 100$$
$$x = y$$

This system not only may be graphed in the same manner as the earlier ones, but is also a natural beginning for the introduction of substitution, since the second equation, $x = y$, would permit the substitution of either variable for the other. Thus, a single-variable equation is quickly deduced. The same would apply to the following situations:

When would the centigrade and Fahrenheit thermometers give the same number reading?

$$C = \tfrac{5}{9}(F - 32)$$
$$C = F$$

When would the candle height give the same number as the length of time it is burning?

$$h = 8 - 1\tfrac{1}{2}t$$
$$h = t$$

When would the "normal" adult have, numerically, the same height and weight?

$$2W = 11(H - 40)$$
$$W = H$$

In the centigrade-Fahrenheit and the burning candle situations, a rather easy introduction to the comparison method is available. For example, in the burning candle relationship,

$$h = 8 - 1\tfrac{1}{2}t$$
$$h = t$$

the student is presented with two statements indicating representations for h. Since both expressions are equal to h, by the equality axiom they must be equal to each other. A comparison of the two statements results in a new equation:

$$8 - 1\tfrac{1}{2}t = t$$

There are many ways in which the solution of systems can be introduced. The Scrabble pieces mentioned earlier can also be helpful at this time.[3]

238

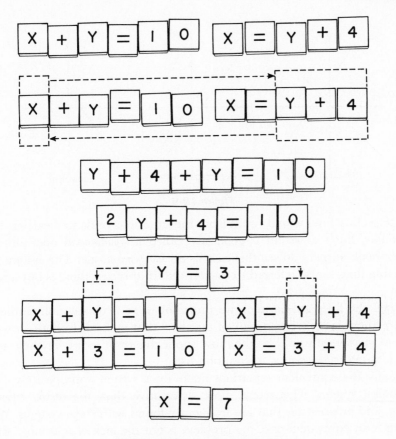

Figure 12-8. *Scrabble solved system.*

If the student uses these pieces to represent the equations to be solved, he will be able to provide a physical movement for many of the mathematical processes. When a substitution is made, a piece is physically placed in the position of another piece. When supposed roots are checked, they are actually put into the variable's place in the equation. Similar outcomes would result from the various solution methods and the use of the equality axioms (Fig. 12-8).

GRAPHING

If we were to graph the two functions just described, how may the lines be related? Either the lines intersect or they are parallel, since we are limiting ourselves to working in the plane. But there is yet another possibility and that is that the two equations are equivalent ones. (See Fig. 12-9.) As a matter of fact, the entire notion of equivalent equations takes on more meaning here. But let us first look at the three possibilities. What kind of situation would result in each of these graphs?

239

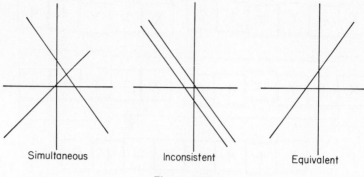

Figure 12-9

Intersecting lines would result from the situations presented earlier; these are familiar. Such a system is generally called a *simultaneous* one, although some textbook authors do see this case as an *independent* one. The system with intersecting lines is also referred to as *consistent*. In this case there is but a single solution.

When the lines are parallel, we find that there is no solution to the system since there is no ordered pair of numbers that will satisfy both. It would seem that *inconsistent* would be the most applicable term to use for these equations, although *independent* is in common use.

Finally the equivalent equations make up a system appropriately called an *equivalent* system. This seems more descriptive than the terms *dependent, consistent,* and *indeterminate* that are frequently found with these systems. When a system is an equivalent one, the problem is not the lack of solutions but the fact that there are an infinite number of ordered pairs that satisfy both equations. After all, that is what we mean by equivalent: Any solution of one equation is also the solution of the other.[4]

SOLVING PROBLEMS WITH SYSTEMS

The use of two variables in the solution of problems opens up a whole host of new problem areas traditionally found in algebra textbooks. These include the familiar digit problems, age problems, motion problems, mixture problems, investment problems, and many others. Often the problems that may be posed from this grouping have great puzzle value for students if students are encouraged to think through to solutions of their own. Unfortunately, it is often the case that students have been bombarded with these problems after first learning the required abstract skills needed to solve them. In this way the entire process is seen by the student as a distasteful kind of "drill" experience. The difficulties encountered by mathematics students when faced with verbal problems is well known. What teacher has not struggled manfully to teach such problems? Perhaps one important reason for student difficulty has been this complete separation of skills and problem solving. We generally expect the students to be able to bring forth previously

240

learned mathematical skills as needed. It is not quite as simple as we might expect. Furthermore, we are often more concerned with a single solution than we are with encouraging our students to create varieties of solutions. The net result is that we place the emphasis upon the ability to remember rather than upon the ability to think.

An attempt has been made here to develop mathematics from interesting situations. The problems are an integral part of our considerations and have been the generator of the mathematical examples. Perhaps in this way we may offer the students every opportunity to succeed in completing the mathematical tasks at hand. At the same time, it has been our intent to strive consistently for the goals so often stated as being fundamental to the learning of mathematics: the ability to reason, as well as the understanding and appreciation of mathematics and its significance.

By all means, use the many problem situations that were mentioned earlier, but use them with wisdom. Provide students with the necessary freedom to attack these in their own ways. Emphasize the puzzle value inherent in some of these. Help students visualize in any possible manner, what is going on in the problem. Take time to discuss what is going on so that all may know. Substitute excitement about solutions for the frequently encountered boredom caused by fear and lack of immediacy. If science can help provide interesting and important settings, let us use science. Typical are the following problems found in a School Mathematics Study Group publication:[5]

> Fresh plant tissue is weighed, dried out, and weighed again. The difference between the dry weight and the fresh weight was 100 grams. If the dry weight was 2/27 of the fresh weight, find the weight of the tissue when it was fresh.
>
> A tree increases in radius 50 mm. in 365 days. This is the ring you see when it is cut open. On days of rapid growth, it increases .25 mm. per day, on the average. On slow growth days the average increase is .10 mm. per day. How many days of rapid and slow growth were there in the 365 days?
>
> Two groups of snails contain 90 percent red snails and 75 percent red snails, respectively. If a new colony of snails is formed from these groups that has 200 snails of which 78 percent are red, how many of each group made up the new colony?

Granted that these are difficult problems, but nevertheless, they are concerned with life around us. Perhaps we add something of consequence when we draw upon such real-life problems.[6]

AN ASIDE ON GRAPHS OF LINEAR FUNCTIONS

Everyone is familiar with the graphical solution of quadratic equations. This process will be discussed later. Perhaps it would be well to explore

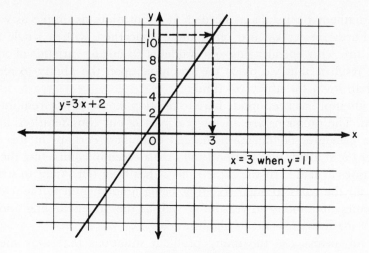

Figure 12-10

graphical solutions of linear equations. These techniques do not add to the power of the student to solve equations. They are of interest, however, because they add clarification to the notion of equivalent equations and provide a point of interest bordering on recreation that will help with later graphical solutions of quadratic functions.

If one of the situations we organize were to yield an equation to be solved, such as $3x + 2 = 11$, the students would probably solve the equation as follows:

$$3x + 2 = 11$$
$$3x = 9$$
$$x = 3$$

In the mathematical procedures, two equivalent equations were constructed. The root of the last equation almost "jumps out" at you, with the result that you thereby know the root of the first equation. Students have a tendency to say that the equations are the same. They think in terms of a single equation being altered in order to find a solution. While this kind of thinking is acceptable at first, eventually it is in need of refinement. To help students see that these are actually three equations, we may proceed to carry out graphing of the indicated functions in the following manner:

In order to draw the graph, we think about the function in this way: The rule for the function is seen to be $3x + 2 = y$. Since 11 is a specific result, granted the one in which we have particular interest, we may identify the particular x-value that results in a value of 11 for $3x + 2$ by graphing all the values of $3x + 2$ as x changes. Once we have the entire pattern, we can seek out the value in question (see Fig. 12-10); we find that $x = 3$.

242

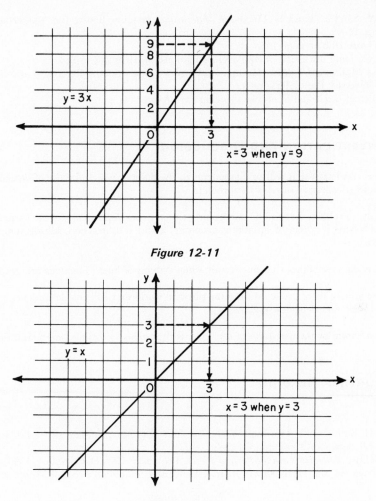

Figure 12-11

Figure 12-12

In the case of $3x = 9$ and $x = 3$, the same process is carried out. Graph the function described by $y = 3x$. Then locate 9 on the y-axis and find the corresponding x-value exactly as was done before. Again we find that $x = 3$ (Fig. 12-11). Completing this process by graphing $y = x$ and by locating the x-value that corresponds to $y = 3$ concludes the work (Fig. 12-12).

We have made a clear picture of the differences between the three equivalent equations, and at the same time emphasis has been placed upon the way in which they are related. The process also offered us graphical solution of the linear equation. We now turn to the quadratic function.

FOOTNOTES

1. Levers may be ordered from W. M. Welch Scientific Co., 1515 Sedgewick St., Chicago, Ill., and from Central Scientific Co., 1700 Irving Park Rd., Chicago, Ill.

Systems of Equations

2. W. W. Sawyer. *Vision in Elementary Mathematics.* Penguin Books, Inc. (paperback), 1964, pp. 40–45.
3. See Figure 10-8 on page 193.
4. See additional discussion of equivalent equations on pages 242 to 243.
5. School Mathematics Study Group. *Mathematics Through Science,* Parts 1, 2 and 3. Stanford University Press, 1963–1964.
6. For further discussion of problem solving see Chapter 14.

For Investigation and Discussion

1. Construct a lesson that will bring students to the point at which the use of systems of equations is necessary to solve the problem.

2. Identify a problem that will be particularly suited to developing each of the various methods of solving a system of equations: graphing, addition-subtraction, substitution, and comparison.

3. Discuss the possibilities that may result when systems of linear functions are graphed.

4. Devise at least three problems from the physical world that will enable students to make use of their knowledge of systems.

5. Plan a lesson for the extension of the work with systems to include one quadratic function.

For Further Reading

Books

Charles H. Butler and F. Lynwood Wren. *The Teaching of Secondary Mathematics,* Ed. 4. McGraw-Hill Book Co., 1960, pp. 354–360.
Morris Kline. *Mathematics and the Physical World.* Thomas Y. Crowell Company, 1959, pp. 63–65.
E. H. Lockwood and D. K. Down. *Algebra.* University of London Press, 1954, pp. 122–130.

Periodicals

A. R. Jerbert. "Simultaneous Linear Equations." *The Mathematics Teacher.* Vol. 45 (January, 1952), pp. 48–50.
John N. Meighan. "Methods of Solving Elementary Systems of Equations in Two Unknowns." *School Science and Mathematics.* Vol. 47 (November, 1947), pp. 709–714.

THE QUADRATIC FUNCTION

THE SIMPLE QUADRATIC FUNCTION

The relationships under consideration are now extended to include those whose graphs result in nonlinear curves. The basic approach that was developed in the study of linear functions is continued here with one major change: It becomes extremely difficult to describe patterns found in tables that are nonlinear, and so although the student is encouraged to continue his search for patterns, he will also be asked to determine relationships through careful reasoning about the situation.

In this section the quadratic functions of form $y = ax^2$ will be investigated. After a study of some simple cases of this relationship, the solution of quadratic equations will be considered algebraically, as well as graphically. All this is built upon the foundation laid as the linear function was explored. The process of finding square roots and the reverse process of squaring will also be given careful attention, as these processes are an essential part of any study of second-degree functions. But the basic idea of exploring relationships, drawing graphs, and making predictions will continue to be an integral part of all the work done. Later, more complicated quadratic forms will be introduced that will create a need for more powerful methods of solution. It is then, and not before, that factoring and completing the square will be developed and the quadratic formula finally presented as another alternative in the development of methods for dealing with this new form: the quadratic function.

245

INTRODUCTION

The study of the quadratic function may begin with the presentation of a number of relationships. Perhaps the simplest and most familiar one to the student would be the area of a square. How does the area of a square change as the length of a side is changed? Since the formula $A = s^2$ is well known to the student, it is possible to begin with the formula. The student can then carry out any necessary computations, compile a table of data, and draw the graph. His data might have these values:

s	A
0	0
1	1
2	4
3	9
4	16

A graph of these data is shown in Figure 13-1. In this instance, the first quadrant would suffice since the ideas of negative line segments and negative areas would be meaningless to the student.

Once the graph has been drawn, many interesting questions can be pursued: What is the shape of the curve? How does it differ from earlier work? As the side length increases, what happens to the area? If we double the side length, what happens to the area?

These are but a few of the considerations that may be undertaken. The first "curved" line graph is an important event to the student and as such should not be dismissed lightly. As before, the process of prediction may then

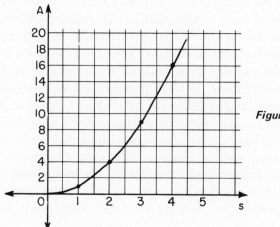

Figure 13-1

be carried out. If the length of a side is 10, find the area. Suppose the length is 12 or 15; find the area. Once again the students may decide to substitute in the formula, simply extend the table, or read the values from an extension of the graph; this choice should be a personal one. They should be encouraged to check their results by using an alternative method.

Finally, areas are given and the value of s is to be determined. And so a beginning is made on the solution of quadratic equations. It is important that no attempt be made to formalize the work done at this stage. If the students are encouraged to attack these problems in the best way that they can, they will have an opportunity to think for themselves and call into play much of their previous learning in mathematics. The formal techniques and vocabulary will be introduced as needed. Certainly a first look at quadratic functions is hardly sufficient to acquaint students with the ideas involved.

Other relationships that are examples of the quadratic function of form $y = ax^2$ and that are suitable for investigation at this time are:

The weight (W) in 100-pound units that can be lifted
by a rope of diameter d: $\qquad W = d^2$

The distance (d) traveled by a dropped object after t
seconds of falling: $\qquad d = 16t^2$

The area of a projected picture (A) from a projector
x feet away from the screen: $\qquad A = \frac{1}{9}x^2$

The weight (W) in 100-pound units that can be supported by a wood plank 6 feet long, 8 inches wide,
and d inches thick: $\qquad W = d^2$

The distance formula is a particularly fruitful one to explore for a variety of reasons. Motion relationships were met earlier in the study of linear functions; hence, they are familiar. A continuing physical theme is present as the mathematical knowledge is extended. Once again, while this formula holds at or near the surface of the earth, it changes if a different planet is considered. Thus, once the distance-time relationship has been considered, an unlimited number of mathematically repetitive situations can be created with a constantly changing physical environment, one that catches the interest of most students: the planets, moon, and sun of outer space.

The introduction of the distance formula so that students may clearly see how it has been formed requires careful attention. It is possible to present a picture or diagram of an object falling through space close to the surface of our planet so that the students have the opportunity to gather their own data to tabulate. An inclined plane and simple pendulum may also be employed to provide an active experience with the variables of this situation. A string 39 inches long has a period of about 1 second. After some practice, the students working in teams would begin to get fairly accurate results regarding the distance a ball would roll down this inclined plane in a given number of seconds as measured by the pendulum. In any event, once the information is

247

collected, the students will have before them a table of values. Here is one in seconds and feet:

t	d
0	0
1	16
2	64
3	144
4	256

Certainly the pattern of these numbers is not as readily observable as were the patterns of the linear relationships. A bit of reasoning comes to the aid of the student. From the velocity formula he is able to determine the speed with which the object is falling at any unit of time ($v = 32t$). Thus, after 1 second the velocity is 32 ft./sec., yet in the table the distance traveled is seen to be 16 feet. Is there some mistake? Shouldn't the distance traveled be 32? Did the ball drop with a speed of 32 ft./sec. for the entire second? No. It reached this speed at precisely 1 second in time. As a matter of fact, after $\frac{1}{2}$ second the speed of the ball was only 16 ft./sec. The speed goes from zero to 32 in 1 second and in between it passes through all the intermediary speeds. In this way we turn the attention of the student toward using the average speed over the interval and also find this by any one of a variety of techniques, such as:

To find the mean of any collection of numbers with a constant increase, such as 2, 4, 6, 8, 10, 12 . . . or 1, 2, 3, 4, 5, 6, 7 . . ., simply take the average of the first and last terms. For example, in the instances just mentioned:

$$\frac{2 + 12}{2} = 7 \qquad \text{Check:} \qquad 2 + 4 + 6 + 8 + 10 + 12 = 42$$
$$42 \div 6 = 7$$

$$\frac{1 + 7}{2} = 4 \qquad \text{Check:} \qquad 1 + 2 + 3 + 4 + 5 + 6 + 7 = 28$$
$$28 \div 7 = 4$$

Since the velocity changes at a constant rate from 0 to 32, the average speed for the first second interval is

$$\frac{0 + 32t}{2} = 16t$$

If this is the average speed for an interval of t-seconds, then the distance traveled is *rate* $\times$ *time* or

$$(16t)(t) = 16t^2$$

This is certainly not the only way in which the result can be arrived at, but it is one that will work. It also brings into sharp focus the symbolism of the quadratic function: t^2. While this concept has been developed in the arithmetic section, the experiences here serve to reinforce what was done earlier and to prepare for an extensive study of the use of radicals. We have derived the statement $d = 16t^2$ as a description of how the distance fallen by a dropped object varies with the length of time it has been falling. After graphing, prediction is undertaken to find the resulting distance fallen after various time periods. Eventually we arrive at predictions requiring the calculation of the number of seconds of time required for the object to fall any given distance. We turn once more to the solution of a simple quadratic equation:

> How long would it take a ball dropped from the roof of the Yankee Stadium, 192 feet high, to strike the ground?

Although the table pattern and the graphs could be used to find the desired number, we also make use of the formula; hence,

$$d = 16t^2$$
$$\text{If } d = 192,$$
$$192 = 16t^2$$

If we translate the symbols, we are looking for a number that will be multiplied by itself and then multiplied by 16 to give a final product of 192. This is a rather difficult equation to solve through our understanding of the language. Consequently, those who need to will make use of the division axiom to get to:

$$192 = 16t^2$$
$$\frac{192}{16} = \frac{16t^2}{16}$$
$$12 = t^2$$

The student finds that he is encountering a number that is not a perfect square, an irrational number. At this point we make use of the radical sign to indicate what we want without computation: $t = \sqrt{12}$.

It is important to be clear about the meaning of the expression $\sqrt{12}$. The radical sign indicates that we are considering the principal square root of 12, which is the positive root.

> For example, if we are asked what the square root of 16 is, the answer is ± 4. Both roots are necessary, $+4$ and -4. However, if the question reads $\sqrt{16} = $ _____, the answer is 4. The use of the radical sign ($\sqrt{}$) indicates that only the positive root is required.

It may be well to simply estimate the value of $\sqrt{12}$ for the time being, indicating that it is somewhere between 3 (whose square is 9) and 4 (whose square is 16) and somewhat closer to 3. We could say about 3.4, perhaps, and let it go at that. For all the student knows this may be a rare occurrence and most numbers will be easily handled perfect squares.

It is only after repeated introduction of these irrationals that time should be taken to explore them in detail to indicate the significance of what has occurred and to become more involved with radicals, as well as with the various ways of classifying the sets of numbers with which we have been working. This work will be developed in greater detail later. For the moment, the important idea is the introduction of another axiom: If $a = b$ (a, b nonnegative real numbers), $\sqrt{a} = \sqrt{b}$. The reverse process of squaring may now be discussed. After careful discussion of the effects of these last two operations on the signs of the numbers, another axiom may be developed for squaring. It would not be necessary to become involved in an extended study of extraneous roots. On the contrary, it would be best simply to point out the possibilities and hold any extended analysis until such time as a situation is introduced involving such roots.

The students are now solving these limited form quadratic equations involving motion problems. The numbers with radical signs are occurring frequently, and estimations are employed for the irrational numbers as predictions are carried out. Student involvement with the real numbers is under way. A change in celestial body provides a rich fund of simple quadratic equations, offering drill without tedium.

FINDING SQUARE ROOTS

We are now prepared for a closer look at these "radical" numbers. Is there some way to be more exact about their values? How might we calculate $\sqrt{12}$ so that it is accurate to the nearest tenth, for example? While the process may have been developed in an earlier grade, lack of use sometimes results in almost complete forgetting. It may be well to proceed as if this were a new problem, bringing the students along as necessary. Two simple methods are mentioned here since they are based upon the meaning of square root itself. Both involve estimation.

Guess-Average Method

The idea behind this method is to guess what the square root will be and check by dividing the original number by your guess. In order to refine your guess take the average of it and the result of the division. Repeat the process as often as necessary to gain accuracy to any desired place. Here is an example:

Find $\sqrt{12}$ correct to the nearest tenth.
1. Guess: 3.3
2. Divide:

```
                  3.6 3   (rounds off to 3.64)
          3.3)1 2.0,0 0 0
                9 9
                2 1 0
                1 9 8
                  1 2 0
                    9 9
                    2 1 0
```

Carry your work to one place more than is contained in your guess.

3. Compare: guess 3.3, quotient 3.64

If your guess had been exact, what would the quotient be?

Since the quotient here is larger than the guess, what can you say about the guess? We know $\sqrt{12}$ is between 3.3 and 3.64. We halve the difference by finding the mean.

4. Average $3.3 + 3.64 = 6.94$
$$6.94 \div 2 = 3.47$$

5. We repeat the entire process using 3.47 as our new guess.

Divide:

$$3.4\,7.\overline{)1\,2.0\,0.0}\quad\begin{array}{c}3.458\end{array}$$

Compare: $\sqrt{12}$ lies between 3.47 and 3.458

Average: $3.47 + 3.458 = 6.928$
$$6.928 \div 2 = 3.464$$

If we are in need of $\sqrt{12}$ correct to the nearest tenth, the averaging process is really unnecessary. When we compare we can see that to the nearest tenth $\sqrt{12} = 3.5$. Should we require greater accuracy, the process may again be repeated with 3.464 as our new guess.

This method is surprisingly powerful and brings one close to the desired square root rather quickly, despite poor guessing. For example, if a student failed to see that $\sqrt{12}$ was between 3 and 4 and chose, say, 6 as a guess, he would not be in trouble at all:

$$6\overline{)1\,2.0\,0}\quad\begin{array}{c}2.0\end{array}$$

Divide:

Compare: $\sqrt{12}$ lies between 2 and 6

Average: $\quad 2.0 + 6 = 8.0$
$$8.0 \div 2 = 4.0$$

Repeating: $\quad 12 \div 4.0 = 3.00$
$$3.00 + 4.0 = 7.00$$
$$7.00 \div 2 = 3.5$$

Repeating: $12.0 \div 3.5 = 3.43$
$$3.43 + 3.5 = 6.93$$
$$6.93 \div 2 = 3.465$$

Thus, in three divisions we have gone from a guess that was completely out of the area to a number that is correct in the tenths and hundredths places. This is a powerful method indeed.

Guess-Multiply Method

The second method of approximation may even be simpler. Here again we guess the desired root; this time we check our estimate by multiplying it by itself, i.e., square it. If we have guessed correctly, the product will be the number we are finding the square root of. If not, we refine our guess and multiply to check again. Here is an example of this method:

Find $\sqrt{12}$ correct to the nearest tenth.
1. Guess: between 3 and 4, say 3.2.
2. Multiply: $3.2 \times 3.2 = 10.24$
3. Compare: 3.2 is too small, but 4.0 is too large:
$$(3.2)^2 = 10.24; (4.0)^2 = 16.00$$
   Thus, our desired root is between 3.2 and 4.0.
4. Revised guess: 3.5. Repeat the process.
5. Multiply: $3.5 \times 3.5 = 12.25$
6. Compare: 3.5 is also too large. The root now lies between 3.2 and 3.5.
7. New guess: 3.35 (halfway between)
8. Multiply: $3.35 \times 3.35 = 11.2225$
   The root lies between 3.35 and 3.50.

Eventually, by repetition and examination of products, the desired accuracy is achieved.

A side road may be explored briefly here. All through their study of mathematics the students have been carrying out four basic operations: addition, subtraction, multiplication, and division. When the processes of squaring and finding the square root are encountered, this becomes the first time new operations are being introduced. The term *binary operation* can now take on meaning since, in contrast, the new operations are uniary operations. In each of the four basic operations, one number describes the result of performing a given operation with *two* numbers; i.e., when you do addition with 2 and 5, the result is 7. These new operations, however, are carried out on but *one* number. Whatever it is we are going to do, we do it to a single number. We may square 10, we may find the square root of 12. Each time only one number is operated upon. Aside from the earlier work with arithmetic, this is the first time we have undertaken such operations. This is, therefore, an event of some consequence and should be appropriately recognized as such. We have taken a step forward. Of course, we also want to continue to build upon the ideas previously developed. Addition was rapid counting. Multiplication was rapid addition, repeated addition at that. Squaring may be thought of as rapid multiplication, and repeated multiplication too. Newly encountered ideas fit rather nicely into our overall framework.

It is appropriate at this point, if student interest warrants, to extend this discussion about operations into the explorations of the abstraction of operation itself. The introduction of finite arithmetics, for example, could bring into focus arbitrarily defined operations and lend greater meaning to the entire process.

We are now prepared to turn our attention to the numbers containing radical signs.

OPERATIONS WITH RADICALS

After a good deal of experience solving quadratic equations of the form $y = ax^2$ using the motion formula and the situations listed on page 247, we are ready to become more deeply involved with radicals. Any of the previous situations would provide a suitable starting point. Let us make use of the changing area of a projected picture as the projector is moved away from the screen. This is an interesting relationship since it is one that can actually be undertaken in the classroom, with the measurements leading to a collection of data. If it is not quite possible to actually carry out the experiment, the teacher can present scale drawings of what is happening and in this way establish procedures for the students to gather their data. In any case, we have an interesting concrete representation of the mathematical ideas under consideration.

If the students are asked to determine many different distance values given a variety of projection areas (for example, If the projected picture must be 9 square feet, how far must the projector be from the screen?), it would be helpful to invert the x formula first and "change its subject" in order to simplify the work. Thus, the original formula

$$A = \tfrac{1}{9}x^2$$

is inverted through application of the axioms to become

$$x^2 = 9A$$
$$x = \pm\sqrt{9A}$$

After a brief discussion indicating that the negative values will be meaningless in this physical situation, we eliminate these values and reduce the formula to

$$x = \sqrt{9A}$$

Now the student is prepared to introduce many different values for A and determine the corresponding x-values. After completing a few of these we might ask,

> Since 9 is a perfect square, may we take the square root of it and then take the square root of A and multiply the results? Or will this give a different result than carrying out multiplication first?

Symbolically, the question asks, Is $\sqrt{9A} = (\sqrt{9})(\sqrt{A})$? How shall the student answer? It would seem that working the problem both ways will enable us to see if the result has been altered. If the picture area were 25 square feet, the two approaches yield the following:

$$\sqrt{9 \cdot 25} = \sqrt{225} \qquad\qquad \sqrt{9} \cdot \sqrt{25} = 3 \cdot 5$$

Answer: 15   Answer: 15

253

In this instance, the result appears to have been unchanged when we altered the order of events. *But*, will it always work in this manner? Additional cases are worked out and compared, and our tentative result holds up. Can we now say for sure that it is always true that: $\sqrt{a \cdot b} = \sqrt{a}\sqrt{b}$? Not quite. How can we be sure that somewhere, somehow, a number will not turn up that fails to satisfy what we have found to be true? Can we try all the possible numbers? Then can we ever be sure? We invite the student to take his first glimpse of the power of deductive proof.

There are not many instances in this world of ours when we can say things with absolute assurance that they are so, but in mathematics we have this power! Through the use of what we call *proof*, we will try to show that a given condition will always hold. Let us be fully aware of what is taking place here. We began by observing individual events. These events led us to a conjecture that was verified again and again by individual observations. At this point—prior to our attempt at proof—we are virtually convinced that what we have found will always hold. We will now attempt a deductive demonstration to confirm our conjecture and dispel all doubts. The important misconception about deductive proof is the notion that such a demonstration will enable us to uncover something that we did not previously know or suspect. This is misleading. While it may occasionally happen that a proof provides us with a surprising result, by and large, deductive techniques add to our information by verifying and legitimizing that which we already have accepted to be so. As a matter of fact, if we were not convinced ourselves that a particular relationship was true, we would probably not undertake the deductive demonstration in the first place! Thus, intuition becomes the creator of ideas while deduction serves to verify that which has already been found. In this situation concerning radicals we have a good opportunity to introduce the student to his first deductive "proof." There is a real need for the proof at this point since we cannot possibly try all the numbers in order to see if they will work as expected. We proceed here in an informal manner.

Does $\sqrt{ab} = \sqrt{a}\sqrt{b}$ $(a \geq 0, b \geq 0)$?

1. Let $\sqrt{a} = x$; then $a = x^2$
2. Let $\sqrt{b} = y$; then $b = y^2$

$$x^2 y^2 = ab \qquad \text{multiplication axiom}$$
$$(xy)^2 = ab$$
$$xy = \sqrt{ab} \qquad \text{by square root axiom}$$

But from steps 1 and 2 $xy = \sqrt{a}\sqrt{b}$.

$$\therefore \ \sqrt{a}\sqrt{b} = \sqrt{ab}$$

We may now proceed in confidence to use $\sqrt{a}\sqrt{b} = \sqrt{ab}$ any time it is to our advantage to do so, since our proof has indicated that this relationship will hold. Of course, what we have proven will be most valuable in finding the square root of numbers that are not perfect squares and yet contain factors that are perfect squares. We have laid the groundwork for the simplification of radicals, ($\sqrt{50} = \sqrt{25}\sqrt{2}$). Once again it is the pattern of the development that is important. The relationship under consideration generated the problem that gave rise to the radicals. We became interested in a possible simplification of the expression encountered and so turned to a proof *after* many individual cases were explored so as to add to our conviction that the relationship was indeed valid. Our work may therefore be extended to include the simplification of radicals with fractions in much the same manner.

One way of introducing such a problem is to investigate the horizon-distance relation. How far can you see if the land is flat before you? If you were at the beach on either coast of our country, how far would you be able to see? An application of the Pythagorean theorem and some approximation provides us with an interesting relationship (Fig. 13-2). Since light rays travel in a straight line, if you were to stand at point A, you would be able to see to the horizon—a tangent line (d) from eye level to the curve of the earth. But how long is line d? If we use the Pythagorean theorem, since the radius of the earth forms a right angle with line d at point B, we find that

$$d^2 + r^2 = (r + h)^2$$

Solving for d,

$$d^2 = (r + h)^2 - r^2$$
$$d^2 = r^2 + 2hr + h^2 - r^2$$
$$d^2 = 2hr + h^2$$

By the distributive law,

$$d^2 = h(2r + h)$$

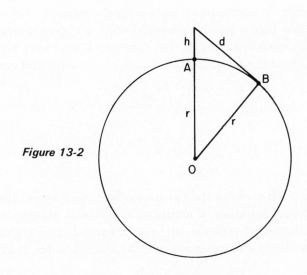

Figure 13-2

The Quadratic Function

If your eyes were 5 feet above the earth, then $h = 5$ feet, or to be correct, since the radius of the earth is in miles, $h = .00094+$ miles. Since h is so small in comparison with r, the value of $(2r + h)$ is extremely close to $2r$; so we may say that a good approximation of the distance you can see to the horizon is offered by $d^2 = 2rh$. If we now take this formula and express the radius of the earth as 4000 miles and change the height into units of feet, we can get a simple formula that will enable us to arrive at quick approximations:

$$d^2 = 2rh$$

$$d^2 = (2)(4000)\,\frac{h}{5280} = \frac{8000}{5280}\,h$$

or

$$d^2 = \frac{100}{66}\,h$$

which we can approximate to

$$d^2 = \frac{3}{2}\,h$$

and finally

$$d = \sqrt{\frac{3}{2}\,(h)}$$

We have finally arrived at a fairly close approximation of how to find the distance (in miles) to the horizon when we know the height (in feet) above the surface of the earth:

$$d = \sqrt{\frac{3}{2}\,h}$$

This development is primarily for the teacher's understanding and is not necessarily intended for students. However, it may well be that some classes of students would be interested in such a development.

The formula that is finally conceived offers an opportunity to introduce many problems involving radicals. For example, if your eyes are 5 feet above the earth, how far can you see? Since $d = \sqrt{\frac{3}{2}h}$, we solve and get

$$d = \sqrt{\frac{3}{2}\,(5)}$$

$$d = \sqrt{\frac{15}{2}} = \sqrt{7.5}$$

$$d = 2.7$$

If your eyes are 5 feet above the earth's surface, you can see about 2.7 miles.

With a proper selection of numbers, a discussion similar to that carried out for multiplication of radicals can now be carried out for division. In each case the relationships are important and the simplification makes good sense.

256

If we are to concern ourselves with distances to the horizon from much larger heights, then we may return to a formula found earlier to add to our accuracy. For example, how far would an astronaut be able to see to the horizon if he were 25 miles high? It may be better in this instance to use

$$d^2 = 2rh + h^2$$

or

$$d = \sqrt{2rh + h^2}$$

Not only is the accuracy of the result improved (and a larger h may require such a revision) but we now have before us the problem of finding the square root of a sum. Just as we did earlier with multiplication and division, we could now explore the question, Is $\sqrt{a + b} = \sqrt{a} + \sqrt{b}$? Thus, we reinforce the importance of the earlier processes since in this instance we must take the sum first or else our work will be incorrect. For example, is $\sqrt{9 + 16} = \sqrt{9} + \sqrt{16}$?

$$\sqrt{9 + 16} = \sqrt{25} = 5$$
$$\sqrt{9} = 3, \sqrt{16} = 4, 3 + 4 = 7$$

At this point the investigation might be extended to include subtraction, after which it would be timely to present the students with a series of examples involving operations with numbers in radical form, emphasizing the process of simplification. Additional practice situations may be presented by inverting any of the quadratic relations mentioned earlier.

RADICAL EQUATIONS

The area of a picture projection may well serve as the basis for an introduction to the study of radical equations.

$$A = \tfrac{1}{9}x^2$$
$$x = \pm\sqrt{9A} = \pm 3\sqrt{a}$$
$$x = 3\sqrt{a} \text{ (only the positive value has meaning here)}$$

As we focus upon these functions involving radicals and consider the solutions of radical equations, we also examine the graphs and compare them with the graph of the changed-subject formula. The situation of projection area-distance is a good place to start since it is familiar. We consider the question, How far shall the projector be from the screen if it is to fill an area of 16 square feet? We then move on to consider questions such as, If I must place the projector 15 feet away, what will the area of the projection be? Of course, if necessary, it would be helpful to actually use a projector here. The

257

fact that a good deal of mathematics has already been learned is no license to ignore the concreteness of ideas. At this point, the need for such experiences may be somewhat lessened, but still necessary.

Questions asking for the distance are easily answered:

$$x = 3\sqrt{a}$$

If $a = 16$,

$$x = 3\sqrt{16}$$
$$x = 3 \times 4$$
$$x = 12$$

Place the projector 12 feet away.

Questions calling for the student to find the area hold more interest:

$$x = 3\sqrt{a}$$

If $x = 15$,

$$15 = 3\sqrt{a}$$
$$5 = \sqrt{a}$$

From all of the work done previously with quadratic equations it would seem natural to expect to reverse the processes developed there: Instead of taking the square root, square both sides. Is this an acceptable axiom? Several arithmetic examples can result in the feeling that it is indeed a possible axiom for equation solution. Of course, the students may well solve this simple radical equation through their understanding of the language of algebra:

$$5 = \sqrt{a}$$

5 is the square root of what number?

$$a = 25$$

In any case, when a root has been found, it must be tested to determine whether or not it is indeed a root of the original equation:

$$15 = 3\sqrt{a}$$
$$15 = 3\sqrt{25}$$
$$15 = 3 \times 5$$
$$15 = 15$$

This checking process becomes extremely important in working with radical equations, for some interesting things happen when we raise expressions to a given power. We have already seen how a linear (first degree) equation has one root, and a quadratic or second degree equation has two roots. If our original equation were linear and if we were to square both sides, the result will usually be a quadratic equation. Hence, we will not have equivalent equations, since one has a single root and the other has two. Evidently this squaring process (or cubing, or raising to any other power) may result in the introduction of additional roots. These are the *extraneous roots*. Perhaps the best way to introduce such roots to the students is to provide them with a situation in which they suddenly find that a correctly calculated root simply does not satisfy the original equation. The effect should be startling, to say the least. But first we may emphasize the importance of checking each root. The more exact formula relating the height and distance seen to the horizon offers such an opportunity: $d = \sqrt{2rh + h^2}$.

How high above the surface of the earth would you have to go to be able to see from New York to California, a distance of about 3000 miles?

If we use 4000 miles as the radius of the earth, we find we must solve the equation:

$$3000 = \sqrt{8000h + h^2}$$

We proceed to square both sides:

$$9,000,000 = 8000h + h^2$$

$$h^2 + 8000h - 9,000,000 = 0$$

The roots are:
$$h = -9000$$
$$h = 1000$$

Checking each of these roots leads to a surprise:

If
$$h = -9000$$
$$3000 = \sqrt{8000 \cdot (-9000) + (-9000)^2}$$
$$3000 = \sqrt{-72,000,000 + 81,000,000}$$
$$3000 = 3000; \text{ it checks.}$$

And if
$$h = 1000$$
$$3000 = \sqrt{(8000)(1000) + (1000)^2}$$
$$3000 = \sqrt{8,000,000 + 1,000,000}$$
$$3000 = \sqrt{9,000,000}$$
$$3000 = 3000; \text{ it checks.}$$

The answer to our problem would seem to be that you would have to rise to a position 1000 miles above the surface of the planet to be able to see the required 3000 miles. But what of the other root, -9000? It is a good root of the equation. Does it have any meaning in the physical situation? Despite an initial inclination to say that it is meaningless, it also fits the situation. For if we seek the point 9000 miles *below* the surface of the earth, since the radius is 4000 miles, we will again end up in a position 1000 miles above the surface! (Fig. 13-3). Thus, each root may have pertinence to the physical counterpart. We cannot simply jump to the conclusion that all negative roots are to be cast aside. We must examine each resulting root in the light of the situation.

259

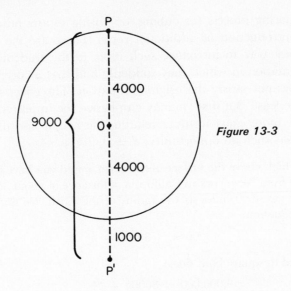

Figure 13-3

As for roots that do not check in the original equation, we simply present an equation and ask for the solution. An abstract equation is acceptable here since there has already been extended experience with the ideas. Such an equation may even appear as one of a list for practice. Student reaction should be interesting, to say the least.

Solve: $\qquad x - 1 = \sqrt{x + 5}$

Squaring $\qquad (x - 1)^2 = x + 5$

$$x^2 - 2x + 1 = x + 5$$

$$x^2 - 3x - 4 = 0$$

$$(x - 4)(x + 1) = 0$$

we get $\qquad x = 4$

and $\qquad x = -1$

We have found two roots, 4 and -1. We now proceed to check these roots:

If $\qquad x = 4$

$$x - 1 = \sqrt{x + 5}$$

$$4 - 1 = \sqrt{4 + 5}$$

$\qquad 3 = 3$; this root checks.

If $\qquad x = -1$

$$x - 1 = \sqrt{x + 5}$$

$$-1 - 1 = \sqrt{-1 + 5}$$

$\qquad -2 = 2$; this root does *not* check.

260

We have found two roots, only one of which will satisfy the original equation. This may be shocking to some students and they will probably search for possible errors in calculation. It is well to allow them to wonder about this for a time. The squaring process, however, has introduced a root that simply does not "work." We have thus presented material that serves to emphasize the importance of checking roots in both the mathematical and physical environment: *Not all roots satisfy the original equation. All roots may have physical meaning.*

HARDER QUADRATIC FUNCTIONS: FACTORING

If we were to investigate the height above ground of objects dropped from a balloon, airplane, or building top, we would encounter a more complicated quadratic function. For example, if a balloon 300 feet high dropped flares, how high above ground would they be at each second of their drop to the earth? Earlier we saw that all dropped objects under certain conditions

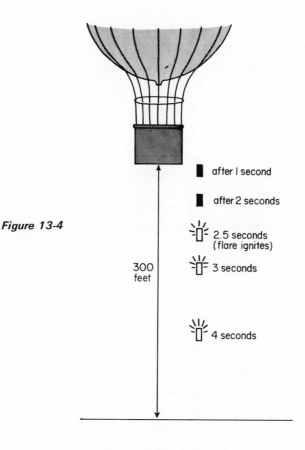

Figure 13-4

300 feet

■ after 1 second

■ after 2 seconds

2.5 seconds (flare ignites)

3 seconds

4 seconds

The Quadratic Function

fall in accordance with the formula $d = 16t^2$. This would tell us how far the object fell in a given time. If we subtract this from the 300 feet of height of the balloon, we can arrive at the height at any instant (Fig. 13-4). Consequently, the formula $d = 300 - 16t^2$ would seem to yield the function we seek. If tables are made and graphs drawn, we have a good view of what is happening. The introduction of prediction problems (perhaps a fuse is set to ignite the flare at a specified height) requires the solution of more difficult quadratic equations:

> We would like the flare to ignite at a height of 200 feet. How many seconds should elapse before the flare ignites?

$$d = 300 - 16t^2$$

$$200 = 300 - 16t^2$$

It is possible to solve this equation and find its roots in the same manner as before. This would require using the axioms to eventually arrive at:

$$\frac{100}{16} = t^2$$

$$t = \frac{10}{4} \quad \text{or} \quad 2\tfrac{1}{2} \text{ seconds}$$

Would it be possible to solve this equation without invoking the equality axioms as we did previously? At this point we introduce as a possible alternative the process of factoring known as *factoring the difference between two squares:*
We first make one side zero. (The reason for this will be clear shortly.)

$$0 = 100 - 16t^2$$

Look at the right side. Both terms are special kinds of numbers: They are perfect squares. Since the left side is zero this may help. If we must find factors that yield a zero product, we know something about these factors; that is, we know that one or both must be zero. How else can we arrive at a zero product? Is this true of all numbers? If two numbers have a product of 6, must one of the numbers be 6? This is a special property of those factors whose

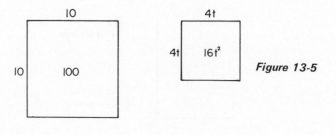

Figure 13-5

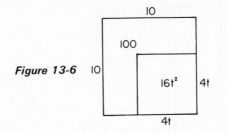

Figure 13-6

product is zero. But can we find the factors of $100 - 16t^2$? If we recall our work with polynomials, we remember that we represented products as areas of rectangles and squares. Since both $16t^2$ and 100 are perfect squares, let us show these as areas (Fig. 13-5). What is the length of each side? The statement $100 - 16t^2$ actually calls for the difference in area between these two squares. Place the smaller square inside the larger and see what is involved (Fig. 13-6).

The total area we are interested in is the difference between the areas of the two squares. If we remove the area of the smaller square altogether ($16t^2$), we are left with the area indicated in Figure 13-7. This area is $100 - 16t^2$. Can we rearrange this area to form a rectangle? If we can, the length and width of that rectangle will give us the factors we seek. We proceed in the following manner: We cut off the shaded piece and place it below the remaining rectangle. In this way we have not changed the total amount of area ($100 - 16t^2$), but we have changed the shape to one that is rectangular. (Notice how the side $10 - 4t$ is placed along a side of equal length [Fig. 13-8].) The area is known; therefore the length and width of this newly formed rectangle must provide us with the factors whose product is this area. Reading from the diagram we find that $(10 - 4t)(10 + 4t) = 100 - 16t^2$. In effect, then, we have factored the difference of two squares. We now return to the original problem, $0 = 100 - 16t^2$. We substitute the factors and

$$0 = (10 - 4t)(10 + 4t)$$

How does this help? Now we can make use of the special property of factors

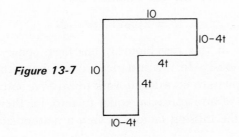

Figure 13-7

263

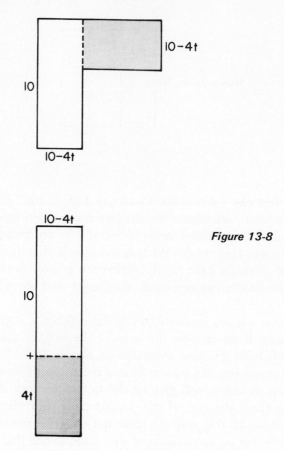

Figure 13-8

with a zero product. We know that at least one of the two factors above *must be zero!* Let us assume that the first factor is zero:

$$10 - 4t = 0$$

What is the value of t? If $t = 2\frac{1}{2}$, then $10 - 4t = 0$. We have found a possible solution. What happens if the other factor is zero?

$$10 + 4t = 0$$

What is the value of t? If $t = -2\frac{1}{2}$, then $10 + 4t = 0$, a second solution. The two roots of the original equation are

$$t = 2\frac{1}{2} \text{ and } t = -2\frac{1}{2}$$

The emphasis in this development has been somewhat different from that discussed previously. In this instance we are fixing things to happen the way that we want them to in order to work toward an outcome that we desire. (We set the factors of an expression equal to zero, for then we may be better able to determine the missing factors.) Often a mathematician manufactures a particular expression to help him get where he wants to go. In effect, he is working backward from his desired end to the original problem, but this is perfectly acceptable as long as the problems worked on are equivalent to the original one. Trial and error is a frequent and respectable partner in such a process.

Once a single quadratic expression has been factored, others are also, using the diagrams of squares and rearranging partial areas without altering the total area. After doing many such problems, the students may be directed to attempt to find the factors without the diagrams. Perhaps an examination of those already done correctly will generate relationships that will lead students to the desired factors, without the necessity of drawing and manipulating squares. The work with squares could, incidentally, be carried out by actually cutting pieces of cardboard. The teacher will decide if the needs of the students warrant such experiences. It is most important for teachers to maintain flexibility as to the exact moment for each student to discard the use of squares (drawings or pieces of cardboard). All children cannot be expected to see relationships at the same time. If we are attempting to help students to "discover" as many concepts as possible, we are also assuming that each student will have the opportunity to do so, which in turn implies differing lengths of time to reach certain guideposts in a given course. These problems and proposed solutions will be discussed in detail in the chapter devoted to individualization of instruction. Suffice it to say here that all students do not discover at the same instant, if at all. Permit students to use the squares as long as they feel the need. Encourage the discontinuance of such use. Later the squares can be used for checking or for testing ideas you may get. But eventually a point will be reached when all children need to proceed without any representation.

THE COMPLETE QUADRATIC

We have used the distributive law, which is sometimes referred to as finding a common monomial factor. We have seen how the difference between two squares can be factored. We turn now to the factoring of a trinomial and introduce functions in the complete quadratic form of $ax^2 + bx + c = 0$, as well as the solution of the derivative equations.

We may continue the work with motion problems at this point, or if a change is desired we may select other relationships. Here are some possible situations that may be introduced to involve students with the general quadratic and to establish the need for additional factoring techniques:

An object thrown down with an initial velocity
of 32 ft./sec.: $\qquad d = 16t^2 + 32t$

Possible areas of a rectangular plot enclosed by
100 feet of fencing: $\qquad A = 50x - x^2$

Surface area of a box 1 foot high with a square
base of side x :

$$S = 4x + x^2$$

A variety of motion problems involving the computation of maximum heights are also available.

An object thrown upward with initial velocity
of 96 ft./sec.:

$$h = 96t - 16t^2$$

If we select one of these situations to focus upon, the process may be clarified.

An open box with a square base must contain a total of 5 square feet. If the box is 1 foot high, what must be its dimensions?

Substitution in the formula yields:

$$S = 4x + x^2$$
$$\text{If } S = 5,$$
$$5 = 4x + x^2$$

If we proceed as before and use the equality axioms to reduce one side to zero, we arrive at

$$x^2 + 4x - 5 = 0$$

Once again, if we can find factors that give a product of $x^2 + 4x - 5$, we can work toward the solution on the same basis that we did earlier; one of the factors (or both) must be zero. But we cannot proceed for we no longer have before us the difference between two squares. We have a trinomial. The student is in need of help, since he cannot continue. We teach to satisfy this need and turn to factoring a trinomial.

Earlier, we saw that when we multiplied two binomials together we frequently ended up with a product that was a trinomial. As a matter of fact the only exception was the case of the difference between two squares. Therefore, we might expect that the factors we seek will be two binomial factors. Perhaps we can use the same devices that were used to carry out the multiplication of binomials and simply reverse the process; that is, if we think of $x^2 + 4x - 5$ as a product and represent it as the area of a rectangle and if we can find such a rectangle, its length and width should provide us with our missing factors. Let us try.

The best development here would be one that enables the students to manipulate something physical, and the procedures here do permit just that. The pieces shown may easily be cut from heavy cardboard or even wood, but enough pieces should be provided for the students to work in small groups at their seats, if not individually. Of course diagrams will have to suffice if the construction of the pieces becomes troublesome. At any rate, we move

x^2 may be shown as the area of a square with side x.

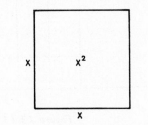

$4x$ is made up of four rectangles, I by x.

Figure 13-9

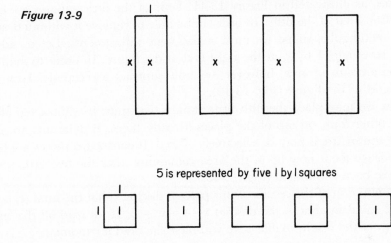

5 is represented by five I by I squares

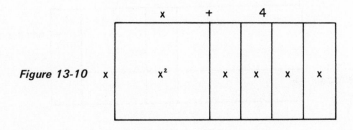

on by representing each term of the trinomial by an area using pieces of cardboard or diagrams (Fig. 13-9). In this way $x^2 + 4x - 5$ is represented by adding the first two terms and subtracting the third. The sum of the first two terms is easy enough to show (Fig. 13-10). We simply place the pieces alongside each other to form a single figure. But how shall we subtract the last term? Since this term is represented by the five 1 inch by 1 inch squares,

Figure 13-10

267

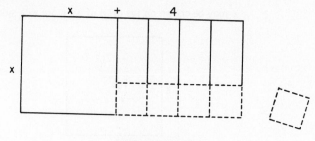

Figure 13-11

we take these pieces and place them on top of the figure formed by the first two terms, as illustrated in Figure 13-11. Four of the little squares are easily placed. But what of the fifth? In order to be able to remove it without destroying the rectangular shape we must make some adjustments. Let us add on another rectangle, 1 by x, at the right end of the figure. In order to maintain the same amount of area, however, we now subtract a rectangle, 1 by x, at the left end of the figure (Fig. 13-12).

Now we may place the fifth little square that must be subtracted alongside the other four, on top of the pieces already there. If diagrams are used, the little square areas may be effectively erased. If cardboard pieces are being employed, we focus now upon the area remaining after the five little square areas have been eliminated (Fig. 13-13).

Examination of the results of this process discloses that the final rectangle is indeed equal in area to the desired $x^2 + 4x - 5$. If we read off the length and width of the result, in effect we will have factored a trinomial:

$$x^2 + 4x - 5 = (x + 5)(x - 1)$$

Now we may return to the problem that initiated the investigation in the first place—the problem requiring that the base of a box be determined. Follow the pattern developed earlier with the factoring of the difference of two squares:

$$(x + 5)(x - 1) = 0$$

If the first factor $(x + 5)$ is to be zero, then $x = -5$; if the second factor

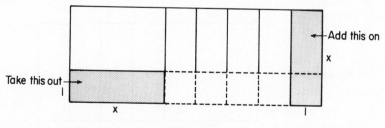

Figure 13-12

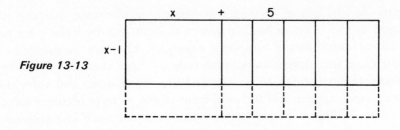

Figure 13-13

$(x - 1)$ is to be zero, then $x = 1$. In this case the negative root is meaningless; hence, the base is a square, 1 foot on a side.

If we were to change the surface area of the box in question, we would find it necessary to factor still another trinomial. The same method of using representative materials may be employed in order to complete the factoring. After several examples we focus exclusively upon this process of finding factors and turn our attention to abstract collections of trinomials. A good starting point involves addition signs only. The rectangular cardboard pieces or diagrams will enable students to find the factors. Two examples are completed in Figure 13-14.

These are but two of a wide variety of examples that may be done by

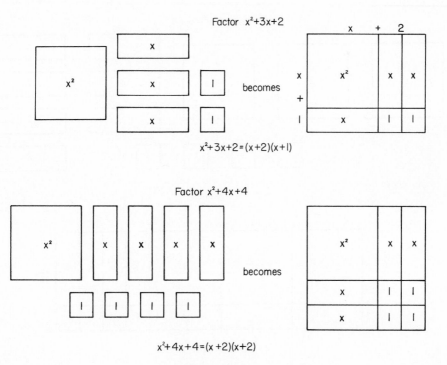

Figure 13-14

269

students. As the pieces or diagrams become burdensome, students are encouraged to seek ways of finding factors without aids by looking for patterns in neatly arranged lists of completed examples. They are encouraged to guess and then use the representative materials to check themselves. As the work progresses the trinomials to be factored are made more and more difficult. Negative signs appear and the coefficient of the x^2 term becomes some value other than 1. Figure 13-15 demonstrates how one such example might be completed using the materials.

The use of these aids not only encourages the students to build their own methods but also provides evidence for the unique factorization theorem. No matter how the pieces may be arranged (there are many alternative arrangements), the factors are always the same. For example, in finding the factors of $x^2 + 3x + 2$, the pieces might have been arranged as indicated in Figure 13-16. While the arrangement may vary, the resulting factors do not. In this interesting, intuitive fashion we begin to build an understanding of an important theorem.

We have been finding factors by making use of visual or manipulative materials. It is quite possible at this stage to put the algebra itself to work for us and make use of a brief algebraic analysis. Let us reexamine our initial equation, $x^2 + 4x - 5 = 0$.

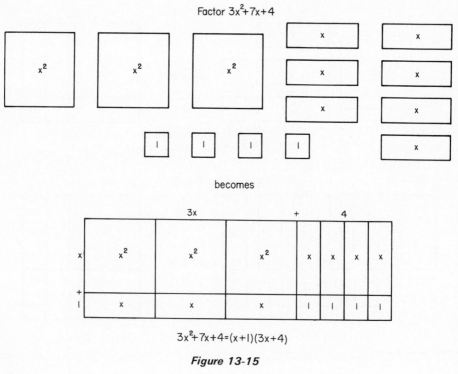

Factor $3x^2 + 7x + 4$

becomes

$3x^2 + 7x + 4 = (x+1)(3x+4)$

Figure 13-15

x^2+3x+2 may be arranged as follows:

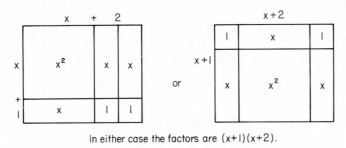

In either case the factors are $(x+1)(x+2)$.

Figure 13-16

How shall we express the polynomial $(x^2 + 4x - 5)$ as the product of two binomials? In other words, we would like to find two factors of form $(x + a)(x + b)$, where a, b are integers. How shall we proceed? Perhaps we may learn more about the missing numbers a and b if we carry out the indicated multiplication. (We may also employ the distributive law.)

$$(x + a)(x + b) = x^2 + ax + bx + ab$$

Factoring yields:

$$x^2 + (a + b)x + ab$$

If this expression is compared with the original trinomial,

$$x^2 + 4x - 5 \quad \text{and} \quad x^2 + (a + b)x + ab$$

we see that $(a + b)$ must yield 4, while ab must total -5. Thus, we have learned a good deal about our missing numbers, a and b. We now know their sum and their product. Trial and error, or any other method, may now be employed:

For a sum of 4, we might use $(2, 2)$, $(3, 1)$, $(4, 0)$, $(5, -1)$, or a whole host of possibilities. For a product of -5, we might use $(5, -1)$ or $(-5, 1)$. The desired pair of numbers is a single pair satisfying both conditions. Checking the two conditions we see that one pair is common to both: 5 and -1. We let $a = 5$ and $b = -1$, and the factors are:

$$(x + 5)(x - 1)$$

If we multiply out as a check, we find that the factors do indeed "work." We then proceed as before. If the a and b values were reversed, the conditions would be satisfied. Would we have the correct factors? The students might try this and discuss their findings.

This method has much to recommend it. It is one of the first times that we are letting the symbols and the techniques do the work for us. In addition,

271

after doing a number of examples in this manner, it soon becomes apparent that we have hit upon a general approach for factoring trinomials with an x^2 term with a coefficient of 1. Thus, it may well be that such an approach leads to more rapid discovery of patterns for dealing with all factorable trinomials. It is also possible to use the rectangular pieces and diagrams to help students use the approach.

COMPLETING THE SQUARES

But all trinomials are not factorable, and we present a problem to the students that will involve them with just such a trinomial:

A ball is thrown straight downward with a velocity of 96 ft./sec. from the top of a cliff. How long will it take to fall 48 feet?

Here the student will use the motion relationships mentioned earlier:

$$d = 16t^2 + 96t$$
$$48 = 16t^2 + 96t$$
$$16t^2 + 96t - 48 = 0$$

We may simplify by using the division axiom with 16:

$$t^2 + 6t - 3 = 0$$

It soon becomes evident to the student that all his methods of attack fail with this equation. He might want to explore the function described by $h = t^2 + 6t - 3$ (or $d = 16t^2 + 96t$) and attempt graphically to locate the t-value corresponding to the desired h-value. This is a valid approach, although lengthy and inaccurate. Such students should be commended for excellent thinking and ingenuity. Most students will require help and we offer this help in the form of completing the squares. What better way to introduce this idea than to do exactly what the name suggests, actually complete given squares. With the work already carried out using squared material, this development follows easily. A brief outline is presented here.

The solutions of the first quadratic equations met were accomplished by simply taking the square root of both sides of the equation:

$$x^2 = 49 \qquad\qquad x^2 = 30$$
$$x = \pm 7 \qquad\qquad x = \pm \sqrt{30}$$

If we could somehow employ this method with the complete quadratic, we could work to a solution rather handily. This approach seems to be helpful when the left-hand side is a perfect square. We quickly find an equivalent equation providing the desired x-values. Can we, then, make a perfect square of the left-hand side? In effect, can we alter the left side so that it becomes

272

a trinomial that has two equal factors? Let us see. The equation to be solved is

$$t^2 + 6t - 3 = 0$$

To aid our analysis, eliminate the negative 3 from the left-hand side and concentrate on the t-terms. We now make use of the geometric shapes to gain insight. First, use representative materials to show $t^2 + 6t$. Then try to form a square, so that the length and width would give us the desired equal factors (Fig. 13-17). In order to complete the square it is necessary to add to our areas as shown in Figure 13-18. We need to add nine square units in order to complete the formation of the desired square. Thus, the equation becomes

$$t^2 + 6t + 9 = 3 + 9$$

To maintain the equality, nine units must also be added to the right side. We now must solve the equation

$$t^2 + 6t + 9 = 12$$

or

$$(t + 3)^2 = 12$$

We may proceed as we did with simpler equations: Take the square root of both sides and simplify

$$t + 3 = \sqrt{12} \qquad\qquad t + 3 = -\sqrt{12}$$

In this manner we find the desired roots. Of course, we proceed to do large

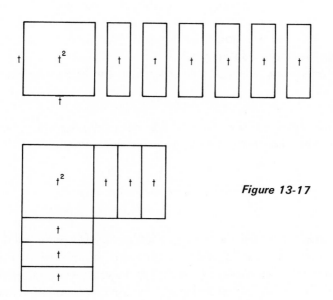

Figure 13-17

273

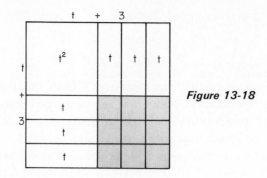

Figure 13-18

numbers of problems that involve these same ideas and then encourage the students to look for methods that will enable them to eliminate the use of drawings and cardboard pieces representing geometric figures. Their conjectures about methods of completing the squares may be applied to collections of quadratic equations and verified by use of the geometric figures. The student is finding his way with the new processes at the same time that he is reinforcing previous learnings. Work with radicals is heavily involved in these situations.

A WORD ABOUT GRAPHING

Once students have learned how to complete the squares with quadratic expressions, they have a short cut to the drawing of graphs. The effect is similar to that achieved through the use of the slope-intercept form of the linear function when drawing linear graphs. This method was recommended by the Commission on Mathematics.[1]

If we reexamine a graph made earlier, the difference becomes clear:

$$x^2 + 4x - 5 = y$$

We begin by arranging the terms to facilitate the process of completing the squares, and then we carry out the necessary adjustments:

$$x^2 + 4x - 5 = y$$
$$x^2 + 4x + 4 - 5 - 4 = y$$
$$(x + 2)^2 - 9 = y$$

This final form, $(x + 2)^2 - 9 = y$, enables us to learn a good deal about the graph: Since the first expression is squared, by inserting values for x we can make the entire expression $(x + 2)^2$ as large as we wish. How small can we make it? No matter what value of x is used, we cannot make the value

274

less than zero. Hence this graph will have a minimum point and will open upward. What value of x will result in a zero value for the entire squared expression? Evidently $x = -2$ will reduce the expression inside the parentheses to zero and will result in the minimum value. In one quick stroke we have found the equation of the axis of symmetry, as well as the abscissa of the turning point. How can we locate the y-value of the turning point? This value fairly jumps out at us: -9. In short order we know the general shape of the curve (opens upward), its axis of symmetry ($x = -2$), and its turning point ($-2, -9$). If we now select any convenient value for x or y, we find not only one additional point but two, because of the symmetry of the parabola, and we may sketch the curve (Fig. 13-19).

We have made a quick sketch of the desired curve. We may now also find the roots of the equation $y = x^2 + 4x - 5$ for any value of y simply by locating the x-values corresponding to the y-value in question. In the case of the equation $x^2 + 4x - 5 = +7$, we draw the graph of $y = 7$ (a straight line parallel to the x-axis, seven units above it) and mark the intersections of this line with the curve (Fig. 13-20). The same process could be carried out for any other values of y. Frequently it is the zeros in which we have our interest: $y = 0$. In this case we simply observe the intersections with the x-axis. Perhaps this kind of development eliminates some of the mystery frequently present in the minds of students as they solve quadratic equations by graphing techniques. In addition, the sudden appearance of y in the equation is most confusing. How often have you heard students cry in dismay, "Where'd the y come from?" when they attempted to solve equations like $x^2 + 4x - 5 = 0$ by graphing? Where *does* the y come from? Using the ideas just presented, perhaps it will be somewhat more reasonable to students to

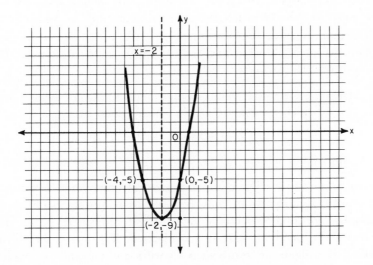

Figure 13-19

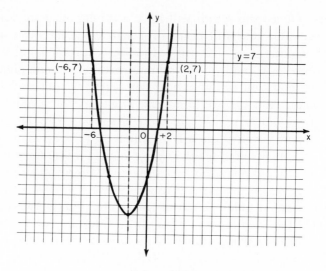

Figure 13-20

find that we graph the function $x^2 + 4x - 5 = y$ and then seek out the particular y-values in which we have some interest.

THE QUADRATIC FORMULA

When we attempt to use the method of completing the squares to solve quadratic equations, we find that our work becomes rather tedious and labored when coefficients other than 1 appear in the x^2-term and when fractional coefficients appear in any of the terms. All of our standard methods, including graphing, become lengthy and tiresome and, in addition, leave us open to calculation errors. Perhaps more powerful methods can be developed. Once again, we create a need and then teach to satisfy that need. One way to begin is to use this problem:

When ice is removed from a storage house in town it begins to melt. The rate at which it melts (in lbs./hr.) is described by

$$R = 40 - 4h + .1h^2$$

How long would it take for the melting rate to become 10 lbs./hr.?

Attempting to use the earlier methods proves extremely cumbersome, granted that the multiplication axiom may be used to eliminate decimal fractions. The quadratic formula provides a more direct approach, although it may not eliminate the need for careful calculations. To derive the formula, we again allow the algebraic symbolism to work for us, and we make use of completing the squares to solve the complete quadratic equation $ax^2 + bx$

$+ c = 0$. Some light may be shed on this process for students if an examination is made of carrying out this notion with linear equations. The general linear equation would be of form $ax + b = 0$. Since we wish to solve for x,

$$ax + b = 0$$
$$ax = -b$$
$$x = \frac{-b}{a}$$

We have solved the equation and can determine x for any given a and b values. In other words, we are expressing the x-values as a function of the coefficients of the equation. For example, solve

$$\frac{3x}{4} + 5 = 8$$

Changing the form and multiplying by 4 we get

$$3x - 12 = 0$$

We now apply the formula using $a = 3$ and $b = -12$

$$x = \frac{-b}{a}$$

$$x = \frac{-(-12)}{3} = 4$$

If we compare this solution with that arrived at by the usual means, we find that it is indeed the same:

$$\frac{3x}{4} + 5 = 8$$
$$3x + 20 = 32$$
$$3x = 12$$
$$x = 4$$

We have, in effect, found a "linear formula." Of course, such a formula adds little to our ability to solve linear equations. The only reason for its discussion here is to help shed light upon the process of finding a quadratic formula, which will indeed add to our ability to solve equations. The development of this formula is a familiar one. It is based upon completing the squares.

We begin with

$$ax^2 + bx + c = 0; a \neq 0$$

Using the division axiom, we get

$$x^2 + \frac{b}{a}x + \frac{c}{a} = 0 \quad \text{or} \quad x^2 + \frac{b}{a}x = -\frac{c}{a}$$

The Quadratic Function

Complete the squares:

$$\text{half of } \frac{b}{a} \text{ is } \frac{b}{2a}$$

Squaring this gives

$$\frac{b^2}{4a^2}$$

Adding this to both sides, we get

$$x^2 + \frac{b}{a}x + \frac{b^2}{4a^2} = -\frac{c}{a} + \frac{b^2}{4a^2}$$

$$\left(x + \frac{b}{2a}\right)^2 = \frac{b^2 - 4ac}{4a^2}$$

Using the square root axiom gives

$$x + \frac{b}{2a} = \pm \sqrt{\frac{b^2 - 4ac}{4a^2}}$$

$$x = \frac{-b}{2a} \pm \sqrt{\frac{b^2 - 4ac}{4a^2}}$$

$$x = \frac{-b \pm \sqrt{b^2 - 4ac}}{2a}$$

We have expressed the roots of the quadratic equation in terms of the coefficients a, b, and c. A host of quadratic equations may now be solved and these are presented to students. First we consider those involving familiar situations. Later, the abstract equations alone are considered. The repetition necessary to fix learning is achieved initially through the introduction of a variety of applications. The following is a list of applications that may be used.

Automobile Functions

A car hitting a pole at r m.p.h. is equivalent to one falling h feet:

$$h = .0336r^2$$

The stopping distance, d, of a car moving r m.p.h.:

$$d = .055r^2 + 1.1r$$

The horsepower, H, generated by an auto engine at n r.p.m.:

$$H = 15 - \frac{(n - 2000)^2}{150,000}$$

The spacing of autos (S) in feet on a busy road with average speed v ft./sec.:

$$S = 18 + v + \frac{v^2}{32}$$

278

Miscellaneous Functions

The stopping distance (d) of a train t seconds after braking:

$$d = 44t - 4t^2$$

The volume of a particular tree (v) in terms of its diameter (x):

$$v = 3.1x^2$$

The cost ($\$y$) of producing x tons of metal in a particular factory:

$$y = 20 + 60x - .075x^2$$

Functions Involving Geometry

The rectangle considered most pleasing to the eye has length l and width w:

$$w^2 + wl - l^2 = 0$$

The number of diagonals (d) in a polygon of n sides:

$$d = \frac{n^2 - 3n}{2}$$

The total number of intersections (x) possible with n straight lines:

$$x = \frac{n(n - 1)}{2}$$

The greatest number of regions (R) created by the intersection of n straight lines:

$$R = \frac{n^2 + n + 2}{2}$$

The radius of a circular arch (r) whose span is $2s$ and whose crown is h (Fig. 13-21):

$$r = \frac{s^2 + h^2}{2h}$$

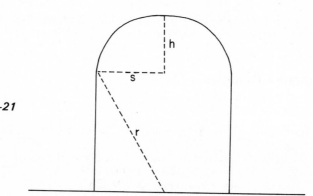

Figure 13-21

279

The Quadratic Function

This list can provide a virtually endless stream of quadratic equations to solve. In addition, graphs may be drawn and the physical ideas involved may undergo careful discussion. In this way, meaningful practice is provided at the same time that the diverse role of mathematics is constantly being emphasized.

FOOTNOTES

1. See the Report of the Commission on Mathematics. *Appendices*. College Entrance Examination Board, 1959, pp. 50–54.

FOR INVESTIGATION AND DISCUSSION

1. Plan a lesson for the introduction of the quadratic function based upon the distance formula $d = 16t^2$.

2. Indicate how interesting practice experiences may be provided by using situations involving the other planets and the moon.

3. Plan a lesson that will result in the need to work with radicals by selecting a situation in which radicals are inherent.

4. Devise problems that will necessitate the use of operations with radicals.

5. Devise a formula for the distance that can be seen from the surface of the moon. (Use a radius = 1000 miles.)

6. Construct a problem leading to a radical equation whose solution involves extraneous roots.

7. Demonstrate how rectangular areas may be used to aid student understanding of the process of factoring trinomials.

8. Make a lesson plan to enable students to make use of completing the squares, in order to analyze the function for graphing purposes.

9. Make a lesson plan for a review session prior to completion of the unit on the quadratic function. Select problems from the list at the end of the chapter.

FOR FURTHER READING

Books

Report of the Commission on Mathematics. *Appendices*. College Entrance Examination Board, 1959, pp. 47–57.
Lauren G. Woodby. "How Far Can You See?" *In* National Council of Teachers of Mathematics, 27th Yearbook: *Enrichment Mathematics For the Grades*. The National Council of Teachers of Mathematics, 1963, pp. 269–272.

Periodicals

George Barnes. "An Easily Constructed Chart for Finding the Roots of Quadratic Equations." *The Mathematics Teacher*. Vol. 50 (January, 1957), pp. 40–42.

Joseph F. Hohlfeld. "An Analysis of the Quadratic." *The Mathematics Teacher*. Vol. 54 (March, 1961), pp. 138–141.

Douglas Ingram. "An Investigation." *The Mathematics Student Journal*. Vol. 8 (November, 1960), pp. 6–8.

Arthur Pedley. "A Radical Approach to $\sqrt{ab} = \sqrt{a}\sqrt{b}$." *The Mathematics Teacher*. Vol. 58 (October, 1965), pp. 512–513.

Lawrence A. Ringenberg. "A Portrait of $\sqrt{2}$." *The Mathematics Teacher*. Vol. 58 (November, 1965), pp. 586–595.

14

OTHER TOPICS IN ALGEBRA

VARIATION

We have made use of mathematics in studying a broad variety of natural phenomena. We have explored linear relationships, quadratic relationships, and relationships described with the use of radicals. Many new types of functions will have to be explored if we are to study the diverse relationships present in nature.

One way in which functions can be classified is to focus upon the way in which one variable changes with another. We should do this in more general terms than we have undertaken thus far. While it is true that the classification "linear function" is a general category including an infinite number of relationships, mathematically, when you take the point of view of variation, still broader classifications can be seen. For example, we have explored and carried out many calculations with the area-distance relationship for a picture projected upon a wall. Although this was an example of a quadratic function, it involved a specific case—the use of a particular projector. If we were to describe this situation using the language of variation we would say that the area of the picture varies directly with the square of the distance. We would then symbolically describe this function with $A = kx^2$. It is true that this formula describes a quadratic relationship, but it does more than that: It describes how the area of a projected picture will change as the distance from the screen is changed, and it does so for *all projectors,* not merely the case in which $\frac{1}{9}$ was the value of k. That was a specific case. Thus, working with variation makes the dependency of a relationship more apparent, emphasizes

282

the meaning of functional relationship in its essence, and classifies various kinds of relationships.

One interesting situation can introduce the student to many types of variation in a single stroke, for example, the amount of weight that can be supported by a wooden plank.[1] To test the strength of the plank, it is set up as a bridge, resting upon two supports (Fig. 14-1). The formula that relates the weight with the dimensions of the board would be

$$N = \tfrac{3}{4}\frac{Wd^2}{L}$$

where

N = weight in 100-pound units

W = width of board in inches

L = length of board in feet

d = thickness of board in inches

In order to simplify our work, we may drop the $\frac{3}{4}$ factor in the formula, since this is close to one, without distorting the results too much for our purposes. This would provide us with a simpler formula: $N = \dfrac{Wd^2}{L}$. What kind of variation is this? Since there are several variables (W, d, and L) that determine the weight that may be supported (N), this is an example of *joint variation*. But let us examine the effect upon the weight if we hold all things constant with the exception of a single variable, taking each variable in turn.

The width (W) varies: If the plank is 10 feet long and 1 inch thick, for the sake of this discussion, how does the weight supported (N) change as we alter the width (W)? (See Fig. 14-2.) IMPORTANT: The students can calculate the effect of changing W by using the formula and then setting up a table of results. They might follow up by drawing the graph. This general procedure would apply to each case demonstrated here. Thus, students readily see the changes taking place.

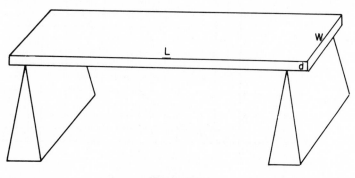

Figure 14-1

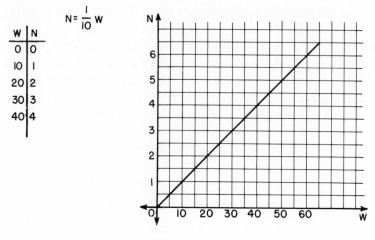

$$N = \frac{1}{10}\,W$$

W	N
0	0
10	1
20	2
30	3
40	4

Figure 14-2

The thickness (*d*) *varies:* If we fix the width at 10 inches and maintain the length at 10 feet, what happens to the weight (*N*) as we alter the thickness (*d*)? (See Fig. 14-3.)

The length (*L*) *varies:* If we fix the width at 10 inches and the thickness at 1 inch, how does the weight (*N*) change as the length (*L*) is changed? (See Fig. 14-4.)

A summary of the results of this investigation is presented in the chart shown on the next page.

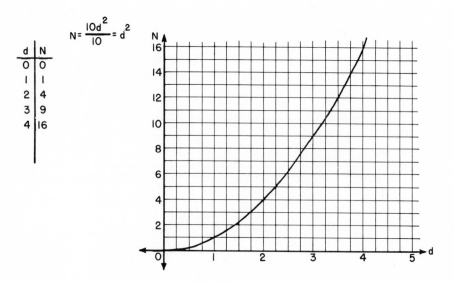

$$N = \frac{10d^2}{10} = d^2$$

d	N
0	0
1	1
2	4
3	9
4	16

Figure 14-3

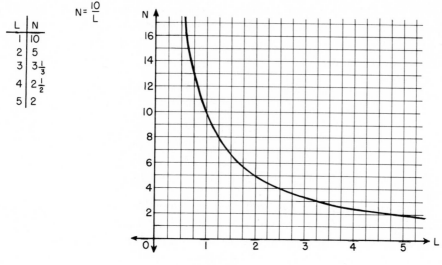

Figure 14-4

Formula	Graph	Kind of variation
$N = \dfrac{1}{10} W$	straight line	direct
$N = d^2$	curved line	direct
$N = \dfrac{10}{L}$	curved line	inverse

The first two formulas in the chart describe familiar functions. The last, however, is a new one. We have not yet examined functions that contained a variable in the denominator, but we shall investigate this function in detail soon. First, students should examine the three situations carefully and satisfy themselves about the different relationships involved, as well as the apparent effects upon the graphs. Additional experiences will enable the students to compute the constant of variation as needed and to begin to see clearly the differences between each of the following:

> varying directly as . . .
> varying directly as the square of . . .
> varying inversely as . . .
> varying inversely as the square of . . .
> varying jointly as . . .

In each instance the graph adds to our understanding of the relationship. As a matter of fact, recognition of the general type of variation involved in a given situation will enable the student to describe tabulated data by a for-

285

mula, if the data have been gathered by direct observation. Thus, the entire process of pattern recognition receives some powerful assistance. For example, if physical experiments had led to the collection of the data that follows, how could we fit a formula?

Time of fall (t)	Distance fallen (d)
0	0
1	16
2	64
3	144
4	256

If we draw a graph of this information, something most interesting takes place (Fig. 14-5). From our previous work with variation and functions we can see that this seems to be a case of "varying directly as the square of . . .," which indicates the formula is of the form $d = kt^2$. If we can compute k, we will have found the desired formula. This is an interesting problem for students, who should be encouraged to check the table for possible help. At any rate, substitution of any of the ordered pairs of the table will yield an equation with only k unknown. If we choose (1, 16), we get

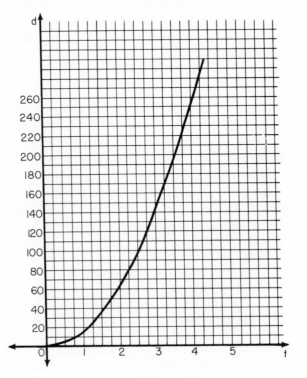

Figure 14-5

$$d = kt^2$$
$$16 = k(1)$$
$$k = 16$$

Thus, we may conclude that the data are described by the formula $d = 16t^2$. Of course, once we have found k, we may calculate any set of values for t and d. Many examples should follow this work; each time the student should be presented with another table of data.

Earlier a new kind of formula was encountered, one with a variable located in the denominator. Let us take a brief but close look at this situation. The formula in question was

$$N = \frac{10}{L}$$

The graph proved most unusual (Fig. 14-6). If we continue to select larger values of L, we see that the resulting N-values are getting smaller and smaller so that the curve will be getting closer and closer to the L-axis (or x-axis). The same seems to be true at the other end, for as the L-values get smaller the N-values get larger and larger and the curve seems to be closing in on the N-axis (or y-axis). Will it ever touch either axis? Can $L = 0$? Why not? Can $N = 0$? What number divided into 10 gives a quotient of zero? Is there such a number? The graph clearly reflects these facts. The axes in this case are special lines called asymptotes. There is no need to dwell on this here. Repeated examples of this kind of variation will make such lines familiar. Later work in analytical geometry will provide a better mathematical description.

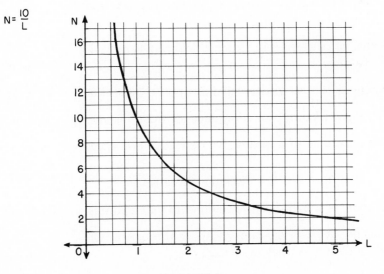

Figure 14-6

Finally, a whole host of problems involving ratio and proportion may be attacked as variation problems. In the general equation of variation, k becomes the constant of proportionality. As indicated before, it can be computed, if necessary, thereby providing access to any desired values of either variable. The approach through variation becomes a most powerful ally in curve fitting, equation solution, and solution of proportions, as well as in helping students with their intuitive understanding of the nature of functional relationships. The following list is a collection of situations involving variation that would prove fruitful in trying to select interesting, meaningful situations for student study:

Direct Variation ($y = kx$)

Spring-stretch-weight:	$s = kw$
Velocity-time for dropped objects:	$v = kt$
Weight of stone block is proportional to length:	$w = kL$
Shadow length varies with height of object:	$L = kh$
Pressure of a liquid varies with the depth in feet:	$P = kd$
Food required (in pounds) to maintain body temperature depends upon weight:	$F = kw$
Volume of water in tank depends on depth:	$V = kd$

Direct Variation ($y = kx^2$)

Distance fallen by a dropped object depends upon time:	$d = kt^2$
Value of a silver coin (same thickness) varies with diameter:	$V = kd^2$
Strength of steel girder depends upon cross section:	$s = kx^2$
Area of a picture projection depends upon distance:	$A = kx^2$
Air resistance to a locomotive depends upon speed:	$A = kv^2$

Other Direct Variation

Estimate of weight-height relationship for elephants:	$W = kh^3$
Velocity (ft./sec.) of water escaping through a hole in a dam h feet below surface:	$v = k\sqrt{h}$
Volume of a sphere depends upon its radius:	$V = kr^3$

288

Distance to horizon (miles) depends upon height above sea level (feet):

$$d = k\sqrt{H}$$

Value of blue whales depends upon length:

$$V = kL^3$$

Inverse Variation

Weight needed to balance a lever depends upon distance from fulcrum:

$$w = \frac{k}{d}$$

Number of ball bearings to a pound depends upon diameter:

$$N = \frac{k}{d^3}$$

Weight of a body depends upon distance from center of earth:

$$w = \frac{k}{r^2}$$

Number of plants to an acre depends upon distance apart:

$$N = \frac{k}{d^2}$$

Joint Variation

Volume of wood in a tree depends on height and girth:

$$V = khg^2$$

Time for a procession to pass a point depends on its length and speed:

$$T = \frac{kL}{r}$$

Altitude of a triangle varies directly as its area and inversely as its base:

$$h = \frac{kA}{b}$$

INEQUALITIES

One of the more interesting topics that has been emphasized by many of the modern programs is the topic of inequalities. In working with this idea, many of the suggestions of the various improvement studies for changing symbolism, vocabulary, and techniques begin to assume some significance in a manner that aids student thinking.[2] One-dimensional graphing, the clear definition of possible replacement sets, the intersection and union of sets, and the notion of set itself are some of the concepts that become interesting when inequalities are considered. Perhaps as we develop this area the ideas will come into sharper focus.

Once again we look for a significant entrance into this topic, and as before we find that there is much in nature that we may call upon. The amount of food (in pounds per day) that the body requires to maintain a constant temperature of 98.6° F is approximately described by the inequality

$$F \geq \frac{1}{50} W$$

where W = body weight in pounds and F = food in pounds. The following problem requires the solution of a linear inequality:

> How much food must a 200-pound man eat in order to maintain his body temperature?

Using the relation we get

$$F \geq \frac{1}{50} W$$

$$F \geq \frac{1}{50} \cdot 200$$

$$F \geq 4$$

The man in question must eat at least 4 pounds of food. Thus, his body temperature is maintained by 4 pounds of food as well as by any greater amount of food, e.g., 5, 6, or more pounds. In this case, our answers are a collection of numbers and so it is natural to describe them as a set of numbers. Indeed, since these numbers are the solution to the problem, we may well call them collectively a *solution set*. The nature of the problem dictates the possible numbers which may be used to select members of this solution set. In this case—measurement of weights—the real numbers are the numbers from which we shall select our answers. Since the inequality contained a single variable, we may draw a one-dimensional graph to illustrate the answers (Fig. 14-7).

The graph indicates that any of the values from 4 to the right satisfy the inequality, including 4. (This is why we shade in the circle at the left end of the graph, instead of using an unshaded circle if 4 were not included.) The graph is a line. This same graph might have been a collection of discrete points if the data had referred to discrete objects like people, tickets, or cars. For example, the maximum weight that an elevator can hold is 1500 pounds. In a particular office building it is determined that those using the elevator average 150 pounds. How many people form a "safe load"? The elevator operator cannot weigh the people, but he can count them. We are now dealing

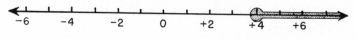

Figure 14-7. *A graph of the solution set* F ≥ *4.*

with the counting or natural numbers. The inequality that describes this situation and its solution is presented here:

$$1500 \geq 150n$$

$$\frac{1500}{150} \geq n$$

$$10 \geq n$$

A picture of the numbers that make up the correct answers (solution set) to this problem is included in Figure 14-8. Thus the elevator is safe for one person to ride alone and for two, three, and on up to, but not more than, 10 people. The graph is now a set of discrete points since we are referring to people rather than measurement numbers. The solution set may also be represented by showing each element included using the set bracket notation:

$$F \geq 4 \qquad \text{or} \qquad \{F \mid F \geq 4\}$$
$$n \leq 10 \qquad \text{or} \qquad \{1, 2, 3, 4, 5, 6, 7, 8, 9, 10\}$$

When the nature of the number system is clear because of the particular problem involved, we need not indicate this any further. If there is question, however, it may be best to clearly indicate these possibilities called the universal or replacement set and make this a part of the symbolism used to present the problem. For example, the problems mentioned before may be written $\{F \varepsilon R \mid F \geq 4\}$ which is read:

The set of all F that belongs to the real numbers such that F is greater than or equal to 4.
$\{\ F \qquad\qquad \varepsilon \qquad\qquad R \qquad\qquad F \qquad\qquad\qquad \geq \qquad 4\}$

By the same token:

$$\{n \varepsilon N \mid 1500 \geq 150n\}$$

The set of all n that belong to the natural numbers such that 1500 is greater than or equal to 150n.

It is very important to use only those symbols that are needed to communicate the ideas. It is possible to take another look at all the work completed earlier and to convert the equations and formulas into this relatively "modern" form. These forms were not introduced earlier because they would have clouded rather than clarified the ideas contained therein. Here the

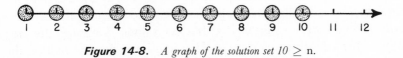

Figure 14-8. *A graph of the solution set 10 ≥ n.*

291

symbolism may add to the student's understanding. This is our test! If indeed understanding is aided, let us make use of it. If not, let us ignore these symbols.

How was the second inequality, $1500 \geq 150n$, solved? What methods were used? If common sense reasoning fails to help the students, we shall explore formal techniques. In the preceding problems these seem hardly necessary. However, we may soon provide problems in inequalities that will surely create a need for more powerful techniques, and then we can consider the equality axioms developed earlier and determine whether or not they may be applied to inequalities as well. But first, the two-dimensional graph of inequalities grows naturally out of the work done and poses some interesting questions. For this let us return to the relationship introduced earlier.

An approximate formula for the amount of food required for maintenance of body temperature is $F \geq \frac{1}{50}W$. The minimum amount of food needed varies from animal to animal; thus, a mouse's food requirements would be described by the inequality $F \geq \frac{1}{2}W$. Although the mouse certainly requires less total food to maintain his body temperature than does man, proportionally with his size, he requires a good deal more. The inequality indicates that a mouse must eat at least half his weight to maintain his body temperature, which may account for his persistent search for food, as compared with a man who must consume only one fiftieth of his total weight to accomplish the same purpose.

In studying this relationship we once again turn to the graph in order to arrive at a picture of this information. We have two variables here, so we will construct the familiar graph on the two-coordinate axes system. In this case we shall graph F as a function of W. It may be well to introduce the notation $F = f(W)$, which is to be read, "F depends upon, or is a function of, W." It is helpful to place $f(W)$ on the vertical axis as a label and begin to use this function notation in the table of values if one is to be made. But first, the student is faced with a rather difficult problem: How shall the graph of $F \geq \frac{1}{2}W$ be made? Where are the values that satisfy this inequality? How many are there? At this point the students require time to think and wonder for themselves. Such time should be provided. The important test for any suggested methods will be: Can we be sure that we have located all such values or ordered pairs? A suggestion about drawing the graph of the function described by the equation $F = \frac{1}{2}W$ may be a good beginning after the students have had time to see the difficulties for themselves. Once the relationship has been graphed, we have part of the desired picture. In the "greater than or equal to" statement we have thus provided for "equal to." But where are the "greater than" points? Here the students use the process of trial and error, selecting and testing points to determine the part of the coordinate plane that is included in the graph (Fig. 14-9). The shaded area is included, as is the line itself. Once the graph has been completed, it may be helpful to pause and consider carefully what has been done. To graph the inequality, a graph of the equality was drawn. This line immediately divided the plane

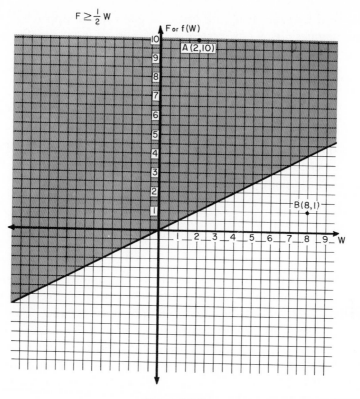

Figure 14-9

into three parts: the region above the line, the line itself, and the region below the line. We have the line and two half-planes created by the line. There are apparently three possibilities present to relate F and $\frac{1}{2}W$:

$$F \text{ is greater than } (>) \tfrac{1}{2}W$$

or

$$F \text{ is equal to } (=) \tfrac{1}{2}W$$

or

$$F \text{ is less than } (<) \tfrac{1}{2}W$$

These would seem to correspond to the three divisions of the plane just described. In the inequality under consideration we see that we are required to illustrate two of these three possibilities: "equal to" and "greater than." The line provided the ordered pairs fitting the "equal to" description. This is the only consideration we have had in the past as we worked with equations. But in this instance we are also concerned with "greater than." Evidently, the two half planes above and below the line will satisfy the "greater than" and "less than" situations. But which is to be which? A good question. This ques-

293

tion is resolved by using trial and error. A point in the upper half is selected and its coordinates (W, F) are tested to determine if the inequality is satisfied: Choose point A (2, 10). Substitution results in

$$F > \tfrac{1}{2}W$$
$$10 > \tfrac{1}{2}(2)$$
$$10 > 1 \quad \text{True}$$

And, indeed the statement is true. The inequality is satisfied. For further assurance we choose a point below the line and not in the upper half-plane and test it: Choose point B (8, 1).

$$F > \tfrac{1}{2}W$$
$$1 > \tfrac{1}{2}(8)$$
$$1 > 4 \quad \text{False}$$

As anticipated this point does not satisfy the inequality. Of course, the students may wish to test many more points before becoming convinced that the upper half-plane is indeed the region we have been seeking. This, of course, should be a student decision that is honored in class. To indicate the desired portions of the graph, shading lines are drawn and the line itself is kept as a solid line. Had the inequality been $F > \tfrac{1}{2}W$, without the equality, the equality line would appear as a broken line. By looking at the graph we see instantly what is and what is not included.

It is important to note here that the graph is a mathematical description of the inequality under consideration. It has included in it many meaningless values as far as the situation generating the inequality is concerned. For example, negative values are meaningless in discussing amounts of food to be consumed. Consequently, we need only the first quadrant to satisfy the physical situation. In addition, many of the ordered pairs in this quadrant are without physical meaning: A mouse weighing in excess of 10 pounds is not likely to be found. Once again we have a very real opportunity to keep clearly before the students the important differences between things mathematical and things physical.

The process of graphing may in turn be applied to each inequality considered, so that solutions are being found algebraically and graphically. The three divisions of the plane should be pointed out each time so that an intuitive feeling for the idea that the line is a boundary line of the two half-planes develops. After several such graphs many students may attempt to abandon the trial and error method of finding the desired half-plane. All well and good. The only criterion to apply to such methods is the pragmatic "does it work" test. The elegance, or lack of elegance, should not become part of judging the validity of a student-constructed idea.

To extend the work with inequalities we move in much the same fashion as we did with equations. We proceed from inequalities of form $y > ax$ to

$y > ax + b$ and then into the area of quadratic inequalities. As we increase the complexity of the form, we create the need on the students' part for more and more powerful techniques in order to arrive at solutions. In this way we eventually come to the point of testing the axioms for equality and trying to determine their applicability here. For example:

The percentage of bacteria left in a culture (p) depends upon the number of seconds (t) it is exposed to ultraviolet rays. This relationship may be described as

$$p = 100 - \tfrac{19}{2}t$$

A particular culture was not safe to use unless there was less than 24 percent bacteria remaining in it. What lengths of time render the culture safe?

$$24 > 100 - \tfrac{19}{2}t$$

Solving this particular inequality may require the use of some method more powerful than simply using an understanding of the symbolism.

Such a problem, or one equally difficult, enables the teacher to bring about a situation ripe for a new technique. As was done earlier when the students were thwarted, we turn to familiar forms and try to determine a strategy based upon our methods with previous work. How would we solve the equation $24 = 100 - \tfrac{19}{2}t$? May we use the axioms of equality here? That is, to cite but one case, if we employ the addition axiom, do we destroy the inequality or alter the sense of it? (The sense being the order of the inequality: greater than-less than.) Simple trial and error experimentation should be our guide here, and we should operate upon simple numbers in order that the outcome shall be clear. For example, we know that $10 > 5$. If we add equal quantities

$$10 + 3 > 5 + 3$$
$$13 > 8 \qquad \text{True}$$

After we have tested many different positive and negative numbers, a feeling that addition is permissable as described becomes entrenched. The same process should follow for each of the operations of subtraction, division, and multiplication. These activities are designed to result in some basic assumptions to be used in dealing with inequalities:

If $a > b$ and $c = d$, then

1. $a + c > b + d$
2. $a - c > b - d$

If $a > b$ and $c > 0$, then

3. $ac > bc$

295

If $a > b$ and $c < 0$, then

4. $ac < bc$

If $a > b$ and $c > 0$, then

5. $\dfrac{a}{c} > \dfrac{b}{c}$

If $a > b$ and $c < 0$, then

6. $\dfrac{a}{c} < \dfrac{b}{c}$

The inequality used before as an example may serve to illustrate the multiplication and division assumptions:

$$10 > 5$$
$$2 \times 10 \boxed{?} 2 \times 5$$
$$20 > 10$$

$$10 > 5$$
$$-2 \times 10 \boxed{?} -2 \times 5$$
$$-20 < -10$$

$$10 > 5$$
$$10 \div 5 \boxed{?} 5 \div 5$$
$$2 > 1$$

$$10 > 5$$
$$10 \div -5 \boxed{?} 5 \div (-5)$$
$$-2 < -1$$

The students see that the inequality sign is reversed when the multiplication or division by a negative quantity is carried out. The original problem of the bacteria is therefore solved as follows:

$$24 > 100 - \frac{19}{2}t$$

Multiply by 2: $\qquad 48 > 200 - 19\,t$

Subtract 200: $\qquad -152 > -19\,t$

Divide by -19: $\qquad \dfrac{-152}{-19} < \dfrac{-19\,t}{-19}$

$$8 < t$$

More than 8 seconds of exposure is required.

This problem, as well as those completed earlier, helps to make many ideas more meaningful. The notion of the range and domain of variables mentioned previously may be explored again. What are the values of t that have meaning in this situation? Can t, for instance, be negative? What of the p-values. Can they be negative? Is there a maximum or minimum value for each?

Since we are thinking of $p = f(t)$, t is the independent variable (horizontal axis on the graph) and therefore we speak of its *domain*.

The domain consists of the real numbers from zero and up: $t \geq 0$.

The *range* consists of the real numbers from zero to 100: $0 \leq p \leq 100$.

The latter inequality indicates that 100 percent is the maximum amount of bacteria that may be present and zero is the least amount.

In this way, the concepts of range and domain aid our ability to focus upon values that are meaningful in the physical situation.

The squaring and taking of square roots may also be investigated when quadratic inequalities are encountered, in order to determine the effects upon the inequality. The solution of quadratic inequalities poses some interesting questions. A brief look will be taken at this shortly; but first, the work just described should be followed by a variety of problems involving additional work with linear inequalities. Besides the bacteria culture relationship, the following situations may yield fruitful inequalities as well as interesting environments in which to house mathematical problems:

1. The British post office will not accept a package larger than 72 inches in girth and length. If the base of the box to be used by a manufacturer is square, this relationship is

$$4W + L \leq 72$$

   Draw a graph of all possible box sizes. Find the possible lengths if a side of the base is 10 inches, 12 inches, and 15 inches.

2. A faulty centigrade thermometer does not record temperatures above $30°$. What will the Fahrenheit temperatures be that can be found with this thermometer?

$$\tfrac{5}{9}(F - 32 = C$$
$$\tfrac{5}{9}(F - 32) \leq 30$$

3. An 80-pound boy named Bob sits on a 9-foot seesaw. He is 5 feet from the fulcrum. If Bob is able to keep his friend up in the air, even though his friend is at the end of the seesaw, how much will Bob's friend have to weigh?

$$80 \times 5 > W \times 4$$
$$400 > 4W$$

A reexamination of many of the linear relationships considered when we discussed equation solution may yield many more practical problems in inequalities similar to that just presented in which temperature readings were converted. Of course, the introduction of abstract inequalities will follow, posing a variety of problems for solution and graphing. The quadratic inequality is particularly interesting. A brief discussion of this type follows.

Inequalities of simple quadratic form hold no hidden surprises for the student. Consider the following problem:

The area of my projection screen is 16 sq. ft. If I am going to project a picture that will fit on my screen, what are the allowable distances from projector to screen? We use the function discussed earlier, and get

$$A \geq \tfrac{1}{9}x^2$$

and in particular

$$16 \geq \tfrac{1}{9}x^2$$

If he had to solve this problem, the student would proceed to find the square root of both sides as he had done with equations. The negative root would not be applicable to this physical situation. Thus, the solution would appear somewhat like the following:

$$16 \geq \tfrac{1}{9}x^2$$

or

$$x^2 \leq 9 \cdot 16$$

$$x \leq \pm(3 \cdot 4)$$

$$x \leq \pm12$$

I would have to place the projector no further than 12 feet from the screen.

When the quadratic inequality is more complicated, the solution becomes more complicated too. The basis for our main attack on the quadratic equation was that if the product of two numbers was zero, one of the factors (or both) had to be zero. In solving quadratic inequalities, however, we will be faced with the dilemma that two factors provide a product that is either greater or less than zero. How shall we deal with this condition? An example may clarify:

A manufacturer finds it necessary because of cost to limit his packing boxes to an area less than 5 sq. ft., without a special top panel (Fig. 14-10). If the height must be 1 foot high and the base must be square, what dimensions may he use for the base?

The total area is made up of four rectangles, 1 by x, and the square bottom is x by x. Thus, the problem is described by $x^2 + 4x < 5$.

To solve:

$$x^2 + 4x - 5 < 0$$
$$(x + 5)(x - 1) < 0$$

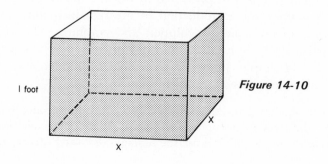

I foot

Figure 14-10

x

x

But where do we go from here?

An examination of the inequality indicates that the product of two factors is negative, that is, less than zero. Therefore, we are not in the dark at all. Our two factors must be of opposite sign since their product is a negative number; hence, we proceed on this basis: We list all the alternatives:

$$\text{If } (x + 5) > 0, \text{ then } (x - 1) < 0$$
$$\text{If } (x + 5) < 0, \text{ then } (x - 1) > 0$$

We then determine the consequences of each:

$$
\begin{array}{ll}
x + 5 > 0 & \qquad x - 1 < 0 \\
\quad x > -5 & \qquad \quad x < 1
\end{array}
$$

$$
\begin{array}{ll}
x + 5 < 0 & \qquad x - 1 > 0 \\
\quad x < -5 & \qquad \quad x > 1
\end{array}
$$

We have defined four sets as possible solution sets. Are they all solutions, or are only some of them solutions? Checking the values against our original inequality (or against the factors, whichever is preferred) will enable us to answer the question. Indeed we find that the two inequations, $x > -5$ and $x < 1$, describe sets that satisfy the inequality. This checking process is a kind of guided trial and error that is so much a part of mathematics and all too often discouraged by teachers. Our results are most interesting. If we locate the values of x on the number line, we find that we have a curious graph (Fig. 14-11).

The only numbers that are roots of the inequality are those in the overlap section of the two sets, and these values are described by $-5 < x < 1$. If we try values outside this segment, we find that they do not work. Only those values that are common to both solution sets will satisfy the inequality. What a clear definition of the intersection of sets! Thus, we come upon an idea usually pressed upon students rather early in their mathematics studies, despite the fact that this idea begins to assume importance much later. Is it any wonder that our students see mathematics—of traditional and modern vintage —as so much symbol juggling? But to return to the quadratic: Will all quad-

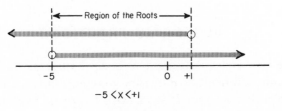

$$-5 < x < +1$$

Figure 14-11

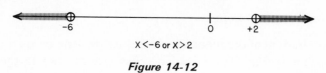

X < −6 or X > 2

Figure 14-12

ratics be resolved this way? Let us explore another problem, built upon the first.

Under the same conditions as in the previous problem, the manufacturer needs a box that will be greater than 12 sq. ft. in area. Thus, we now find that $x^2 + 4x > 12$.

To solve:

$$x^2 + 4x - 12 > 0$$
$$(x + 6)(x - 2) > 0$$

We apply the same idea as before, but the situation is different. The product of two factors is positive (greater than zero); therefore the factors agree in sign. The possibilities here are:

$x + 6 > 0$	$x - 2 > 0$
$x > -6$	$x > 2$
$x + 6 < 0$	$x - 2 < 0$
$x < -6$	$x < 2$

Testing values in the various ranges results in the selection of $x > 2$ or $x < -6$ as the descriptions of the solution sets. A graph is of interest (Fig. 14-12). This time the solution of the inequality may be described as $x < -6$ or $x > 2$. There is no overlap at all here and we find that the union of the two solution sets forms the solution set for the original inequality.

A number of abstract inequalities could be presented for solution here in order to provide additional experiences. The graphs point up the ability of the equation function to divide the plane into three distinct parts: the two half-planes and their boundary. A raft of new ideas and symbols have been employed in building upon the work done earlier in as natural a manner as possible. Our important guide post has not been ignored: *What we do has got to make sense to the student.*

ALGEBRAIC FRACTIONS

There are two topics that seem to bedevil students to a degree that far outstrips any other difficulties that they may encounter. One is the solution of verbal problems; the other is work with fractions. How many times have you seen a student execute a cancellation such as this one:

$$\frac{\dfrac{1}{\cancel{a}}}{\dfrac{\cancel{a}+b}{1}} = \frac{1}{1+b}$$

How many times have you seen fractions combined when denominators were to be eliminated and vice versa?

There are no simple pathways around such difficulties; but if any help is to be provided at all, the symptoms must be seen for what they are: rather clear statements that the manipulation of symbols is a process devoid of much reason for the student.

W. W. Sawyer states that two things are necessary if students are to be successful in working with algebraic fractions. These two things are ". . . an understanding of fractions in arithmetic, and the ability to see the connection between fractions in arithmetic and fractions in algebra."[3]

We seem to be up against several causes for trouble in dealing with algebraic fractions: The symbols are without meaning, arithmetic fractions are not understood, and the connection between algebra and arithmetic is a mystery. The first of these problems has been under attack throughout this section on algebra. The point has been that the students must "speak the language." A translation of symbols has been the starting point for much of the work undertaken. How well the students have understood fractions in arithmetic is, of course, a crucial question. The importance for algebra teachers is the recognition of the fact that what appears to be an immediate problem may well have had its roots in years gone by. If so, the teacher has got to retrace some steps and hit at the root of the matter if he is to make a difference. The last notion about connecting the processes of arithmetic and algebra is not as simple as it may appear. There are things that we do with algebraic fractions that are hidden processes when we work with fractions in arithmetic; so, in effect, it becomes necessary to reexamine the ideas involved in working with arithmetic fractions in order to clarify the algebraic processes. On the other hand, certain notions remain constant throughout arithmetic and algebra, and they are clearly seen as such. For example, multiplying the top and bottom of a fraction by the same number (the identity element) does not alter the fraction value, although it does lead to another numeral for the same number:

$$\frac{3 \times 2}{4 \times 2} = \frac{6}{8} \qquad \frac{(a+b)x}{(c+d)x} = \frac{ax+bx}{cx+dx}$$

With these cautions at hand we move into the study of algebraic fractions. A formula that has been used in traffic engineering is

$$Q = \frac{3600 \cdot V \cdot N}{C}$$

where $\qquad Q$ = number of vehicles per hour

$$V = \text{ their average speed in ft./sec.}$$

$$N = \text{ number of traffic lanes}$$

$$C = \text{ spacing between cars in feet}$$

Consider the following problem:

On a certain highway there is concern over the spacing between cars. Since 20,000 cars are moved per hour on the four lanes, where the average speed is 88 ft./sec. (60 m.p.h.), how much spacing does this permit between cars?

$$Q = \frac{3600 \cdot V \cdot N}{C}$$

$$20{,}000 = \frac{3600 \cdot 4 \cdot 88}{C}$$

Solving for C involves the student with an expression that contains a variable in the denominator. The student is free to do what he has done previously when faced with fractions: He uses the multiplication axiom with the denominator. Thus we have

$$20{,}000\,C = 3600 \cdot 4 \cdot 88$$

We then proceed as we have all through the work with equations. The result in this case is 63.36 feet, which is not ample spacing. Other combinations of values could provide additional practice with these equations. Cross-multiplication, if employed by students, should be accepted as a valid method.

Other situations of interest for dealing with simple fractional equations include:

1. The number of steel ball bearings to the pound depends upon the diameter of each ball bearing. A formula relating these is

$$N = \frac{225}{32d}$$

where N = the number of bearings to the pound
d = the diameter in inches per ball bearing

If we find that there are 450 ball bearings to a pound, what is the diameter of each one?

2. The length of time in minutes it will take for a parade to pass a given point depends upon how long the parade is and how fast the marchers can walk. A formula for one group of marchers 150 yards long is

$$t = \frac{150}{20s}$$

where t = time to pass a point in minutes
s = speed in feet per second

If the parade must pass the reviewing stand in 3 minutes, how fast must the marchers walk?

3. A gardener wanted to plant 176 flowers in a rectangular garden 20 feet by 30 feet. How far apart should they be planted?

In this case it may help students to find a formula by examining a similar but simpler situation: If we put flowers 1 foot apart in a garden 8 feet by 4 feet, how many flowers could be planted (Fig. 14-13)? If we placed them 2 feet apart? 4 feet apart?

Let us examine this problem carefully: If we can find a pattern we may have a formula. Let us see. Arranging the information in a table gives:

Length	Width	Distance apart	Number of plants
8	4	1 foot	$9 \times 5 = 45$
8	4	2 feet	$5 \times 3 = 15$
8	4	4 feet	$3 \times 2 = 6$

The Garden: 4 Feet by 8 Feet

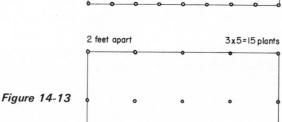

1 foot apart   5 x 9 = 45 plants

2 feet apart   3 x 5 = 15 plants

Figure 14-13

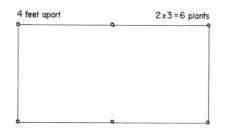

4 feet apart   2 x 3 = 6 plants

The numbers to be multiplied appear to be one more than the length or width divided by the distance apart.

Distance apart	Length	Width	Multiply
1 foot	$8 \div 1 = 8$	$4 \div 1 = 4$	9×5
2 feet	$8 \div 2 = 4$	$4 \div 2 = 2$	5×3
4 feet	$8 \div 4 = 2$	$4 \div 4 = 1$	3×2

The formula for the number of plants is

$$N = \left(\frac{L}{d} + 1\right)\left(\frac{w}{d} + 1\right)$$

In this problem we are looking for d; hence,

$$176 = \left(\frac{20}{d} + 1\right)\left(\frac{30}{d} + 1\right)$$

This problem is particularly fruitful since it introduces a multitude of new ideas, and the students may proceed in a variety of ways: using the multiplication axiom, combining and then multiplying, and possibly others. A rich variety of problems may be constructed here.

Finally, we turn to more complicated situations. A familiar formula from optics serves as a vehicle of interest:

$$\frac{1}{v} + \frac{1}{u} = \frac{1}{f}$$

where v is the distance of the image from the lens; u is the distance of the object from the lens; and f is the focal length of the lens, that is, the distance from the common point of all reflected light rays and the center of the lens (Fig. 14-14).

How far would the image have to be from the lens if we use a lens with a 2-inch focal length and if the object is placed 3 inches from the lens?

$$\frac{1}{v} + \frac{1}{3} = \frac{1}{2}$$

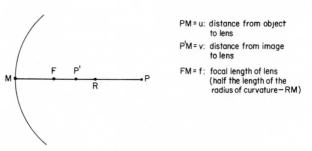

PM = u: distance from object to lens

P'M = v: distance from image to lens

FM = f: focal length of lens (half the length of the radius of curvature—RM)

Figure 14-14

We begin to make use of the lowest common denominator in order to solve through simplification. Settings such as those just listed are difficult to come by with fractions, and so after some work with these functions, abstract situations will have to be introduced to extend the work to include most of the important notions to be considered. The idea of factoring first, in order that common denominators may be more easily discovered, is most important. For example, to combine

$$\frac{x}{x^2 + 3x + 2} \quad \text{and} \quad \frac{x}{x + 2}$$

we first factor the trinomial since the lowest common denominator (l.c.d.) will contain all the factors of each denominator no more frequently than it appears in any single denominator. The factoring process indicates clearly that $(x + 2)$ is a common factor of the two denominators in our example.

This also holds true for the work done with fractions in arithmetic. For example:

$$\frac{1}{8} + \frac{1}{6} = \frac{1}{2 \cdot 2 \cdot 2} + \frac{1}{2 \cdot 3}$$

Our quest for the l.c.d. is greatly facilitated by factoring, in much the same manner as it is in algebraic fraction work. From the factors just given, we see that the l.c.d. must contain the factors $2 \cdot 2 \cdot 2 \cdot 3$ and is therefore 24. Indeed, this method of determining the l.c.d. was once in great favor in arithmetic texts. It gradually disappeared but was resurrected by the "modern mathematics" curriculum suggestions. The process of simplifying fractions is also aided by this examination of factors:

$$\frac{a + b}{a^2 - 3ab - 4b^2} = \frac{a + b}{(a - 4b)(a + b)} = \frac{1}{a - 4b}$$

It may be of interest to make use of the distributive law in helping students to understand combining like fractions or fractions with equal denominators:

$$\frac{3}{x} + \frac{5}{x} = \frac{1}{x}(3 + 5) = \frac{8}{x}$$

Here we are pointing out another role played by an important fundamental law, without emphasizing the law itself. Thus, the distributive law gains in importance by virtue of the ideas it enables us to understand.

The study of algebraic fractions may have been emphasized unnecessarily in the past. Certainly it is not as useful a collection of techniques as other ideas of algebra. Perhaps it is one area that may be preserved for those who are planning to follow a career in mathematics or an allied field, but for the most part it may be best to keep any work with these ideas to a minimum for the public at large. In this way we will not interfere with the important notions we struggle to develop about the significance of mathematics.

MORE ABOUT PROBLEM SOLVING

It has not been an oversight that up to this point there has been little in this discussion of algebra that deals with a topic known as "problem solving." It is customary in algebra courses to spend a good deal of time learning to carry out numerous kinds of manipulations with the symbols of algebra in order to be able to solve some interesting problems that generally appear in the textbook and in the teacher's plans at the end of the segment of work. The lack, until now, of a topic called "problem solving" has been no oversight: It has been intentional. It is certainly questionable that algebra should be taught with a separate topic such as this. Problem solving is an integral part of virtually all the work undertaken in algebra. When we approach new ideas, we meet them in the context of a problem. The same must hold true for the large variety and number of techniques to be learned. In the past we have differentiated these skills by calling the former "verbal problem solving." This is caused, it seems, by our inability to present the study of techniques as a legitimate problem for the student to solve. It has been the aim of this section to provide some ideas as to how this might be undertaken. If we are to interest our students in the tasks we are bringing before them, they must see what has to be done as some sort of challenge growing out of an idea of consequence.

But a word about the process of problem solving is in order, and it is no simple process to attempt to comprehend. A good deal of work has been carried out in this area by people like George Polya and Z. P. Dienes, among others.[4, 5] Consequently we have some guides for our efforts to help children improve their ability in this area, but there is also a good deal that remains to be done before teachers will no longer list this area as one of the areas of greatest difficulty for their students. A few such guidelines are presented here.

First, to reiterate the earlier point, problem solving is a natural part of all the work in algebra. If it is seen in this context over the course of a semester or a year, perhaps students will not feel it to be such a difficult task. But we must ask why the task appears so inordinately hard for students.

Perhaps one cause is the inability of the students to be able to read the problem properly. A first law, if there are any in this area, would be to be certain that the student can read what is before him. Closely allied with this is the question of whether or not what is read makes any sense at all. Granted that a student can read all the words in a given problem, but does he understand the action described by the problem? Is the situation something from his experience, or is it a totally new situation to him? I am constantly reminded of the youngster in elementary school who when asked how big a cow was held up two fingers about 3 inches apart! The only cows this child had ever seen were those in the pictures in her reader. Does your student understand what is happening in the problem before him? Perhaps a brief discussion of what is taking place without numbers will help each student to know what the problem is all about.

Now, can he decide how to represent the information before him in terms of mathematical symbolism? If he can manage this, all he has left to do is to put to work his many skills with symbols and derive the desired answer. But in the movement from words to mathematical symbols we have the most difficult step to be taken in this chain of events.

Many teachers have bravely tried to list the English words and their corresponding symbols one below the other. This may be helpful to some students. In the work with algebra described here, a good deal of emphasis was given to the idea that the language of algebra must be learned because this is one important prerequisite for "doing" algebra with understanding. A mastery of the language should also be an aid to the translation of information into the symbols of mathematics. But this process is a most creative one, and as such, there is no one way that will enable all to meet success.

What causes even greater complication in any attempt to identify "helpful hints" is the uncanny ability of many students to suddenly receive a flash of insight that lays the innermost secrets of the problem bare to them despite the fact that they may well be unable to provide a coherent explanation for what has transpired! This is a treasured skill to be sure; and while we are unable to cause such insights to occur, we are able to prevent them from ever taking place. Here lies an important lesson for us. When we approach the business of problem solving with the notion of getting the students to solve problems in the way that we want them to, we may be creating effective blocks to the adventurous kind of thinking described earlier. How many times have we, as teachers, tried to impress upon the students the fact that certain solutions were more preferable than others, although all were mathematically sound? In geometry, how many times have we taught particular proofs, rather than providing the opportunity for students to think about a theorem for themselves? If we want to be sure that the climate is right for insightful thinking, we will have to provide a good deal of freedom for students to think for themselves, and we must create an atmosphere of acceptance that will minimize their fear of ridicule for what may be termed "wild thoughts."

Alternate solutions should be presented to students without any evaluative remarks other than the fact that the mathematics is sound. Methods need not be compared to see which involves fewer steps or takes less time. Allow the students the freedom to select methods for themselves and problem solving may not pose the big threat it has always posed. In this way we may work toward the development of thinking and away from the remembering tasks which seem to make up the bulk of a student's involvement with mathematics.

To provide a common base from which to approach a given problem, techniques of analysis may be employed. That is, at times it can be helpful when solving problems to attempt to answer such questions as:

1. What does the problem tell us?
2. What are we to find?
3. What information is given to us?
4. Can I express the relationships in equation form?
5. Can I solve the particular equation?
6. Does the answer satisfy the conditions of the problem?

But we must also face the fact that students may well be able to answer the first three questions and still be at a loss as to what to do. Forming equations and deciding upon the operations to carry out are creative acts that can be aided by freedom to think without fear of ridicule or failure. Indeed the ingenuity of students to come up with varieties of approaches is an astounding fact for teachers who have opened up the classroom to encourage such thoughts! Contributions of this kind do not always depend upon previous success or ability with mathematics. This is but one more indication that we have only begun to scratch the surface in uncovering the mathematical abilities of our students. Perhaps the thoughts presented here will help some teachers begin to look upon this area a bit differently.

One final word about problem solving: Many times I have been in classrooms in which a student provides a most insightful solution to a given problem. Often the solution is ingenious. What generally happens is that the teacher then turns to this student and asks for greater clarity of explanation and perhaps even a justification of what has been done. Unable to provide this as required, the student flounders and often withdraws, convinced that he really does not know after all. Why should a student who can present evidence of excellent thinking be made to feel as though he has failed because his verbal ability does not match his thinking power? This can be a most destructive force. As teachers we have the difficult task of listening not only to what is being said, but to what is *not* being said. We do business with ideas. Words and symbols are not our points of focus. Let us honor ideas at all times and praise lavishly all incidents of good thinking, perhaps even to the extent of culling the interesting thoughts behind incorrect statements. In this way we may provide for student involvement with ideas at all levels.

FOOTNOTES

1. W. W. Sawyer (Editor). *Mathematics in Theory and Practice.* Odhams Press Ltd., pp. 180–187.
2. Report of the Commission on Mathematics. College Entrance Examination Board, *Appendices.* 1959, pp. 8–27. See also School Mathematics Study Group. *First Course in Algebra,* Part 1. A. C. Vroman, 1960.
3. W. W. Sawyer. *Vision in Elementary Mathematics.* Penguin Books, Inc. (paperback), 1964, p. 335.
4. George Polya. *How to Solve It,* Ed. 2. Doubleday & Company, Inc. (paperback), 1957.
5. Z. P. Dienes. *Building Up Mathematics.* Hutchinson & Co. Ltd., 1960.

For Investigation and Discussion

1. Select an example(s) of direct variation from the list provided and make a plan for an introductory lesson in this area.

2. Do the same for inverse variation.

3. Contrast the use of set vocabulary and symbolism in the study of inequalities and the study of equations. Indicate arguments for and against the use of these "modern" terms.

4. Select a physical situation involving inequalities, outline the procedures to be used to establish a need for formal techniques of solution, and then illustrate how the need will be met. (Use linear inequalities.)

5. Show how the solution of a quadratic inequality may involve the concepts of intersection and union of sets.

6. Demonstrate how the process of factoring may simplify work with algebraic functions. Evaluate the application of this method to work with arithmetic fractions.

7. Describe three possible causes for difficulty with verbal problem solving. Indicate what you might do to enable students to overcome each of these difficulties.

For Further Reading

Books

Edwin Beckenbach and Richard Bellman. *An Introduction to Inequalities*. New Mathematical Library. The L. W. Singer Company, Inc., 1961.
J. W. Getzels. "Creative Thinking, Problem Solving, and Instruction." *In* National Society for the Study of Education, 63rd Yearbook: *Theories of Learning and Instruction*, Part I. The National Society for the Study of Education, 1964, pp. 240–267.
Kenneth B. Henderson and Robert E. Pingry. "Problem-Solving in Mathematics." *In* National Council of Teachers of Mathematics, 21st Yearbook: *The Learning of Mathematics. Its Theory and Practice*. The National Council of Teachers of Mathematics, 1953, pp. 228–270.
E. H. C. Hilderbrandt. "Mathematical Modes of Thought." *In* National Council of Teachers of Mathematics, 24th Yearbook: *The Growth of Mathematical Ideas, Grades K–12*. The National Council of Teachers of Mathematics, 1959, pp. 370–404.
Donovan Johnson and Gerald Rising. *Guidelines for Teaching Mathematics*. Wadsworth Publishing Co. Inc., 1967, pp. 104–125.
G. Polya. *How to Solve It*, Ed. 2. Doubleday & Company, Inc. (paperback), 1957.
G. Polya. *Mathematics and Plausible Reasoning*, Vols. 1 and 2. Princeton University Press, 1954.

Periodicals

Richard Bellman. "On the Concepts of a Problem and Problem Solving." *The American Mathematical Monthly*. Vol. 67 (February, 1960), pp. 119–134.
Truman Botts. "Problem Solving in Mathematics, 1." *The Mathematics Teacher*. Vol. 58 (October, 1965), pp. 496–500.
Peter Braunfeld, Clyde Dilley, and Walter Rucker. "A New UICSM Approach to Fractions for the Junior High School." *The Mathematics Teacher*. Vol. 60 (March, 1967), pp. 215–221.
William P. Hull. "Learning Strategy and the Skills of Thought." *Mathematics Teaching*. (Summer, 1967), pp. 52–56.
L. H. Lange. "Some Inequality Problems." *The Mathematics Teacher*. Vol. 56 (November, 1963), pp. 490–494.
W. J. Lyda and Frances M. Duncan. "Quantitative Vocabulary and Problem Solving." *The Arithmetic Teacher*. Vol. 14 (April, 1967), pp. 289–291.

Other Topics in Algebra

G. Polya. "The Minimum Fraction of Popular Vote That Can Elect the President of the United States." *The Mathematics Teacher.* Vol. 54 (March, 1961), pp. 130–133.

Henry D. Snyder. "Problem Solutions That Ask Questions." *School Science and Mathematics.* Vol. 66 (April, 1966), pp. 373–376.

Harold C. Trimble. "Problems as Means." *The Mathematics Teacher.* Vol. 59 (January, 1966), pp. 6–8.

David Wallin. "An Approach to Inequalities." *The Mathematics Teacher.* Vol. 53 (February, 1960), pp. 134–135.

Pamphlet

The Development of Mathematical Activity in Children; the Place of the Problem in this Development. Report of Sub-Committee on Mathematical Instruction. British National Committee for Mathematics, Association of Teachers of Mathematics, November, 1966.

310

PART THREE

GEOMETRY

15

THE TRIANGLE

OVERTURE

We now turn our attention to another vital branch of mathematics: geometry. In studying algebra, the students learned a great deal about the world in which they live. They found out about the laws of motion that seem to govern falling bodies on our planet and on other planets. They examined how a spring would stretch as weights were added to it. They saw how their ability to lift heavy objects increased as they made use of levers. In short, the students made use of algebra to work with laws describing relationships in the physical world, and as a result they learned a good deal about that world as well as about mathematics.

Through the use of algebra, we were able to predict what would happen in nature with great accuracy. There were times when the use of mathematics to solve physical problems yielded answers that had no meaning in the physical situation despite the fact that the result was a good one mathematically. An attempt was made to help students begin to see that mathematics and physical situations were two very different entities. Negative roots led to good examples emphasizing such differences. These roots generally have little meaning when one works with the lengths of sides of squares and rectangles.

On the whole, the work done in algebra has been primarily concerned with the notion of number. How fast does a dropped baseball fall? How long is the stretch of a spring? How much weight can I lift? All these questions and the many others encountered in the study of algebra refer to the idea of number. Geometry is going to carry us a step further as we explore the world in which we live through the eyes of mathematics. In geometry we will concern ourselves with the sizes and shapes of things. Once again, the ideas are abstract, but like the concept of number, the ideas are suggested over and over again in nature. The sun, the moon, and the earth itself suggest spheres and circles. The banks of a river seem to be parallel lines. The surface of a body of water appears to be a plane. Tree trunks are cylinders and mountains seem to indicate cones and triangles. Everywhere you look, you can find the stuff of which geometry is made. These physical objects yield the ideas (circles, parallels, triangles, and so on) that the students will carefully examine as they undertake the study of geometry. As with algebra, the more you study nature, the more mathematical ideas become apparent and, in turn, the more you will find out about this world in which you live. This never-ending cycle is right now adding to man's knowledge of the universe and, at the same time, adding to man's development of mathematics. We have before us, then, some of the more important reasons for the study of geometry by all students—not only the informal geometry of the early grades examined previously, but the formal plane geometry generally found in the tenth year of school.

In addition, there are other significant reasons for the study of geometry. It is perhaps the foremost example of what man can accomplish when he uses his powers of reason. The entire edifice of geometry is a monument to the power of logical thinking. By identifying some undefined terms, then making definitions and establishing basic assumptions, we build up a tremendous body of knowledge piece by piece, theorem by theorem, until the totality that we call geometry (including the allied geometries) has grown to the position we find it in today. And herein lies the story of all of mathematics as attempts are made to unify the many branches into a single discipline and to derive all our knowledge of mathematics from a compact set of basic assumptions. It is this process that is peculiar to mathematics—this process of a logical, deductive demonstration to verify the certainty of propositions. It is this process that is being called into play in other disciplines as they attempt to establish themselves on the solid foundation offered by logic. It is not uncommon today to read about such dissimilar fields as biology and economics and encounter virtually the same quest: mathematization of the separate and numerous relationships that abound in any area of human investigation.

There are, however, some cautions to be observed. Typically, if students who had completed four years of high school mathematics were asked where we prove things in mathematics, the reply "geometry" would be offered without a moment of hesitation. While this branch of mathematics has furnished the opportunity for a careful study of the use and meaning of logical deduction, there are many today who feel that geometry may no longer offer us the best opportunity to help students appreciate the power of proof. Many teachers of mathematics are well aware that they have not been able to successfully develop the all-important intuitive feeling for and appreciation of proof to the extent that they would like. This lack, coupled with the several limitations that are now apparent in Euclidean geometry, has resulted in the suggestion that there may well be more suitable vehicles for the teaching of logical deduction and proof.

As a matter of fact, many writers have seriously questioned the continued teaching of Euclidean geometry when, in their view, other geometries may be much more appropriate. Hogben states that Euclidean geometry "does not give us the best possible way of measuring space."[1] The concepts of this geometry are no longer useful in the microcosm, the world of the atom, and in the macrocosm, the magnitudes involved in outer space. What is more, Allendoerfer explains that ". . . today there seems to be no compelling reason for using Euclidean geometry as the principle example of the deductive method of logical reasoning."[2] He goes on to indicate that it may well be better to use the notion of "group" as an example of deductive theory since it is closely allied with arithmetic and algebra. However, it would seem to be a mistake to turn away from the basic Euclidean geometry since this has historically been the foremost example of what could be accomplished with logical thought and reasoning, a lesson not completely learned by man to this day. Furthermore, geometry, more than any other branch of mathematics, is actually dealing with idealized versions of our physical world. It has ready-made visual counterparts for its abstractions—visual counterparts that play a vital role in the establishment of relationships that are later certified with proof.

As Hogben himself later states, "For many things Greek geometry remains the best tool we have."[1] Thus Euclidean geometry is still able to provide much important information about the world between the very small and the very large. As we study this "in-between world," we seem to have an optimum combination of factors present for the study of mathematical proof.

Why do students experience difficulties understanding the notion of proof? Could it be that we have made the course a melange of facts and a collection of theorems to be committed to memory without any real comprehension? Is this why we frequently find students including the very statement they are trying to prove as an intermediate step in their proof? Could this be one of the reasons why we frequently find students establishing in a proof what they had set out to do, only to continue to add more steps and not realize that they had already proven the proposition in question? If we are attempting to develop the student's ability to think for himself, how is it that he feels he has to learn "required proofs" rather than concentrate on proving a given theorem in the best way he can, as long as his mathematics is sound? The learning of "required proofs" shouts out that memorization is the chief operational technique, yet we find the expression in common use by many students of geometry. In light of this, it seems that we should continue to consider the notion of proof in all mathematics work but that we should also maintain the tenth year course in geometry (eleventh year in some schools) as *the point of emphasis* for helping students gain better insight into what is meant by deductive proof. This important mathematical concept must be seen in its proper context and must be taught in a manner that reflects what we know about how children learn.

The informal geometry described earlier in the section on prealgebra mathematics provides the foundation upon which we will build the geometry experiences that follow. As W. W. Sawyer has explained, "The best way to learn geometry is to follow the road which the human race originally followed: do things, make things, notice things, arrange things and only then—reason about things." [3]

The informal geometry discussed earlier provided a beginning in the "doing," "making," and "arranging" areas. This is a necessary prerequisite to reasoning. In the geometry to be studied here we will continue to build active experiences while we involve the "noticing—reasoning" processes a great deal more.

In the past there has been a great deal of misunderstanding by teachers of mathematics about what is good mathematics and what is good teaching. It is only natural for a teacher of mathematics to plan to begin the study of geometry with the necessary definitions and then to proceed to make assumptions about these and to attempt to prove propositions involving relationships between these entities. This is the logical order of things as they are known in mathematics. And herein lies what appears to be the important notion in the statement by Sawyer. While the logical order just described makes good mathematical sense, it may not provide good learning experiences for students; for the logical order that we find so obvious today was not at all the way in which mathematical ideas have historically developed over the years. Rather, it is an artificial framework brought to a multitude of mathematical ideas *after* they had been developed and were in use for some time. The order has been brought to organize those things that were known and used for many years. To present the finished product to students in just that way is to ignore the lessons of the development of the race as well as what we know about how our students learn. Further support for this observation appears in a publication of the British Ministry of Education:

> The historical order of development often proves to be the most natural: the gropings of the pioneers are often closely allied to those of the schoolboy. The knowledge that the human race took three hundred years to clarify the concepts we now call momentum and kinetic energy should prevent the teacher from becoming impatient with his pupil for not grasping the notions in a few minutes. [4]

314

How splendidly put! How important is the "groping" to the proper development of mathematical insight! And when we consider how little "groping" is allowed and the frequently misunderstood notion about the role of proof, we begin to become aware of some causes for the reactions of students to the study of geometry. But what of the concept of proof and the role of intuition in its development?

Students often believe that if they use deductive proof in mathematics they will be able to find out something that they were not aware of previously. They are also frequently informed that the mathematician uses deductive proof in this manner, that is, to find out what he did not know before he started. While this statement has some truth in it, it is also misleading. When we arrive at a proof, we have established the permanency and the certainty of a given proposition. That is one of the gains derived from doing the proof. But the concept contained within the proof itself, the proposition under consideration, is generally accepted *before* the attempt is made to create a deductive demonstration. Is it not usually the case that a mathematician will not undertake to find a proof for a proposition until he believes it to be true?

For the most part, geometrical relationships should be fully known to and accepted by our students before they undertake to prove them. As a matter of fact, a recent report of the British Mathematical Association goes so far as to state that "until this has been to some extent acquired, attempts to reason on the facts are constantly hampered. The paradox may also be ventured that in many cases until a fact is obvious, argument will be of little avail." [5] The report later goes on to say that ". . . a boy ought to feel fully convinced by mere intuition . . . conviction should be reached without formal proof and by his own activity." [6] The report flatly states that the purpose of proof is neither the discovery nor the realization of the fact. Rather, the role of proof is seen to be an aid to understanding why things are what they are, as well as to confirm a fact and to settle all doubt about it. Thus, intuition is the creator and logic is the vehicle for confirmation; or, in the words of the same report, ". . . the path is blazed by the one, consolidated by the other." [7] What a far cry from the notion that deduction will enable us to uncover hitherto unseen facts!

Many educators have expressed concern over the fact that students are attempting to prove relationships that are obvious. Hence, geometry is seen as a form of nonsense task. Why bother to "prove" something you know is true? While there is no desire to bother students about proving obvious relationships, the role of proof as just discussed is verification. In addition, since proof also adds to our understanding of why things are what they are, it would seem to be an important undertaking for most propositions. The proof confirms for all to see that a given proposition is indeed a theorem, that a statement will always hold (or fail to hold, as the case may be). It is a means of convincing others—a means that could eliminate much sorrow were it only available to us in other fields, such as politics and international relations. And this is also what makes mathematics unique. In what other area of life can we so effectively establish the certainty of ideas?

The importance of the free development of ideas through the use of intuition based upon geometrical perceptions cannot be overemphasized. This is one of the major reasons for the study of geometry in the first place. In a most unusual work probing into the very heart of the invention of mathematical ideas, Hadamard has pointed out that most mathematicians think in terms of geometrical representations of the ideas under consideration. Visual images in the mind serve as the stuff from which mathematical inventions are realized. The importance of this for teachers of mathematics is plainly stated by Hadamard: "Between the work of the student who tries to solve a problem in geometry or algebra and a work of invention, one can say that there is only a difference of degree, a difference of level, both works being of a similar nature."[8] Thus, the previous statement of the British Mathematical Association would seem to be reemphasized here. Indeed, the entire process of invention growing out of the intuitive consideration of mental, visual images is considered to be so vital by Hadamard that he leaves little room for question as he concludes that this process ". . . gives the leading thread, without which one would be like the blind man who can walk but would never know in what direction to go."[9] How interesting a parallel for describing the behavior of many of our students in geometry today.

There may be some who wonder about the absence of the claim that the study of geometry per se will help students to think more logically in all areas of life. This has not been an accidental ommission. We are presently at a point of development where few educators, if any, believe this to be a tenable position. If one really thinks that the study of geometry will, as such, result in logical thinking in other areas, all he need do is to read the local newspapers to find out how unscientifically many scientists will attack problems in politics and human affairs. The objections to this goal are well stated in a recent report considering the improvement of the secondary school mathematics curriculum. The Commission on Mathematics of the College Entrance Examination Board asserts,

> Training in mathematics based on deductive logic does not necessarily lead to an increased ability to argue logically in situations where insufficient data exist, and where strong emotions are present. It is a disservice to the student and to mathematics for geometry to be presented as though its study would enable a student to solve a substantial number of his life problems by syllogistic and deductive reasoning.[10]

But this is not to say that geometry cannot be taught in a manner that would result in such transfer of the use of logic. On the contrary, it can. Perhaps the prime example of just such an achievement is the work of Harold Fawcett, who conducted a class in geometry in the laboratory school at Ohio State University and accomplished much in helping his students face all problems more logically.[11] However, the outcome was a product of the methods of Fawcett rather than of the content of geometry. Therefore, while it is possible to emphasize critical thinking in the teaching of geometry, children will not think more logically simply because they have undertaken the study of it. Exercise may build muscles, but mental exercises will not strengthen the mind in the same way.

Let us briefly review the important ideas to be considered as geometry is developed. First and foremost, geometry will enable us to add to our knowledge of nature as we study the size and shape of forms, as well as the interdependence of form and function. This is an outcome that flows directly from our work in algebra. Second, geometry (Euclidean geometry) has offered mankind a prime example of what the mind of man can accomplish when reason rather than passion is his guiding force. Third, historically geometry has been the vehicle for the development of deductive proof, and as such, it offers a fine opportunity to help students develop an understanding and appreciation of deductive logic in mathematics. An important beginning is made in emphasizing the significance of proof in mathematics. Finally, and much more subtly, we again point up the difference between the mathematical thing and the physical thing, as the interaction between these two is once again clarified in a number of meaningful situations.

Before turning to the study of the geometry itself, let us take a moment to consider rigor. One of the chief concerns of the many curriculum improvement studies has been an improvement of the degree of rigor in the school program. We are seldom as rigorous as we would like to be in undertaking the teaching of mathematics, but is this necessarily a weakness in our program? The important question would seem to be, Are we as rigorous as we have to be at the moment? Probably each of us has been a student in a class in which the teacher's standard of rigor for his students far exceeded that which he demanded of himself. You can well imagine the feeling of frustration and resentment experienced by each student as he found that one man's rigor was another man's excuses. But the instructor was not solely at fault. It is the very nature of mathematics that makes such occurrences commonplace. Willoughby, in considering rigor, has put the problem into an interesting perspective by indicating that he was "willing to agree that rigor may be central to mathematics. However, when it is simply memorized, without an understanding and appreciation of its need, it is central in the same sense that the hole is central in the doughnut. Sterile rigor is neither more appetizing nor more nutritious to the young mind than the hole in the doughnut is to the young body."[12]

In his discussion, Willoughby also points out some of the well-known weaknesses in Euclid, but he follows this with the important idea that the "ultimate justification" of mathematics lies in the fact that "it works" when applied to the real world. This shall be our watchword throughout.

Finally, the work in geometry offers us an excellent opportunity to demonstrate the relationships that exist between various branches of mathematics. The interplay possible between geometry and algebra will be emphasized, and concepts from solid geometry and coordinate geometry will be considered. An introduction to vectors will also be presented. The involvement of these several mathematical areas is not meant to diminish the vital importance of the ideas of plane geometry. Rather, it is an attempt to place all the concepts into better perspective with the hoped-for result that students will see more in each branch of mathematics and thereby more in mathematics as a whole. A highlight of this work will be a geometric consideration of the conic sections. This may appear to be out of place here, but plane geometry seems to provide an opportunity for an interesting introduction into this important area of study, which shall be treated in greater depth analytically.

In the chapters to follow, the significant areas of plane geometry will be considered in turn, with suggestions presented later as to where and how the ideas may be extended to consider solid and coordinate geometry concepts. No attempt will be made in the limited space given to geometry here to consider all the important concepts of a tenth year course in plane geometry. That is a book in itself. Instead, those ideas deemed to be of greatest significance will be examined and specific suggestions will be presented for the active involvement of students with the concepts in question. This, in itself, poses a task of no small proportion. We are now ready to get on with just that task.

INTRODUCTION

It would seem that a natural beginning would be one that grows out of the work done in informal geometry prior to the study of algebra. The experimental kind of exploration of the various shapes and figures that are found all about us leads nicely to the consideration of the following question: What is the best shape to use if we had to construct an oil tank that must hold 7500 gallons of oil? Shall we make the tank a rectangular solid? a sphere? some other shape? What shall we do? How shall we proceed?

Since 7500 gallons would occupy a volume of some 1000 cu. ft., let us use the latter figure for the sake of convenience. What shall determine the shape to use? One important criterion will be the amount of metal that will have to be used to make the tank. If you were the manufacturer, you certainly would want to use as little metal as you needed to do the job in order to keep your costs down. Will the shape affect the amount of metal needed? For example, will a sphere require more metal to hold the same amount of oil as a cube? Students should be allowed time for guessing and discussing before becoming involved in more formal work. Guessing offers good incentive to find out who is correct in his theorizing. It serves to increase the desire to know.

Perhaps a good way to "take hold" of the problem would be to explore several figures and observe the results. We know that the volume will be fixed: 1000 cu. ft. We are concerned with the surface areas of the various containers that will enclose such a volume. Let us arbitrarily choose to explore three shapes as a start: a rectangular solid, a cube, and a sphere. Any others would also be suitable. In order to be better able to examine the results, a chart is constructed, such as that shown in Figure 15-1. Remember that in each case the volume is 1000 cu. ft., so we may choose dimensions accordingly. At this point the students compute the various surface areas and enter the results into the chart and compare. If the work is done correctly, the following results will be found:

> Rectangular solid: 850 sq. ft. (for the given solid)
> Cube: 600 sq. ft.
> Sphere: about 483 sq. ft.

Other rectangular solids with a volume of 1000 cu. ft. are also checked. It appears that the sphere would make use of a good deal less material in order to hold within it an equal amount of oil. While there is a substantial saving on just one tank, this mounts up sharply when we think in terms of producing large quantities of such items. The shape of things may well be determined by the fact that a given shape is more pleasing to the eye, but it may also be be-

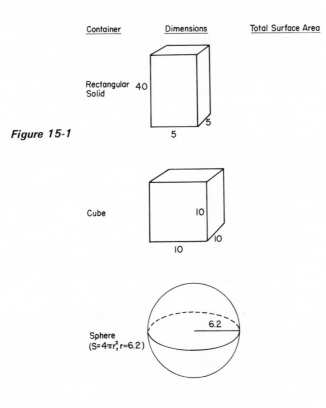

Figure 15-1

cause of some additional considerations that are equally important. We may then proceed to explore similar situations including: Why is a teapot round? Why are soap bubbles shaped like spheres? What is the largest area a farmer can enclose with 88 feet of fencing?

In each case, the point is made that the shapes of natural or man-made objects are very important and are in no small way related to the function, use, and (in the case of man-made objects) construction of the things in question. This is a theme we shall return to often as we develop the work of geometry. It is no less surprising to find that nature too is a fine architect and is apparently aware of these all-important considerations. The soap bubble is but one example of this. We shall meet more later.

This beginning work can be made as brief or as extensive as desired. For example, the entire discussion can be translated into two-dimensional space as the farmer's problem about the fence enclosing maximum area is considered. Some of the many questions that can be pursued are:

> If a sphere encloses the greatest amount of volume for the least surface area, does it follow that a circle encloses the greatest area for the least amount of circumference?
> If we keep the perimeter constant (88 sq. ft.), what will happen to the area as we increase the number of sides of the polygon?
> If we limit the discussion to triangles, does any special triangle enclose greater area if the perimeter is fixed?

This work also lends itself to exploration and construction. In working with the solids it may be very helpful to have the students construct the various forms in question and then proceed to measure in order to compare areas and volumes. Using squared paper and drawing plane figures can lead to the same kind of experiences in two dimensions. At this point we wish to present as little assistance to students as possible, at the same time that we provide experiences to enable the students to satisfy themselves as to what is taking place. Construction with compasses, drawing on squared paper and measuring, and making solids and measuring are all respectable activities to be encouraged.

USING TRIANGLES

In our study of shapes we now turn our attention to a most familiar form: the triangle. Why is this the shape that carpenters use when support is needed for shelves or cabinets? If we look at water towers, bridges, and light towers we again find that the supporting structures are always full of triangular-shaped bracing. Why are these supports not squares or rectangles or perhaps even pentagons? Is there something special about this particular shape, or is it that the triangle is a most appealing form to look upon? The answers to these questions may be found by conducting simple experiments using any one of a variety of materials. The common Erector set and Tinkertoys that are favorites of young boys are excellent devices. The familiar carpenter's rule is another. Simply connecting Popsicle sticks or cardboard strips with paper fasteners, will also serve equally as well. If we attach three strips together to form a triangle, and do the same for four or even five strips, we notice something surprising about the triangle (Fig. 15-2). It is a rigid shape. Somehow, we cannot change this shape without breaking the strips or the connections. This is not true of the other figures. The four strips bound together will "give" with the result that the shape may vary as indicated. We could hardly expect a shelf to remain upright with such a support. The students may like to experiment with a variety of shapes, using a variety of materials. The rigidity of the triangle will then become "known" to them in every sense of the word.

This beginning work could be extended to other uses of the triangle, such as that made by the Egyptians in building. Here the students may recreate the act of "rope-pulling" in order to establish a right angle. If it does not seem feasible to take a class outside and carry out the "rope-pulling" on a life-size basis, then certainly each student can do his or her own rope-pulling on a pegboard (Fig. 15-3). All that is required is a loop of rope with 12 equally spaced knots. If a pegboard is used, place two pegs into the board along the line of one side of the desired right angle. Loop the rope over the two pegs and, using a third peg, pull the rope until it is in a position that results in three equal spaces between knots on one side of the two original pegs and four equal spaces along the other. Then put the third peg in place. The next time these

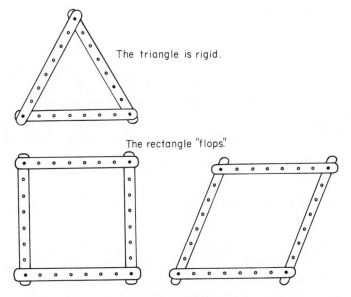

The triangle is rigid.

The rectangle "flops."

Figure 15-2

321

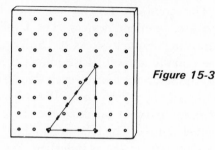

Figure 15-3

students hear about the Egyptian "rope-pullers" they will have a clear understanding of just what happened.

Students can also readily point out the numerous triangles they see all about them. As they enumerate the many different triangles in the room, in the school, in their homes, and outside, we not only help them to realize how useful a shape this is but we also open their eyes so that they can now see things that they have been looking at for years without taking notice. What a feeling of satisfaction it is for one to recognize familiar shapes that he was unaware of before. This is one small way in which geometry adds to our understanding and appreciation of nature.

CONGRUENCE

The triangles used for building, the triangles formed of rope, or the earlier triangles formed of metal or cardboard strips all have something in common. That something is the abstract idea of triangle that we will study more closely as we explore the important ideas of geometry. After many experiences with physical triangles, we begin to move toward the study of the geometrical triangle. Following a pattern that has generally been adhered to throughout the development here, we may begin with a problem that has within it as an integral part those ideas we wish to examine. One such problem follows:

> How could we measure the distance across a river without getting wet (Fig. 15-4)?

After the usual gestation period for student thought, a possible approach to a solution is presented for consideration:

> We wish to measure *AB*. Along the shore pace off some distance (for example, 10 feet) from *B* to a point *C*. Mark *C* with a stake or rock. Then walk off another 10 feet to point *D* and mark it. Now walk away from the river (and point *D*) at a right angle to *BD* until you reach a point in line with points *A* and *C*. Call this point *E* (Fig. 15-5).

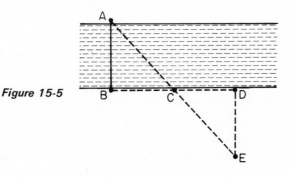

Figure 15-4

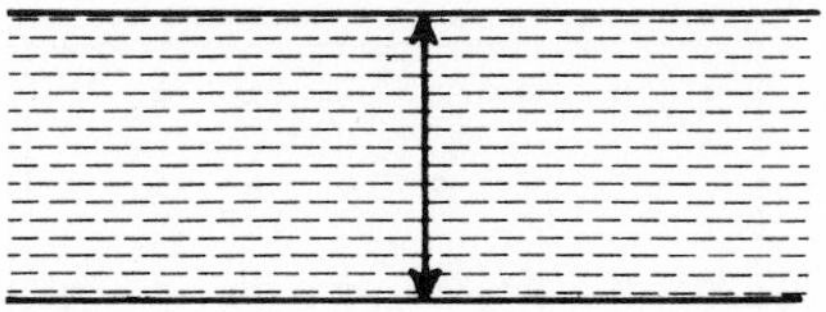

What is the reason for all of this pacing and marking? Have we made two triangles that may be considered equal? Look at $\triangle ABC$ and $\triangle CDE$. If one is a replica of the other, we may have the solution to the problem simply by measuring line *DE*. And this may be done without getting wet!

If the students are provided with a square foot of common pegboard and some golf tees and rubber bands or elastic cord, each one may lay out the problem and mark it off to scale. They are then in a better position to think about what is happening. Measurement may also be an aid to the formulation of ideas. A geoboard may serve equally well. These boards will be used frequently during the study of geometry (Fig. 15-6).

We now focus upon the key question: Is $\triangle ABC = \triangle CDE$? At this point, a consideration of the meaning of "equal" very nicely lays the groundwork for the introduction of the notion of congruence:

> Do equal triangles have the same shape?
> Do equal triangles have the same size?
> Do equal triangles have equal areas?

After a brief exploration of triangles that are shaped alike but of different sizes, as well as of triangles whose areas are equal but whose shapes are different, definitions of equal and congruent emerge:

Congruent triangles are triangles all of whose corresponding angles and sides are equal.
Equal triangles are triangles with equal areas.

The initial problem about measuring the distance across the river may be temporarily resolved by stating that indeed these triangles are congruent;

Figure 15-5

323

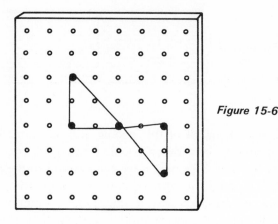

Figure 15-6

therefore, if we measure *DE* we will have a good approximation of the distance we sought—but we will examine this more carefully shortly. A brief word about the use of symbols is in order here.

We have already mentioned equal angles and equal lines in formulating the congruence definition. Recent suggestions for the improvement of geometry curricula have included the recommendation that we state that $m\angle A = m\angle B$, instead of $\angle A = \angle B$. In addition, line segments are described using horizontal bars above the letters; thus we see $\overline{AB} = \overline{DE}$, where once we saw $AB = DE$. Furthermore, in recent textbooks we will find such symbols as $\overrightarrow{AB}$, $\overleftrightarrow{AB}$, $\angle A \cong \angle B$, $\overline{BC} \cong \overline{DE}$, and $d(A,C)$.[13] All of these changes in symbolism resulting from the studies of the School Mathematics Study Group and the University of Illinois Committee on School Mathematics, among others, are attempts to add to the preciseness of mathematical statements and to eliminate ambiguity. In addition, changing definitions of the geometric forms themselves have resulted in the changing symbolism that may be found in many current textbooks, as well as in the publications of the several groups just mentioned. For example, recall the recommendation just cited: Students should write $m\angle A = m\angle B$, rather than $\angle A = \angle B$. In this way it is stated that the measures of the two angles are equal, rather than the angles themselves, which are defined to be made up of the union of two sets of points, the two rays.

This new notation differentiates between the set of points and the real number associated with them; and although it is not the intention here to diminish the importance of this, no attempt will be made to use the new symbolic forms unless they, in addition to serving an important mathematical goal, also serve an important learning goal from the students' point of view. Thus, to separate the measure of an angle from the angle would seem, at this point, to be an undesirable practice; for in addition to adding symbols and words (as the symbols are verbalized), it appears that little is gained in terms of meaningful acceptable ideas that are of consequence at the moment. On the contrary, in the students' eyes we once more seem to be splitting mathematical hairs—a practice that is familiar to all students of mathematics. In the manner of the development of algebra, the symbolism must be meaningful and we shall use only what at this time can be so understood. Later, as the need for additional precision becomes clear, we can help students rethink that with which they are already familiar and extend their knowledge.

The more familiar notation used to express equality of angles and the usual notation for expressing line segments and lines will be employed here. This is not to say that the revised notation is not desirable. It is simply not necessary at this stage. When the need can be made clear to the students and when the use of the symbols clarifies ideas, then the symbolism and vocabulary shall certainly be introduced.

The same general guidelines will be employed in the development of definitions. These ought to be as correct as we can make them and still keep them understandable to students, and they should enable us to make a maximum appeal to student intuition. Examples will be presented as the work in geometry develops. The logical weaknesses that we know to exist in Euclid's *Elements* will also be approached in this same manner. Even though we are aware of the fact that Euclid failed to deal with the concepts of betweenness (a point that is located between two other points), order, and separation, with resulting logical incompleteness, these omissions will be corrected only as and when the need to do so arises.[14] Once more, by need, reference is made to the requirements of the student at a given stage of his mathematical development. It is the chief criterion. This does not mean that we knowingly will teach incorrect ideas. Rather, we shall provide as much rigor and preciseness as the student may be able to deal with intelligently at a given level. Later, concepts shall be extended. It is the overall "feel" that the student will get for geometry that is primary. As he continues his studies, his ideas will be continually refined and made more precise.

After working with a variety of examples involving the differentiation between congruent and equal triangles, the students are ready to focus their attention on the important concept of congruence.

One of the problems with Euclidean geometry involved the "proofs" for the congruence theorems which concerned the notion of superposition.[15] Euclid did not provide the necessary postulates to clearly indicate how plane figures were to be moved about. In order to avoid this problem altogether, it is common practice for high school textbooks to simply take the congruence theorems as axioms and then to proceed from there. It is possible to assume one of the congruence theorems and then to prove the others, but the proofs are not really simple enough to use at this stage of the student's development. The activities to select are those involving students in attempts to intuitively establish just which triangle conditions are necessary for congruence. In this way, the appeal to intuition may help provide students with a good insight into the notion of congruence, as well as with an understanding of the congruence axioms.

It would be possible to use a compass and straight edge and by experimentation determine which equal parts result in congruence. Trying to construct triangles after having been given various parts in order to find out if the given parts determine a unique triangle would point out vividly which conditions are and are not tenable. But it is also good practice to introduce varieties of problems involving the conditions of the several congruence axioms in order to make the work at hand more meaningful. The combination of such problems and construction is developed more fully in the paragraphs that follow. Whatever the approach, a good deal of experience should be provided with these important congruence axioms before accepting and using them.

The problem requiring the width of a river to be measured could serve to initiate such an exploration of congruence, or a similar problem such as that which follows might be helpful:

> To find the distance across a pond, a boy put stakes at points A and B and at a convenient point C (Fig. 15-7). Walking along BC, he put another stake at D so that $BC = CD$. He did the same at E so that $AC = CE$. Will DE provide the distance wanted? (Once again, the pegboards may be used.)

The definition of congruence indicates that all the corresponding angles and corresponding sides must be equal. But the students may now consider the question of whether or not all these parts are necessary to establish congruence. Does the boy in the problem have enough information to conclude that the triangles he made are indeed congruent? Extracting the geometry from the situation, we focus upon two triangles with two pairs of equal length sides (Fig. 15-8).

How shall the question be resolved? Construction can play an important

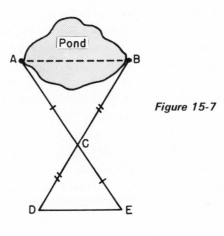

Figure 15-7

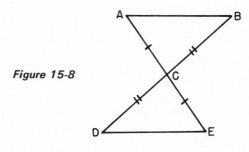

Figure 15-8

role here; and there are several possibilities, one of which would be to make a scale drawing on squared paper using compasses. The students could then measure *AB* and *DE* and compare. This may be repeated, changing the lengths and the angle at *C* but maintaining the conditions of the problem. What about the angles at point *C*? Are they equal? A protractor can provide some idea. After this investigation the students should explore additional cases before trying to draw conclusions. Here is another example:

> A farmer would like to know if two triangular parcels of land are identical in size. What is the least number of parts he has to measure, or must he measure all three angles and all three sides?

First, he measures one side of each parcel and finds that they are of equal length, 210 feet. Can he now conclude that the parcels are the same size? If we fix one side of a triangle, how many triangles of different size can we draw? (Students may construct or draw triangles here.)

Next, he measures a second side of each and finds that they each measure 150 feet. Can he now conclude that the pieces of land are the same size? Are the triangles congruent? Again, construction or drawing should enable students to test this for themselves. The farmer needs additional measures.

Finally, using a transit, he finds that the angles between the two measured sides are equal in measure. Can he now conclude that the triangles are congruent, that is, that the land parcels are identical in size? Once again the students may construct a scale drawing or simply use the methods for construction of triangles, given particular parts, to decide. If it seems that this information "fixes" the triangle, additional constructions could be undertaken with these same parts in order to demonstrate conclusively that the resulting triangle always has the given shape and size.

In this way we actually make several beginnings. Of course, there is a need for additional problems of this sort to establish firmly what is happening, but basically these things take place:

1. We establish an intuitive base for congruence in general and the congruence axioms in particular.
2. We review, by application, several basic constructions of informal geometry: constructing a line segment equal to a given line segment

and constructing an angle equal to a given angle, as well as construct-ing a triangle given two sides and the included angle.

As we proceed, we will also review our notation: the way in which we designate equal angles and equal sides and the manner in which we label the diagrams. But what is more important, in each case we will have abstracted a geometric diagram from a physical situation, again emphasizing the differ-ence between mathematics and physical things. These ideas have been revisited as a result of new classroom activities undertaken by the students. We have tried to involve the students in problems of interest with the neces-sary review growing out of the tasks at hand. Now that we have a fund of experiences to draw upon we can proceed to develop the other congruence axioms in a similar manner. Some problems that may be used are provided here.

To establish angle-side-angle (ASA):

A river and three trees (a cherry, a birch, and an oak) are in a field. If you had to construct a scale plan showing these, could you complete your plan without crossing the river? (See Fig. 15-9.)

Some boys at the beach wanted to measure the distance of a ship from the shore (AB). One boy paced off $CD = 60$ feet and then he and his friend measured the angles to the boat at C and D. They then walked away from the shore at equal angles until they met at E. Which line pro-vides the distance desired? Why? (See Fig. 15-10.)

To establish side-side-side (SSS):

If the farmer in the earlier problem, in which he was attempting to determine if two plots of land were identical, had measured the three sides of the triangular plot, would this have provided the necessary information?

To map an area bounded by straight lines ($ABCDE$) the area was divided into triangles by drawing the diagonals from a single point. Measure all lines and diagonals. Will this method provide enough infor-mation? (See Fig. 15-11.)

An interesting exercise along these lines appears in a recent publication from Canada.[16] A scalene triangle is drawn on the chalkboard and the stu-

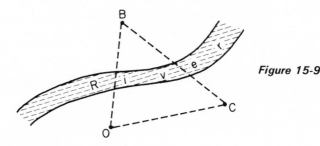

Figure 15-9

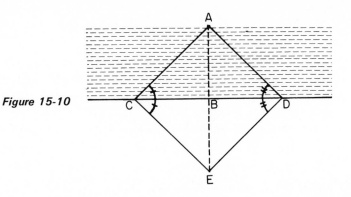

Figure 15-10

dents are asked to make a scale drawing of the triangle at their seats. The students are permitted to come to the board and perform any desired measurements of sides or angles in an attempt to discover the minimum number of parts they need in order to be able to fix the triangle. As they try various combinations of parts, the students become aware of the congruence axioms as well as those combinations that will not establish the triangle. Additional examples are explored as needed in order to verify any findings.

Proceeding in the manner described soon results in the study of the question, Will any three parts of a triangle enable us to establish congruence? In addition to experimentation through measurement and construction, some curious problems may be presented that emphasize the need for careful consideration of the importance of correspondence of equal parts. Here are two such examples that appeared in a New York State Bulletin:[17]

$\triangle ABC$ has $AB = BC$ and $\angle A = \angle C$ (Fig. 15-12). Any line from point B intersecting side AC (such as BE) divides the triangle into two triangles with three equal parts, but the triangles are not necessarily congruent. In Figure 15-13 the altitude to the hypotenuse (CD) also creates two triangles which agree in four equal parts, and yet the triangles are not congruent. In the first case the angle is not the included angle. In the second case, angle-side-angle

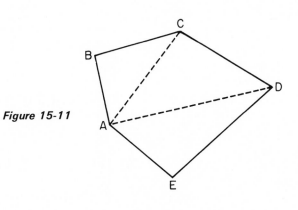

Figure 15-11

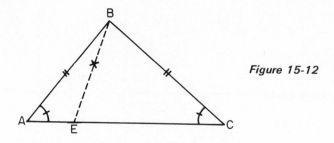

Figure 15-12

is present but these parts are not corresponding parts. This is a good time to emphasize what is meant by the word *corresponding*. The students must know that corresponding parts may be identified by looking opposite the equal angles or sides. These parts are in the same relative position with respect to the other angles and sides of the triangle. For example, in the second problem the following would be the case:

Correspondences		Equalities	
$\triangle BCD$	$\triangle ACD$	$\triangle BCD$	$\triangle ACD$
$\angle 3 \longleftrightarrow \angle 4$		$\angle 3 = \angle 4$	
$\angle B \longleftrightarrow \angle A$		$\angle B = \angle 1$	
$\angle 2 \longleftrightarrow \angle 1$		$\angle 2 = \angle A$	
$BC \longleftrightarrow AC$		$CD = CD$	
$BD \longleftrightarrow AD$			
$CD \longleftrightarrow CD$			

In this case it is the right angle that serves as an indicator of the corresponding parts. Since BC is opposite the right angle in $\triangle BCD$, the corresponding side would be that opposite the right angle in the other triangle, i.e., AC. The other corresponding parts may be determined in like manner.

The first case we cited, often called the side-side-angle (SSA) case (although another arrangement of the letters generally helps students to remember to avoid this situation), is also referred to as the ambiguous case. Construction is an excellent way for students to become acutely aware of

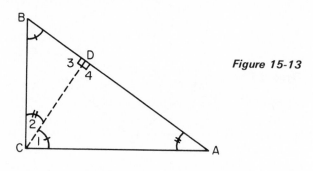

Figure 15-13

the fact that with these given parts, not one but two triangles are a distinct possibility. Hence, the given parts are not sufficient to establish a congruence. We will discuss this further, as well as the AAS and right triangle congruences, in the chapter on parallels.

PROOFS

Armed with the congruence postulates, we are prepared to begin to examine "proofs." It is the custom in courses in geometry to use the famous T-bar proof, the statement-reason format. This rigid form and the attempts at logical perfection, which are desirable at advanced levels, are at best questionable in the secondary school. It may well be that demanding each step in a proof to be carefully justified is actually creating results that are opposite from what was intended. The Canadian publication cited earlier explains this situation in an elegant manner:

> In school, the avoidance of certain logical subtleties is not a serious offence and may even be a virtue. What is a serious offence is to give the student the impression that mathematics is just a waste of time. . . . The majority of students who write out proofs of such results with the authority for each step carefully cited, do so to oblige the teacher or to keep out of trouble. Very few do it because they feel in their hearts that such a result needs careful proof. They are not thinking, nor are they learning to think; they are carrying out a prescribed ritual. When students feel their time is being wasted, they are being driven away from mathematics and logical thinking.[18]

The report goes on to suggest that geometry be taught as an exercise in "informal reasoning."

For the many reasons stated previously, deductive proof is seen to be an important part of the development of geometry to be presented here. In order to keep the important ideas in focus, however, we shall try not to become victims of rigid formulations for the proofs that are considered.

The Report of the Commission on Mathematics, in considering the case for a "logically unimpeachable treatment of Euclidean geometry suitable for use in secondary schools," arrived at the conclusion that no such treatment exists. What is more, the report cautioned against "boring students with logical subtleties" and goes on to recommend that "textbook writers and teachers should feel free to modify the Euclidean development to attain a more incisive and interesting program."[19] That is exactly what will be set forth here.

Since it is the reasoning that is primary and not the form in which it is cast, the key ideas in the development of proofs will be brought out, with reasons stated wherever they may not be obvious. Perhaps the presentation of one such proof will make the intent clear.

The Triangle

In the work with triangles completed thus far, we had occasion to deal with intersecting lines. The problem which involved the attempt to find the width of a pond was a case in point. What of the relationship between the angles formed by such lines? For example, is $\angle ACB$ equal to $\angle DCE$? (See Fig. 15-14.) In the problem mentioned, these angles were equal. Let us try another pair of lines to determine if this relationship will hold. The students may examine several different pairs of intersecting lines and by measurement determine that the vertical angles always appear to be equal. Can we try all such possible pairs of lines? Unless we approach the problem in some other way we may never be absolutely certain that a pair of lines does not exist somewhere that will form unequal vertical angles. Logical deduction can help us. If we can provide "proof," we can be sure for all time. A proof of this relationship is presented to establish certainty and to illustrate the point of the earlier discussion of form and degree of rigor.

> **Prove:** $\angle 1 = \angle 2$
> **We Know:** AB and CD are straight lines intersecting at E (Fig. 15-15).
>
> $\angle 1$ is a supplement of $\angle 3$
> $\angle 2$ is a supplement of $\angle 3$
> Therefore: $\angle 1 + \angle 3 = 180°$
> $\angle 2 + \angle 3 = 180°$
>
> $\angle 1 + \angle 3 = \angle 2 + \angle 3$ Since both sums are 180°, they are equal.
> $\angle 1 = \angle 2$ Subtract $\angle 3$ from each side.

Now that we have completed our deductive demonstration, we have changed the proposition regarding vertical angles into a theorem. But what is more important, we have eliminated any doubt about the fact that whenever any two straight lines intersect, vertical angles formed will always be equal angles. We need not try any more specific cases: We now know this property holds in all cases. There is no other way in which this fact could have been established (aside from different proofs) since we could not possibly have examined every situation.

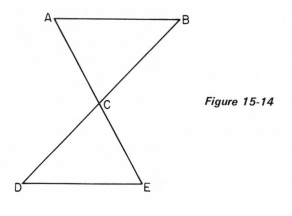

Figure 15-14

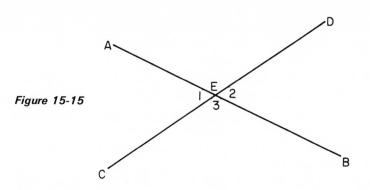

Figure 15-15

The form of the preceding proof is much like that generally employed when one works with algebraic ideas. It does not follow the strict statement-reason form so often found in geometry textbooks. It does, however, present just about everything that is necessary to make the argument clear to the reader. It would seem helpful to students to refrain from writing the obvious but to be specifically clear about questionable statements. For example, instead of stating "things equal to the same or equal quantities are equal to each other," it may be more beneficial to students if they present the specific parts under discussion. In the proof we just completed, the simple statement that both sums are 180° tells more, in fewer words, than does the equality axiom. The same is true of the final statement. Rather than use the general statement of the subtraction axiom, let us state specifically what *is* being so subtracted. Thus, there need be little mystery in the mind of the student about what is or is not being added or subtracted, as the case may be. At the same time that we seek to eliminate unnecessary formalism, we also wish to add to the clarity of ideas.

The use of the diagrams in developing the deductive argument has often come under fire. The figures we draw are not the concepts of geometry but merely a representation of these concepts. As such it is quite possible to be misled by a diagram since we may be unaware of using many unstated assumptions about the ideas under consideration. To highlight this danger, the proof of the fact that all triangles are isosceles is generally offered together with the caution that pure logic must persist rather than the intuitive notions contained in or derived from any representative pictures. Allendoerfer discusses just this point and states that "the student is taught that figures are only a crutch to his insight, but that his reasoning is supposed to be independent of the figures which he has drawn."[20]

This same matter is considered by Sitomer, who recommends that students should or should not be admonished for drawing conclusions from the diagrams instead of by pure logic, according to their mathematical ability.[21] Do not permit the top mathematics students to use conclusions based upon observation, says Sitomer, but do accept this as valid from those less able. These are interesting arguments.

The Triangle

Considering the importance of visualization in the act of creating mathematics, as discussed earlier, and considering our goals of maximum appeal to the intuition and de-emphasis of the strictly logical form, it would seem that, despite some shortcomings, the use of diagrams to gain both sight and insight into what is happening would be virtually a necessity. Make the necessary cautions if you are so inclined, but encourage the use and construction of diagrams by the students, virtually all students. Here is a splendid visual representation for the mathematical ideas under consideration. Let us take advantage of it and indeed encourage reliance upon figures, rather than turn away from them in order to serve the needs of logic. Evidently, seeing and reasoning are integral parts of a single process for the majority of our students. Let us try to develop such abilities rather than discourage them.

In discussing proof, we should mention the proof of the theorem concerning the base angles of an isosceles triangle. This famous theorem, which was called the *pons asinorum*, is a good case in point with regard to suggestions for the improvement of school geometry. (The pons asinorum, or "bridge of asses," was a turning point in the career of budding mathematicians: Those who could master the theorem crossed the bridge into the study of mathematics; those who could not, failed to go on.) Traditionally, this theorem has been proven by adding a line to the diagram—either by drawing the angle bisector of the vertex angle or by using the median to the base. The former results in congruence by SSS (Fig. 15-16).

The School Mathematics Study Group (SMSG), however, has attempted to avoid certain logical problems entailed in these proofs by using a different approach. In an attempt to overcome the criticism of superposition as em-

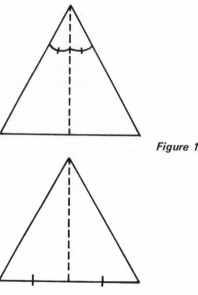

Figure 15-16

334

ployed by Euclid, the SMSG geometry specifically defines how the vertices are matched as one figure is thought of as being moved onto another.[22] For example, if we were to show which vertices go where in describing the congruence between two triangles, $\triangle ABC$ and $\triangle DEF$, we would write the following:

$$A \longleftrightarrow E$$
$$B \longleftrightarrow F$$
$$C \longleftrightarrow D$$

When the triangles "fit" perfectly, the correspondence is called a congruence. The order in which the vertices are listed affects the matching of vertices. Thus, the first letter of one triangle is A, which corresponds to the first listed letter of the second triangle, E. If we wished A and F to correspond, we would list the F first. The proof of the isosceles triangle theorem is then undertaken in the following manner:

Prove: $\angle B = \angle C$
Given: $\triangle ABC$ with $AB = AC$ (Fig. 15-17).

The plan behind the proof is to show that the following correspondence between $\triangle ABC$ and $\triangle ACB$ is a congruence: $ABC \longleftrightarrow ACB$. Under this correspondence we see that

$$AB \longleftrightarrow AC$$
$$AC \longleftrightarrow AB$$
$$A \longleftrightarrow A$$

This results in the equality of two sides and the included angle of $\triangle ABC$ with the corresponding parts of $\triangle ACB$. Thus by the SAS axiom of congruence

$$\triangle ABC \cong \triangle ACB$$

and

$$\angle B = \angle C$$

since they are corresponding parts of congruent triangles.

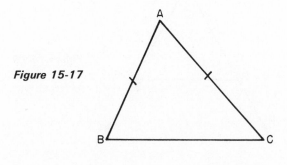

Figure 15-17

It may seem strange to learn that, in effect, the triangle is shown to be congruent to itself. But this will be true only of triangles with at least two sides of equal lengths.

The use of the angle bisector in attempting the proof of this theorem results in circular reasoning, for the proof that every angle has a bisector is based upon the "base angles of an isosceles triangle" theorem. The SMSG proof avoids this criticism. But the logical correctness of the SMSG approach seems to be out of place at this point in the mathematics curriculum. As far as our students are concerned, it may well seem to make too much of too little.

Another alternative for the proof of this particular theorem follows. It makes use of neither the angle bisector nor the median.

Prove: $\angle B = \angle C$

We Know: $\triangle ABC$ is isosceles with $AB = AC$ (Fig. 15-18)

Our Plan: If we can show that $\angle 1 = \angle 2$, then $\angle B = \angle C$ since the supplements of equal angles are equal to each other. This we will attempt through congruent triangles.

Extend AB and AC equal lengths to points D and E respectively.

Draw BE and CD. The diagram now appears as in Figure 15-19.

We focus on the two overlapping triangles, $\triangle ADC$ and ABE. Separating these triangles may add to the clarity of the proof (Fig. 15-20).

We have corresponding parts equal: SAS

S: $AB = AC$	Given
A: $\angle A = \angle A$	
S: $AD = AE$	By addition of the following equalities:

$$AB = AC$$
$$\underline{+\ BD = CE}$$
$$AD = AE$$

Thus $\triangle ADC \cong \triangle ABE$ and $\angle D = \angle E$, $DC = EB$

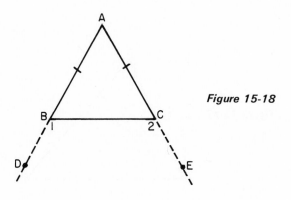

Figure 15-18

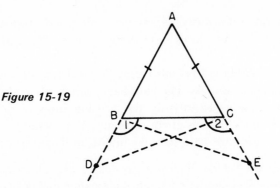

Figure 15-19

This results in $\triangle DBC \cong \triangle ECB$ by SAS

$$\text{S:} \quad DC = EB$$
$$\text{A:} \quad \angle D = \angle E$$
$$\text{S:} \quad BD = CE$$

Thus $\angle 1 = \angle 2$ and $\angle B = \angle C$

We have seen a few of the variety of proofs for the famous pons asinorum or "bridge of asses" of Euclid. The fact that propositions can be established in many different ways is important if students are to be encouraged to search out proofs of their own. The only test to apply to proofs should be the one of logical soundness, interpreted in terms of the particular level of development. There cannot be an abstract logical standard for all students at all times.

The last proof may well be a suitable place for the introduction of overlapping triangles. Bringing out the triangles through separation is facilitated by using colored chalk or using overlays on the overhead projector, each an important aid for the student. Since misconceptions may result from the separation process, care must be exercised. But some way to clearly see the parts involved is needed if the students are to be able to think through this

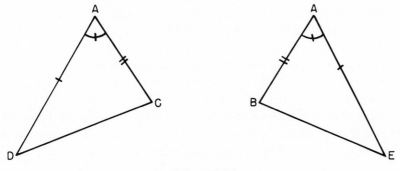

Figure 15-20

kind of situation. Of course, experience will build student confidence and skill in this area. Some things take time; visualizing relationships is one of those things.

The use of analysis may also provide students with an important tool for the discovery of proofs. The familiar process of working backward frequently helps students to identify the missing links in developing a proof. It also guides and channels their thinking. For example, if you wanted to prove that two lines are parallel, you might analyze the situation as follows:

> How can I show lines are parallel? I can do this if I can show (1) that a pair of alternate-interior angles are equal or (2) that a pair of corresponding angles are equal.
>
> How can I show equal angles? I can do this if I can show (1) that the angles are corresponding parts of congruent triangles or (2) that the angles are equal to the same angle.
>
> How can I show the triangles are congruent? I can do this if I can show. . . .

By following this chain of reasoning we may begin with what we seek to prove and work backward until we arrive at the given information, or some link with it. This method will not always aid our thinking, but it does provide us with a starting point as we begin to think about a theorem. It also offers a plan for working with the relationships we have already mastered as a probe for a proof.

INEQUALITIES

We explored the conditions under which triangles were congruent. We now turn our attention to those conditions under which parts of triangles are not equal to each other and seek out pertinent relationships. Our first real connection with science will be made here as we explore some fundamental properties of light rays. In the study of the behavior of light rays, we make use of mathematics in order that we may better understand what is happening. The result of this exploration is to add not only to our knowledge of light rays but also to our list of mathematical theorems. Both mathematics and science grow as a result of this natural partnership.

We begin with a simple problem, one we had investigated before: There are three trees in a field on both sides of a river. In our earlier work, we sought to make an accurate plan of these trees, using $\angle O$ and $\angle C$ and side OC (Fig. 15-21). For the sake of argument, specific values have been assumed for the two known angles: $\angle O = 40°$ and $\angle C = 60°$. The question to consider is, With the information you have before you, can you tell which tree

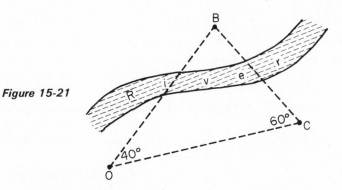

Figure 15-21

is closer to the birch tree? Is it the cherry or the oak? Remember, the distances (*OB* and *CB*) cannot be measured directly.

Look at the diagram and take a guess before you do any work to determine the answer. How can you check your guess? Of course, the same method used before to make a scale drawing could be used here. Measurement of the distances in question could resolve the problem. At this point, the students might be asked if they had correctly anticipated the outcome. In effect we are asking if a knowledge of the size of the angles of a triangle will provide us with information about the relative sizes of the sides of this same triangle. Since it is impossible to generalize from a single observation, we add several similar examples, varying the angle sizes, and in each case first try to guess which side is larger. We then verify the guess by constructing the triangle to scale and measuring. The problem may also vary. Indeed, after a few changes in angle size, the students may drop the problem situation entirely and concentrate on the abstract triangle and the relative measures of its angles and sides. Two notions are investigated: Does knowing the relative lengths of the sides give us any indication of the relative measures of the angles? Conversely, if we know the angle measurements, can we conclude anything about the lengths of the sides?

Once the students are virtually convinced that a given relationship holds, the question of proof arises in order to remove all doubt. As with most theorems, the proof of this particular relationship may be accomplished in a variety of ways. Both direct and indirect proofs are possible.

In any case, there are theorems about inequalities that usually precede the proof of this theorem. The basic theorem for inequalities, that of the exterior angle of a triangle being greater than either opposite interior angle, must be established if a logical order is to be maintained. We now have several choices as to how to order our theorems and postulates so that we do not fall prey to circular reasoning. As a matter of fact it may be of interest to note how these theorems and postulates have been arranged in various texts. The chart that follows shows the way in which the theorems were ordered in an old, classic textbook, in the SMSG textbook, and in a contemporary textbook:

Hall and Stevens (1903)[23]	SMSG (1960)[22]	Fehr and Carnahan (1961)[24]
Exterior angle theorem	Exterior angle theorem	Exterior angle theorem
Unequal sides theorem	Unequal sides theorem	Postulate: straight line is the shortest distance between two points
Unequal angles theorem	Unequal angles theorem	Corollary: two sides greater than the third
Theorem: two sides greater than the third	Theorem: two sides greater than the third	Unequal sides theorem
		Unequal angles theorem

Both the SMSG textbook and the Hall and Stevens textbook present indirect proofs for the unequal angles theorem. Of the three textbooks listed, only Fehr and Carnahan present a direct proof. They postulate the proposition that a straight line is the shortest distance between two points and from it derive the fact that two sides of a triangle are greater than the third. They then proceed to use this corollary in their proof. In the other two textbooks the proof of the sides of a triangle is derived through the use of the inequality theorems. So we see that we have more freedom to develop our own order of events than we might have suspected—provided we have adhered to the rules of logic. It is interesting to see how closely the work of Hall and Stevens (based on Euclid's *Elements*) matches that of the SMSG text. The term "modern" when applied to mathematics is indeed a strange word. But let us move on to the proofs themselves.

DIRECT AND INDIRECT PROOFS

Let us first examine a direct proof. We may then take a careful look at the meaning and importance of the indirect proof. A restatement of the proposition will keep our task clearly before us: If two angles of a triangle are unequal, the sides opposite them are unequal in the same order (Fig. 15-22).

Prove: $CB > CA$
We Know: $\triangle ABC$ with $\angle A > \angle B$

We begin by constructing $\angle BAD = \angle B$. Therefore, $\triangle ADB$ is isosceles and $DA = DB$.

$CD + DA > CA$	Sum of two sides of a triangle is greater than the third
$CD + DB > CA$	Substitution of DB for DA
$CB > CA$	$CB = CD + DB$

Thus, the direct proof is complete. Once we may use the fact that the sum of two sides of a triangle is greater than the third, the proof becomes a rather simple matter. The indirect proof is a bit more involved but it does not require

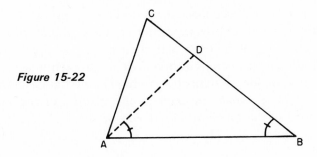

Figure 15-22

the "two sides greater than the third," theorem. In addition, the method of indirect reasoning is of special interest. Let us now examine this proof. Once again we state the proposition: If two angles of a triangle are unequal, the sides opposite them are unequal in the same order (Fig. 15-23).

Prove: $CB > CA$
Given: $\triangle ABC$ with $\angle A > \angle B$

There are three possibilities in comparing the lengths of the sides:

1. $CB < CA$
2. $CB = CA$
3. $CB > CA$

If the first possibility were true, then $\angle A$, which is opposite CB, would be less than $\angle B$, which is opposite CA, because of the theorem about unequal sides of a triangle. This is impossible, since we were given that $\angle A > \angle B$.

If the second possibility were true, then $\triangle ABC$ would be isosceles and $\angle A = \angle B$. But this contradicts the given information that $\angle A > \angle B$.

The only remaining possibility is the third.

Thus, it can be seen that the converse theorem that begins with the sides given unequal must be proved before this indirect proof can be established. In order to prove the converse of the theorem just presented, we first need to prove the basic theorem on triangle inequalities: the exterior angle of a triangle theorem. You can begin to get a sense of the relative order of ideas and their respective requirements.

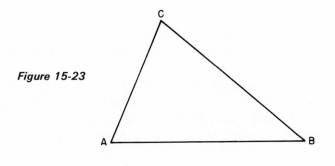

Figure 15-23

341

But let us take a closer look at the indirect proof, which we have just employed for the first time. It seems rather paradoxical that students generally experience a good deal of difficulty with these proofs, despite the fact that most reasoning outside the geometry classroom would proceed in a similar manner. For example, if a car simply stopped running, the mechanic, in trying to make the necessary repairs, would proceed in the manner of the indirect proof. Here is the proof of the theorem placed side by side with the thinking of the mechanic:

Proof	**Mechanic**
1. List all possibilities:	1. List all possibilities:
$$CB < CA$$ $$CB = CA$$ $$CB > CA$$	no gas clogged gas line broken fuel pump
2. Test the consequences of each: If $CB < CA$, then $\angle A < \angle B$, which is impossible since it was given that $\angle A > \angle B$. If $CB = CA$, then $\angle A = \angle B$, which is impossible since it was given that $\angle A > \angle B$.	2. Test the consequences of each: Put gas in car. It still does not start. Take apart all gas lines; clean and replace them. The car still does not start.
3. $CB > CA$ must be true since it is the only remaining possibility.	3. The trouble must be with the fuel pump. Replace it and the car works!

Of course, it may very well be that there are many other possibilities for the auto trouble that were not listed. A few causes were chosen to emphasize the comparison presented. This is, after all, the key consideration when one attempts to make use of the indirect method of proof: Have you considered all possibilities? At times it may not be so easy to answer that question; but when you can definitely list all the possibilities, the method is a powerful tool for proof. Not only is this type of reasoning employed by mechanics as they try to diagnose car troubles, but it is also used by many other members of our society. Doctors do exactly what the mechanic has done when they ask you for the symptoms you have with regard to an illness. They then make a tentative diagnosis and prescribe medicine. If you feel better, that is the end of it. If not, their assumption is contradicted and another possibility is explored.

The method of indirect proof is a natural thought process. If our students find it difficult, perhaps it is because they do not see that any of the patterns of thought we are attempting to develop in mathematics classes have any connection whatsoever with anything outside of that mathematics class. If we take the time to point out these similarities, we may have better opportunities for the development of such understandings.

LIGHT PATH THEOREMS

At the beginning of this section, it was mentioned that the study of inequalities enables us to become involved with important science concepts in an easy way. What could be of greater importance to man than the simple, and everywhere present, phenomenon of light? Though there is still a good deal that is unknown about the nature of light, one successful approach is to think of light as traveling along rays. Sunlight through a window and the light from a flashlight—both seem to move through the air in straight lines that appear to be parallel. As we employ the tools of geometry to learn more about this basic natural phenomenon, we are demonstrating directly one of the most important goals for the study of geometry: The interaction of mathematics with the physical world results in advances in each area. To clarify this, let us turn to some of the discoveries of the Greeks with regard to light as described by Euclid in his book *Optics*. Euclid observed what is now known as the law of reflection: If light rays strike a flat mirror, they are reflected so that the angle of incidence is equal to the angle of reflection. In Figure 15-24, a light ray from point A hits the mirror and is reflected to point B. Here $\angle 1$ is the angle of incidence (the angle made by the light ray and a perpendicular to the mirror surface as the light enters the mirror) and $\angle 2$ is the angle of reflection (the angle formed in the same manner as the ray leaves the surface of the mirror). Euclid observed that these angles were always equal. (Sometimes angles 3 and 4 are referred to as the angles of incidence and reflection. Since they too are equal we may use either pair.)

Using this basic law of light rays, and the facts of geometry, we may add to our knowledge of each. When you look into a mirror, you see the reflection of objects. In the preceding situation, if you were at point B, as you looked into the mirror you would see the reflection of the object at A. The light rays from A spread out in all directions and strike the mirror at many points, each ray being reflected in accordance with the reflection law. How many rays are reflected from point A to you at point B? Here is a ques-

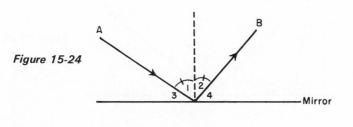

Figure 15-24

tion that our knowledge of geometry can help us to pursue. In fact, of all the rays only one such ray is reflected to point *B*. We will use the indirect method to establish this proof: We will assume that there are many such rays reflected to the observer, and we will examine the logical consequences of this assumption. Using a geometric arrangement for this particular proposition, we proceed.

> **Prove:** There is but one light ray reflected from point *A* to the mirror to point *B*.
>
> **We Know:** The angle of reflection must equal the angle of incidence. *AP* is a ray reflected to point *B* (Fig. 15-25).

Assume there is another ray, *AP′*, reflected to point *B*. Then $\angle 3 = \angle 4$ by the law of reflection, but this is impossible because $\angle 3$ is an exterior angle of $\triangle AP'P$; thus $\angle 3$ is greater than $\angle 1$. $\angle 2$ is an exterior angle of $\triangle BP'P$; thus $\angle 2$ is greater than $\angle 4$.

We now have contradictory statements:

$$\angle 3 > \angle 1$$
$$\angle 2 > \angle 4$$
$$\angle 1 = \angle 2 \qquad \text{(the reflection law)}$$

So $\angle 3$ must be greater than $\angle 4$, and by the reflection law if $\angle 3 \neq \angle 4$, *P′B* cannot be the reflected ray of incident ray *AP′*.

We must therefore conclude that of all the rays from point *A* to the mirror, only one is reflected to you at point *B* because only one can satisfy the law of reflection!

We carry this investigation a step further and ask the following question about this light ray path: Of all the possible paths that may be followed to get from point *A* to the mirror to point *B*, how does this one compare? Is it the shortest? the longest? What do you think? Here is an excellent place for the use of measurement to gain insight into the relationship. The students may draw several different pathways from *A* to the mirror to *B* and measure each to see how they compare (Fig. 15-26). The results may be kept in a table such as that which is shown on the top of the next page.

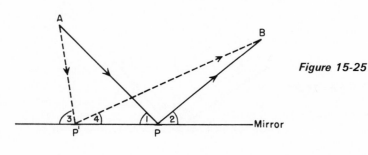

Figure 15-25

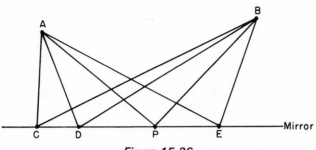

Figure 15-26

Pathway	Measure
light ray *APB*	
ACB	
ADB	
AEB	
AFB	
etc.	

Of course, the light ray path would have to be constructed to be certain of the equality of the angles of incidence and reflection. This in itself is interesting practice. The other lines may be drawn with a straightedge. The diagram should also be large enough (cover an $8\frac{1}{2} \times 11$ sheet) so that small differences of measure will be apparent. In this way the students may convince themselves of a fact that was found by the Greek mathematician Heron (about A.D. 100): The path of this ray is indeed the shortest path from the object to the mirror to a given point. In addition to everything else we may gain from such a study, we find that nature is economical. Although it is somewhat involved, the proof developed by Heron may be of interest to teachers. It confirms what the students have established experimentally. In order to develop his proof, Heron took advantage of a keen observation:

> He noticed that if an observer at *B* sees an object at *A*, in the mirror he seems to see the object at *A'*. Thus, the image of the object appears to be as far behind the mirror as the object itself is in front (Fig. 15-27). (This could be proved by showing that $\triangle ARP \cong \triangle A'RP$, an exercise the students could probably complete.)

Heron's argument was developed along these lines:

Given: The path of the light ray from *A* to the mirror to *B* is $AC + CB$. Any other path is $AD + DB$ (Fig. 15-28).

Prove: $AC + CB < AD + DB$

1. *F* is the image of *A* so that *AE* is $\perp m$, and $AE = EF$. (The image is as far behind mirror as the object is in front.)

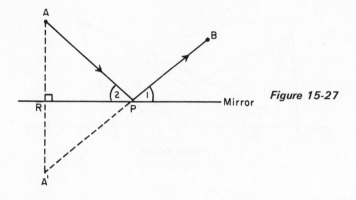

Figure 15-27

2. Heron concluded that $\triangle EAD \cong \triangle EFD$ by SAS: (S) $EA = EF$, (A) $\angle DEA = \angle DEF$, and (S) DE is a common side.
3. By the same reasoning $\triangle EAC \cong \triangle EFC$ by SAS.
4. Thus our proof is complete if we can show that

(a) $AC + CB < AD + DB$

or

(b) $FC + CB < FD + DB$

since $AC = FC$ and $AD = FD$ by congruent triangles.
5. Statement (b) is true if FCB is a straight line.
6. The mirror was represented by straight line m, thus $\angle 1 + \angle 4 + \angle 2 = 180°$.

$\angle 1 = \angle 3$: congruent triangles

$\angle 1 = \angle 2$: angles of incidence and reflection
7. Hence $\angle 3 + \angle 4 + \angle 1 = 180°$ or a straight angle by substitution of $\angle 3$ for $\angle 1$ and $\angle 1$ for $\angle 2$.
8. Thus FCB is a straight line $\longrightarrow FC + CB < FD + DB \longrightarrow AC + CB < AD + DB$. Q.E.D.

Let us step back a moment and take a good look at what we have done. On the face of it, it would seem that we have discussed some interesting applications of the inequality theorems. This is true, but we have accomplished much more. In physics we have added two laws about the behavior

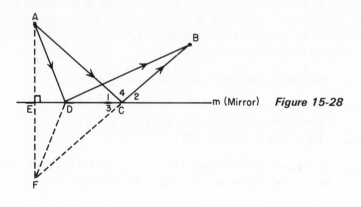

Figure 15-28

of light rays. In geometry we have added two theorems about the inequality of lines. These are listed here:

> **Theorem:** Of all broken line paths from point A to any point P on line m, and then to B, only one path is such that AP and PB make equal angles with m.
>
> **Theorem:** Of all broken line paths from point A to any point P on line m, and then to B, the path APB for which AP and PB make equal angles with m is the shortest path.
>
> **Physics Law:** There is only one light ray from an object that is reflected from a mirror to an observer.
>
> **Physics Law:** The lone light ray is the shortest path from the object to the mirror to the observer.

In effect we have provided a very real demonstration of the interaction of mathematics and the physical world in such a way as to add to our knowledge in each field, as well as to our understanding of our environment. This is far more than simply examining an application of a mathematical concept. Mathematics shapes our understanding of the world and is in turn affected by these findings. This is a message that must be shared with students of mathematics at every level if we are to tell the whole story of mathematics.

If the teacher finds that class interest and ability so warrant, this work with the paths of light rays can be extended to include the converse of one of the previous theorems. Briefly the statement would be:

> **Theorem:** If the path from point A to a point P on line m to point B is the shortest path from A to m to B, then the angles made with m by AP and BP are equal.

Physically, this theorem states that if the path of the light ray is the shortest path, then its angle of incidence is equal to the angle of reflection.

In addition, it is now possible to investigate a somewhat more complex reflection that we find in everyday use. Clothing stores sometimes have two mirrors hinged together (often three) so that a person can look at his side or back in order to see how well a suit or dress fits. If Figure 15-29 indicates the position of the mirrors, is it possible for a person standing at P to look into the mirror n and see the side of his body that faces mirror m? If a person at P is to see his left side in the mirror n, the light ray would have to travel from P to mirror m to mirror n and back to P again, as shown in the diagram. How can we be sure that the light ray leaving P and striking the mirror at some point X will be reflected to mirror n? And if it should be so reflected, how can we be sure that it will be reflected in such a way that it will eventually return to P? This is far from obvious, and it forms an interesting exercise for those who are able to consider it.

There are many interesting problems that can grow out of this discussion of light rays. The reflection laws do not apply only to light rays. They would,

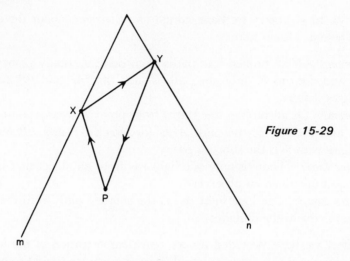

Figure 15-29

for example, explain the rebounding of a billiard ball on a pool table. Some sample problems for use are presented here.

1. A trucking company delivers merchandise from boats on a river to two towns, *A* and *B* (Fig. 15-30). If it wishes to build a single pier along the bank *m* to serve both towns, where should the pier be located so that the trucking distance will be shortest? (In this problem we may thank Heron for the solution. Build the pier at the point *P* on *m* which makes *AP* and *BP* form equal angles with *m*. How many such points are there?)

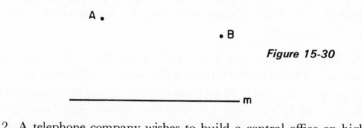

Figure 15-30

2. A telephone company wishes to build a central office on highway *h*, serving towns *A* and *B*. Where should *h* be located to keep the amount of wire needed as small as is possible? (See Fig. 15-31.)

Figure 15-31

3. A dress shop mirror extends down to the floor so that the customers can see their entire body as they try on dresses. Must the mirror be full length? How long must it be to do the job? (Perhaps Figure 15-32 will help. *AB* represents the person looking into mirror *m*. *A'B'* is the person's image. Prove your answer is correct.)

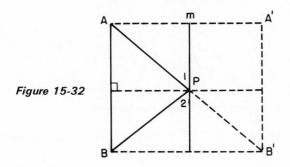

Figure 15-32

4. Two billiard balls are on the pool table as shown in Figure 15-33. Explain how the ball at *A* should be directed so that it will hit a side of the table and rebound to hit the ball at *B*.

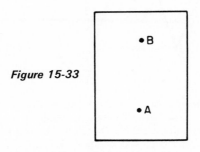

Figure 15-33

5. An observer at *A* looks into mirror *m* and sees the image of a clock at *B*. Explain how to find the point *P* on the mirror where the ray of light from the object is reflected to the observer (Fig. 15-34).

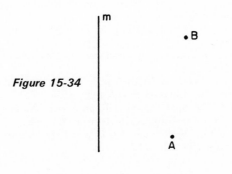

Figure 15-34

6. From town *A* there are two roads; each is 3 miles to the state highway *h*. Prove that a new road built to the state highway at a point *P* (between *B* and *C*) will be less than 3 miles, while one that meets the state highway at *R* must be greater than 3 miles (Fig. 15-35).

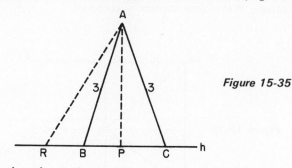

Figure 15-35

7. Prove that the perimeter of pentagon *ABCDE* is greater than the perimeter of triangle *ACE* (Fig. 15-36).

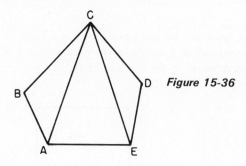

Figure 15-36

FOOTNOTES

1. Lancelot Hogben. *Mathematics for the Million*. W. W. Norton & Co., 1937, p. 114.
2. Carl B. Allendoerfer. "Deductive Methods in Mathematics." *In* National Council of Teachers of Mathematics, 23rd Yearbook: *Insights Into Modern Mathematics*. The National Council of Teachers of Mathematics, 1957, pp. 65–66.
3. W. W. Sawyer. *Mathematician's Delight*. Penguin Books, Inc. (paperback), 1943, p. 17.
4. *Teaching Mathematics in the Secondary Schools*. Ministry of Education Pamphlet No. 36, Her Majesty's Stationery Office, 1958, pp. 80–81.
5. *A Second Report on the Teaching of Geometry in Schools*. Mathematical Association (England), G. Bell and Sons, 1951, p. 5.
6. *A Second Report on the Teaching of Geometry in Schools*. Mathematical Association (England), G. Bell and Sons, 1951, p. 6.
7. *A Second Report on the Teaching of Geometry in Schools*. Mathematical Association (England), G. Bell and Sons, 1951, p. 9.
8. Jacques Hadamard. *The Psychology of Invention in the Mathematical Field*. Dover Publications, Inc., 1954, p. 104.
9. Jacques Hadamard. *The Psychology of Invention in the Mathematical Field*. Dover Publications, Inc., 1954, p. 105.
10. Report of the Commission on Mathematics. *Program for College Preparatory Mathematics*. College Entrance Examination Board, 1959, p. 23.
11. Harold P. Fawcett. *The Nature of Proof*. Reprint from National Council of Teachers of Mathematics, 13th Yearbook. AMS Reprint Co., 1966.
12. Stephen S. Willoughby. "Revolution, Rigor, and Rigor Mortis." *The Mathematics Teacher*. Vol. 60 (February, 1967), p. 108.

13. $\overrightarrow{AB}$: the ray with A as its end point and containing B.
    $\overleftrightarrow{AB}$: the line containing the two points A and B.
    $\angle A \cong \angle B$: angle A is congruent to angle B.
    $BC \cong DE$: line segment BC is congruent to line segment DE.
    $d(A,C)$: the distance from point A to point C.
14. See the following:
    Report of the Commission on Mathematics. *Appendices*. College Entrance Examination Board, 1959, pp. 109–111.
    Stephen S. Willoughby. *Contemporary Teaching of Secondary School Mathematics*. John Wiley & Sons, Inc., 1967, pp. 298–304.
    Paul H. Daus. "Why and How We Should Correct the Mistakes of Euclid." *The Mathematics Teacher*. Vol. 53, (November, 1960), pp. 576–581.
15. Carl B. Allendoerfer. "Deductive Methods in Mathematics." *In* National Council of Teachers of Mathematics, 23rd Yearbook: *Insights Into Modern Mathematics*. The National Council of Teachers of Mathematics, 1957, pp. 94–97.
16. *Geometry, Kindergarten to Grade Thirteen*. Report of (K–13) Geometry Committee. The Ontario Institute for Studies in Education, 1967, p. 65.
17. *Mathematics 10: Handbook*. Bureau of Secondary Curriculum Development. N. Y. State Education Department, 1962, p. 27.
18. *Geometry, Kindergarten to Grade Thirteen*. Report of (K–13) Geometry Committee. The Ontario Institute for Studies in Education, 1967, pp. 19–20.
19. Report of the Commission on Mathematics. *Appendices*. College Entrance Examination Board, 1959, p. 24.
20. Carl B. Allendoerfer. "Deductive Methods in Mathematics." *In* National Council of Teachers of Mathematics, 23rd Yearbook: *Insights Into Modern Mathematics*. The National Council of Teachers of Mathematics, 1957, p. 95.
21. Harry Sitomer. "Sight Versus Insight." *The Mathematics Teacher*. Vol. 60 (May, 1967), pp. 474–478.
22. School Mathematics Study Group. *Mathematics for High School: Geometry*, Part I. Student's Text, Yale University Press, 1961, pp. 97–100.
23. H. S. Hall and F. H. Stevens. *A School Geometry*, Parts I–IV. MacMillan and Co. Ltd. (London); St. Martin's Press (New York), 1961.
24. Howard F. Fehr and Walter H. Carnahan. *Geometry*. D. C. Heath & Company, 1961.

FOR INVESTIGATION AND DISCUSSION

1. What changes take place in the purposes of the study of geometry as we move from informal geometry to the more formal course of the senior high school?

2. Discuss whether the notion of "proof" is better taught in geometry or algebra classes.

3. Compare the arguments for and against the teaching of Euclidean geometry. Which of these arguments do you agree with? Why?

4. The logical order of mathematical ideas and the development of effective learning sequences may be in conflict. Discuss the nature of this conflict and present a single specific example to illustrate what is involved.

5. Describe the role of "proof" in mathematics and select a specific topic in plane geometry to illustrate how the role of proof will influence the manner in which the topic may be taught.

6. Critical thinking is often mentioned as one of the outcomes of the study of geometry. Discuss the feasibility of helping students to think more logically in general, as a result of studying plane geometry.

351

7. Select a topic that you have repeatedly met at different levels of your study of mathematics from grades one to 12. Show how your understanding was expanded each time the topic was restudied (i.e., grade five: $8 - 10$ can't be done; grade nine: $8 - 10 = -2$).

8. Select a topic from plane geometry and demonstrate how students will add to their understanding of this topic as they continue their training in mathematics beyond the high school.

9. Devise a lesson plan to help students to intuitively accept the congruence theorems: ASA, SSS, SAA.

10. Using the rebounding behavior of billiard balls, develop a lesson plan to help students begin to realize the interaction between mathematics and science.

11. Prove the converse of the theorem about the light ray path being the shortest distance. See the statement on page 347.

FOR FURTHER READING

Books

A Second Report on the Teaching of Geometry in Schools. Mathematical Association (England), G. Bell and Sons, 1951.

Nathan A. Court. *Mathematics in Fun and in Earnest.* The Dial Press, Inc., 1958.

Harold P. Fawcett. *The Nature of Proof.* Reprint from National Council of Teachers of Mathematics, 13th Yearbook. AMS Reprint Co., 1966.

Geometry: Kindergarten to Grade Thirteen. Report of the (K–13) Geometry Committee. The Ontario Institute for Studies in Education, 1967.

S. H. Gould. "Origins and Development of Concepts of Geometry." *In* National Council of Teachers of Mathematics, 23rd Yearbook: *Insights Into Modern Mathematics.* The National Council of Teachers of Mathematics, 1957, pp. 273–305.

Lancelot Hogben. *Mathematics for the Million.* W. W. Norton & Co., 1937, pp. 111–188.

Morris Kline. *Mathematics and the Physical World.* Thomas Y. Crowell Company, 1959, pp. 73–89.

Mathematics 10: Handbook. Bureau of Secondary Curriculum Development. N. Y. State Education Department, 1962.

National Council of Teachers of Mathematics, 17th Yearbook: *A Source Book of Mathematical Applications.* AMS Reprint Co., 1966, pp. 145–212.

Report of the Commission on Mathematics. *Appendices.* College Entrance Examination Board, 1959, pp. 109–174.

Periodicals

A. Henry Albaugh. "The Game of Euclid." *The Mathematics Teacher.* Vol. 54 (October, 1961), pp. 436–439.

Paul E. Cantonwine. "How To Develop Critical Thinking About Inter-Group Relations in the Geometry Classroom." *The Mathematics Teacher.* Vol. 42 (May, 1949), pp. 247–251.

Hope H. Chipman. "When I Teach Geometry." *The Mathematics Teacher.* Vol. 53 (February, 1960), pp. 140–142.

Harold P. Fawcett. "Quod Erat Demonstrandum." *The Mathematics Teacher.* Vol. 49 (January, 1956), pp. 2–14.

Stanley B. Jackson. "Congruence and Measurement." *The Arithmetic Teacher.* Vol. 14 (February, 1967), pp. 94–102.

Max Jeger. "The Present Conflict in the Reform of Geometry Teaching." *Mathematics Teaching.* (Autumn, 1965), pp. 22–32.

Morton R. Kenner. "Helmholtz and the Nature of Geometrical Axioms: A Segment in the History of Mathematics." *The Mathematics Teacher.* Vol. 50 (February, 1957), pp. 98–104.

Morris Klein. "The Straight Line." *Scientific American.* Vol. 194 (March, 1956), pp. 104–114.

Oswald Veblen. "The Modern Approach to Elementary Geometry." *The Mathematics Teacher.* Vol. 60 (February, 1967), pp. 98–104.

R. L. Wilder. "The Role of the Axiomatic Method." *The American Mathematical Monthly.* Vol. 74 (February, 1967), pp. 115–127.

16

PARALLELS AND QUADRILATERALS

PARALLEL LINES

We turn now to another important idea that can be extracted from nature: parallel lines. Here is a concept that is in everyone's experience. The paper in a notebook has lines upon it that seem to behave like the rays of the sun shining through your living room window. The tracks of a railroad, the opposite edges of the bricks in a building, and the banks of a river—all seem to share the characteristics of the sun's rays: The lines appear to be the same distance apart; they seem to move in the same direction; and no matter how far they are extended, they do not intersect each other. Parallel lines are indeed familiar.

As we explore the relationships inherent in parallel lines, we encounter both familiar and new ideas, including the method of indirect proof and the paths of light rays we met earlier. One of the important points to be discussed will be the development of proof for the angle sum of a triangle. This will lead us directly to consider some new additions to the number of congruence relationships we have available. We will also mark an important signpost when, in this chapter, we encounter the most famous postulate of all: Euclid's fifth postulate.

In order to continue our concentration upon areas common to student experience, we may make use of railroad tracks: Can we be sure that railroad tracks are parallel? Certainly if you stand between them and look down the

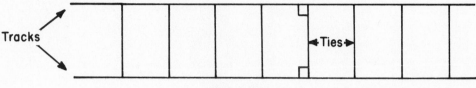

Figure 16-1

right of way, the tracks seem to meet. Geometry can help us to establish the parallelism. If we look at the tracks, we notice that they are joined by ties. Each railroad tie seems to be perpendicular to both tracks (Fig. 16-1). This can be checked by measuring, if necessary. Perhaps this in itself will provide us with sufficient information to show that the tracks must be parallel to each other. As we have now done many times, let us once again strip away the physical and concentrate upon the suggested geometrical ideas. We have two lines, each perpendicular to a third line. Can we prove that the two lines are parallel?

> ***Prove:*** $m \parallel n$ (Fig. 16-2)
> ***We Know:*** Lines m and n are each perpendicular to line T.

Let us assume that the lines are not parallel and observe the consequences of such an assumption.

Assume m and n are not parallel. They must therefore meet. Call their point of intersection A. How many lines from point A are perpendicular to T? Here we have two such lines, which is impossible because of the theorem that there can be only one such line from a point perpendicular to a given line.

Therefore lines m and n cannot meet; hence, $m \parallel n$.

We have taken a physical situation, extracted the geometry contained therein, and used our method of analysis to establish that since the tracks of the railroad are perpendicular to the railroad ties, they are parallel to each other. Indeed, this is one way in which the tracks can be properly laid. If we were to put down a single rail of track and choose any point not on the rail, we can always place at least one rail through the chosen point parallel to the first rail by the way in which we place the tie that connects them.

A periscope offers us still additional opportunities to add interest and

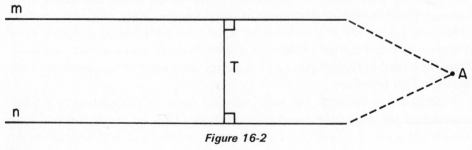

Figure 16-2

354

importance to the ideas of geometry as we deal with parallel lines. It is an instrument simple enough to be made by the students in the class and yet useful enough to be an important precision instrument aboard a submarine. In order to make the periscope work, it is necessary to construct a situation resulting in parallel light rays. A light ray from an object at *P* is reflected by a mirror (*m*) to a second mirror (*n*) to the eye of the observer at *A* (Fig. 16-3). A long tube and two simple mirrors are all that is needed. This could become an interesting construction problem for the entire class.

The problem to be considered, once the idea behind the periscope is understood, is: How shall the mirrors be placed so that the light ray that leaves the tube is parallel to the path it took upon entering? In our diagram, how can we be assured that *PX* || *YA*? We have the reflection law available for use, but how can we be sure that the mirrors will be placed so that the light ray will be reflected and observed as desired? Of course we could use trial and error and continue to move the mirror about until it "works"; indeed this is

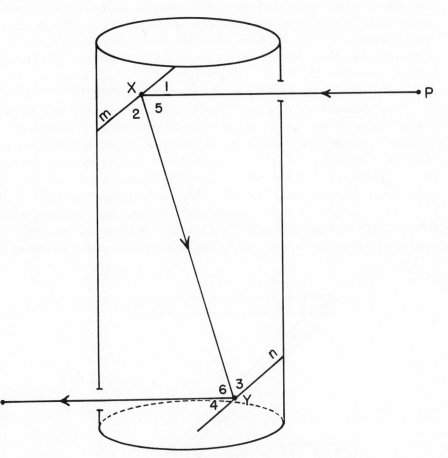

Figure 16-3

355

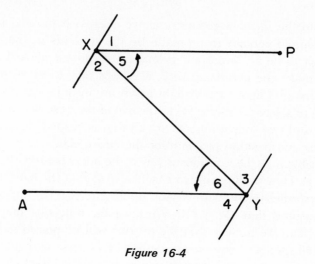

Figure 16-4

undoubtedly what most students would actually do if they undertook this construction. But perhaps our knowledge of geometry can offer us some important assistance. Once again we focus upon the purely mathematical aspect of the situation. We have two lines, *PX* and *YA*, and another line intersecting each of these lines at *X* and *Y*, respectively (Fig. 16-4). Thus, we have two lines cut by transversal *XY*. Our aim here is to make *PX* ∥ *YA*.

As we examine our diagram, it begins to appear that ∠5 and ∠6 are the crucial angles. If they can be made equal to each other, it appears that the lines will be parallel. Let us examine a variety of situations involving parallel lines cut by a transversal and focus upon the angles located in the same comparative position to test for some relationship. Measurement may once again assist us in this exploration. The adjustable quadrilaterals commercially available may be helpful here. Erector set strips, straight-line drawings, and protractors may serve equally well (Fig. 16-5). It is important to compare the measures of alternate interior angles for both parallel and intersecting lines.

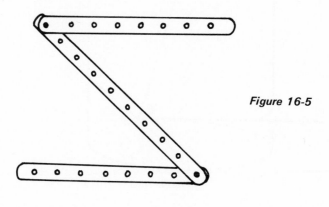

Figure 16-5

In this way added importance is given to the case in which the angles turn out to be equal. After enough experimentation to convince the students that if the alternate interior angles are equal, the lines are parallel, we turn to a proof of this proposition in order to confirm our findings. Once again the proof is an indirect one and appears below.

    Prove: $m \parallel n$ (Fig. 16-6)
    Given: lines m and n cut by transversal t so that $\angle 5 = \angle 6$

    Let us assume that the lines are not parallel and see if a contradiction will result.

    Assume that line m intersects line n at A.

    We have thus formed triangle ABC, of which $\angle 6$ is an exterior angle.

    $\angle 6 > \angle 5$ since $\angle 5$ is an opposite interior angle. But this contradicts the given information: $\angle 6 = \angle 5$.

    Therefore lines m and n cannot intersect; it must be true that $m \parallel n$.

    To return to the periscope, if we place the two mirrors so that $\angle 5 = \angle 6$, then we can be assured that the periscope will work as intended and that the entering and departing rays will be parallel. In the actual construction of a periscope, it would be advisable to construct $\angle 1 = 45°$. This would cause the light ray to travel straight down the length of the tube and would result in $\angle 5 = 90°$ (Fig. 16-7). The advantage offered by this would be to enable one to use a narrower tube. Another item of interest that results from this construction is that if $\angle 2 = \angle 3$, we once again have an equal pair of alternate interior angles and, as a consequence, we have parallel lines. The parallel lines in this case are the two mirrors themselves. This work could be followed by exercises using the properties developed.

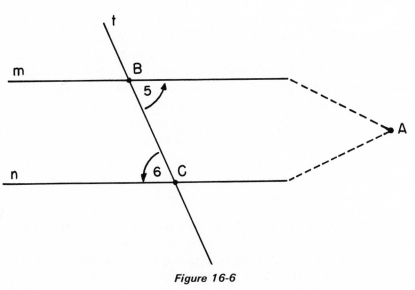

Figure 16-6

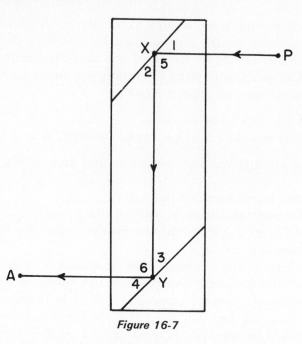

Figure 16-7

While the periscope provides an interesting approach to the study of alternate interior angles, we can investigate the corresponding angles through the use of navigation problems. A ship at point *A* is directly north of a ship at point *B* (Fig. 16-8). If both ships are following the same course of 70° (the angle made with the North line), how will the lines of direction compare with each other? Will they intersect? Are they parallel? It would seem that if the ships follow the same course, their paths will not cross. Let us examine the geometry of this problem.

Here too, many similar situations can be explored using the materials described earlier and measuring in order to provide evidence for the students that would help them determine that equal corresponding angles also result in parallel lines. After such experimentation, we may attempt to support our intuitive feeling about these course lines with deductive proof. The angles, designated $\angle 1$ and $\angle 2$ (Fig. 16-9), are called corresponding angles since they are found to be in corresponding positions with relationship to the lines that form them. The lines look parallel. Let us attempt a proof.

> **Prove:** $AC \parallel BD$
> **Given:** lines AC and BD cut by transversal T so that the corresponding angles are equal, i.e., $\angle 1 = \angle 2$

If we extend the lines in our figure and introduce $\angle 3$, the proof is readily attained using the theorem on alternate interior angles.

We have shown that if the corresponding angles formed by two lines cut by a transversal are equal, the lines are parallel. The suspicions resulting from

358

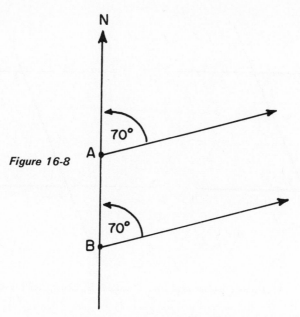

Figure 16-8

the navigation problem are confirmed and the course lines are now known to be parallel. To aid students in identifying pairs of corresponding and alternate interior angles, it is often pointed out that familiar shapes are present (Fig. 16-10).

Additional navigation problems could then be presented for solution to help students to fix this information in their minds. Of course, other theorems

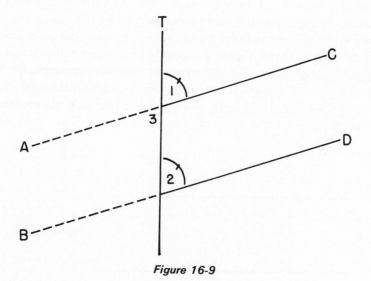

Figure 16-9

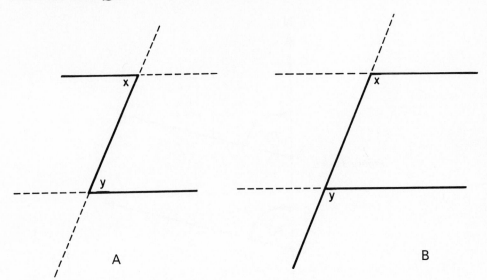

Figure 16-10. A, *Alternate interior angles are Z-shaped.* B, *Corresponding angles are F-shaped.*

involving angles formed by transversals would be explored, including that involving the interior angles on the same side of the transversal as well as that concerning any other pairs of angles that may be in special relationship.

THE FIFTH POSTULATE

Earlier, we questioned the method for laying the rails of a railroad track parallel to a given rail. The use of perpendicular lines enabled us to find the correct position for the rail. In the diagram the rail we sought can be thought of as passing through point P and being parallel to the rail, r (Fig. 16-11). Thus, we know that one parallel exists through a point not on a line to that line. But are there others? Could we possibly lay other rails through P that would also be parallel to r? To ask the same question geometrically: Given a line, r, and a point P not on r, how many lines can pass through P that are parallel to r? (See Fig. 16-12.) An attempt to answer this question results in some excellent construction exercises for the students. They may decide to

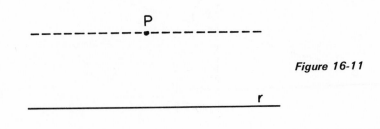

Figure 16-11

360

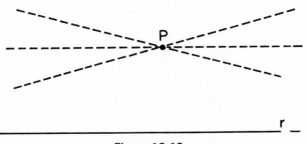

Figure 16-12

use the corresponding angles theorem (Fig. 16-13) or perhaps the earlier theorem about two lines perpendicular to the same line (Fig. 16-14). It is even conceivable that some other method of construction will be found. As a matter of fact, it may be of interest for students to carry out more than one construction. In this way they may build physical experiences to accept the idea that there appears to be only one line through *P* that is parallel to *r*. Every other line will intersect *r* if it is extended far enough.

We have presented two important ideas. We have extended the use of the ruler and compass to include construction of parallels. We have provided experiences that form the basis for the acceptance of Euclid's fifth postulate. This postulate is stated in Playfair's formulation:[1]

> Given a line *r* and a point *P* not on *r*, there is just one line through *P* which does not meet *r*, that is, which is parallel to *r*.

The constructions described, as well as our own experience, would seem to indicate that the postulate is a reflection of the physical world. We leave it

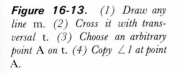

Figure 16-13. *(1) Draw any line* m. *(2) Cross it with transversal* t. *(3) Choose an arbitrary point* A *on* t. *(4) Copy* ∠1 *at point* A.

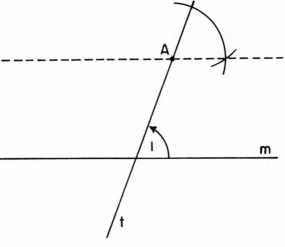

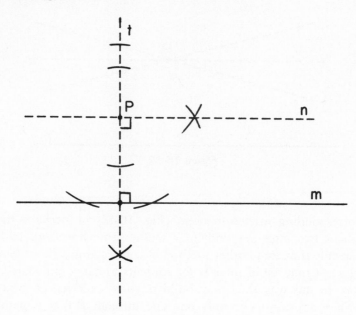

Figure 16-14. *(1) Draw any line* m *and a point* P *not on* m. *(2) At* P *drop a perpendicular to* m. *(3) Then at* P *erect a perpendicular to that line* (t).

at this point for the time being. For now, it should be pointed out to students that mathematicians tried for more than 2000 years to establish that this postulate was a theorem. However, although they failed in attempts to provide a proof, they happened upon an entirely new world, not too much unlike Alice who passed through the looking glass.

At this point, the students might enjoy examining a "proof" of the fifth postulate in order to find where the demonstration goes astray. Besides the interest-value in finding the error, the students may gain in their understanding of and their criteria for proof if they are given opportunities to criticize "proofs." One such "proof" is presented here.

Criticize the following "proof" that there is just one parallel line to a given line through a given point *P*.

> **Given:** line *AB* and point *C* not on *AB*
> **Prove:** There is one and only one line through *C* parallel to *AB* (Fig. 16-15).

> **Proof**
> 1. From *C* drop a perpendicular, *CD*, to line *AB*.
> 2. Also at *C* now construct a perpendicular, *CE*, to *CD*.
> 3. *CE* ∥ *AB*. *AB* and *CE* are both perpendicular to *CD*. Thus we have
> a parallel.

362

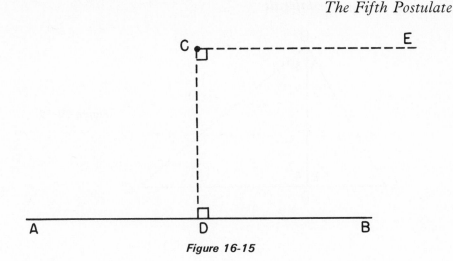

Figure 16-15

4. Now we must prove that *CE* is the only such parallel. There is only one perpendicular from *C* to *AB*, and only one perpendicular at point *C* on line *CD*.

5. Therefore *CE* is the only parallel.

The converses of the corresponding angle and alternate-interior angle theorems may be proved by returning to the original situations created for them here: the periscope and the navigation problem. The important theorem about the angle sum of the triangle may then be considered. A minimum of preliminary experience is required for this theorem because of the work done with this concept in the study of informal geometry. Students have a wide choice of proofs, offering a good opportunity for students to proceed as they think best in attempting to find their own way in establishing this theorem. Once again we may offer the students a so-called "proof" and ask for criticism.

Here is a "proof" of this same theorem that was written by a student. Is it a good proof?

Given: $\triangle ABC$
Prove: $\angle A + \angle B + \angle C = 180°$ (Fig. 16-16)

Proof
1. Draw line *BD*.
2. Let us say that the sum of the angles of any triangle is *x*. Then $\angle A + \angle 1 + \angle 2 = x$.
3. What holds for one triangle holds for another, so $\angle 3 + \angle 4 + \angle C = x$
4. Adding: $\angle A + \angle 1 + \angle 2 + \angle 3 + \angle 4 + \angle C = 2x$
5. But $\angle A + \angle 1 + \angle 3 + \angle C = x$ since it too is the sum of the angles of a triangle (the large one, *ABC*).
6. $\angle 2 + \angle 4 = 180°$ because they are supplementary.
7. By substitution we get:

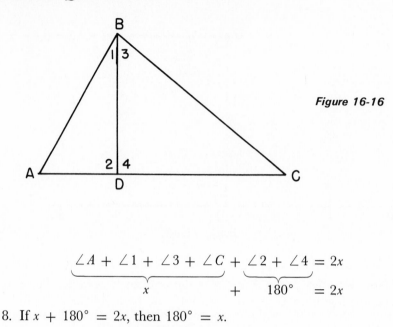

Figure 16-16

$$\underbrace{\angle A + \angle 1 + \angle 3 + \angle C}_{x} + \underbrace{\angle 2 + \angle 4}_{180°} = 2x$$
$$+ \quad 180° \quad = 2x$$

8. If $x + 180° = 2x$, then $180° = x$.

Is the proof acceptable? Note that it does not even use parallel lines and so does not depend upon the parallel axiom. Reconsider the third statement. In making proofs we must be very careful not to make any unwarranted assumptions. Not all series of logical statements make up a proof.

The angle-sum theorem is little short of amazing, and teachers should not treat the theorem indifferently. Consider what we have established: Our proof tells us that no matter how large a triangle or how small a triangle, the sum of its angles will always be the same—a straight angle or 180°! Thus, the triangle formed by using New York, San Francisco, and New Orleans as vertices in a plane has angles whose sum is equal to that of a triangle drawn on a small piece of paper! There is nothing like an exuberant teacher to create student excitement about ideas considered.

MORE ABOUT CONGRUENCE

The angle-sum theorem and its corollaries make the proof of the angle-angle-side congruence theorem a relatively simple matter. This particular congruence relationship would probably come up for consideration as a result of the activities described earlier. At this point, however, the proof of the relationship becomes a possibility. The problem could be put to the students in just that way: Let us take another look at this relationship and see if we cannot find a proof now that we have many new theorems and postulates to call upon. The proof is left to the student.

This return to the notion of congruence can be expanded to include the hypotenuse-leg theorem. The ambiguous SSA situation can be used as an

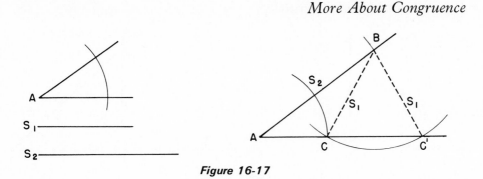

Figure 16-17

introduction to this theorem. The construction is generally carried out by students to make them sharply aware of the fact that these parts result in two possible triangles (Fig. 16-17). We may pose the question again, this time with the condition that the angle be a right angle. While two triangles again result (Fig. 16-18), this time the two triangles are congruent. Some additional construction exercises will indicate that the result is not a chance happening; and since we are convinced so far, we turn to proof. This proof has often been accomplished by moving one triangle and placing it adjacent to the other. Because of the earlier-mentioned criticism of Euclid for not clearly defining this movement, we may wish to avoid using this method. There are several proofs available in school textbooks that do not attempt to move the triangle. A proof based upon the SMSG text is presented here.[2]

> ***Prove:*** $\triangle ABC \cong \triangle DEF$ (Fig. 16-19)
> ***Given:*** rt. $\triangle ABC$: $\angle C = 90°$, hypotenuse AB
> rt. $\triangle DEF$: $\angle F = 90°$, hypotenuse DE
> $AB = DE, BC = EF$

Extend DF to point G, so that $CA = FG$.
Draw GE, forming $\triangle GEF$ with a right angle at F.
$\triangle GEF \cong \triangle ABC$ by SAS.

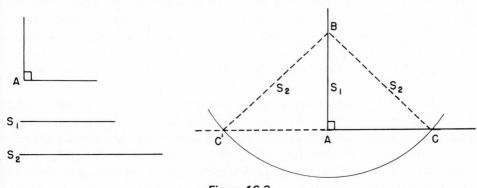

Figure 16-8

365

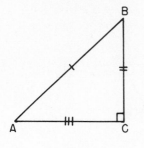
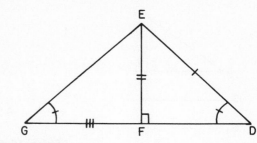

Figure 16-19

> S: $BC = EF$, as given
> A: $\angle ACB = \angle GFE = 90°$
> S: $CA = FG$

Thus $AB = GE$, by definition of congruence.
This makes $\triangle GED$ an isosceles triangle, since it was given that $AB = DE$.
Thus $\angle G = \angle D$, and $\triangle GEF \cong \triangle DEF$ by AAS.

> A: $\angle GFE = \angle DFE = 90°$
> A: $\angle G = \angle D$
> S: $EF = EF$

Since $\triangle GEF \cong \triangle ABC$ and $\triangle GEF \cong \triangle DEF$, then $\triangle ABC \cong \triangle DEF$.

The topic of parallels is brought to a close by returning once more to the use of light rays. An interesting situation may be explored that involves the two hinged mirrors mentioned earlier when we considered the possibility of being able to see a particular side of our body. What would happen to the light rays in question if the mirrors were hinged so as to form a right angle? After a discussion that encourages student guessing, the students may locate point P and proceed to make a scale drawing of the various light rays emanating from P and reflecting from one mirror to the other and out again (Fig. 16-20). For example, they might carry out the work as follows:

From P draw any light ray to mirror m. Using a protractor, measure the angle made with m. Then draw the path of the reflection by making the angle of reflection equal to the angle of incidence ($\angle 1 = \angle 2$). Do the same for the ray on mirror n ($\angle 3 = \angle 4$). Is there anything special about the entering path (PX) and exiting path (QY)? Repeat the process, tracing another ray from P to mirror m.

The students may draw as many different rays from P as they wish. Careful drawing of the reflections will eventually provide the impression that every light ray from P that is reflected successively by m and n travels out parallel to the incident ray $(PX \parallel QY)$. A small pair of hinged mirrors could serve as a desk demonstrator for each student. Thus, if you were to stand at P and if two mirrors were hinged to form a $90°$ angle, you would

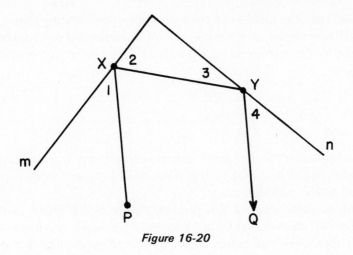

Figure 16-20

be unable to see your right side reflected in the mirror at the left. As we turn from mirrors and light rays to geometry, we find that we have an interesting application of the theorem about the sum of the angles of a triangle.

> ***Prove:***   *PA* || *BR* (Fig. 16-21)
> ***Given:***   line *m* ⊥ line *n*
>   *PA-AB-BR* is any path from *P* to *m* to *n* to *R*
>   ∠1 = ∠2, ∠3 = ∠4

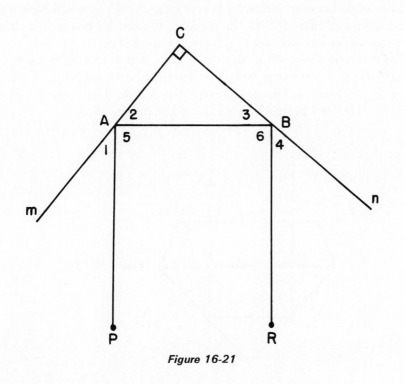

Figure 16-21

367

Parallels and Quadrilaterals

We find that one method of proof depends upon showing that $\angle 5 + \angle 6 = 180°$. (If two angles on the same side of a transversal are supplementary, the lines cut by the transversal are parallel.) This can be accomplished using the facts that:

1. $\angle 1 + \angle 2 + \angle 5 = 180°$
2. $\angle 3 + \angle 4 + \angle 6 = 180°$
   and $\angle 2 + \angle 3 = 90°$

The completion of this proof can be carried out by the students. We have thereby established that in this instance, a light ray from P is reflected out parallel to the incident ray.

A curious application of this physical "theorem" is found in the highly skilled area of diamond-cutting. Strangely enough, heirloom diamonds (diamonds that were cut before 1870, a year of great diamond discoveries in South Africa) do not have the beautiful sparkle of modern diamonds. The reason for this is that it was falsely believed that the deeper the diamond, the more brilliant its shine. Today we know better. The angles and proportions of the diamond that are necessary for proper cutting have been scientifically determined, using our knowledge of light rays. The general shape of a diamond provides us with a situation much like that of the hinged mirrors (Fig. 16-22). If the sparkle of a diamond results from light reflected from facet to facet and back through its tip, what should the angle be between the facets? The preceding theorem provides a rather good reason for thinking that if the angle between the facets is kept close to 90°, you will have a properly cut diamond (Fig. 16-23). In practice, the dimensions in the diagram are thought to be necessary for a well-cut diamond (Fig. 16-24).

The theorems discussed in this chapter, as well as related theorems, offer a broad variety of interesting problems for solution by students. A sampling of these is presented in the paragraphs that follow. The teacher can build numerous additional problems based on those presented here.

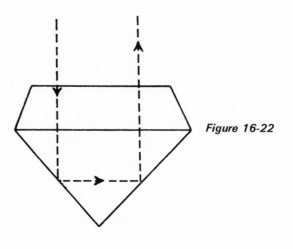

Figure 16-22

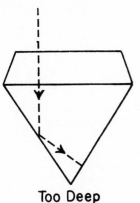

Too Deep

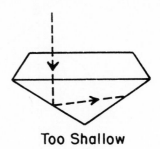

Too Shallow

Figure 16-23

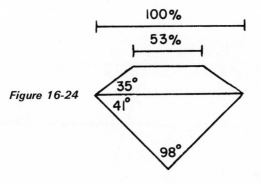

Figure 16-24

1. To save time in digging a tunnel under a mountain, the contractors decided to dig from both ends simultaneously. However, they had to be sure that the diggers would work along the same straight line and so meet somewhere in the middle of the tunnel. They followed a plan first suggested by the Greek mathematician Heron (first century A.D.). They chose points A and B (at the same elevation) near the points at which they wished to begin the tunnel, and then they chose point C so that $\angle C$ was 90° and so that $AC = BC$ (Fig. 16-25). They then knew what direction to take at A and at B in order to have the diggers work along one line and meet. What were the directions?

2. A ship sailed east from A to B going 30 m.p.h. If the ship left A at noon and arrived at B at 3 P.M. and if $A = 38°$ and $B = 76°$, how far is the ship from port P? (See Fig. 16-26.)

3. Can you find the mistake in this proof? (See Fig. 16-27.)

Given: $AB \parallel CD$
Prove: sum of the interior angles on same side of transversal is 180°, or $\angle 1 + \angle 2 = 180°$

369

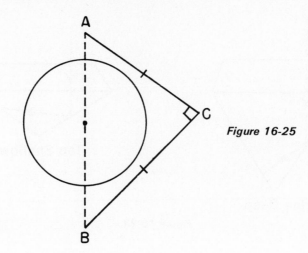

Figure 16-25

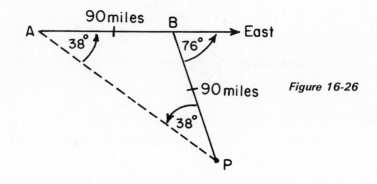

Figure 16-26

Proof

Either $\angle 1 + \angle 2 > 180°$, $\angle 1 + \angle 2 = 180°$, or $\angle 1 + \angle 2 < 180°$.

Assume $\angle 1 + \angle 2 > 180°$.

Then $\angle 3 + \angle 4 > 180°$ and $\angle 1 + \angle 2 + \angle 3 + \angle 4 > 360°$.

But $\angle 1 + \angle 3 = 180°$ because they form a straight line, and $\angle 2 + \angle 4 = 180°$ for the same reason.

Therefore $\angle 1 + \angle 2 + \angle 3 + \angle 4 = 360°$, which is a contradiction. Therefore, $\angle 1 + \angle 2 > 180°$ is false.

The same argument applies to $\angle 1 + \angle 2 < 180°$.

Therefore, $\angle 1 + \angle 2 = 180°$.

4. In order to mark a line of plants parallel to one already up (AB), a farmer did the following: He set up rods at C and D on line AB. He then chose G at random and marked off GE and GF so that $GE = GD$ and $GF = GC$; then he drew EF. Will it work? Explain. (See Fig. 16-28.)

370

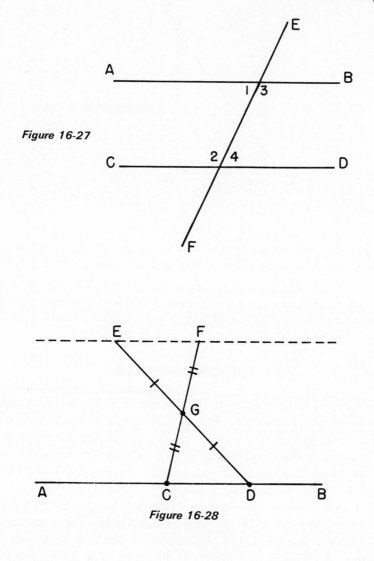

Figure 16-27

Figure 16-28

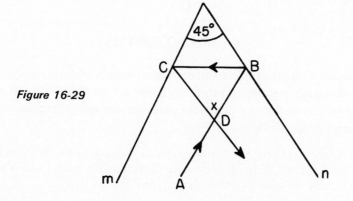

Figure 16-29

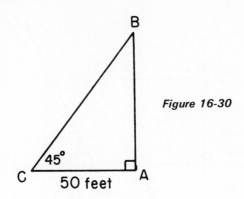

Figure 16-30

5. Two mirrors are hinged at a 45° angle. If angle x equals 55°, find all the other angles. How are AB and CD related? (See Fig. 16-29.)

6. A boy wishes to obtain the height of a flagpole, AB. He walks away from the base to the point C where $\angle ACB$ is 45°. He then measures CA and finds it to be 50 feet. How long is the flagpole? (See Fig. 16-30.)

QUADRILATERALS

The study of quadrilaterals offers another area that is rich in experiences demonstrating the relationship between nature and mathematics. To aid us in this development, the concept of the vector will be introduced. The idea of a vector is described by the Commission on Mathematics as a basic idea of the physical sciences. The commission proposed the study of vectors in high school for a number of reasons, perhaps the most important of which is the fact that "vectors are dynamic concepts that appeal to the intuition and therefore provide vivid illustrations, and easily comprehensible ones, of both physical and geometric phenomena."[3] Nothing could suit our purposes better, or be more consistent with the pattern of development that has taken shape in this section on geometry.

PARALLELOGRAMS

By focusing upon problems involving a variety of forces and considering the representative parallelograms, we have an entrance into the study of quadrilaterals, as well as a convenient place for the use of vectors. A particular problem may help to clarify.

A boy rows directly across a river at 8 m.p.h., and the river has a 6 m.p.h. current. What path does the boat actually follow and how fast is it moving relative to either shore? (See Fig. 16-31.)

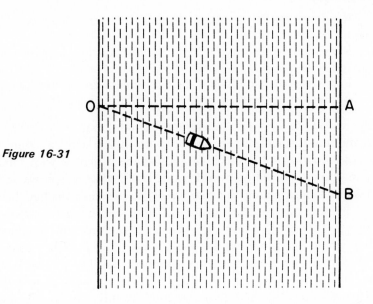

Figure 16-31

After providing time for thinking and discussing student conjectures, we attempt an analysis of the problem. If the boy headed across the river perpendicular to the shoreline and if the current was flowing downstream, we would expect the boy to reach the opposite shore somewhere below the point at which the perpendicular from his starting point intersects the opposite shoreline, point A. The current will certainly carry him downstream in this situation. But, under the conditions of this problem, can we determine exactly where he will land on the opposite shore? To do this we would need additional information—the width of the river. Can we then show the route that will be followed by the boat as a result of the rowing velocity and the current? A diagram of this information is presented in Figure 16-32.

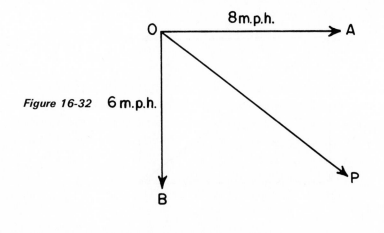

Figure 16-32

Represent the boy's rowing velocity with a line segment 8 units long.

Represent the velocity of the current with a line segment 6 units long.

Let us assume that if both of these velocities were in force for 1 hour, the boy would have been carried by the stream to point *P*.

After rowing for 1 hour, the student travels from *O* to *P*. Therefore we say that the line segment *OP* represents, both in size and direction, the effect (or the resultant) of both velocities. Our concern here is with change from the starting point: started at *O* and ended at *P*. That is why we say that *OP* is the resultant of applying the two forces. If the diagram had been drawn to scale, the students could measure *OP* and determine the velocity in the given direction in order to answer that part of the problem. To do this, however, they would need to know the exact location of *P*. *P* can be determined geometrically by drawing two line segments parallel to the two velocity segments from the end points of each (one from *A* parallel to *OB* and one from *B* parallel to *OA*). The figure formed in this way is a rectangle since the forces were operating at right angles to each other (Fig. 16-33). If we draw the diagonal of the rectangle from point *O*, we will have found the desired result of the simultaneous action of the two forces (rowing and current) upon the boat.

Before getting involved with the ideas in any greater depth, the students should undertake additional problems. Here is one that changes the situation slightly.

An airplane heads due east at 200 m.p.h., and a wind blows northeast at 100 m.p.h. What direction does the plane actually take? What is its velocity relative to the ground? (See Fig. 16-34.)

If we represent these velocities as we did earlier, *OA* will be a vector 200 units long and *OB* will be a vector 100 units long. The segments point in the indicated directions. What path will the plane follow? After the stu-

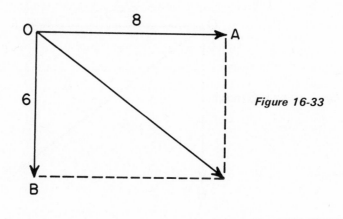

Figure 16-33

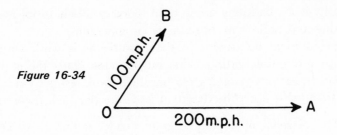

Figure 16-34

dents have had sufficient time to think and discuss, we consider the fact that the resulting direction will be somewhere between the two given vectors. We can locate the point *P* (the position of the plane after 1 hour of flying in accordance with the conditions of the problem) by drawing lines parallel to the force lines, as we did earlier: a parallel to *OB* from *A* and a parallel to *OA* from *B*.

In this instance, the force lines were not perpendicular to each other, so the resulting figure is not a rectangle but a parallelogram (Fig. 16-35). Diagonal *OP* provides us with the distance traveled by the plane in 1 hour, as well as its direction. (Scale drawings enable students to determine the distance through measurement.)

As many additional examples as you feel are necessary may be considered here. Later, we can step back and take a good look at what we have accomplished. At this point we emphasize that the line segments in use here are not quite the same as those encountered earlier: These segments have a size or magnitude (represented by length), but they also have a direction. This is how we define the *vector*. We have also performed an operation upon these vectors by finding the resultant of two given vectors. This we call the *addition of vectors*. It is important to emphasize that the familiar word "addition" is being used in a new way here: It is not the same as addition applied to numbers. We also refer to adding velocities represented as vectors as "applying the parallelogram law." In this way, we have not only made a concrete introduction to an important physical-geometrical concept (vector) but we have involved parallelograms in our work.

It may be wise here to present many additional problems to our students,

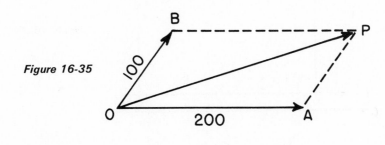

Figure 16-35

involving physical quantities other than velocity. Such problems might involve pushing and pulling by humans or by machines.

The geometrical outgrowth of these problems is work with parallelograms in an interesting setting. This introduction leads the student to the study of many questions involving the parallelogram, resulting in its definition. We could then focus upon the diagonal and consider such theorems as:

> The diagonal of a parallelogram divides it into two congruent triangles.
>
> The diagonals of a parallelogram bisect each other.

In addition, proof of the several corollaries of these theorems may also be attempted (opposite angles are equal, opposite sides are equal, and so on), as well as the important converses of these theorems. In this way we begin to accumulate information about the conditions that are necessary and sufficient for the broad variety of quadrilaterals to be studied. In addition to the problems involving forces of all kinds, as well as the abstract geometric problems usually introduced at this point, we may also pose problems like the two listed below.

1. If we wish to fasten two rulers AB and CD to each other by connecting strips EF and GH so that AB and CD will always be parallel, what conditions should we place on the strips? (See Fig. 16-36.)
2. A boy wishes to make a kite in the shape of a parallelogram. How should he choose the four slats which make up the frame to be sure that the frame is a parallelogram?

The presentation of a problem with two perpendicular forces can enable the students to turn their attention to the study of special parallelograms. Such a problem was presented earlier concerning the forces of the rowing and the current in crossing a river. Extending the conditions of these problems to include equal forces can focus attention on the square and the rhombus. Here are some problems together with the theorems to which they apply:

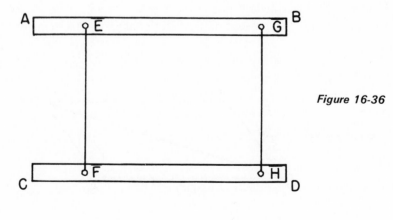

Figure 16-36

Introduction to the square:

1. A light plane is flying due south at a rate of 60 m.p.h. A strong wind of equal velocity, 60 m.p.h., is blowing directly east. Using a scale of 1 inch = 30 m.p.h., draw the parallelogram of forces and estimate the resultant speed and direction.

Introduction to the rectangle:

2. If a boy rows across a river at 3 m.p.h. and the river current is 4 m.p.h., find the speed and direction of his trip.

Diagonals of a rectangle are equal (and the converse):

3. In order to make a rectangular frame, an artist applied glue to two pairs of equal lengths of wood which were to form the sides. Just before the glue hardened, he moved the four pieces until the two diagonals were equal to each other. Criticize this method.

Diagonals of a square are perpendicular to each other (and the converse):

4. A carpenter arranges two cross slats designed to add strength to a gate so that they are perpendicular to each other as well as being of equal length. What shape must the gate have? Explain.

Introduction to the rhombus:

5. A plane is flying south with a velocity of 60 m.p.h. and a wind is blowing southeast at a velocity of 60 m.p.h. Find the magnitude and direction of the resultant velocity.

The process of using protractors and rulers can also provide exercises designed to build understandings of the many relationships involved in the study of quadrilaterals. For example, what is the minimum number of right angles a parallelogram must have before we can conclude that it is a rectangle? Attempting to construct the parallelogram by making only one of its angles a right angle enables students to draw their own conclusions about such situations. The same process could be applied to many other theorems prior to attempts at proof, including:

> The diagonals of a square bisect the angles.
> If the opposite angles of a quadrilateral are equal, the figure is a parallelogram.

Where construction becomes difficult, measurement is available. In this way we continue to involve the students in the necessary experiences to establish their understanding of the relationships in question. As a matter of fact, it is quite possible for the students to organize their own theorems by investigating the relationships between sides, angles, and diagonals, as they study quadrilaterals. They may well make their initial conjecture about a relationship on the basis of what they have done with the tools of geometry: compass, straight edge, and protractor.

377

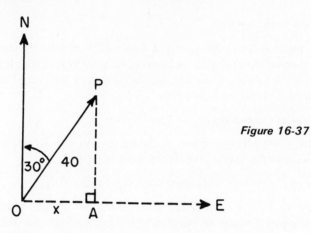

Figure 16-37

Additional work with vectors and the resulting parallelograms of forces could be introduced if the 30°–60°–90° triangle theorem has been developed prior to this work. These problems are the reverse of the earlier vector problems we had explored: Given the resultant, find the individual or component forces that yield the given resultant. For example:

> A ship moving under its own power and the effect of a current travels at a velocity of 40 m.p.h. in a direction making an angle of 30° with the north line. At what velocity is the ship traveling eastward? (See Fig. 16-37.)
>
> In 1 hour, this ship travels 40 miles in a northeast direction. If we drop a perpendicular to the east line (*OE*), then *OA* (i.e., *x*) represents the actual distance traveled eastward in 1 hour. Since *x* is opposite the 30° angle (∠*P*), it is half the hypotenuse. The desired velocity is 20 m.p.h.

We have found the *component* of *OP* in the direction of *OA*. The vector *OP* (which is usually written $\overrightarrow{OP}$ to distinguish it from a line) is the resultant of two. velocities. We have found one, $\overrightarrow{OA}$. We could indicate the other vector by dropping a perpendicular from *P* to the north line. This would provide us with the component of $\overrightarrow{OP}$ in the direction of *ON*. Thus we have reversed the process employed earlier with vector problems. In order to be able to determine the individual vectors, the angle formed by a vector and the resultant must be given. If this angle is 30° or 60°, as in the example above, the desired value is easily computed, using the 30°–60°–90° triangle relationship: The length of the side opposite the 30° angle is half of the length of hypotenuse. This theorem would also enable the students to consider push-pull forces, such as those involved with inclined planes. When trigonometry is employed to arrive at solutions, we can consider many more problems since the angle

378

need no longer be limited to any special size. A detailed discussion of the use of such problems in working with vectors will be included in the chapter on trigonometry. Here is an example using the special angle triangle:

> An object weighing 100 pounds rests on a hill. We know that this weight is the force of gravity and acts straight down (Fig. 16-38). What force causes the object to slide down the hill? Since the only force acting is gravity and since this acts straight down, only some component of gravity can be effective along the hill. To find this component force, drop a perpendicular from P to the hill line, XO. $\overrightarrow{OA}$ is the force along the hill. Use 30° for the inclination of the hill and determine the missing component. (The students may wonder if $\overrightarrow{OR}$, the second vector, isn't also responsible for pushing the object down the hill. Since this force is acting perpendicular to the hill, it cannot cause downhill motion.)

At times it may seem that the science concepts involved in a particular problem require too much discussion for the amount of mathematical learning to be gained. Our goal has been to offer insight into the importance of mathematics to the scientist. Work with science concepts to some slight depth cannot be avoided if we are to help each student share in such experiences. We have made rather brief visits to a host of scientific ideas. It has been the intent to keep this work clear, simple, and to the point, without trying to make penetrating analyses of the science concepts encountered. Our focus is mathematics, not science; but the ideas concerned with the physical world cannot be treated too lightly. They are important ideas. The time spent clarifying science in order to help students understand the problems is time well-spent for the insights offered into both mathematics and science. Perhaps a by-product of better understanding of science ideas will offer us an extra dividend.

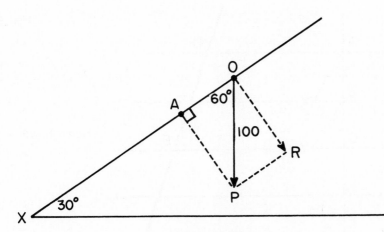

Figure 16-38

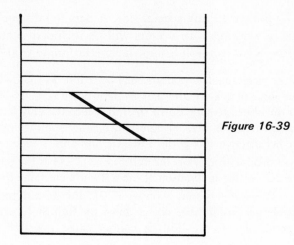

Figure 16-39

The work with parallelograms may be concluded with an interesting activity:

>In order to divide a string into three equal parts, a boy placed the string on a piece of lined composition paper so that it just covered three spaces. He then cut the string at the two points where the lines intersected the string. Does this work? Why? (See Fig. 16-39.)

This is certainly an activity that students can do at their seats. After several trials we may turn from string and paper to geometry, as we ask the question, Why does it work? We have straight lines and a transversal (the red margin). Laying the string down is the same as drawing another transversal. It seems that since the lines cut off equal segments on one transversal (the margin), they also do it on any other transversal (the string).

One possible proof is the familiar one involving the construction of lines

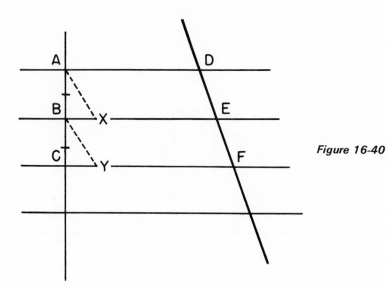

Figure 16-40

AX and BY parallel, respectively, to DE and EF (Fig. 16-40). With this theorem the students gain the ability to divide a line into any desired number of equal parts by construction.

TRAPEZOIDS

The consideration of the topic of quadrilaterals is concluded with an examination of trapezoids and brief mention of polygons other than quadrilaterals. This work presents further opportunities for organizing active experiences for students as we study several important theorems. We direct the attention of the student to these relationships with a typical problem that can be represented in a variety of ways:

> In staking pole AB, which is 12 feet long, a scout attaches two guy lines to be sure that the pole is held firmly (Fig. 16-41). The smaller guy line, 10 feet, is attached to the pole at its midpoint and is staked to the ground halfway between the pole and the second line. If the lines are attached as indicated, how much rope is needed?

In attempting a solution to a problem like this, the students could make good use of some of the devices and representative materials introduced earlier: Erector sets, pegboards, graph paper. Measurement would be the means for determining the answer. The results here are somewhat surprising. The line BE is twice the length of CD and is apparently parallel to it. Is this a coincidence? Using the materials described, the students could try various lengths to see if the relationship holds; they might also vary the conditions —change the position of CD—and observe what happens. The net result of all of this is the intuitive establishment of another theorem: A line joining

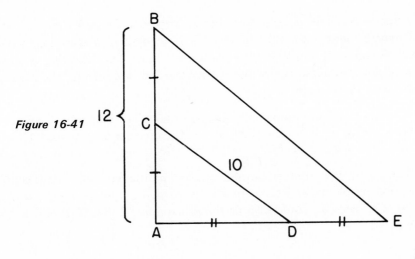

Figure 16-41

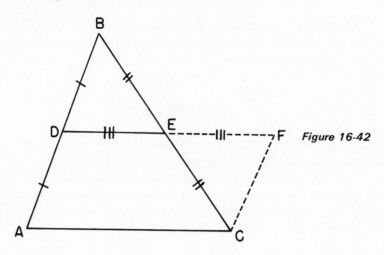

Figure 16-42

the midpoints of two sides of a triangle is parallel to the third side and equal to half of it. The proof is generally accomplished by extending the line joining the midpoints, its own length, and demonstrating that *ACFD* is a parallelogram (Fig. 16-42).

Besides the important relationship introduced in the earlier problem, we have also brought into focus another geometric form: the trapezoid (*ACED* in Figure 16-42). This is an unusual quadrilateral. Unlike the others we have met, it has only two sides parallel. We proceed to explore this new figure and its angles and diagonals, and we make use of the theorem about joining the midpoints of a triangle by exploring a similar property of the median of a trapezoid.

> A carpenter is building a magazine rack for the school library. (A side view of the rack is contained in Figure 16-43.) He wants to build in a shelf, *XY*, that connects the midpoints of *AD* and *BC*. How wide is this shelf and how can the carpenter be sure that the shelf will be parallel to *AB* and *CD*?

After experimental activities (graph paper, pegboard, and so on), a proof may be sought for the theorem: The median of a trapezoid is equal to half the sum of the bases and is parallel to them. The following is an indication of how we make use of the earlier theorem concerning the midpoints of two sides of a triangle.

> Draw *BY* and extend it to intersect *AD* (Fig. 16-44). If *Y* can be shown to be the midpoint of *BE*, the earlier theorem may be used. Can you show that *DE* = *BC*?

The work with quadrilaterals can be culminated with a collection of application problems, as well as problems involving only geometric concepts. The proof of originals could also be undertaken as all the work of this unit is summarized.

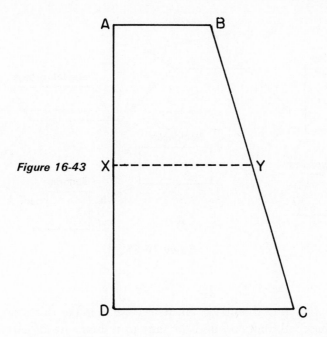

Figure 16-43

To clarify the hierarchy of relationships that exist between the many quadrilaterals investigated in this chapter, a flow diagram of the family of quadrilaterals may be constructed (Fig. 16-45).

OTHER POLYGONS

A brief word about polygons other than triangles and quadrilaterals closes out this part of the work. These figures are common to the experiences

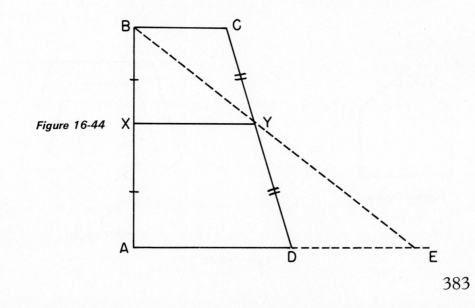

Figure 16-44

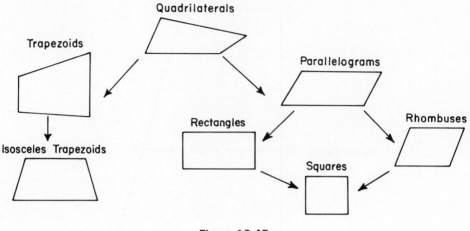

Figure 16-45

of all of us, and time should be taken in class to make this clear. The home plate on a baseball diamond and the famous military headquarters in Washington, D.C. are both pentagons (Fig. 16-46). Card tables, gardens, and even bars of soap are frequently found with shapes of other polygons: hexagons, septagons, and octagons. If we were to add still more sides we could create new polygons—a process that could go on indefinitely. These shapes may be a good deal more difficult to find around us.

The angle-sum theorem for all polygons is one of the most important theorems to be considered in this area. An interesting introduction to this relationship results from an apparently unrelated problem:

There are five telephone users: A, B, C, D, and E (Fig. 16-47). How many possible phone connections can be made using any two of them?

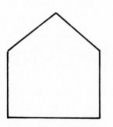

Home Plate

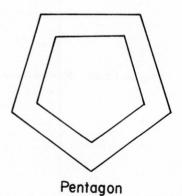

Pentagon

Figure 16-46

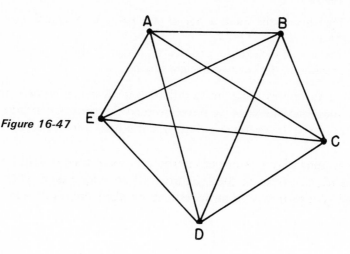

Figure 16-47

If we make a picture of all the possible phone connections between these five parties, we find that that we have a curious diagram. The pentagon, *ABCDE*, together with five diagonals, is present. We see that the answer is 10 possible connections. Now if we change the number of families with phones, how does the number of connections change? There is a good opportunity for the students to determine the relationship for themselves. They can carry out experiments, record results, and look for patterns in much the same manner as was done in the algebra section. The students should have the task clearly before them:

1. How many diagonals may be drawn from a single vertex of a polygon of *n* sides?
2. How many diagonals are there altogether in a polygon of *n* sides?
3. What is the total number of possible connections for *n* telephone subscribers?

Similar procedures would be followed to find the sums of the interior angles and the exterior angles of a polygon. For example, a table for the interior angles might be:

Number of sides	Number of triangles	Number of straight angles

The findings of these "experiments" could then be verified by attempts at proofs. The resulting theorems would be:

The sum of the interior angles of a polygon of *n*-sides is $(n - 2)$ straight angles.

The sum of the exterior angles of a polygon, if the sides are extended in succession, is $360°$ or two straight angles.

Here is an opportune time to differentiate between convex and concave polygons—emphasizing that we have assumed the convex condition in all our work so that the theorems we have established refer only to the convex polygons.

The regular polygons are of interest and some time should be allotted to them. Additional study of these figures will be undertaken when circles are considered. We turn now to an investigation of the areas of polygonal figures.

FOOTNOTES

1. Euclid's statement of the parallel postulate was as follows:
   If a straight line falling on two straight lines makes the interior angles on the same side less than two right angles, the two straight lines, if produced indefinitely, will meet on that side on which the angles are less than two right angles.
   This is hardly a "self-evident" truth—hence, the attempts to prove this postulate.
2. School Mathematics Study Group. *Mathematics for High School: Geometry,* Part I. Student's Text, Yale University Press, 1961, pp. 198–199.
3. Report of the Commission on Mathematics. *Appendices.* College Entrance Examination Board, 1959, p. 176.

FOR INVESTIGATION AND DISCUSSION

1. Make a plan utilizing the construction of a periscope by the students in order to emphasize conditions necessary and sufficient for parallel lines.

2. Outline the experiences that may enable students to develop for themselves and accept the notion that if two lines are cut by a transversal so that the alternate interior angles are equal, the lines are parallel.

3. Do the same for the corresponding angles relationship.

4. Use construction to enable students to see that the side-side-angle congruence relationship holds only for right triangles.

5. Describe an investigation based upon two mirrors hinged at a $60°$ angle to determine whether or not the exiting and entering light rays are parallel.

6. Construct two additional problems that may be used to introduce the concept of the quadrilateral through the study of vectors.

7. Indicate how quadrilaterals may be introduced in a meaningful way without involving vectors. Compare the two methods.

8. Select one of the problems listed for use in the introduction of a given quadrilateral. Make a lesson plan to demonstrate how the problem may be so used.

386

9. Explain with a specific problem how an inclined plane involves the concept of vectors. Outline how students may be aided to discover this.

10. Investigate the attempts made to prove the fifth postulate of Euclid. What was the outcome of these attempts? How did they influence the development of mathematics?

FOR FURTHER READING

Books

Banesh Hoffmann. *About Vectors*. Prentice-Hall, Inc., 1966.
Constance Reid. *A Long Way From Euclid*. Thomas Y. Crowell Company, 1963, pp. 16–28.
H. E. Wolfe. *Introduction to Non-Euclidean Geometry*. Dryden Press, 1945.

Periodicals

Paul W. Avers. "A Unit in High School Geometry Without the Textbook." *The Mathematics Teacher*. Vol. 57 (March, 1964), pp. 139–142.
Roslyn M. Berman and Martin Berman. "Concave Polygons." *The Mathematics Teacher*. Vol. 56 (October, 1963), pp. 403–406.
Denis Crawforth. "What Is a Quadrilateral." *Mathematics Teaching*. (Summer, 1967), pp. 18–20.
Francis G. Lankford, Jr. "Optional Proofs of Theorems in Plane Geometry." *The Mathematics Teacher*. Vol. 48 (December, 1955), pp. 578–580.
Wesley W. Maiers. "Introduction to Non-Euclidean Geometry." *The Mathematics Teacher*. Vol. 57 (November, 1964), pp. 457–461.
Charles G. Moore. "Pierced Polygons." *The Mathematics Teacher*. Vol. 61 (January, 1968), pp. 31–35.
Don Ryoti. "Congruency of Triangles by AAS." *The Mathematics Teacher*. Vol. 59 (March, 1966), pp. 246–247.
Dan Smith. "Vectors—An Aid to Mathematical Understanding." *The Mathematics Teacher*. Vol. 52 (December, 1959), pp. 608–612.
Steven Zabo. "An Approach to Euclidean Geometry Through Vectors." *The Mathematics Teacher*. Vol. 59 (March, 1966), pp. 218–235.

17

AREAS OF POLYGONAL
FIGURES AND SIMILARITY

THE RECTANGLE

If we wanted to measure the area of our classroom directly, in the same way that we use a ruler to measure the length of a line, how should we proceed? Most students would reply to this question by suggesting that the length and width be measured with a tape measure or yardstick. This answer is, however, incorrect. Such a process would directly measure the length and width of the room—the linear measures. How does one measure an area directly? As was suggested earlier in the discussion of area, it may be well to attempt to cover at least a portion of the surface of the classroom floor using 1-foot squares. Asbestos or vinyl tiles (usually 9 inches by 9 inches) may be used to clarify the process. The important idea is the use of square units to measure the amount of surface in a given instance. While it is often inconvenient and difficult to measure linear dimensions directly, it is virtually impossible to do so with area measures; that is why there is a great need for formulas enabling us to determine the required areas without attempting direct measurement.

The students of geometry at this level are, at the least, acquainted with a variety of formulas that may be used to determine the areas of geometric figures. In this section we will provide verification for some of the less familiar relationships, in addition to exploring problems of maximum areas, emphasizing the interrelatedness of algebra and geometry.

388

It is customary in geometry textbooks to first postulate the rectangle area relationship ($A = bh$) and then to prove the parallelogram, triangle, and trapezoid area relationships. It is possible to begin by postulating the formula for the area of a square (or by stating it as a definition) and then prove the rectangle area theorem. What is a postulate in one instance becomes a theorem in another. It does seem that since the area of a rectangle is so well known to the students that it may be better to assume this property and go on from there. Whichever path we choose to follow, we will make good use of the equality axioms of algebra as we establish the area theorems.

There is a whole host of physical problems that involve the concept of area. The size of land for farming or building, the construction of parts for machines and equipment, and the amounts of material to be used in floor or wall covering are some of the kinds of experiences from which you may construct pertinent problems. Since the cost of a material, as well as its weight and thickness, is influenced by its area, we have a basis for important applications, as well as an extension of our work into three dimensions, i.e., solid geometry. Much of this work holds a pleasant change for students, in that calculation once more becomes an important part of the problem-solving work. In this way the students get a chance to put into use their arithmetic and algebra skills.

It may be of interest to examine a proof for the area of a rectangle should you decide to accept the area of a square as a postulate. The proof is of interest because it is typical of most area theorem proofs.

Prove: area of rectangle $PQRS = bh$ (Fig. 17-1)
Given: rectangle $PQRS$ with base b and altitude h

Let A be the area of the rectangle with base b and altitude h. Construct a square as shown in Figure 17-2.

If we sum the areas and use the postulate for the area of a square,

$$b^2 + 2A + h^2 = (b + h)^2$$

To find A, we simplify:

$$b^2 + 2A + h^2 = b^2 + 2bh + h^2$$
$$2A = 2bh$$
$$A = bh$$

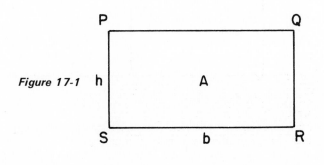

Figure 17-1

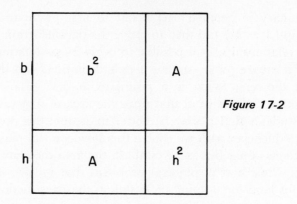

Figure 17-2

The interplay between geometry and algebra is dramatically brought out in this proof, as is the use of the diagram in the entire process. Thus, from the students' point of view, we bring together two different subjects, algebra and geometry; and the word *mathematics* becomes increasingly meaningful.

This is a good place to present a problem on maximum areas similar to those encountered in the study of algebra.

> A rancher has a given amount of fencing. He wishes to use this fencing to enclose a rectangle of the greatest amount of area. This problem is complicated by the fact that one side of the rectangle lies along a river. If no fencing is needed along the river, what shape yields the maximum area? (See Fig. 17-3.)

In the chapter on algebra, we saw that the rectangle of greatest area was a square. We have two questions before us:

1. Can we now prove that it must be a square?
2. Does the lack of fencing on one side alter the picture?

Of course, it would be wise to try numbers first and observe the resulting areas. We may even tabulate these in the same manner we did earlier. For example, we might fix the fencing at 100 feet; our tabulation would be as follows: (Remember we only fence three sides.)

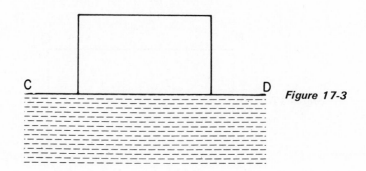

Figure 17-3

Base	Height	Area
10	45	450
20	40	800
30	35	1050
40	30	1200
50	25	1250
60	20	1200
70	15	1050
80	10	800
90	5	450

The maximum area appears to result when the base is double the size of the height. Does this mean that our earlier work showing a square as the rectangle of greatest area is incorrect? Let us attempt a proof of the fact that we earlier accepted intuitively and see what happens. In other words, can we prove that the rectangle of greatest area, considering all rectangles as being of equal perimeter, is a square?

Prove: area of rectangle $ABCD$, with perimeter p, is greatest when $ABCD$ is a square (Fig. 17-4)

Given: rectangle $ABCD$ with perimeter p

If rectangle $ABCD$ is not a square, one side, say AB, is longer than the other, AD. On AB construct the square with perimeter p, i.e., construct $EBHG$.

$$AE + EB + BC = \frac{p}{2} \text{ (semiperimeter of rectangle)}$$

$$EB + BC + CH = \frac{p}{2} \text{ (semiperimeter of square)}$$

Thus,

$$AE = CH \left(\text{each can be set equal to } \frac{p}{2} - EB - BC \right)$$

The smaller side, AD, of the rectangle must be less than a side of the square:

$$AD < GH$$

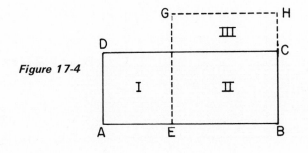

Figure 17-4

Multiplying by the previous equality, we get

$$AD \cdot AE < GH \cdot CH$$

That is,

$$\text{area I} < \text{area III}$$

Then,

$$\text{area II} + \text{area I} < \text{area II} + \text{area III (adding equals)}$$

The area of any rectangle of equal perimeter must be less than that of a square with the same perimeter. Thus, we have established a proof for the maximum area of the square. Before we return to the ranch-fence problem, it may be a good idea to present students with the construction problem used in the proof: "On *AB* construct the square with perimeter *p*." There are many ways to carry out such a construction, but enabling students to undertake this renders the use of the construction in the proof more plausible. It is also an interesting exercise for the students.

Let us return to our problem of fencing an area along a river: How is it that trial and error seems to indicate that the maximum area results when the base length is double that of the height? Doesn't this appear to contradict the theorem we have just proven? Not exactly. If you take another look at the problem and think of the land to be enclosed as lying on *both* sides of the river, it becomes apparent that the square is the best shape to use (Fig. 17-5). For a perimeter of 2*p*, the square is best; otherwise the theorem about maximum area is contradicted. We see now why the base turned out to be double the height.

Some problems concerned with these same ideas would be in order here; and the theorems establishing the areas of the right triangle, any triangle, the parallelogram, and the trapezoid would follow. The particular order in which these theorems are arranged varies from textbook to textbook, so there seems to be no reason why you may not select an order that makes good sense to you. As a matter of fact, there is a good deal more flexibility available here than many teachers are aware of. The overall listing of topics varies greatly from author to author. It is frequently the case that similarity is introduced before

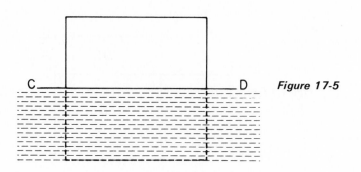

Figure 17-5

area, although the reverse has been the case here. The order, so important to the work of geometry, may well lead to a number of different arrangements, all equally effective in getting where we are headed.

THE PYTHAGOREAN THEOREM

A good example of this flexibility is provided by what is perhaps the single most important theorem of plane geometry: the Pythagorean theorem. Since the theorem and Pythagoras were discussed in Chapter 2, we turn directly to the theorem itself.[1] There are many, many different proofs now available for this landmark theorem. In school texts, it is sometimes found in the area section, but often it is a part of the work on similarity. The SMSG text introduces the proof under the topic of area, whereas the Commission on Mathematics establishes this theorem in the sequence of similarity theorems. Let us examine an area proof here and later we can take a look at an alternative proof in the chapter on similarity.[2]

Prove: $a^2 + b^2 = c^2$ (Fig. 17-6)
Given: right triangle ABC with a right angle at C
Construct a square with side $a + b$. In this square draw four right triangles with legs a and b (Fig. 17-7).
Each of these four triangles is congruent to the original triangle by SAS.

$$
\begin{array}{ll}
\text{S:} & a = a \\
\text{A:} & \text{right angles} \\
\text{S:} & b = b
\end{array}
$$

Therefore, they each have an hypotenuse equal to C. The quadrilateral formed by these hypotenuses is a square since

$$\angle 1 + \angle 2 = 90° \text{ (acute angles of a right triangle)}$$
$$\therefore \angle 3 = 90° \ (180° - 90° = 90°)$$

The same can be said for each angle of the quadrilateral.

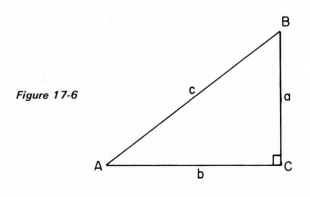

Figure 17-6

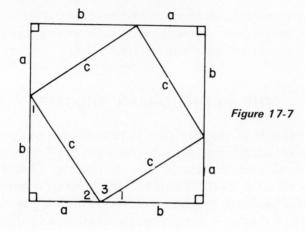

Figure 17-7

Since the area of the large square is equal to the sum of the areas of the small square plus the four triangles,

$$(a + b)^2 = c^2 + 4(\tfrac{1}{2}ab)$$

or

$$a^2 + 2ab + b^2 = c^2 + 2ab$$

and so

$$a^2 + b^2 = c^2$$

Again the use of algebraic and geometric ideas enables us to achieve our desired goal. The two together form a powerful team.

DISTANCE AS AREA

The study of area offers us an opportunity to introduce another concept that ties arithmetic, algebra, and geometry together—the concept of motion. Every school child knows the formula

$$r \cdot t = d$$

We can represent the distance as the area of a rectangle if r and t are the measures of its sides. Placing the entire situation on the coordinate axes system simplifies it still further. For example, if an auto moved at a constant rate of speed, say 30 m.p.h., and traveled 6 hours, the auto would travel 180 miles. The graph of this situation is a straight line parallel to the horizontal axis (t-axis) at the level $v = 30$ (Fig. 17-8). The area of this rectangle is equal to the distance, 180. If we follow this general plan but vary the speed, we encounter some interesting ideas:

The auto travels 15 m.p.h. for 3 hours and 30 m.p.h. for 3 more hours (Fig. 17-9). The areas of the two rectangles ($3 \times 15 = 45$ and $3 \times 30 = 90$) represent the total distance traveled.

394

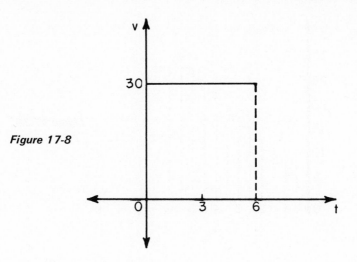

Figure 17-8

The auto starts at $2\frac{1}{2}$ m.p.h. and increases velocity in sudden jumps of $2\frac{1}{2}$ m.p.h. every half hour for 6 hours. Again the sum of the areas of all these rectangles would be the distance traveled (Fig. 17-10).

If we were to continue this pattern of reducing the time interval and the velocity for the corresponding interval but maintain the idea of the sudden increases in speed, the graph of these separate velocities comes very close to being the graph of a straight line. The narrower the rectangle, the more the

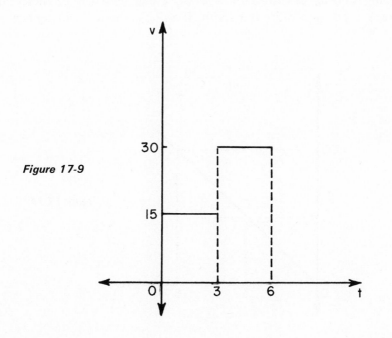

Figure 17-9

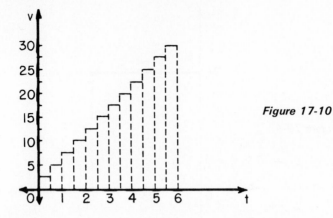

Figure 17-10

series of "steps" approximates the straight line. Hence, the area under the straight line from $t = 0$ to $t = 6$ should represent the distance traveled during this time interval (Fig. 17-11). However, the area of the triangle formed is $\frac{1}{2}(30)(6)$ or 90 miles. Thus, 90 miles is the distance traveled.

If we take the midpoint of the interval from $t = 0$ to $t = 6$, erect the perpendicular BC, and draw a line through C parallel to the t-axis, we obtain rectangle $ODEF$ (Fig. 17-12). The area of this rectangle equals the area of $\triangle OAF$. (Show that $\triangle OCD \cong \triangle ACE$.) We may then say that rectangle $ODEF$ represents the distance traveled. Its base and height are 6 and 15, respectively; so once again 90 miles is the distance traveled. It appears, then, that a constant velocity of 15 m.p.h. is equivalent to the continuously increasing velocity described by $v = 5t$. Using both the geometry and the algebra, we may generalize this result. If an object moves with velocity $v = at$

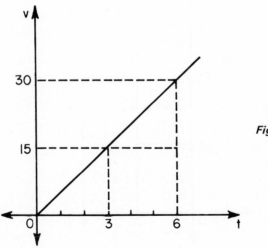

Figure 17-11

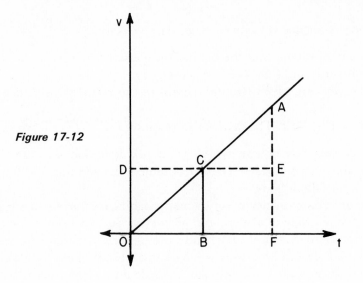

Figure 17-12

from $t = 0$ to $t = T$, the area under the straight line from $t = 0$ to $t = T$ indicates the distance traveled. If we erect a perpendicular BC at $\dfrac{T}{2}$ and construct DE, we have a rectangle whose area is equal to that of $\triangle OAT$ (Fig. 17-13). If we determine the area of this rectangle, we will, in effect, have found a statement for the distance covered in the given interval. But what is the height and base of this rectangle? In determining the height, we see that it is BC. Its length is the value of $v(v = at)$ at $t = \dfrac{T}{2}$. By substitution we get $v = a\left(\dfrac{T}{2}\right)$. Thus, the constant velocity of $\dfrac{aT}{2}$ continued for T hours is equiva-

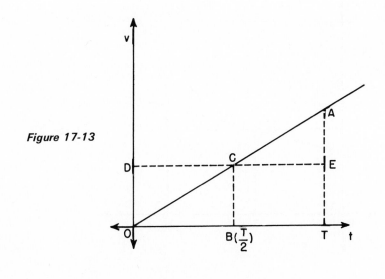

Figure 17-13

lent to the changing velocity $v = at$. The velocity $\dfrac{aT}{2} = \dfrac{0 + aT}{2}$, which is another way of saying that the equivalent constant velocity is the average of the initial (zero) and final (aT) velocities.

Since we were given that the length of the rectangle is T, the area becomes $bh = \left(\dfrac{aT}{2}\right)(T)$. The distance in question is $d = \dfrac{aT^2}{2}$. If we now substitute the acceleration of gravity $(a = 32)$ we find that $d = 16T^2$. This is precisely the way in which Galileo obtained the formula for the distance traveled by a falling body!

The preceding discussion serves many significant purposes. Already mentioned is the wedding of algebra and geometry. But what of the use of mathematics here to analyze and understand the physical situation? Concepts from geometry and algebra both were needed; and what is more, we have made an intuitive start on some of the ideas of the calculus. There appear to be many advantages that can accrue from such a discussion.

It is possible, if interest warrants, to extend this work to include trapezoids. For example, if an object is thrown downward with a velocity of 10 ft./sec., the velocity is described as $v = 10 + 32t$. The object falls for 6 seconds. Represent the distance traveled geometrically as an area and calculate the area (Fig. 17-14).

In solving such a problem, the students have a choice of finding the area of a trapezoid or a rectangle. These areas are equal and also provide the distance traveled. One figure can be used for finding an answer and the other can serve as a check.

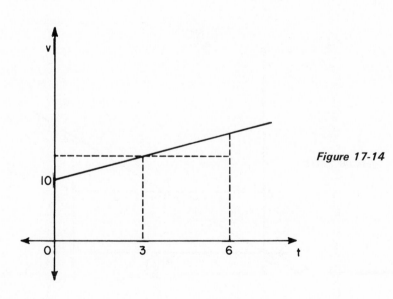

Figure 17-14

This situation may be generalized in the manner described earlier. A rich variety of problems involving the calculation of area and the determination of distances traveled, as well as proofs of pertinent originals, may be presented here.

SIMILARITY

The construction of the model of a building or a plane, the making of a map, and the enlargement of a photograph all involve the concept of similarity. It is curious that this notion, which pervades everyday life in so many ways, should cause such difficulties for students of geometry. Whatever the reason, we may maximize student opportunities for successful work in this area by making the work as meaningful and active as possible. There are ample experiences available to set the mathematics in a context of some significance.

In paragraphs to follow we will examine the important similarity theorems, building upon the earlier work in congruence. An alternate approach to the proof of the Pythagorean theorem will be considered, and the previous work with vectors will be expanded. Thus, we will make frequent use of concepts that were developed earlier, including those of algebra, as we continue to extend the students' gradual awareness of the many important ways in which mathematics sheds light on natural phenomena and aids man in a broad variety of tasks.

How could a commonly used surveyor's instrument have anything to do with one of the important theorems on similarity? It may seem odd, at first, that these two things should be related, but they are. In order to measure the height of a tall tree, a surveyor may use a very old and very simple instrument known as a Jacob's staff (Fig. 17-15). It is actually two intersecting rods in the shape of a cross, which is probably why it is sometimes known as a cross-staff. Let us see how the surveyor proceeds. He holds the instrument vertically before himself and slides the smaller rod on the larger, parallel to the tree and perpendicular to the ground, toward himself or away, until he is able to sight the top of the tree along the top of the rod (C) and the bottom

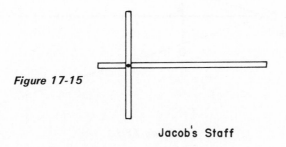

Figure 17-15

Jacob's Staff

of the tree along the bottom of the rod (*D*) (Fig. 17-16). He examines the Jacob's staff, does some calculations, and has the height of the tree. How does he do it?

Since the vertical adjustable rod is parallel to the tree, the surveyor is able to conclude that all the corresponding angles of $\triangle OEC$ and $\triangle OFB$ are equal. In this way he knows that the corresponding sides of the two triangles are proportional. He can then set up the following proportion: $\dfrac{BF}{CE} = \dfrac{FO}{EO}$. Since the lengths of *EO*, *CE*, and *FO* are easily measured, the surveyor is able to calculate *BF*, which is half of the desired length.

This is the kind of experience that may easily be duplicated if you are able to take your students outside the classroom. A rough Jacob's staff may easily be made.[3] It is also possible to use the staff in the classroom or have students use squared paper to simulate the surveyor's work at their seats. After working several problems of this kind, we may well ask how it is that these techniques enable us to calculate the missing length. How do we know this method gives us what we are looking for? How can we be sure that it will always work?

If the students are asked to recall the earlier work with congruent triangles, they may remember their experimentation from which they found that many different sets of equal corresponding parts resulted in congruence. At the same time, they also found that some sets did not. In the problem investigated here, we have equal corresponding angles. Was AAA one of the congruence relationships?

If constructions of a triangle are attempted, given the three angles, many different sizes of triangles will result. Hence, this is certainly not a congruence situation. But if these resulting triangles are examined carefully to see if there is any relationship that exists between them, what might we find? Most students will be quick to notice that all these triangles seem to have the same

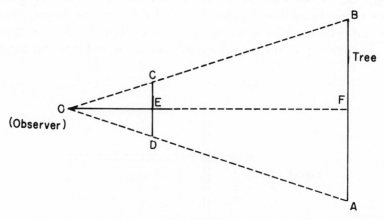

Figure 17-16

general shape. The students may wish to measure the lengths of the sides of the triangles and compare, or the teacher might suggest that they do so. If the results are recorded in tabular fashion, such as in the chart that follows, any inherent relationships are easy to discern.

In $\triangle ABC$	In $\triangle A'B'C'$	In $\triangle A''B''C''$
$AB =$	$A'B' =$	$A''B'' =$
$BC =$	$B'C' =$	$B''C'' =$
$BA =$	$B'A' =$	$B''A'' =$

In this way we have a sampling of activities that lead the students to an introduction to similarity, with the result that it can be defined: Triangle *ABC* is similar to triangle $A'B'C'$ if $\angle A = \angle A'$, $\angle B = \angle B'$, and $\angle C = \angle C'$ and if $\dfrac{a}{a'} = \dfrac{b}{b'} = \dfrac{c}{c'}$.

But we have not as yet established a proof that would shed light on the problem of finding tree height by using a Jacob's staff. If we focus upon the geometry of that situation and strip away the physical components, there are several questions that may be considered. As we take them in turn, we move from the fundamental theorem of proportionality and its converse to the basic similarity theorems: In $\triangle OAB$ if CD is parallel to AB, must $\dfrac{OB}{OC} = \dfrac{OA}{OD}$? (See Fig. 17-17.)

Theorem: If a line parallel to one side of a triangle intersects the other two sides in distinct points, then it cuts off segments which are proportional to these sides (fundamental proportionality theorem).

In $\triangle OAB$ if CD intersects OA and OB so that $\dfrac{OB}{OC} = \dfrac{OA}{OD}$, must it follow that $CD \parallel BA$?

Theorem: If a line intersects two sides of a triangle and cuts off seg-

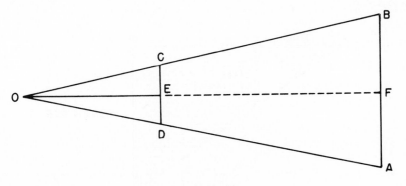

Figure 17-17

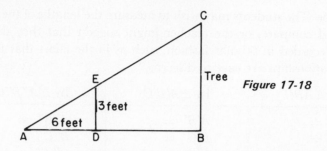

Figure 17-18

ments proportional to these two sides, then it is parallel to the third side.

If $\angle C = \angle B$ and $\angle D = \angle A$ and if $\angle O$ is common to both triangles OCD and OBA, are the triangles similar?

> **Theorem:** If the corresponding angles of two triangles are equal, the triangles are similar (AAA).

This pattern could be followed to include the SAS similarity theorem (two pairs of corresponding sides proportional and the included angles equal), as well as the SSS theorem (all corresponding sides proportional). In addition to the multitude of surveying problems, you can also introduce a variety of problems of indirect measure involving shadow lengths, cliff heights, water depths, and well depths. A list of sample problems follows:

1. The shadow (AB) of a tree (BC) is 50 feet (Fig. 17-18). At D, a yard-stick is held vertically so that a boy lying flat on the ground at A sees C along AE. If AD is 6 feet, how tall is the tree? Explain.
2. From point A on shore, the ground under the water slopes down. At B, a point 5 feet from A, the water depth is 2 feet. How deep is the water at C, 100 feet from A? (See Fig. 17-19.)
3. A builder intends to construct a triangle out of steel beams. He makes a model with the necessary shape that has sides that measure 2, 3,

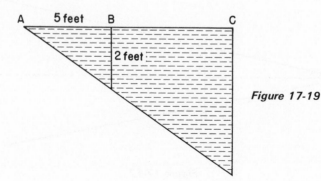

Figure 17-19

402

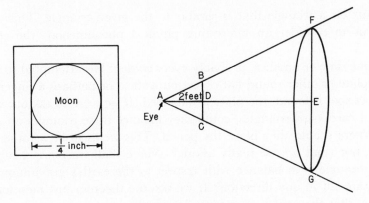

Figure 17-20

and 4 feet. The base, and longest side, of the actual structure is 120 feet. What are the lengths of its sides?

4. An astronomer cuts a $\frac{1}{4}$ inch square hole in a piece of cardboard and by holding it about 2 feet from his eye, the circular shape of the moon fits exactly into the square hole (Fig. 17-20). If we use 240,000 miles as the distance to the moon, what is its radius? (Be careful of the units.)

5. To find the depth of a well 15 feet wide, a boy places a rod, *AB*, horizontally under his foot. He places the rod so that its end point (*B*) is on a line with his eye (*C*) and the base of the opposite wall (*D*). If *OC* = 4 feet and *OB* = 3 feet, find the depth of the well and explain why you answer as you do (Fig. 17-21).

MEDIANS OF A TRIANGLE

One of the corollaries of the AAA similarity theorem indicates that a line parallel to one side of a triangle intersecting the other two sides in distinct

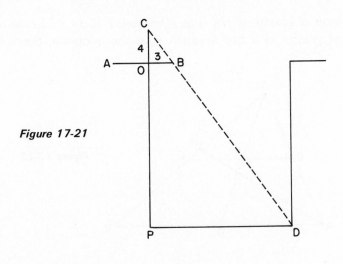

Figure 17-21

403

points cuts off a triangle that is similar to the given triangle. This theorem enables us to consider an interesting physical phenomenon: the center of gravity.

At one time or another, probably every student has attempted to balance a paper plate or other round flat object on a stick, or perhaps a finger. When the correct spot is found, the plate is balanced. If we were to ask our students to cut out cardboard triangles, could they balance these triangles on a pencil point? Where should they place the pencil? This seems to be a rather simple problem, but what are we really asking? Where shall we place a support so that the triangle is in balance with respect to the earth's gravitational force and will not tilt in any direction? If we use the theorem just mentioned, we can prove that the center of gravity lies on the intersection of the medians. Indeed, the students can construct the medians; and if their work is carefully done, the point of concurrency would be very close to, if not actually on, the center of gravity, as tested by cutting out the triangle and balancing. A proof of this follows:

> ***Prove:*** center of gravity of $\triangle ABC$ lies on the intersection of the medians (Fig. 17-22)
> ***Given:*** $\triangle ABC$

Let CG be the median from C to side AB. Let DE be parallel to AB.

$\triangle CDF \sim \triangle CAG$ by the theorem about a line parallel to one side of a triangle

In the same way $\triangle CFE \sim \triangle CGB$

Then
$$\frac{GB}{FE} = \frac{GC}{FC} \quad \text{and} \quad \frac{AG}{DF} = \frac{GC}{FC}$$
$$AG = GB \quad \text{by definition of median}$$
Hence
$$DF = FE$$

The center of gravity of DE is at F because F is the midpoint of DE and the center of gravity of a line segment is at the midpoint. Since the center

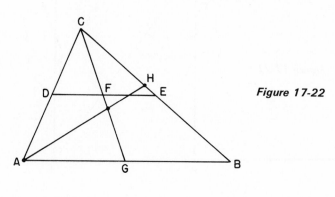

Figure 17-22

404

of any such segment is on the median, the center of gravity of the triangle is on the median. Repeating the same argument for median *AH* indicates that the center of gravity of the triangle is on the intersection of the medians.

SIMILAR RIGHT TRIANGLES— PYTHAGOREAN THEOREM

One of the more interesting applications of similar right triangles involves the method used for finding the height of the pyramids ascribed to Thales.[4] A stick placed in the ground vertically casts a shadow, as does the pyramid. The imaginary line from the end of the shadow to the top of the stick and to the top of the pyramid completes the right triangles (Fig. 17-23). The students may be able to recreate Thales' method if they are given this information and are allowed to attempt to solve the problem unaided. Thales measured the stick and its shadow and then measured the shadow of the pyramid. (It is said that he forgot to include half the width of the base of the pyramid in his calculations.) In this way, because of the similar triangles, he had three terms of a proportion and was able to calculate the fourth one. This same method was also used by the Greeks to find the heights of mountains.

As we focus upon the right triangle in particular, we encounter some important relationships that, among other things, will enable us to formulate another proof of the Pythagorean theorem. These relationships concern the altitude of a right triangle drawn to the hypotenuse. An interesting entry into this area may be made by presenting an additional method for finding an inaccessible length: In order to measure the distance across a river (*AB*), an engineer followed this plan (Fig. 17-24): At *B* he walked in a line perpendicular to *AB* until he reached a convenient point *C*. He then walked perpendicular to line *AC* until, at *D*, he intersected *AB* extended. He then used the lengths *BC* and *BD* and computed *AB*. How does this work?

This problem could lead students to consider several theorems, including:

> The altitude to the hypotenuse in any right triangle divides that triangle into two triangles which are similar to each other and the original triangle.

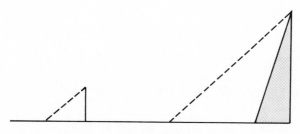

Figure 17-23

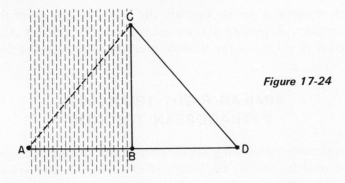

Figure 17-24

The altitude to the hypotenuse in any right triangle is the mean proportional between the segments of the base.

Of course, the single problem is not sufficient experience for students to undertake the proof of the theorems mentioned. In addition to other such problems, varieties of right triangles can be measured and ratios calculated to add to the conviction of the students that these relationships do indeed hold. After these activities, the proofs may be attempted.

We now turn our attention to a proof of the Pythagorean theorem different in approach from that developed in the chapter on area.

Prove: $a^2 + b^2 = c^2$

Given: right triangle ABC, with a right angle at C, $CD \perp AB$ (Fig. 17-25)

Since $\triangle ACD \sim \triangle ABC$ (both contain right angles and $\angle A$)

$$\frac{x}{b} = \frac{b}{c}$$

By the same token, $\triangle CBD \sim \triangle ABC$

$$\frac{y}{a} = \frac{a}{c}$$

Using algebra we get

$$x = \frac{b^2}{c} \qquad \text{and} \qquad y = \frac{a^2}{c}$$

By addition

$$x + y = \frac{b^2}{c} + \frac{a^2}{c} = \frac{a^2 + b^2}{c}$$

Since $x + y = c$,

$$c = \frac{a^2 + b^2}{c} \qquad \text{or} \qquad c^2 = a^2 + b^2$$

406

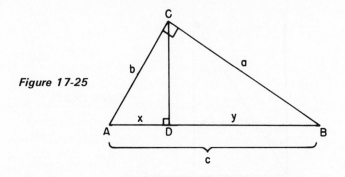

Figure 17-25

There are, as indicated before, many other ways to prove the Pythagorean theorem. It would be an interesting and fruitful exercise for the students to experiment with the ratios in attempts to find their own way to a proof. It is also valuable to once again demonstrate the interplay between algebra and geometry. The proof of the converse of the Pythagorean theorem offers an irresistible challenge: If the sides of a triangle are in the relationship $a^2 + b^2 = c^2$, the triangle must be a right triangle with c the hypotenuse. The relationships inherent in a 30°–60°–90° triangle, as well as in a 45°–45°–90° triangle, may also be established here, leading to a rich supply of computational exercises such as the following:

1. A tunnel is to be dug under a mountain by working from both ends (A and B) simultaneously (Fig. 17-26). C is chosen on a level with A and B so that C is a right angle and $AC = BC = 200$ feet. How long is the distance from A to B?

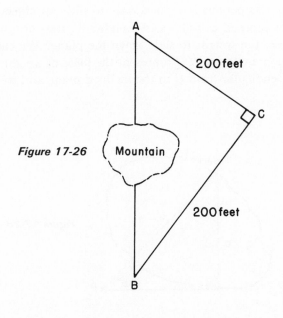

Figure 17-26

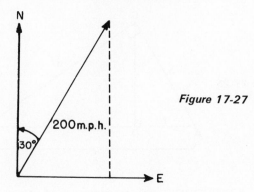

Figure 17-27

2. An airplane is flying due east while a wind is blowing due north so that the actual flight of the plane is at a rate of 200 m.p.h. in a northeast direction along a line making a 30° angle with the north line. Find the component due to the wind (Fig. 17-27).

3. In order to measure the distance across a canyon, a ranger selects a tree on the opposite side as a reference point (Fig. 17-28). He then walks along the rim at a right angle to the line of the tree and his starting point, until he reaches a point (P) which makes a 45° angle with the tree and the rim. How does this help him find the distance across the canyon?

Some of the exercises just mentioned may involve the use of vectors. At this point a revisit to the topic of vectors results in the consideration of many interesting applications of the geometric ideas. The similarity theorems and the Pythagorean theorem add greatly to our ability to deal with a broad variety of problems dealing with the component forces involved in moving objects up or down an inclined plane. For example, if we were concerned with finding the component force necessary to slide an object up an inclined plane, we might proceed as follows: A weight, W, rests on an inclined plane. What force causes the weight to slide down the plane? We can find the component of the force by letting PQ represent the force of weight W (Fig. 17-29). We drop a perpendicular from Q to the inclined plane and we get component

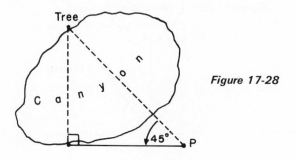

Figure 17-28

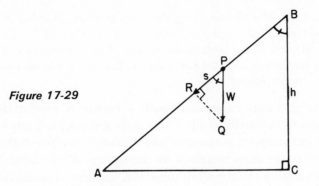

Figure 17-29

PR of W along the plane. But how much is PR, or s? If the inclined plane rises h feet in distance AB, by similar triangles ACB and QRP we have:

$$\frac{s}{W} = \frac{h}{AB} \qquad \text{or} \qquad s = W \cdot \frac{h}{AB}$$

If the inclined plane rises 5 feet in a distance of 20 feet along the plane, then

$$s = W\tfrac{5}{20} = \tfrac{1}{4}W$$

Thus, if W is 100 pounds, only 25 pounds of force acts down the plane. This is the force necessary to slide the object up the plane. If we return to the previous equation and perform one algebraic manipulation, we arrive at a curious result:

$$s = W\tfrac{5}{20}$$
$$20s = 5W$$

This result is curious because it appears to indicate that the work necessary to raise a weight W straight upward to a height of 5 feet is the same as that done by sliding the weight along the plane for 20 feet, in order to reach the same height. This conclusion applies to any inclined plane of any slope. A similar investigation can be carried out to study motion down an inclined plane. Additional problems may be presented if the students' interest so warrants. A typical problem follows:

> A weight of 100 pounds must be raised 5 feet. If you have a choice of two inclined planes, one which rises 5 feet in 10 feet of distance and one which rises 5 feet in 20 feet of distance, which would you use? Compute the forces necessary in both cases and explain the method used.

AREAS OF SIMILAR TRIANGLES

We close this discussion of similarity by comparing the areas of two similar triangles. Let us consider the following problem:

You are offered two triangular plots of land. One has dimensions of 30, 40, and 60 feet; and the other has dimensions of 60, 80, and 120 feet. If the cost of the land in the second plot is three times as much as that in the first, which do you think is the better buy in terms of the cost per square foot of area?

The students may experiment with a variety of similar triangles to see what happens to the areas as the dimensions are doubled, tripled, and so on. They may even examine rectangles and squares and observe the same effects. It appears that the area increases as the square of the sides. We may now attempt proof of a relationship observed earlier. A combined algebraic-geometric analysis can shed some light here. Let us examine such an analysis based upon similar triangles.

Given: $\triangle ABC \sim \triangle A'B'C'$

BD is altitude of $\triangle ABC$,

$B'D'$ is altitude of $\triangle A'B'C'$ (Fig. 17-30)

Prove: $\dfrac{\text{Area } \triangle ABC}{\text{Area } \triangle A'B'C'} = \dfrac{c^2}{c'^2} = \dfrac{b^2}{b'^2} = \dfrac{a^2}{a'^2}$

The areas of the triangles are in the following ratio:

$$\frac{A}{A'} = \frac{bh}{b'h'}$$

$\triangle ABD \sim \triangle A'B'D'$ since $\angle A = \angle A'$, right angles at D and D'. Hence, we may state that

$$\frac{h}{c} = \frac{h'}{c'} \qquad \text{or} \qquad \frac{h}{h'} = \frac{c}{c'}$$

From the original triangles we know that

From the original triangles we know that

$$\frac{c}{c'} = \frac{b}{b'}$$

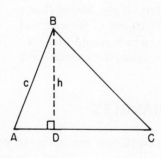
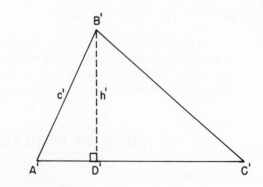

Figure 17-30

410

Therefore we have $\dfrac{h}{h'} = \dfrac{b}{b'}$ by substitution of $\dfrac{b}{b'}$ for $\dfrac{c}{c'}$.

So $\dfrac{A}{A'} = \dfrac{b^2}{b'^2}$, again by substitution.

But $\dfrac{b^2}{b'^2} = \dfrac{c^2}{c'^2} = \dfrac{a^2}{a'^2}$; thus we can conclude that the ratio of the areas of the two similar triangles is the square of the ratio of any two corresponding sides.

Our original problem is answered by indicating that since the sides of the second triangular parcel are double those of the first, the area of the second parcel is four times that of the first. Since the cost is only three times as great, as far as cost per square foot is concerned, the larger triangle is a better buy. We are paying only three times as much for something worth four times as much.

One final word on this topic before we take our leave: It is customary to find a good deal of work devoted to a review of the arithmetic of proportions before getting into the geometric ideas. The process of reviewing is a necessary part of successful mathematics teaching, but there are many different ways to accomplish the ends of review experiences. The position is taken here that no work should be undertaken to aid student ability to deal with proportions except as such need grows out of the work with similar polygons. In this way, you are providing help that the students clearly see is necessary; at the same time you may be avoiding needless repetition. The fact that ideas encountered earlier will recur helps the student to see a unity in all that he is studying. Each time he meets a familiar idea in a new setting it adds to the importance of that idea, as well as adding interest to the new problems under consideration. It is important that we permit difficulties to occur naturally and not try to anticipate problems that have not yet arisen; for if they have not yet arisen, certainly the students see little purpose in what is going on.

FOOTNOTES

1. See Chapter 2, pages 15 to 31.
2. For several proofs of this theorem see *Geometry Growing* by William R. Ransom, a pamphlet of the National Council of Teachers of Mathematics, 1954, pp. 1–7.
3. Edmond R. Kiely. "Surveying Instruments: Their History and Classroom Use." National Council of Teachers of Mathematics, 19th Yearbook: 1947, pp. 194–206.
4. Edmond R. Kiely. "Surveying Instruments: Their History and Classroom Use." National Council of Teachers of Mathematics, 19th Yearbook: 1947, p. 283.

FOR INVESTIGATION AND DISCUSSION

1. If we begin by postulating the area of a square, devise a lesson to help students intuitively determine the area of a rectangle.

2. Make a lesson plan that will enable students to construct a square with a given perimeter.

3. Make an outline indicating how you would move from a proof of the area of a rectangle to the understanding and proof of the areas of a right triangle, a triangle, a parallelogram, and a trapezoid—not necessarily in that order.

4. Develop a proof of the Pythagorean theorem other than the ones presented here.

5. Describe how the distance traveled by a falling object is mathematically related to the area under a curve.

6. Indicate how a lesson may develop to aid student awareness that equal corresponding angles do not necessarily result in congruent triangles. How would you help students uncover the relationship that does exist?

7. Plan an experiment that students can undertake to be able to establish the center of gravity of any cardboard cut-out triangle.

8. Demonstrate how knowledge of vectors may be extended after the basic similarity theorems have been explored. Make use of specific illustrations.

9. Describe physical apparatus that may be employed to experimentally determine the vector-inclined plane relationships discussed on pages 408 to 409.

10. Evaluate the advantages and disadvantages of reviewing ratio and proportion concepts before work with similarity or of waiting until difficulty arises after similarity concepts are explored.

FOR FURTHER READING

Books

E. T. Bell. *Mathematics: Queen and Servant of Science.* McGraw-Hill Book Co., 1951, pp. 188–194.
Constance Reid. *A Long Way From Euclid.* Thomas Y. Crowell Company, 1963, pp. 1–14.

Periodicals

Nelson Gray. "Right Triangle Construction." *The Mathematics Teacher.* Vol. 53 (November, 1960), pp. 533–536.
Philip J. Hart. "Pythagorean Numbers." *The Mathematics Teacher.* Vol. 47 (January, 1954), pp. 16–21.
Paul B. Johnson. "Are Circles Similar?" *The Mathematics Teacher.* Vol. 59 (January, 1966), pp. 9–13.
Donald W. Stover. "Auxiliary Lines and Ratios." *The Mathematics Teacher.* Vol. 60 (February, 1967), pp. 109–114.

Pamphlets

William H. Glenn and Donovan A. Johnson. *The Pythagorean Theorem.* (Exploring Mathematics on Your Own Series), Webster Publishing, 1960.
William R. Ransom. *Geometry Growing.* (National Council of Teachers of Mathematics), 1954, pp. 1–10.

18

CIRCLES

INTRODUCTION TO CIRCLES

We have considered many basic and useful geometric figures, such as the triangle, the rectangle, the parallelogram, and quadrilaterals in general. Of even greater importance than each of these is the circle. The wheels of automobiles and trains are circles, and you can well imagine the consequences of using some other shape. What kind of ride would result from a car with square wheels? The shapes of coins and dishes, the cross sections of tree trunks and cans, and even the moon and sun suggest circles, as does the equator. There is no end to the variety of physical objects that bring the circle to mind, and these provide us with an opportunity to offer the student work of genuine significance.

The mathematical properties of circles will shed light upon an endless number of problems from the physical world. If an auto tire is to fit the wheel properly, we become concerned with circumference, which also involves the size of the earth at the equator as well as the distance around any of the planets and moons of our solar system. In machinery, one wheel is often used to make another wheel move. A circular shape helps to keep this motion smooth. When we are interested in the speed with which the wheels turn, we once again need to know circumference. What better way is there to immerse our students in the concept of circle than to call upon one of these numerous basic, but important, applications? The computation of the circumference of this planet upon which we live offers just such an opportunity.

How would you go about finding the circumference of the earth upon which we live, especially when it is difficult to get off its surface? Direct measurement would require a lot of string and a lot of walking! Yet in about the third century B.C., a Greek mathematician was able to compute the earth's circumference.

The way in which Eratosthenes went about determining the circumference of the earth is interesting and useful and makes clear in no uncertain terms the power of mathematics! Perhaps the best way to help students to build an awareness of the importance of this calculation is to attempt to place them in the position of Eratosthenes: If we assume that the earth is shaped like a sphere and if we cut through the sphere (like cutting an orange), passing our knife through the center, the surfaces of the two halves are circular. How would you go about trying to find the circumference of this circle, the length of the equator?

Many students, having been led to believe that Columbus first thought the earth to be round in 1490, may be quite surprised to learn that more than 2000 years ago there were people on the planet who were aware of its spherical shape!

But how did Eratosthenes proceed? He knew that Alexandria (point A) was due north of, and 500 miles from, the city of Syene (now called Aswan). This is point B in Figure 18-1. Thus, $\overset{\frown}{AB}$ is 500 miles. Eratosthenes also knew that on June 21 (summer solstice) at noon the sun shone directly down into a well at Syene. This meant that the sun's rays came directly along line BO at that time of the year. He also determined that the sun's rays made an angle of $7\frac{1}{2}°$ with line OAD, a line straight up from the surface of the earth at point A.

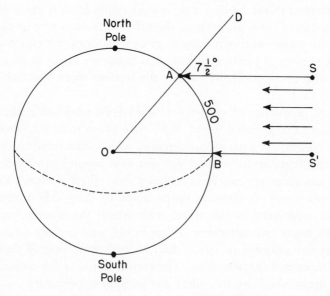

Figure 18-1

Since the sun is so far away, we may consider its rays to be parallel lines when they reach the earth; that is, *SA* and *S'B* are parallel. With this information, can the students do as Eratosthenes did and compute the circumference of the earth? It is important to provide time for "groping" here so that the students will have an opportunity to realize the satisfaction that comes from "cracking" a puzzling problem. The solution presented by Eratosthenes involves the use of corresponding angles to establish $\angle AOB = 7\frac{1}{2}°$. He then solved the proportion,

$$\frac{7\frac{1}{2}}{360} = \frac{500}{x}$$

and finally arrived at the answer: 24,000 miles. This is a remarkable result when you consider that in the time of Columbus, geographers are reputed to have believed that the correct figure for the circumference of the earth was 17,000 miles. As a matter of fact, had Columbus known the correct figure (about 24,900) he might never have undertaken to sail to India!

We have a rather dramatic demonstration of how a little mathematics can certainly go a long way. Although in the case of Columbus, perhaps the lack of such knowledge provided greater assistance. It may be best to suppress this example after all!

The calculation of the time it takes various planets to make a single trip about the sun (the number of days in their respective years, or what is called their *period*) also offers an interesting situation that serves as important introductory work to circles. For example, consider this problem:

> At a certain time, the earth, Mars, and the sun are in a straight line. (Let us assume that the earth and Mars travel a circular orbit.) It takes 780 days for the sun, the earth, and Mars to be in a straight line again. Compute the period of Mars (Fig. 18-2).

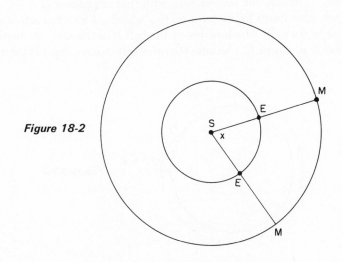

Figure 18-2

It will help the students to add that in 780 days the earth completed two revolutions (730 days) and part of a third ($\frac{50}{365}$). In the same time, Mars completed one revolution and part of a second. If the students are unable to progress, they should be asked to find $\angle x$. However they proceed, one solution involves two proportions in this manner:

$$\frac{x}{360} = \frac{50}{365} \qquad \text{or} \qquad x = 49°$$

Since Mars has made one revolution $+$ 49°, it has turned through 360° $+$ 49°, or 409°.

$$\frac{360}{409} = \frac{p}{780} \qquad \text{or} \qquad p = 687$$

Thus, the period of Mars is about 687 days.

The introductory work with circles has been a demonstration of how, with a little mathematics, we have been able to determine approximations of the circumference of our planet and the periods of other planets under certain conditions. What remarkable returns for our mathematical efforts! In this way we give promise that the work with circles will open new vistas as to the role of mathematics in helping us to "see" nature better.

Many pertinent exercises are available at this point, and the following list is a sample of these:

1. What is the circumference of the path of a satellite that is in a circular orbit 500 miles above the surface of the earth?
2. If a telephone line were constructed around the earth and if the wire were 20 feet above the surface of the earth at each point, how much longer would the wire be than the circumference of the earth? ($r = 4000$ miles.) (See Fig. 18-3.)
3. Same problem as the preceding except based on the moon. ($r = 1080$ miles.) Compare the answer here with that of problem 2.
4. A belt is wrapped tightly around two wheels, A and B, each of which turns on an axle. The function of the belt is to transmit the motion of wheel A to wheel B. (Assume that the belt doesn't slip.) If the radius

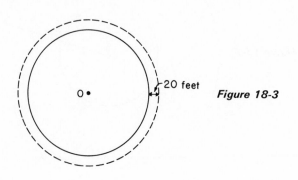

20 feet

Figure 18-3

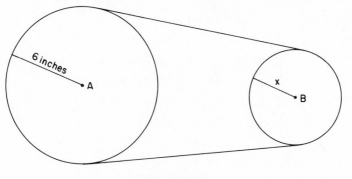

Figure 18-4

of wheel *A* is 6 inches and it revolves 1000 times a minute, what should be the radius of wheel *B* so that it will revolve 1500 times a minute? (See Fig. 18-4.)

5. The sun, the earth, and Venus are in line every 579 days. In that time Venus makes more than two revolutions and the earth more than one. Find the number of days in a year on Venus (Fig. 18-5).

TANGENTS TO CIRCLES

The idea of tangent is a difficult one to define exactly, but an idea that is intuitively quite accessible. A boy stands at the seashore and gazes out to sea. His line of vision is tangent to the earth at the horizon (Fig. 18-6). The moon passes between the sun and the earth, forming an eclipse; the shadow boundary lines are tangent lines (Fig. 18-7). An inclined plane is tangent to a disc that is rolling down its length. These are some familiar situations involving the tangent. Let us begin by recalling a problem we met earlier in the chapter on algebra—the problem of the distance to the horizon. A lookout in the crow's nest of a ship is 100 feet above the sea. How far can he see? In dealing with this situation in algebra,[1] we made several assumptions about the rela-

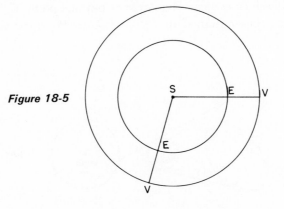

Figure 18-5

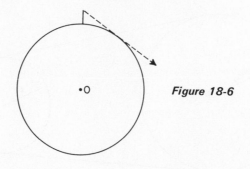

Figure 18-6

tionships present. Perhaps we can now be a bit more precise in explaining what is happening. As the sailor looks out over the sea, his line of vision extends to the horizon: a tangent from his lookout point to the great circle of the earth (Fig. 18-8). Before, we assumed that $\triangle AOB$ was a right triangle with a right angle at B. Can we be sure of this? If we attempt to make a drawing or construction of this situation, we find that since the lookout is on a pole vertical to the earth's surface, if extended (AC), it should pass through the center of the earth. Of course, we are assuming that the earth is a perfect sphere, which it is not in actuality. It does approximate the sphere closely enough for our purpose. If we complete $\triangle AOB$ by drawing OB, it appears that $OB \perp AB$. If this is true, then we may use the Pythagorean theorem to determine any desired lengths. But how can we be sure? Perhaps if the circle is of a particular size or if AC is made a certain length, the line OB (the radius) will not be perpendicular to the tangent AB at the point of contact. And so we attempt a proof by focusing upon the geometry alone.

    Prove: $m \perp PQ$ at Q (Fig. 18-9)
    Given: line m tangent to circle p at Q
    If we can show that PQ is the shortest distance from p to line m, then, since the shortest distance from a point to a line is the perpendicular, we will have shown $PQ \perp m$.

    Compare PQ with PR, where R is any other point on line m. R must be outside the circle since m meets the circle at but one point, Q. Thus, R must be farther from the center than Q or $PR > PQ$. So PQ is the shortest line from p to m.

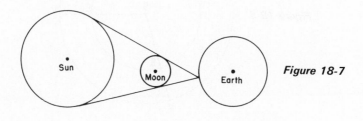

Figure 18-7

418

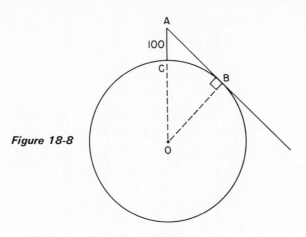

Figure 18-8

The converse of this theorem is also important and is developed in an interesting manner in the SMSG text.[2] A single theorem is considered that involves the three possible relationships between a circle and a line in the same plane: The line is outside the circle, on the circle, or inside the circle. The theorem is stated as follows:

Given a line and a circle in the same plane (Fig. 18-10), let P be the center of the circle; let F be the foot of the perpendicular from P to the line. Then either

1. every point of the line is outside the circle

   or

2. F is on the circle, and the line is tangent to the circle at F

   or

3. F is inside the circle, and the line intersects the circle in exactly two points, which are equidistant from F.

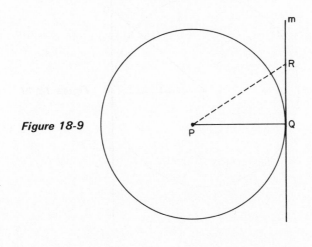

Figure 18-9

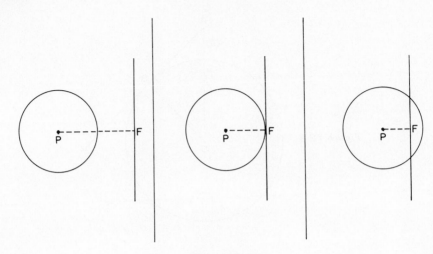

Figure 18-10

This is a rather long statement of a theorem and its proof is equally lengthy, but the text explains that the gains are worth the effort. Once this theorem has been established, all the other theorems about secants, chords, and tangents become corollaries.

Here, only the second case will be presented as it is pertinent to the problem under consideration.

F is on the circle (Fig. 18-11). Here we have $PF = r$. Thus, if Q is any other point on the line, then $PQ > r$. Hence the line is tangent to the circle at point F.

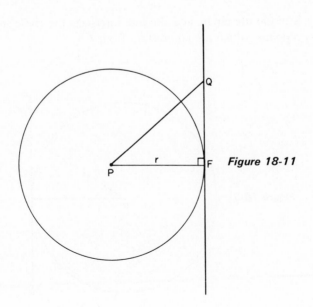

Figure 18-11

Now we have a solid basis upon which to make use of the Pythagorean theorem in order to find the distance that the sailor in the crow's nest can see. The solution is based on Figure 18-8. Since OB and OC are radii of the earth, we may use 4000 miles as an approximation for their length. (Changing to feet, we get 4000×5280, which gives 21,120,000 feet.) The lengths of the sides of the triangle are as follows: $AO = 21{,}120{,}100$; $BO = 21{,}120{,}000$.

$$AB^2 + (21{,}120{,}000)^2 = (21{,}120{,}100)^2$$
$$AB = \sqrt{(21{,}120{,}100)^2 - (21{,}120{,}000)^2}$$
$$AB = \sqrt{100^2 \cdot (211{,}201)^2 - 100^2\,(211{,}200)^2}$$

By factoring, we get
$$AB = 100\sqrt{(211{,}201)^2 - (211{,}200)^2}$$

Factoring again, we get
$$AB = 100\sqrt{(211{,}201 - 211{,}200)(211{,}201 + 211{,}200)}$$
$$AB = 100\sqrt{(1)(422{,}401)}$$
$$AB = 65{,}000 \text{ feet (approximately) or about 12 miles.}$$

Notice how the use of algebra helps us to avoid rather large computations. It may be necessary to point out how algebra can be of service. At any rate, we have found that at 100 feet above the sea the sailor is able to see about 12 miles in every direction!

LATITUDE—LONGITUDE

There are very close ties between geometry and geography. This relationship had been exploited earlier as we frequently considered a variety of surveying problems. Additional work in this area will result from a consideration of locus. We turn now to the study of latitude and longitude, an application of tangents to a circle. If we assume once again that the earth is a sphere and imagine a plane cutting this sphere halfway between the north and south poles perpendicular to the axis, the plane cuts out a circle on the surface of the sphere that we know as the equator. Since latitude and longitude lines are used to identify points on the surface of the earth, let us begin with the equator and assign all its points the value of 0° for latitude. How shall we designate the other latitudes? As we move away from the equator, we shall locate points of north and south latitude as these points lie above or below the equator. The number of degrees above or below the equator is determined by the angle formed at the center of the earth, O, by the radii to the point in question, P, and to the point on the equator directly north or south of the given point, Q (Fig. 18-12). Thus, angle POQ is the angle that determines the latitude. Of course, if we pass a plane through point P parallel to the plane of the equator, we cut off a circle, every point of which shares the same latitude. Besides considering maximum latitudes and distances between points of the same longitudes whose latitudes are known, it is interesting to see how

421

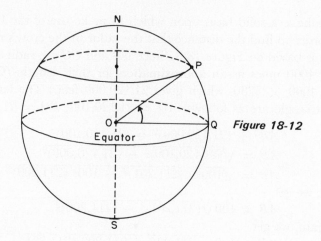

Figure 18-12

we can determine our own latitude both at night and during the day. It is these methods that involve the tangent theorems. Here is a brief presentation of each with the justification left for the students to determine. The diagrams are made using the great circle cross section of the earth.

Determining Latitude at Night

The star known as the North Star always seems to be in the same place. The light rays coming from it are parallel to each other and to the earth's axis. To find your latitude, go out in front of your house and find the angle ($\angle APN$) made by a line to the North Star and a horizontal line, tangent AP (Fig. 18-13). (The angle can be measured using a simple astrolabe, which

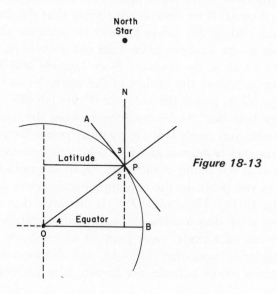

Figure 18-13

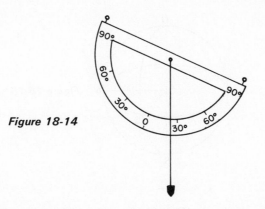

Figure 18-14

is really an enlarged protractor with a plumb line hanging as indicated in Figure 18-14.) Since $\angle POB$ should give the latitude of point P, how is it that $\angle APN$ will work? ($\angle 1 = \angle 2$, $\angle 3 = 90° - \angle 1$, and $\angle 4 = 90° - \angle 2$.)

Determining Latitude During the Day

It is difficult to find your latitude during the day, unless it is done upon one of two special days—those days when the sun's rays at noon are parallel to the equator: about March 21 and September 21. These days are called the spring and fall equinoxes. If you are at point P in Figure 18-15, can you explain why the latitude is easily determined on these special days? Remember $\angle POB$ will give the desired latitude.

Determining Longitude

You may be wondering about the lack of mention of longitude, the vertical lines dividing up the surface of the earth going through the poles. Whereas the equator was the base line for latitude measures, the semicircle made by passing a plane through the earth perpendicular to the plane of the equator and through the city of Greenwich, England (point G), is the base

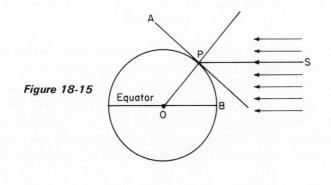

Figure 18-15

423

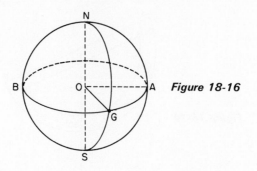

Figure 18-16

line for longitude measures (Fig. 18-16). All points on semicircle *NGS* have a longitude of zero. The longitudes of points not on this semicircle vary from 180° east longitude to 180° west longitude. For example, point *A* has a longitude determined by ∠ *GOA*. When we specify the latitude and longitude of a point, we have pinpointed its location on the earth in the same manner as the *x*- and *y*-coordinates locate a point in the Cartesian plane.

Arriving at your own longitude is done rather handily if you have a clock on Greenwich time. If your time is, say, 5 hours later than Greenwich time, your longitude must be 5 × 15 or 75° west longitude. It takes 24 hours for the earth to complete a rotation or to turn 360°; thus, in each hour it will turn 15°. If we recall that Greenwich has a zero longitude, the computation is simple.

The problems and theorems just presented, including the mathematical analysis of line-circle relationships from the SMSG, make the proofs of a host of theorems a possibility. Such theorems as those involving line segments through the center of the circle intersecting chords are typical:

> Any perpendicular from the center of a circle to a chord bisects the chord.
> The segment joining the center of a circle to the midpoint of a chord is perpendicular to the chord.
> The perpendicular bisector of a chord passes through the center of the circle.

ECLIPSES

You have probably read many stories about how strange and terrifying the sudden darkening of the sun was, and perhaps still is, to primitive peoples. Many were convinced that the end of the world was surely near! Can you imagine the power that might be wielded by one who was able to calculate when such an apparent catastrophe would take place and how long it might last? It would not take much to convince those around that the sun had regained its light on command! The term "godlike" would probably under-

424

estimate the feelings of primitive people towards such a person. Today, eclipses are still major events capturing the attention of laymen and scientists all over the world, but the mystery is gone. The mathematics required to be able to compute the time of the appearance of the eclipse, as well as its length of duration and the position on the earth from which it will become visible, is known to high school mathematics students. With this brief introduction, let us consider the question, How is an eclipse caused?

As the planets and their moons travel through the plane of their orbits about the sun, they assume a variety of relative positions. Using the earth as an example, there are times when the earth is between the sun and the moon. There are also times when the moon in its movement passes between the earth and the sun. These situations bring about eclipses. A diagram may help to clarify (Fig. 18-17). If we think of the sun and the earth as circles, and also assume that each point on the sun is a light source sending out rays in all directions, we may investigate the shadow. The region to the right of the earth, marked with the Roman numeral I, is the region that is in shadow as the earth blocks the sun's rays. We may think of ray AB emanating from A as the last ray illuminating space behind the earth. Approaching from the other side, DE may be considered the last ray illuminating space behind the earth. Both AB and DE are common external tangents, and if they are extended beyond the earth until they intersect, we complete region I, the region in shadow (bounded by these tangents and that portion of the circle, BE, included between them). All the while the moon is in this region, it will be eclipsed. Thus, many relationships can be investigated that will add to our knowledge of the physical phenomenon as well as to our knowledge of geometry. For example, we may consider the comparative sizes of tangents to a circle from a point outside, as well as the segments of the common external tangents.

The common internal tangents help us to identify other regions of interest (Fig. 18-18). Rays coming from part of arc $AFHD$ pass through points such as point X in region III. In fact, as point X moves towards point W in region IV, more rays from the sun can reach it. Thus, point X is partially illuminated. These regions (II and III) of partial illumination are called the *penumbra*.

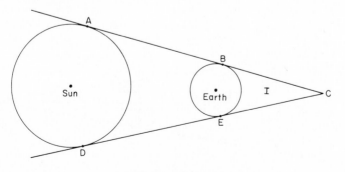

Figure 18-17

425

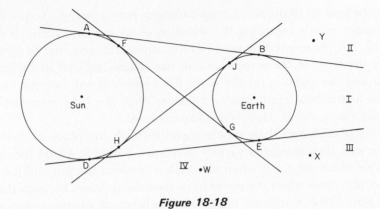

Figure 18-18

But it is the shadow region that is of greatest interest. Since the moon is in eclipse when it is in this region, we may well ask whether or not it does indeed pass through the region. It may well be that the moon is so far away from the earth that when it is to the earth's right, it is beyond the shadow region. How can we be sure? Here we have an interesting application of our knowledge of plane geometry, including similar triangles. How long is the shadow region? We know that the average distance of the moon from the earth as it circles around is about 240,000 miles. Is the shadow region less than or greater than this distance? The problem is solved using Figure 18-19. We will use the following approximations:

BE, radius of earth:	4000 miles
AS, radius of sun:	432,000 miles
SE, average distance of earth to sun:	93,000,000 miles

If we think of *PE* as the length of the shadow (less the length of the radius of the earth), this becomes the important distance to determine. We have learned enough mathematics to be able to determine this length. The theorem about radii drawn to tangents and the similar triangle relationships yield

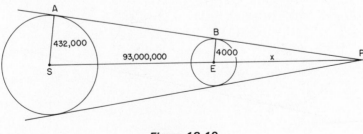

Figure 18-19

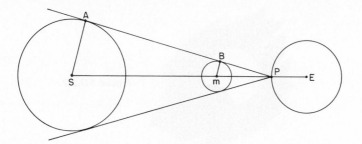

Figure 18-20

$$\frac{PE}{PS} = \frac{BE}{AS}$$

If we let $x = PE$,

$$\frac{x}{x + 93,000,000} = \frac{4000}{432,000}$$

Eventually we arrive at $x = 869,000$ (rounded off). Since the average distance of the moon from the earth is about 240,000 miles, we can see that the moon is, indeed, going to pass through the shadow region; and we can expect an eclipse to take place.

A similar investigation may be undertaken to determine the effects of the moon's passing between the earth and the sun (Fig. 18-20). The moon's shadow, in this instance, is darkening a small portion of the earth's surface. If we determine the distance (PM) of the moon from the earth, using a moon radius of 1080 miles, we find $PM = 233,000$ miles. The mean distance of the earth from the moon is 238,857 miles, but the distance varies from about 221,000 to 253,000 miles. Thus, there is a more critical situation here. In any case, we may now indicate that if an observer on earth is within the moon's shadow, he will observe things differently from one who is not so located. In the first instance we have a total eclipse of the sun. In the second, the sun may be viewed in a variety of ways, depending upon position on the earth's surface. Such a view would range from observation of an annular eclipse (i.e.,

Figure 18-21

427

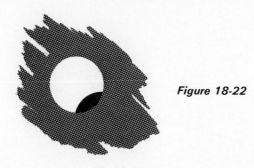

Figure 18-22

a bright ring around the concealed central portion of the sun [Fig. 18-21]) to a partial eclipse, in which a segment of the sun is covered (Fig. 18-22). Of course, where it is night there will be no visible sun at all.

In this way, man is able to calculate when and where an eclipse will occur and how long it might last. You may have read about an impending eclipse of the sun that is causing astronomers to go to a particular place on the earth's surface where they may be afforded a better view.

This natural occurrence of common internal and external tangents leads

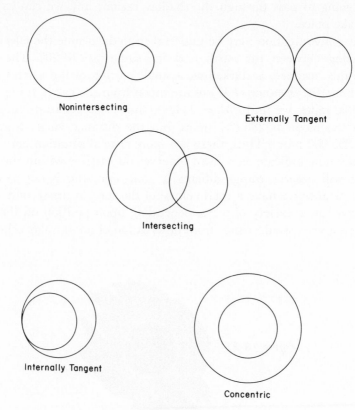

Nonintersecting

Externally Tangent

Intersecting

Internally Tangent

Concentric

Figure 18-23

us to explore the geometric relationships in a purely mathematical way, so we encounter the several relationships that are described by the important theorems about circles. Most of these have already been mentioned.

Before leaving tangency, we may undertake to explore tangent circles and extend this investigation to include the variety of relationships possible between two circles. This is a purely mathematical consideration that asks the question, What are the possible relationships between two circles? If the circles are drawn on plastic sheets, they can actually be maneuvered into a variety of positions and observations can be made (Fig. 18-23). This is an excellent place to encourage student exploration of relationships and the generation of their own propositions which may or may not become theorems. The guiding force shall be the question, "Can you find any relationships at all?" The freedom to add lines should be made clear to the students so that, for example, they might explore lines connecting the centers and common chords. Often, the students' observations are too carefully directed. Here is an opportunity for nondirected exploration.

ANGLE MEASUREMENT

An important problem in ship navigation enables us to consider angle measurement in a most interesting manner. A ship must pass by a rock area in a particular harbor. What course shall the captain follow if he is to keep his ship safe and avoid possible damage from the rocks? One way to aid this captain is to identify two landmarks or to place two buoys in the water and then lay out a circular path encompassing the dangerous rock area which passes through these two points (Fig. 18-24). If the captain traveling along *RS* knows what angle his ship must make with the buoys (*A* and *B*) in order to be safe ($\angle APB$), he can easily set his course in order to do so. This angle is called the danger angle. How shall we instruct this captain? To help us answer the question, we examine such angles in general. First we simplify the situation by placing the ship (*P*) on the circle itself, and then we consider $\angle APB$ (Fig. 18-25). As *P* moves along the circle, what happens to $\angle APB$? Strangely

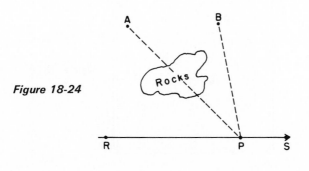

Figure 18-24

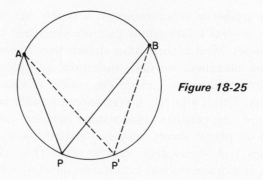

Figure 18-25

enough, it appears to remain the same size. Can this be true? (The use of a device or overlays at this particular point can be most helpful in enabling the students to see for themselves that the angle does not change size. Pegs and elastic angle sides, such as those used in Burns' Boards [Fig. 18-26], dynamic devices [Fig. 18-27], and overlays are all possible aids to be employed here.) After intuitive acceptance we turn to deduction. As we turn to the geometry of the situation, we have to introduce many new terms in order to carry out communication—terms such as central angle, inscribed angle, and so forth. How shall we measure angles formed by two chords, such as $\angle APB$? (See Fig. 18-28.) First we assume that the diameter PQ falls inside the angle. If we draw OB, $\angle 3 \stackrel{\circ}{=} \overset{\frown}{QB}$. It is a central angle.

$$\angle 3 = \angle 1 + \angle 2 \qquad \text{It is an exterior angle of } \triangle POB.$$
$$\angle 1 = \angle 2 \qquad \text{Because } OB = OP \text{ (radii).}$$

Then we may conclude that

$$\angle 1 \stackrel{\circ}{=} \tfrac{1}{2}\angle 3$$

Thus,

$$\angle 1 \stackrel{\circ}{=} \tfrac{1}{2}\overset{\frown}{QB}$$

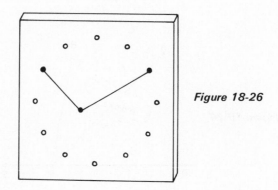

Figure 18-26

430

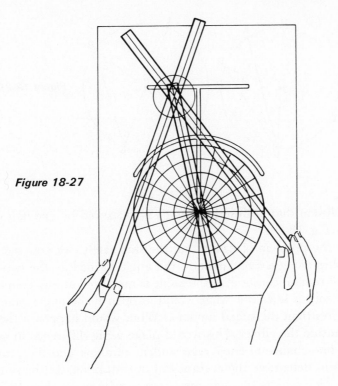

Figure 18-27

In the same manner we arrive at

$$\angle 4 \stackrel{\circ}{=} \tfrac{1}{2}\widehat{AQ}$$

By addition,

$$\angle P \stackrel{\circ}{=} \tfrac{1}{2}\widehat{AQB}$$

A similar consideration of the cases of the diameter from *P* falling outside the angle and the diameter constituting a side of the angle itself would result

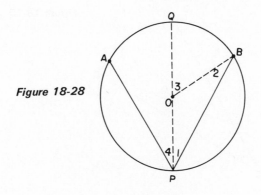

Figure 18-28

431

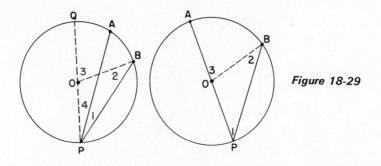

Figure 18-29

in the conclusion that an inscribed angle is measured by one half of its intercepted arc (Fig. 18-29).

As for the problem of navigating the ship safely, we now see that as we move the ship along a circular path, the angle formed by the two buoys and the ship will remain constant. If the angle is measured at any point and maintained, the ship is safe. But what would happen if the angle were permitted to become less than the stated amount? What would happen if the ship were inside or outside the circle? This would make a big difference in safety. Here we have a fine chance to encourage student thinking and then carry out investigations to determine the accuracy of our intuition. At the same time we introduce a rich variety of angle-measurement situations (Fig. 18-30).

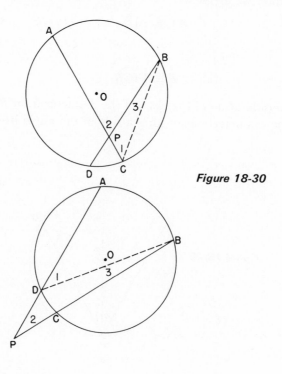

Figure 18-30

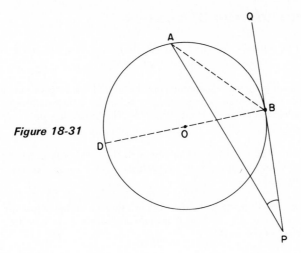

Figure 18-31

If we use the exterior angle of a triangle theorem, we may deduce that if P is inside the circle, $\angle 2 \doteq \frac{1}{2}(\widehat{AB} + \widehat{DC})$. If P is outside the circle, then $\angle 2 \doteq \frac{1}{2}(\widehat{AB} - \widehat{DC})$. Hence, we see that if the ship should stray into the circle, the angle at P would be greater than when P is a point on the circle. When the angle at P becomes smaller, the ship is wandering outside the circle.

At the same time, we have shown that an angle formed by two chords intersecting inside a circle is measured by one-half the sum of the arcs intercepted by it and by its vertical angle. In addition, we have also shown that an angle formed by two secants intersecting outside the circle is measured by one-half the difference of the intercepted arcs.

There is but one situation left to consider. If P is outside the circle so that PB becomes a tangent to the circle (Fig. 18-31), how is the angle measured? This situation permits consideration of the angle formed by a tangent and a chord, as well as the angle formed by a tangent and a secant. We eventually arrive at the general idea that the angle formed by two lines that intersect a circle and intersect each other outside the circle is measured by half the difference of the intercepted arcs.

The consideration of a problem in navigation has provided an interesting base for the exploration of virtually all the important angle-measurement theorems. Problems involving application and abstract mathematical problems providing an opportunity for additional work with these ideas are now in order. We conclude this chapter on circles and angle measurement and turn to the study of locus.

FOOTNOTES

1. See Chapter 13, pages 255 to 260.
2. School Mathematics Study Group. *Mathematics For High School: Geometry,* Part II. Student's Text, Yale University Press, 1961, pp. 414–416.

FOR INVESTIGATION AND DISCUSSION

1. Make a lesson plan for an introductory lesson in circles using one of the problems on pages 416 to 417 as a means for creating student interest.

2. In the discussion of tangents, a theorem from the SMSG textbook was mentioned concerning the possible relationships between a line and a circle in the same plane. Of the three cases considered, only one was discussed. Describe how you would help students to learn the other two.

3. Devise a problem that will involve students with the ideas of latitude and longitude. Then use this problem to outline how to teach students how the latitude designations have been determined.

4. Indicate how you might make use of the student's understanding of graphing in the Cartesian plane to help the understanding of latitude and longitude as a means for locating points on the surface of the earth.

5. Outline the steps you would develop to aid student discovery of the relationships inherent to two circles as they assume different positions in relation to each other, i.e., intersecting, tangent, concentric, and so on.

6. Employing a device that students may or may not construct, plan a sequence of experiences to develop student awareness of the several angle-circle relationships resulting in the angle-measurement theorems.

7. Investigate the life of Eratosthenes. What contributions has he made to mathematics in addition to that mentioned in this chapter?

FOR FURTHER READING

Books

Samuel L. Greitzer. "Computing a Lunar Eclipse: An Exercise in Classical Mathematics." *In* National Council of Teachers of Mathematics, 28th Yearbook: *Enrichment Mathematics for High School.* The National Council of Teachers of Mathematics, 1963, pp. 265–273.
Edwin Moise. *Elementary Geometry from an Advanced Viewpoint.* Addison-Wesley Publishing Co., Inc., 1963, pp. 186–201.
Lauren G. Woodby. "How Far Can You See?" *In* National Council of Teachers of Mathematics, 27th Yearbook: *Enrichment Mathematics for the Grades.* The National Council of Teachers of Mathematics, 1963, pp. 269–272.

Periodicals

Irene Fischer. "How Far is it From Here to There?" *The Mathematics Teacher.* Vol. 58 (February, 1965), pp. 123–130.
Geoffrey Giles. "Locus Sets and Circles." *Mathematics Teaching.* (Winter, 1966), pp. 26–32.
Rodney Hood. "A Chain of Circles." *The Mathematics Teacher.* Vol. 54 (March, 1961), pp. 134–137.
Harry Schor. "An Introduction to the Angle Measurement Theorems in Plane Geometry." *The Mathematics Teacher.* Vol. 56 (February, 1963). pp. 107–108.
Charles H. Smiley and David K. Peterson. "No Space Geometry in the Space Age?" *The Mathematics Teacher.* Vol. 53 (January, 1960), pp. 18–21.

19

LOCUS AND CONIC SECTIONS

LOCUS

Without much fanfare, the danger angle problem of the preceding chapter was actually an introduction to the study of locus. We were asked to locate all the points that satisfied the conditions of the problem, all the points that would make a safe pathway for the ship. This is precisely what is meant by *locus*.

In the past, the students have made frequent contacts with the idea of locus. Each time they drew a graph of a function, each time graphing was used to solve equations, and each time a geometric construction was completed the concept of locus was underlying what was done. The fact that this idea is encountered so often in the study of mathematics makes it somewhat of a paradox that students should have such difficulties with it, but troubled they are when the topic of locus comes up.

Perhaps we may provide some immediate assistance if we point out the similarity in spelling between locus and location. Location is our task when we deal with locus problems: locating the point or set of points that satisfies the given conditions.

> Where is the set of points that lie on the perpendicular bisector of a line segment?
> Where is the set of points that describe a certain path?

In each case we try to locate the set of points in question, thus maintaining the "locus–locate" idea.

435

Locus and Conic Sections

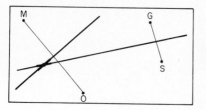

Figure 19-1. M, *Maple tree;* O, *Oak tree;* G, *Giant rock;* S, *Statue.*

There are two ways to think about locus—usually called the "static" approach and the "dynamic" approach. We may think of the set of points that are 5 inches from a fixed point, P, or we may think of the path followed by a point moving so that it is always 5 inches from point P. The moving point is an example of the dynamic point of view. There has been a good deal of discussion about which of these viewpoints we should teach. Lately, it seems that the idea of a static set of points is predominating, possibly because of the popularity of the notion of set altogether.

In their textbook on geometry, Fehr and Carnahan make interesting use of both concepts.[1] They advise that it may be easier to first think of a moving point in order to gain insight into the nature of the locus. Then the set of all the points described by the moving one can be formulated when the motion is completed. Since this seems to be a case calling for personal judgment, I wonder if this judgment cannot be exercised by our students? If we make both points of view clear throughout our work with locus, perhaps the student will think in terms best suited to him. Of course, it may well be advantageous to switch from one approach to the other as the problem changes: We may wish to think of a graph of a function as a set of points, whereas we may prefer to characterize given distances as pathways. It seems that a clarification of the two ideas offers the student greater freedom of thought.

There are many interesting problems that can be explored here and some equally interesting apparatus that can be used to aid the students. Finding the location of a buried treasure never fails to generate a good deal of attention. Here is a typical problem:

> A band of pirates left a message indicating the location of treasure they had buried in a large churchyard. It read, "As far from the maple as from the oak—as far from the statue as from the giant rock." A plan of the churchyard is shown in Figure 19-1. Can you find the spot where the treasure was buried?

In order to locate the required point, it is first necessary to find the set of points described by each condition. We then look for the intersection. This process gets students involved in finding loci and the intersection of loci. The students also are anxious to make up treasure maps of their own, which is an excellent means for getting students to want to know more and more loci. Student problems presented for class consideration may generate a good deal

436

of interest on the part of most students. It may even be possible to hide objects in the classroom and have individuals or groups of youngsters attempt to locate these objects using the loci that are given. In any case, all students can carry out the necessary constructions on plans drawn on plain or squared paper.

Exploring physical loci problems in the classroom can also be carried out by having the designated students either stand or raise their hands. For example, what is the locus (set) of students equidistant from Tom and Irene? Of course, the two given students would have to form a horizontal or vertical line; but as the hands of students go up, we have a living locus line before us that is a physical set of objects. The emphasis is certainly on the pertinent ideas here.

There are other problems of interest that may be considered before we turn to the geometry of locus and work in the abstract. Industry problems are one such source:

> A telephone company is planning for the location of telephone poles in a new housing development. They must place each pole 2 feet from the curb and equidistant from each of two adjacent houses (Fig. 19-2). Can you find the exact spot for the pole in the diagram?

Additional problems may be developed by considering the best location for a railroad station or bus stop or the central location for a hospital clinic, police station, or firehouse. In short, most questions of location may well form a suitable problem for the use of locus concepts. Once again we are stressing the locus-location relationship.

There is also a broad variety of locus problems that are not concerned with intersecting loci. These generally involve the path traced by a moving point. For example, the path traced by a point

> on the rim of a bicycle wheel.
> at the center of a bicycle wheel.
> at the top of your head as you ride an escalator.
> at the top of your head as you move forward on a pogo stick.
> at the top of your head as you ride on a seesaw.

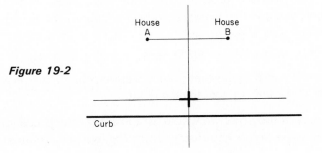

Figure 19-2

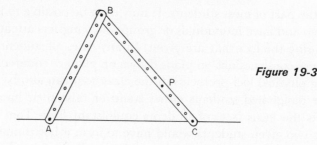

Figure 19-3

In addition to this sampling, there are problems that may be considered with the use of apparatus, such as the Tinkertoys or Erector set mentioned earlier. For example, join two strips from an Erector set as indicated in Figure 19-3. These strips may be moved with a pencil inserted at P that will actually trace out the locus in question; i.e., keep A fixed and rotate AB about A as C moves along fixed line AC. Many other such problem situations may also be constructed, some perhaps by the students themselves.

There are numerous abstract locus problems that may be considered after sufficient experiences with familiar objects and situations have been provided:

> The center of a circle rolling about another circle
> The vertex of a triangle with fixed base and area
> The center of a circle rolling about a triangle

The proofs required for locus theorems frequently puzzle students because they suddenly find that the theorem and its converse must be proved before the proof of the locus is considered complete. They may well ask, "Why is a locus proof made up of two parts?" This question must be answered at the time it first arises and the idea should be clarified each time it comes up, that is, each time a proof is considered.

For example, if we were attempting to prove that

> the locus of points equidistant from the sides of an angle is the ray bisecting the angle,

in the first part of the proof we would establish that the set of points that make up the ray are indeed equidistant from the angle sides. But how can we be sure that there are no other points equidistant from the angle sides? We undertake the second part of the proof.

If we were attempting to prove that

> the locus of points equidistant from two given points is the perpendicular bisector of the line segment joining them,

in the first part of the proof we would establish that the perpendicular bisector is indeed the set of points equidistant from the two given points. But are there

438

any other such points? The second part of the proof demonstrates that if there are such points, they must lie on the perpendicular bisector in question. If we constantly clarify the importance of both parts of the proof we may dispel the mystery so often present in students' minds.

Finally, we should mention a word about locus in three dimensions. Many of the loci problems considered have interesting complications if we provide that three-dimensional space, rather than the plane, shall be the universe in which we function. Students rather enjoy observing and thinking through the implications for a problem if it is placed in space. For example, here is a chart comparing the loci for a given condition in two- and three-dimensional space.

Conditions	In the plane	In space
points a given distance from a fixed point	a circle	a sphere
points a given distance from a straight line	two parallel lines	a cylindrical surface
points equidistant from two fixed points	a line	a plane

All our loci have involved straight lines and circles, but these do not make up the totality of lines and shapes that may be encountered in the physical world. We turn now to some new and interesting shapes.

CONIC SECTIONS

THE PARABOLA

The path of a satellite as it travels around the earth, the path of water squirting from a hose, and the path of a ball thrown from one boy to another are familiar to everyone in our society; yet these paths cannot be described by any of the figures we have so far explored in our investigation of geometry. The figures studied earlier are all made up of line segments and circles; and while these are very important figures, they are not the only ones we must consider as we study the world in which we live. The loci described here are all members of a family of lines called the conic sections, lines that we briefly encountered in algebra. You may be wondering what these familiar loci from analytic geometry are doing here. There is a great deal that can be learned about these curves using a geometric approach. In addition, the study of the conic sections follows directly from the previous work with locus and does help to satisfy our goal of learning more about the physical world. Indeed, the question might be asked, Why do we not find this study included more often in courses on geometry?

Locus and Conic Sections

The variety of uses to which we put these shapes makes it appropriate to begin this topic with a familiar application:

The headlight of a car and the major lens of a giant telescope share the same shape. What is this shape and why are these dissimilar objects using it?

To understand clearly what is going on, we will revisit the realm of light rays explored several times before. When an object is far away, its light rays reaching a small area of the earth are practically parallel. If all these rays could be reflected by a mirror so that the reflected rays would go through a single point, there would be a strong image of the star at that point. This is exactly what happens when the shape of the mirror is parabolic. All the rays are focused upon a single point; therefore, we call that point the focus (Fig. 19-4). In Latin, *focus* means hearth or burning place. It is no mere coincidence that if a piece of paper is placed at the focus of a parabolic mirror that is reflecting the sun's rays, the paper will be set on fire. This focusing of light rays enables us to see images of objects far off in space; that is why the lens of a telescope will be made in this parabolic shape. The shape enables us to concentrate the reflections of the entering light rays. But what of an automobile headlight? Why should it be made in this same shape? It does not receive light rays— rather, it sends them out. The reflecting property of a parabolic mirror can also be used in reverse. If we were to locate a light source at the focus (a light bulb), all its rays would be reflected by the parabolic mirror so as to travel out parallel to what we call the axis of the parabola (Fig. 19-5). In this way all the reflected rays form a powerful beam of light traveling in one direction. These beams can be seen coming from flashlights as well as auto headlights.

The reflecting properties of the parabolic mirror are properties of a three-dimensional surface, while a parabola is a plane figure. Have we made use of the wrong figure? Not really. What we have done is to make use of a surface formed by rotating a parabola about its axis (Fig. 19-6). Such a surface

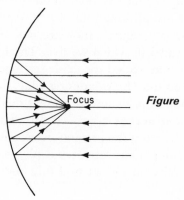

Figure 19-4

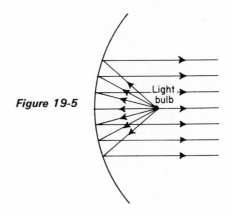

Figure 19-5

is called a paraboloid. The focus of the parabola is also the focus of the paraboloid. Since radio waves and sound waves behave much like light rays, we find this surface is also used in radar antennas and loudspeakers.

But let us take a close look at the parabola and perhaps we may briefly consider the formulation of a proof for the reflection property just described. This is the manner in which the study of the conics may be organized for students. Rather than introducing the definition of the parabola, if we begin with a situation in which it is inherent, we may help the student to gain some perspective and frame his own definition.

How shall we provide a careful description of the parabola? The concept of locus offers us the opportunity to describe a parabola as a set of points and also enables us to construct parabolas. The circle was described as the set of points that are a given distance from a fixed point. The parabola has an analagous definition: It is the set of points equally distant from a fixed point and a fixed line. For example, if we are given line *d* and point *F* (Fig. 19-7),

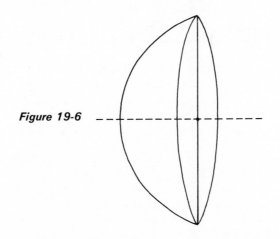

Figure 19-6

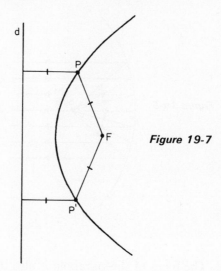

Figure 19-7

each point of the parabola will be just as far from point F as it is from line d. The use of lined paper makes the construction of a parabola a simple task:

Place point F and line d in any position as long as d is parallel to the lines of the paper. Draw the perpendicular AB to line d through point F (Fig. 19-8). Along AB, using a compass, measure the distance from d to

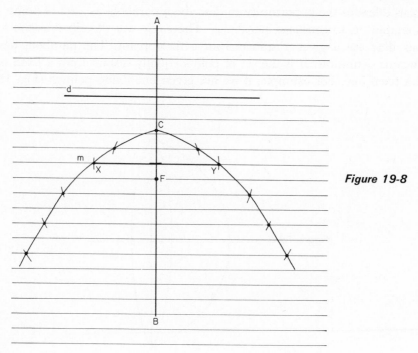

Figure 19-8

any of the parallel lines on the paper, say line *m*. Mark off this same measure from *F* on line *m*, obtaining points *X* and *Y*. These are two points of the parabola. Repeating this process with other parallel lines will provide additional points on the parabola. The set of such points forms the parabola.

How is it that such a process yields the parabola? How do we know where to locate point *C*, the turning point of the parabola? These are questions that may be discussed with students to help them see how the construction is built upon the locus definition.[2] After several parabolas are constructed placing *F* and line *d* in a variety of positions, we can indicate that line *d* is called the directrix, *F* is the focus, and the axis of the parabola is the perpendicular to *d* through *F*. This is the line that we called the axis of symmetry in our study of algebra. Construction of the parabola not only helps to demonstrate the meaning of the locus which defines the parabola, but it also points up the symmetry of the parabola about its axis. Each time a new parallel line is selected, two points are located—one on each side of the axis.

How can we be sure that parallel light rays entering the parabola will all be reflected through the focus and that light rays emanating from the focus will be reflected out parallel to each other and the axis of the parabola? Here our knowledge of geometry comes to our aid. Since the complete proof is lengthy, it will not be presented here but will be included in the appendix. Perhaps a brief indication of the plan will enable you to attempt to work it out for yourself. Once again we make use of Heron's theorem; this time we are concerned with the converse.

Look at Figure 19-9. If we can show that the distance from the focus (*F*) to a point on the parabola (*P*) to the fixed point *V* on a parallel to the axis from *P* is the shortest distance from *F* to the parabola to *V*, then we will have

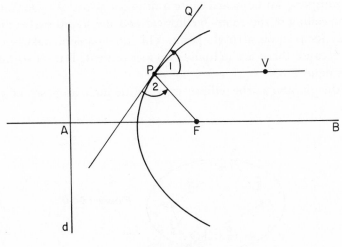

Figure 19-9

established that $\angle 1 = \angle 2$, the angles of incidence and reflection,[3] and according to Heron we can conclude that *PV* must be the reflection of *FP*. The approach to a proof consists of selecting any other point on the tangent line *Q* and demonstrating that $FP + PV < FQ + QV$. This is a challenging proof. You might like to refer back to the earlier work with Heron's theorems.[4]

This unique property of the parabola helps us to understand how astronomers can manage to see the light reflected from stars so many light-years away. If the rays are feeble but are all concentrated at a single point, they become relatively brighter. The same is true of radio signals which may be faint when received but are comparatively strong at the focus of a paraboloid antenna. Finally, if you have ever wondered how such a small light bulb in a flashlight could cast such a strong beam, you now have some insight into what is happening. It would seem that mathematics has again helped us to better understand what is going on about us.

THE ELLIPSE

Another useful curve that has not yet been explored is the ellipse. The path of a satellite moving around the earth, the paths of each of the planets of our solar system as they orbit the sun, and the paths of comets are all described by the ellipse. The ellipse is a figure that also has some surprising reflection properties. If you have ever been on a tour of the Capitol in Washington, D.C., you may have been amazed by a simple demonstration carried out by the guide. After placing the group of people on his tour at a brass plate in the floor of the old House of Representatives, the guide walks some 100 feet away and whispers. Lo and behold, each syllable reaches you as clearly as if a microphone had been used. The same would be true of words spoken by the group to the guide. What makes the human voice travel so that even whispers can be heard quite a distance away? As you might suspect by now, the ceiling of the room is elliptical and the sound waves are reflected so that they focus upon a single point. This phenomenon takes place in two directions because there are actually two foci present. But let us take a closer look at this figure.

Like the parabola, the ellipse may be defined as a set of points that

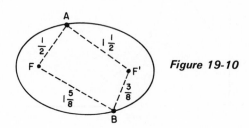

Figure 19-10

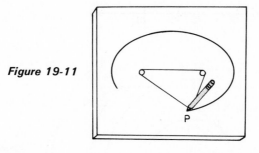

Figure 19-11

satisfy a given condition. In this instance, the ellipse is the set of points whose combined distances from each of two fixed points is constant. For example, if the fixed points are F and F' and if we arbitrarily set the constant distance at, say, 2 inches, point A is a member of the set of points in question since it is $\frac{1}{2}$ inch from F and $1\frac{1}{2}$ inches from F' (Figure 19-10). The same is true of B and any other point, the sum of whose distances from F and F' will be 2 inches. A simple construction emphasizes the definition and demonstrates clearly what shape the ellipse has (Fig. 19-11). Fix two points on a pegboard, or similar material, say 6 inches apart. If we decide on a 10-inch constant, make a loop of string 6 + 10 or 16 inches long. Pass the loop around the pegs and pull it taut with a pencil, as at point P. As the pencil moves with the string taut, it will describe an ellipse. Paper folding is another simple way to construct an ellipse.[5] This construction method also helps to demonstrate the symmetry of the ellipse about its major axis, the line segment AA' through the foci, and the minor axis BB', the segment of the perpendicular bisector of FF' (Fig. 19-12). The two symmetries of the ellipse may be established by geometric proof.

The ellipse may also be constructed using a compass and straightedge. Select any two points as the foci F and F' and choose any distance AB for the constant sum of the distances from the foci, being sure that $AB > FF'$ or there will be no ellipse (Fig. 19-13). Since $AB = PF + PF'$, with the compass divide AB into two lengths of any size. This gives point C. Thus, $AC = PF$ and $CB = PF'$. Place the compass point at F and with opening AC draw an arc. Place the compass point at F' and draw a second arc intersecting the first with opening CB. You will have located two points of the

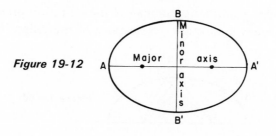

Figure 19-12

A — Major axis — A'

B — Minor axis — B'

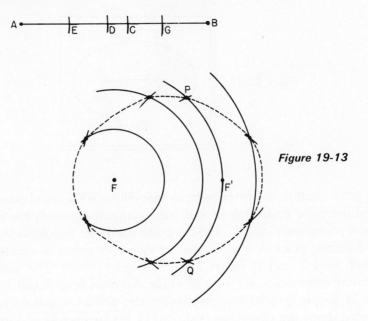

Figure 19-13

ellipse *P* and *Q*. To find additional points, divide *AB* into two different lengths and repeat the procedures just described.

The magnification of the whispers on the Capitol tour was due to the remarkable reflection properties of the ellipse. All sound waves (or light waves) emanating from one focus are reflected off the surface of the ellipse through the other focus. The very weak sound waves of the guide's voice, going out in all directions, were reflected through the other focus (both marked by brass plates) so that we heard very clearly (Fig. 19-14).

This unusual reflection property was also responsible for what I thought at the time was a remarkable demonstration of skill by a student. An elliptically shaped board had a 1 inch fence built around its edge. In one part of the board there was a hole slightly larger than a nickel, a five-cent piece. On the other side of the board was a mark. The student would place a nickel on the mark and shoot it off the fence in a variety of directions, and every time it would bounce off the fence and into the hole! (See Fig. 19-15.) Amazing —but not really, because when I tried it, I too made the coin land in the hole. The mark and the hole were at the foci of the ellipse. The reflection property of the ellipse did the rest. This is an interesting project for a student to attempt because it provides a dramatic example of the reflection property.

There are many important applications of the ellipse besides those in-

Figure 19-14

446

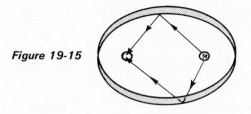

Figure 19-15

volving reflections. Early in the seventeenth century Johann Kepler, a German astronomer, working with the multitude of observations recorded by the Danish astronomer Tycho Brahe, developed three basic laws regarding the motion of the planets. The first of these laws stated that the path of each planet is an ellipse with the sun at one of the foci. The second law provides an estimate of the speed and distance of planets.

Kepler stated that in equal time periods, the planet sweeps out equal areas with the sun. For example, if it takes the planet an equal amount of time to move from A to B as it does to move from C to D, then area ASB is equal to area DSC (Fig. 19-16). The derivation of this law was astounding since it was not easily inferred from observations. Finally, for his third law of motion, Kepler stated that the square of the time it takes a planet to complete an orbit is proportional to the cube of the major axis of the orbit. If the earth's time to complete one orbit is T_1 and if the time for Mars is T_2 (see Fig. 19-16), then the third law states that

$$\frac{T_1{}^2}{(CD)^3} = \frac{T_2{}^2}{(AB)^3}$$

Thus, Kepler formulated three laws that presented new insights into the motion of the planets, and he used mathematics to shed light upon the world in which we live.

There are many problems that can be studied here. The following are typical examples:

1. Let $2a$ be the sum of the distances of any point on an ellipse to the foci. Show that the length of the major axis is $2a$. Let $2a$ be the length of the major axis of an ellipse. Show that the distance from one end of the minor axis B to either focus is a (Fig. 19-17).

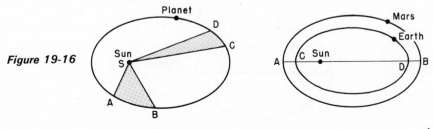

Figure 19-16

447

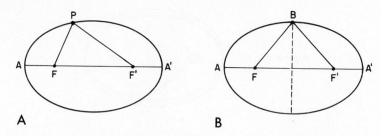

A   **B**

Figure 19-17. *(A) Given* FP + PF′ = 2a, *prove* AA′ = 2a. *(B) Given* AA′ = 2a, *prove* FB = F′B = a.

2. Let Q be any point outside of an ellipse. Prove that QF' + QF is greater than a where a is the sum of the distances of any point P on the ellipse from the foci (Fig. 19-18).
3. Let t be the tangent at any point P of an ellipse and let F' and F be the foci. Prove that PF' and PF make equal angles with the tangent at P (Fig. 19-19).
4. Suppose the foci F and F' coincide. Show that the ellipse becomes a circle.
5. The American artificial satellite Explorer followed an elliptical orbit around the earth. At its closest point to the earth (perigee) it was 230 miles away. Its farthest point (apogee) was 1700 miles away. If 4000 miles is the radius of the earth and the center of the earth is at one focus, find the major and minor axes of this orbit.
6. In its orbit around the sun, the closest the earth comes to the sun (perihelion) is 91,500,000 miles. Its farthest distance (aphelion) is 94,500,000 miles. If the sun is at one focus of the earth's orbit, find the length of the major and minor axes of the earth's orbit. (The diameter of the sun is about 850,000 miles, negligible in this case.)

Finally, if the ellipse is rotated about its major axis, we obtain a surface called an ellipsoid. The shape of a football serves as an excellent example of such a surface. You would be quite correct to say, "Wow, can he kick that ellipsoid!"

THE HYPERBOLA

The last of the conic sections we shall consider is the hyperbola. A pilot in an airliner listens in on two radio stations and notes the time difference

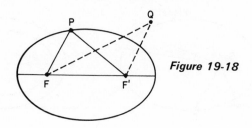

Figure 19-18

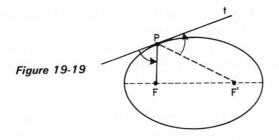

Figure 19-19

between the two signals (low frequency) from these stations. He repeats this process with two other stations and is able to fix his location. A hunter loses his way in the forest and fires his rifle to attract attention. Two forest rangers, a fixed distance apart, record the time they hear the shot and compare this with the time recorded at a third location. They now have a good approximation of the position of the lost hunter.

What do these two situations have to do with a hyperbola? In each case we were involved with the distances from a given point to each of two other points—represented by the time of the radio signals from two stations and the time a shot is heard at two different points. Thus far we seem to be in a situation calling for the ellipse locus. In this instance, however, we are working with the differences between the two distances rather than the sum. Whereas the ellipse was defined in terms of the sum of the distances from two fixed points, the hyperbola is concerned with the differences. If we return to the second situation and look at it more carefully, we see that if the two rangers hear the shot 5 seconds apart, since sound travels at the rate of about 1100 ft./sec., the rifle must be 5500 feet farther from one ranger than it is from the other. This is the difference between the distances from each ranger to the gun (Fig. 19-20). If we try to locate the hunter and ask where are all points whose distances differ by 5500 feet from the two rangers, we find the answer to be the hyperbola. For example, one such point might be 6000 feet from the first ranger and 500 feet from the second. The hunter's position is somewhere on the hyperbola. The time reading at the third location enables us to locate another hyperbola whose intersections with the first one provide

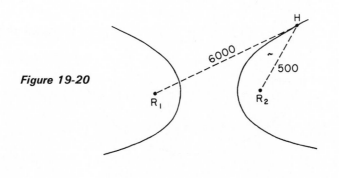

Figure 19-20

449

possible locations for the missing hunter. The implications for the pilot of the first problem will be discussed later.

Can we construct a hyperbola with a compass and straightedge as we did the other conic sections? The answer is yes and the procedures are as follows:

> Choose two fixed points, F and F', that are 8 units apart (Fig. 19-21).
> Let us also assume that the constant difference between distances of points from F and F' will be 6 units.

We begin by taking any length, for example, 10. If we describe a circular arc about F' with a radius of 10 units, we shall have points whose distance from F' is 10 units. We would like to have points whose distance from F' minus their distance from F is 6 units. Hence, let us take the difference $10 - 6$, or 4, and describe an arc with a radius of 4 units and F as the center. Suppose this arc cuts the former arc at P and P'. Now P is 10 units from F' and 4 units from F. Hence,

$$PF' - PF = 6$$

Then P must be a point on the hyperbola. For the same reason, so is P'. We note that for each point of intersection of the two arcs that lies above the line $F'F$ there will be a point below and these two points are symmetric with respect to FF', or we could say one point is the mirror image of the other in the "mirror" $F'F$.

If instead of length 10 we had taken length 11 and then constructed circular arcs with radii 11 and 11-5 or 6, about F' and F respectively, we would have gotten two more points which lie on the hyperbola. In fact,

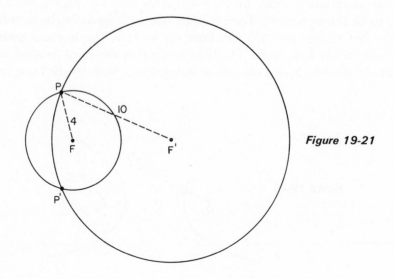

Figure 19-21

if we start with any given length greater than 6 and repeat the construction, we can get points on the hyperbola.

Suppose we reconsider the length 10 and this time describe an arc about F as center with radius 10 and another arc about F' as center with radius 4. Where these two arcs intersect, say at R and R', we shall have points such that

$$RF - RF' = 6$$

and

$$R'F - R'F' = 6$$

Hence, R and R' also lie on the hyperbola (Fig. 19-22).

By constructing a number of points which meet the definition of the hyperbola, we find the curve shown in Figure 19-23. This curve is peculiar in that it consists of two distinct parts or branches. The two branches constitute a single hyperbola.

Of course, the numbers 8 and 6 that we used in the preceding discussion are just special cases. We can start with two points F and F', called foci, which are a fixed distance apart, $2c$; choose a fixed quantity which we denote by $2a$; and define a hyperbola generally as the set of all points whose distances from F and F' differ by the numerical value $2a$. ($|PF' - PF| = 2a$.)

We note that the quantity $2a$ must be less than $2c$ because the difference between any two sides of a triangle must be less than the third side (Fig. 19-24).

Here are some additional problems that may be explored with students.

1. Show that there can be no points of the hyperbola on the perpendicular bisector of FF'.
2. Find the distance PF of the point P on a given hyperbola which lies

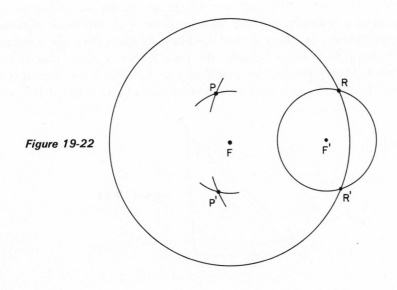

Figure 19-22

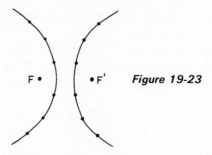

Figure 19-23

on the perpendicular to FF' through F. This distance PF is called semilatus rectum. It is a measure of the width of the hyperbola (Fig. 19-25).

3. What is the curve traced by the third vertex of a triangle whose base is kept fixed while the difference of the other two sides is kept constant?

Other applications of the hyperbola using the same principle as locating a gun occur in navigation by ships and airplanes. An example of this is the pilot who listened in on two radio stations at F and F' and noted the time difference between two low frequency signals from these stations. Since radio waves travel at the speed of light and this speed is known, the difference in time multiplied by the speed of light is the difference in the distances between the airplane and the two stations. Hence, the pilot knows he is on a definite hyperbola (Fig. 19-26). By listening in on signals from two other fixed stations, G and G', and again noting the difference in time at which he receives these signals, the pilot determines another hyperbola on which he must be located. He must then be on the intersection (or intersections) of the two hyperbolas. If there is more than one intersection, he can generally tell from a knowledge of his approximate location which one of the intersections is the relevant one for him.

Since radio waves travel at such a high speed, the time difference must be measured accurately and this can be done with electronic equipment. The system known as Loran is useful within distances from the sending stations of about 1000 miles because the assumption is made that the radio waves travel in straight lines or practically so, but this is not true over great distances. In practice the pilot carries with him charts with all the possible

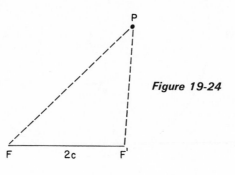

Figure 19-24

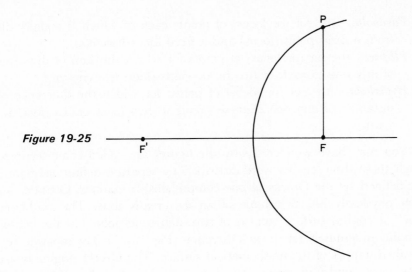

Figure 19-25

hyperbolas mapped out so that by knowing the time differences he can go directly to his chart and determine his location immediately.

THE CONIC SECTIONS: CONCLUSION

In these last three topics we have discussed three very important curves. Each of these figures was defined by describing a set of points (or a locus) that satisfied certain conditions:

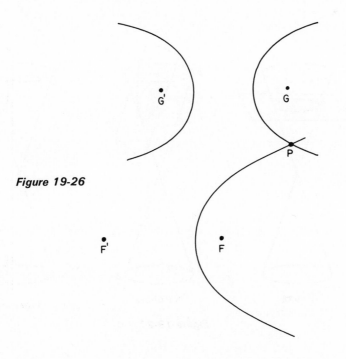

Figure 19-26

453

Parabola: the set (or locus) of points each of which is equally distant from a fixed point (focus) and a fixed line (directrix).

Ellipse: the set (or locus) of points for which the sum of the distances of any one to each of two fixed points (foci) is a constant.

Hyperbola: the set (or locus) of points for which the difference of the distances of any one of these points to two fixed points (foci) is constant.

You may have wondered why the figures are called conic sections. Although these three curves were described by separate definitions here, they were defined by the Greeks in one comprehensive manner. Consider a cone which physically has the shape of an ice cream cone. The mathematical "cone" or conical surface consists of two such cones joined at the vertex and extending indefinitely far in each direction (Fig. 19-27). The separate "cones" are called nappes of the mathematical surface. The Greeks originally arrived at the curves under discussion by slicing the conical curface. When the slice cuts one entire nappe of the cone, the resulting curve is an ellipse. When the cut is made by passing a plane parallel to a generator such as AOA' of the cone, the result is a parabola. Finally, if the plane is passed through the cone so as to intersect both nappes, then the resulting intersection is the two-branched curve, the hyperbola. Thus, the most commonly used name for these three figures is the *conic sections,* or sections of a cone. Both Euclid and Apollonius have done extensive work with these figures and developed many theorems. Johann Kepler was able to establish his three famous laws of planetary motion only because he had available so much information about these

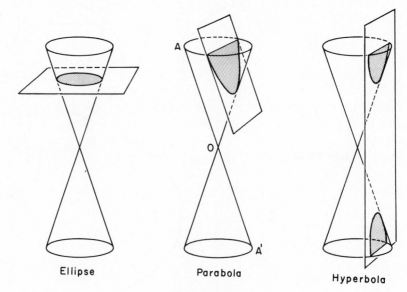

Ellipse   Parabola   Hyperbola

Figure 19-27

454

conic sections. It is an addition to the wonder of mathematics that certain slices through a cone and the paths of the planets are described by a common mathematical element!

SOLID AND COORDINATE GEOMETRY

Before this section on geometry is brought to a close, a word about solid geometry and coordinate geometry is in order. As mathematics curricula have come under close scrutiny, attempts have been made to interweave the several branches of mathematics wherever possible in order to present the picture of a single unified discipline to students of the subject. All too familiar is the compartmentalized, isolated approach to these different mathematics subjects made by the traditional curricula. In geometry, we have a particularly fertile area for such exploitation, as can be seen in the work developed in this section. For example, the vector problems involving the forces at work on an inclined plane offer the student the opportunity to employ concepts from algebra, geometry, and trigonometry as he works towards a solution. And this is how it should be if we are to develop a genuine understanding of both the relationships between the many branches of mathematics and the significance of each of the separate subjects. At the same time, however, we must not lose sight of a most important property of geometry. As Hadamard pointed out in his investigation of creation in mathematics, most mathematicians did their thinking in geometric terms.[6] It would seem that the more geometry the students know, the more visual imagery of mathematical ideas will be available to them. Whereas one of the important roles played by algebra is to provide a symbolic language for communication between scientists, among other things, geometry provides the blocks for building mathematical ideas; so we seek the kind of experience for students that will establish for each a vast reservoir of geometric ideas generating visual representations at the same time that the relationships between the several mathematical areas are emphasized. Coordinate and solid geometry enable us to provide additional experiences, greatly increasing the visualization of mathematical concepts. Let us briefly inquire into each of these two fields.

When Descartes, in the early seventeenth century, decided to question everything that he had known (including his own existence) and begin building ideas anew, there was little reason to expect that he would develop so powerful a tool for binding algebraic and geometric ideas together. But this he did in no uncertain terms. The resulting analytic geometry offers the mathematician the means for describing the curves of geometry in algebraic terms. In this way, all the power of the methods of algebra may be brought to bear on the problems of geometry. What a significant landmark in the development of mathematics!

Each time we approach the proof of a geometry theorem we are faced with a new problem. We have no method to bring to bear upon the problem and simply begin by seeking out relationships. We approach the solution of an algebraic equation in a different manner. Here the symbols and techniques of algebra go to work for us immediately. There are operations that may be employed almost without thinking. Imagine being able to approach a theorem of geometry in the same way—with method and powerful techniques! This is what Descartes has enabled us to do. By translating our geometric entities into their algebraic counterparts, we then may use all our algebraic techniques to reach our destination.

But Descartes has done still more. By presenting us with the medium for exchanging geometric ideas for algebraic ones, he has also offered us visual representations for the concepts of algebra. If, as Hadamard believes, a good deal of the thinking that takes place in the mind of the mathematician, and the student as well, is in terms of geometrical images, many of the ideas of algebra become more readily accessible to us. So we make major gains in a twofold way: We have analytic proofs to supplement or to use instead of the synthetic ones of plane and solid geometry, and we have the ability to think in visual, geometric terms about representations in algebra.

We have many different points from which to begin the introduction of concepts from coordinate geometry in our work with plane geometry. Actually, the work in algebra discussed previously involved a careful introduction to the ideas of coordinate geometry, so we may build upon what was studied earlier. Although this earlier work may no longer be as fresh in the minds of students of plane geometry as we would like, review exercises and lessons would seem to be a waste. It would be a better idea to plunge into coordinate geometry and carry out any necessary "repair" work as the need arises. In this way, the need for such revisitation of concepts is sharply clear to students as well as teacher.

It is possible to extend the work of plane geometry to coordinate geometry easily during the study of triangles, parallel lines, quadrilaterals, polygonal areas, and circles. In truth, there do not seem to be many areas of plane geometry that cannot readily lend themselves to consideration from the point of view of coordinate geometry. The teacher and the students may well allow interest to determine just how much coordinate geometry work will be undertaken. In any event, the topics considered arise readily from the work in plane geometry and serve as a solid foundation upon which to build a later full-fledged course in analytic geometry (see Chapter 20). But let us briefly explore just how some of the concepts of plane geometry may be extended.

In our work with triangles we were concerned with comparing the size and shape of pairs of triangles, i.e., congruence and similarity. If we were to represent two triangles algebraically and place them upon a Cartesian coordinate system, we would have to know the coordinates of their vertices. Once these were known, using the distance formula derived with the Pythagorean theorem, we could readily determine the congruence, similarity, or lack of either for the triangles in question.

A similar situation could result in determination of whether or not lines are parallel ($m_1 = m_2$, equal slopes) or perpendicular ($m_1 m_2 = -1$). These ideas could be extended to include the many quadrilateral properties as well. For example, we may show that the diagonals of a rhombus are perpendicular to each other by demonstrating that their slopes are negative reciprocals of each other. We could continue to extend the introduction of coordinate geometry ideas in much the same manner throughout our study of plane geometry. There is no dearth of opportunities for crossing over.

Many students do have some difficulty deciding how to best place a given figure on the coordinate system. While this is not a life or death decision that must be made, the chances for successfully completing a given problem may certainly be affected. For example, if we were to attempt an analytical proof of the theorem that

> the line segment joining the midpoints of two sides of a triangle is parallel to the third side and equal to one half of it,

where shall we locate the diagram? Where shall we place this triangle in our coordinate system? Two possibilities are presented in Figure 19-28. Which of these two figures do you think facilitates our work toward proof? It would appear that the more zero coordinates we introduce, the easier our work will be. Thus, diagram II may quickly be eliminated because point B does not have any zero coordinates. Therefore, diagram I is the better of the two. In this particular instance it would also be helpful to keep an additional consideration in mind. It will be more convenient to use coordinates $2a$, $2b$, and $2c$, since we will otherwise encounter fractions in using the midpoint formula later on. At any rate, the placement of the axes is a variable in this situation that the student must learn to use to his advantage. If the students should place diagrams so that they complicate the proofs in question, be sure to let them work through the situation before making any suggestions about changing the positions of the axes. In this way, the student can do his own thinking about the problem and arrive at his own realization of the need for help; then any suggestions you may make will be appropriately received.

Coordinate geometry may also be extended into three dimensions but only to a very limited degree because of a lack of time. Finding points in space given three coordinates, finding the missing vertices of a cube whose faces are parallel to given planes, and perhaps finding the lengths and midpoints of line segments in three-dimensional space are some of the elementary ideas to be considered. So much for coordinate geometry.

As for extending our work to include topics from solid geometry, what better instrument is at our disposal for the study of the physical world than the mathematics of space? In introducing such concepts, we should choose

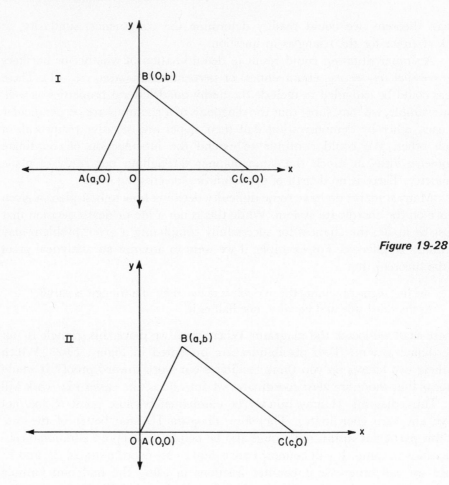

Figure 19-28

our spots carefully in order to maintain a natural transition from two to three dimensions, in much the same manner as from plane to coordinate geometry. Some instances of an extension of plane geometry have already been considered in this section; most notable of these is the exploration of locus in three dimensions. There are numerous other opportunities. When we consider parallel lines, we may just as easily expand this work to the consideration of parallel lines in space, as well as parallel planes. The same can be said for the property of perpendicularity. Our investigation of polygons and their areas may be extended to solid figures whose faces consist of these plane figures (such as cubes, pyramids, and prisms) and to the respective measures of their volume and surface area. Our examination of the circle and its tangents leads directly to an analogous discussion of spheres. There is no shortage of points of intersection between the concepts of plane and solid geometry. There is a shortage of time, however, so the teacher must of necessity choose

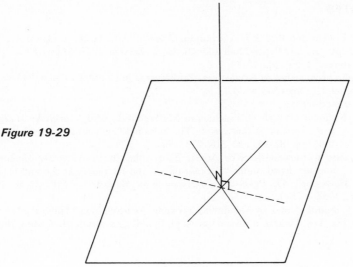

Figure 19-29

which topics shall be included. Once again, perhaps the best guide to be employed in such a situation is the response of the students. Should their interest and enthusiasm be high, the amount of work done with solid geometry may be extended.

In the consideration of figures in space, students often have a good deal of difficulty drawing diagrams and visualizing a given situation. Such problems can be overcome by the construction of three-dimensional models using ordinary coat hangers together with elastic string. If this does not prove handy there are ready-made aids for three-dimensional constructions, such as the Tinkertoy and the D-Stix.[8] For example, in considering the theorem that

> if a line is perpendicular to each of two intersecting lines at their point
> of intersection, it is perpendicular to every other line in the plane of
> these two lines through their point of intersection,

we could make, or have the students make, a three-dimensional model of the theorem (Fig. 19-29). Such a model enables each student to see clearly what is going on so that he may be able to think through the situation for himself and perhaps pose his own questions. A slated globe is also a definite aid.

There are many important advantages to be found in the introduction of coordinate and solid geometry. Of greatest significance, however, is the excellent opportunity to fit together different branches of mathematics. In this way, we take a big step toward helping students realize that there is a unity to the divergent subjects they have been calling mathematics. It is a unity that adds greatly to the power of mathematics to help us understand our world.

459

FOOTNOTES

1. Howard F. Fehr and Walter H. Carnahan. *Geometry*. D. C. Heath & Company, 1961, p. 328.
2. Ethel Saupe. "Simple Paper Models for the Conic Sections." *The Mathematics Teacher*. Vol. 48 (January, 1955), pp. 42–44.
3. The angles of incidence and reflection are discussed in Chapter 15, page 343.
4. See Chapter 15, pages 345 to 347.
5. For other methods see:
   National Council of Teachers of Mathematics, 18th Yearbook: *Multi-Sensory Aids in the Teaching of Mathematics*. The National Council of Teachers of Mathematics, 1945, pp. 82–85, 212–216, 273–279.
   Also see three articles by Adrian Struyk that appeared in *The Mathematics Teacher* and are listed under "Periodicals" in the references at the end of this chapter.
6. Jacques Hadamard. *The Psychology of Invention in the Mathematical Field*. Dover Publications, Inc., 1954, p. 105.
7. "D-Stix," manufactured by Geodestix, Spokane, Washington; "Tinkertoy," manufactured by The Toy Tinkers, a division of A. G. Spalding & Broth., Evanston, Illinois.

FOR INVESTIGATION AND DISCUSSION

1. Make up a "treasure map" of your own that may be used to introduce the notion of locus. Be sure the instructions may be expressed as loci.

2. Devise two problems from the everyday experience of most students that will involve students in physical locus problems.

3. Illustrate how either or both of the problems just devised in number 2 may be used to develop a lesson on locus that emphasizes student thinking.

4. State one locus situation that lends itself to the static set-of-points approach and explain why you feel as you do.

5. Do the same for the dynamic path-of-a-moving-point approach to locus.

6. Making use of an application, plan a lesson that will introduce students to the parabola defined as a locus.

7. Heron's name has appeared several times in this chapter. Investigate the life of this man, focusing on his contributions to mathematics.

8. Plan a lesson around a demonstration to illustrate the reflecting properties of a paraboloid using a flashlight. Light the bulb without the reflector and then do the same with the reflector. Observe the light provided.

9. Briefly outline three lessons designed to help students to construct a parabola, an ellipse, and an hyperbola. Use any of the methods of construction you may prefer.

10. Prove the theorem that the diagonals of a rhombus are perpendicular to each other, synthetically (Euclidean style) and analytically (using coordinate geometry). Compare the two proofs you have constructed.

11. Select a locus theorem and demonstrate the implications of moving from two- to three-dimensional space.

12. Discuss whether or not solid geometry should remain a course in its own right or whether its key ideas should become integrated with the plane geometry course. Be sure to emphasize the strengths and weaknesses of either course of action.

FOR FURTHER READING

Books

Edwin A. Abbott. *Flatland.* Dover Publications, Inc., 1953.
Charles H. Butler and F. Lynwood Wren. *The Teaching of Secondary Mathematics,* Ed. 4. McGraw-Hill Book Co., 1965, pp. 478–502.
I. M. Gelfand, E. G. Glagoleva, and A. A. Kirillov (translated by Leslie Cohn and David Sookne). *The Method of Coordinates,* Vol. 1. Library of School Mathematics, M. I. T. Press, 1967.
Mathematics 10: Handbook. Bureau of Secondary Curriculum Development, N. Y. State Education Department, 1962, pp. 91–129.

Periodicals

Sister M. Annunciata Burbach, C.P.P.S. "Conic Sections and Their Constructions." *The Mathematics Teacher.* Vol. 54 (October, 1963), pp. 443–446.
Sister Maurice Marie Byrne, OSU. "A Geometric Approach to the Conic Sections." *The Mathematics Teacher.* Vol. 59 (April, 1966), pp. 348–350.
Howard Eves. "The Names 'Ellipse,' 'Parabola,' and 'Hyperbola.'" *The Mathematics Teacher.* Vol. 53 (April, 1960), pp. 280–281.
Geoffrey Giles. "Locus Sets and Circles." *Mathematics Teaching.* (Winter, 1966), pp. 26–32.
Adrian Struyk. "Theme Paper, a Ruler, and the Central Conics." *The Mathematics Teacher.* Vol. 47 (March, 1954), pp. 189–193.
Adrian Struyk. "Theme Paper, a Ruler, and the Hyperbole." *The Mathematics Teacher.* Vol. 47 (January, 1954), pp. 29–30.
Adrian Struyk. "Theme Paper and Ruler Finale." *The Mathematics Teacher.* Vol. 47 (October, 1954), pp. 411–413.
John J. Sullivan. "Some Problems in Geometry." *The Arithmetic Teacher.* Vol. 14 (February, 1967), pp. 107–109.
Donald A. Williamson. "Teach Loci with Wire and Paint." *The Mathematics Teacher.* Vol. 51 (November, 1958), pp. 562–563.

461

PART FOUR

UPPER-LEVEL MATHEMATICS

TRIGONOMETRY AND OTHER TOPICS

INTRODUCTION

Until recently, the final high school mathematics course taken by the great majority of students was either elementary algebra or plane geometry. Some students ended their mathematics work with algebra because the school required only one year of mathematics for graduation. Others went on to take an additional year of study (plane geometry) in order to satisfy college admission requirements.

The remainder of the high school program generally consisted of algebra in the third year and trigonometry and solid geometry in the fourth. Some schools offered a combination of intermediate algebra and trigonometry in the third year, with the fourth year made up of advanced algebra and solid geometry.

The newfound emphasis upon science and mathematics in our schools has brought about many changes in both high school and freshman college offerings. For one thing, there are an increasing number of colleges that now set three years as the minimum mathematics requirement for all entering students. The once familiar college freshman offering of college algebra and trigonometry is now used primarily to eliminate freshman deficiencies. An excellent survey of high school offerings on the twelfth-grade level conducted by Lauren Woodby indicates that in high school

> the fourth-year mathematics courses . . . can be characterized generally as algebra and trigonometry. . . . These fourth-year courses in high school appear to have essentially the same function that the first-year courses in college had some 20 years ago: to prepare students for the study of calculus.[1]

Thus, we find that the freshman year of college mathematics has become the senior year of high school mathematics. Solid geometry, for the most part, has become integrated into the course on plane geometry, freeing the senior year for additional algebra work preparatory to the study of calculus.

While this is the pattern in most high schools, there have been a number of courses making their appearance for the first time in high school. Analytic geometry, calculus, probability and statistics, and linear algebra are among these. The Advanced Placement Program, which has been in existence for more than a decade, has concentrated upon offerings for the talented mathematics student. This program of the College Entrance Examination Board consists of a full year of calculus together with analytic geometry. The program has shown continuous growth over the years in the number of participating students.

Of one thing we may be certain: The upper years of high school seem to be in a state of change. The ability of the teacher to be able to provide instruction in a given course has influenced the shape of programs a great deal. More than one school district has undoubtedly had the experience of attempting to introduce new courses into its senior year only to find that there was no teacher on the faculty who could teach them. The National Science Foundation summer and in-service institutes have been helpful in extending teachers' backgrounds and expanding their ability to teach upper level courses, but the progress has been slow. Let us turn our attention to the specific courses just mentioned.

TRIGONOMETRY

The topic of trigonometry generally has two differing roles to play in the school curriculum. There is the trigonometry of the elementary algebra and the plane geometry classes, which is primarily concerned with ratio and similarity, and there is the full-fledged study of trigonometry itself. In the latter, we move outside the rigid triangle and begin to think of the various relationships as functions rather than ratios. In both instances, however, we have before us a subject that should prove to be an exciting challenge for students. The applications are manifold. As we consider this area, we find that problems of inaccessible heights, unreachable distances, navigation, surveying, and the behavior of sound, light, and radio waves are plentiful. What is more, virtually all the mathematics studied by students in the secondary school can be shown to blend together as we attack problems with the use of trigonometry. It is a strong unifying force of the many areas that the students have already had the opportunity to come to know in a more than casual manner. Because of its ability to take a significant role in these two areas, application and unification, trigonometry is uniquely suited to aid in the realization of the establishment of mathematical experiences of significance and consequence.

TRIGONOMETRY AS RATIOS

Why did the concepts of trigonometry appear in the ninth grade algebra course as an added starter at the end of the book? It appears so abruptly and seems so out of place that one may well wonder if it wasn't simply a hangover from days gone by.

What can we do to provide fair treatment for this subject? Several suggestions have already been considered. Certainly the early work with trigonometry can center on the kind of problems that were introduced in geometry as we considered the inclined plane and navigation problems, but perhaps the most fruitful place to initiate this work is in informal geometry. At this point we have an opportunity to combine the concepts of ratio and proportion (similarity) and geometry in an active and meaningful collection of experiences for our students. Here we also have a chance to bring our students out of the confines of the classroom.

Making a map of the immediate school area forms an excellent problem upon which the outside experiences may be based. An informal walk around the school area in order to identify and record the more important landmarks (such as a special tree, statue, pond, water tower, private home, or playground) can bring all students face-to-face with the difficulties of constructing a map. How shall we determine where to place each of these points of reference? The needs are carefully discussed in the classroom and some preliminary exercises are carried out within the room. Perhaps a map is made of the room or floor of the school, indicating clearly any distinguishing features of either. But there are obstructions that block our way. How shall we find the missing distance? If a building or pond prevents the direct measurement of distances, how shall we proceed? And where we are reluctant to go dashing across busy streets, how shall we find the measurement required? A knowledge of the right triangle will help. In this climate we turn to trigonometry as a much needed tool. Here is a possible problem:

464

How shall we find the length of a diagonal from one corner of the room to an opposite corner, if we are unable to measure directly? (A hill, pond, or large boulder may be in our way.)

Working with this sample within the room offers us a chance to focus upon a representative problem, and at the same time direct measure is available as a check of our techniques.

The introduction of the trigonometric ratios can result as one method of solution for this problem. (Scale drawings and proportion offer another alternative.) The indirect measurement exercises of the classroom are a preparation for outside work. Crude instruments may be constructed for use so that all students have enough equipment to carry out the necessary activities when the students leave the classroom. One of the reasons for quick disenchantment with outside surveying on the part of students has been the failure to provide equipment that makes everyone a participant. If some half-dozen students and the teacher are "doing" while the remainder of the class is "watching," you may rest assured the students will soon become bored and restless. However, this can be prevented in two ways: First, there must be enough tools for everyone. Second, each student should be perfectly clear about the problems that he will attempt to solve as he goes outside. Once the students have the tools and the direction, an outside experience can be a source of important instruction for them. It may be well to duplicate the problems so that upon going out each student carries an instruction sheet with him, in addition to any instruments he may use. It is not necessary for all students to solve the same problems, but everyone should have a good idea of what he is going to do when he gets outside. It is also possible to maintain some flexibility by devising additional problems on the spot, but by and large the work should be carefully structured as to activity and purpose.

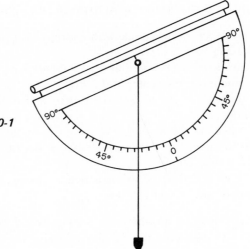

Figure 20-1

The simplest tool for students to construct for themselves is a clinometer, a tool to measure angles being sighted upward or downward (Fig. 20-1). Basically, it is a large protractor with a plumb line hanging from its center. It may also be constructed using an empty paper-towel tube or a thick straw mounted on a pin so that it can rotate in a vertical plane and be used as a sight. In addition, a tape measure at least 100 feet long and several wooden rods varying in size from 3 feet to 6 feet should also be available in quantity, although pacing may be used in place of tape measures if this becomes a problem.

The 19th Yearbook of the National Council of Teachers of Mathematics, entitled *Surveying Instruments: Their History and Classroom Use,* not only has an interesting historical account of a variety of instruments but also contains an invaluable collection of problems arranged by topic for use by the teacher. Other instruments for simple construction are also included, such as the Jacob's staff.[2] Suffice it to say that there is no shortage of problems and activities that may be employed with students. A bit of organization and careful planning, together with an adventurous spirit, will make outdoor work an invaluable mathematics experience.

BUILDING TRIGONOMETRY TABLES

All these experiences serve to provide a setting for our students to become familiar with trigonometric ratios. As they explore the ratios between given sides of right triangles, it soon becomes apparent that it would be quite helpful if these ratios were calculated and tabularized beforehand. Is there some way that we can account for these ratios? A simple device can be constructed by the students that will enable them to make their own table of trigonometric ratios for the sine and the cosine by measuring (Fig. 20-2):

1. On graph paper, draw a circle with a radius of $2\frac{1}{2}$ inches (10 boxes on paper having four boxes per inch).
2. Cut a thin strip of cardboard at least 3 inches long.
3. Draw a line down the center of the strip.
4. Attach one end of the strip to the center of the circle (use a pin or paper fastener).
5. At the other end of the strip, $2\frac{1}{2}$ inches from the point where it is attached to the circle, make a small hole and attach a piece of string at least 5 inches long.
6. At the opposite end of the string, attach a weight to serve as a plumb line (a small nut or bolt will do).

If the entire device is mounted on a thick wood or cardboard base, the use is simplified. As we move the cardboard strip, the cord hangs down and cuts the horizontal axis OA. If the student counts the number of spaces of length of the cord (i.e., BC), since the hypotenuse is fixed at 10 (on paper

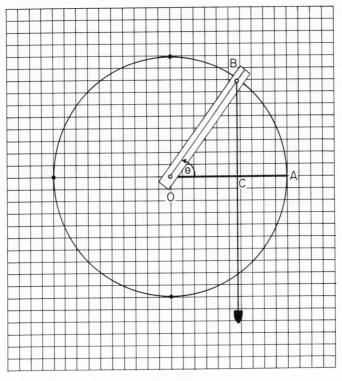

Figure 20-2

having four boxes per inch), he can easily determine an approximation of the sine ratio. As he changes the angle by moving the cardboard strip, he can observe the corresponding changes in the sine. Counting the boxes enables him to set up his ratios and make his table of values. Of course, if he measures the amount of the horizontal axis cut off by the hanging cord, he can also approximate the cosine and construct a table of values for this ratio as well. The entire process should strengthen the student's understanding of these ratios, as well as earn his respect for the true worth of the trigonometric tables. Such a device may also help us to extend our concept of angle size, as well as shed light upon the idea of radian measure.

TRIGONOMETRY AS FUNCTIONS

Looking upon the trigonometric relationships as ratios and constructing tables will provide suitable experiences for the solution of a multitude of problems involving navigation, indirect measurement, and a host of other applications. Throughout these experiences the students have seen how changing the reference angle effects a change in the ratio. Thus, subtly but

467

assuredly, they have been undergoing experiences that are basic to the notion of function. In turning to the concepts of trigonometric functions, we have one more opportunity to extend our work with this significant idea.

If we were to hang a weight from a spring and pull the spring downward and release it, how shall we describe the motion of the spring? It seems to move up and down, moving slower and slower until it eventually comes to a stop. In effect, the spring stretches out and then contracts, and stretches out again and contracts somewhat less than before. Eventually the movement ceases altogether. If we think of the starting position of the spring and examine the different positions it takes, we may consider any change from the at-rest position as a displacement of the spring. Since the displacements of the weight are dependent upon the time that has passed since the spring was set in motion, we may consider the change in position to be a function of time. If we do so, can we find a mathematical description of the function? To aid in this process, let us examine the situation, form a table of corresponding time and displacement values, and draw a graph of the function in order to see if it is recognizable.

Establishing equally spaced time intervals and making stop-action pictures of the motion of the spring results in Figure 20-3. It is possible for the teacher to present such diagrams to the students to enable them to gather their own data about the behavior of the spring, in much the same fashion as was done in algebra. The outcome of this is the table of values and the graph shown in Figure 20-4.

This is a function of a new kind. We have not encountered such a function in any of our previous work. It is periodic in nature, since it passes through a series of values and then repeats; and thus far we have had no occasion to deal with such a function. It must be a new breed of function, and we shall therefore have to find something new if we are to describe it properly. Perhaps trigonometry can help and, of course, it does.

Since we have already studied trigonometric equations, such as $y = \sin x$ or $y = \cos x$, we find that we are describing a different breed of function. Here

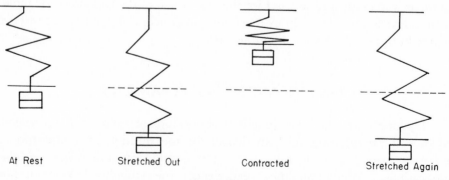

At Rest   Stretched Out   Contracted   Stretched Again

Figure 20-3

468

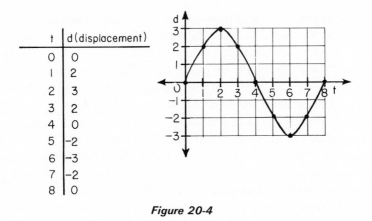

t	d (displacement)
0	0
1	2
2	3
3	2
4	0
5	-2
6	-3
7	-2
8	0

Figure 20-4

the *x* is a placeholder for the measure of an angle. At this time the only possible replacements for *x* are contained in the set of angles from 0 to 90°. Let us explore how the functions derived from these descriptions would look upon the graph. When we construct the table and draw the graph of $y = \sin x$, we see it is a familiar one, as far as it goes (Fig. 20-5). This graph appears to be a replica of the one showing the motion of the weight on a spring, although it is but a small portion of that graph. Is there some way we may extend the graph of the function described by $y = \sin x$? To accomplish this we will, in effect, have to define a new function. To do this it may be well to look at some familiar ideas. The variable *x* in $y = \sin x$ is the measure of an angle. In the situation in which we met the trigonometric ratios, this was an angle of a right triangle. Therefore, it cannot possibly exceed 90°; indeed, it must be less than 90°. Let us take the equation $y = \sin x$ and think of the variable *x* simply as a real number. Each time we identify a new value for *x*, we find a corresponding one for *y*. The domain is now the set of real numbers. Of course, we do not know what the physical meaning of an *x*-value greater than 90° will be, but for now we are concerned only with the mathematical representations. Since we want the values for *x* to reflect the weight motion, they must repeat the displacement values of the weight in the same order. Thus, if we permit

Figure 20-5

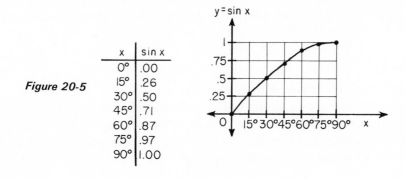

x	sin x
0°	.00
15°	.26
30°	.50
45°	.71
60°	.87
75°	.97
90°	1.00

469

$x = 100$, the resulting y-value must match the value corresponding to $x = 80°$, or .9848. If we choose $x = 120$, the value of y must be the same as that of $x = 60°$; i.e., $y = .8660$. If any other values are chosen for y, the periodic nature of the function would be destroyed. Hence, we complete the table of extended x-values and their corresponding y-values, and we complete the graph as well. In general, we find that $\sin x = \sin (180 - x)$. It appears that selecting x-values up to and including 360 results in a construction that matches the graph in question rather well. The trigonometric functions defined in this way are a perfect description of the periodic function of the oscillating spring. What an excellent development for the demonstration of the inter-dependence of mathematics and science. Beginning with a physical experiment, we explored mathematical descriptions, with the net result of a better understanding of the physical situation as well as the definition of a new function and an extension of our knowledge of mathematics.

Similar developments may extend our concepts of cosine and tangent; and, indeed, once we have moved to the concept of x as a placeholder for a real number, we are free to extend the function to include negative x-values as well. In each instance we may stop and inquire as to the meaning of the ex-pression before us in physical terms, in order to maintain our contact with the physical environment from whence these ideas came. Applications abound in any area concerned with the periodic nature of these functions. Musical sounds, electricity, and radio and television waves are some of these areas.[3] But there are still other ways in which we may look at the trigonometric functions.

VECTORS IN TRIGONOMETRY

Another recommendation of the Commission on Mathematics has been the reorganization of the trigonometry course because of new and vital appli-cations in the fields of statics and dynamics and all kinds of vibration prob-lems—to name but a few. In order to meet these needs it is suggested that

> computational emphasis should shift from triangles to vectors, and analytic emphasis from identities to functional properties. . . . The vital material of the reorganized trigonometry lies in the rectangular and polar descriptions of points, vectors, and complex numbers, and in the addition theorems and periodic character of the circular functions.[4]

Building on the definition of an angle as ". . . the configuration formed by two half-lines (rays) with a common end point," the Commission on Mathematics indicates how the concept of vectors is integrated into the study of trigonometry together with the notions of rectangular and polar coordinate systems.[5] A single diagram may serve to clarify the relationships (Fig. 20-6). Once the standard position for the angle has been established, the trigo-

470

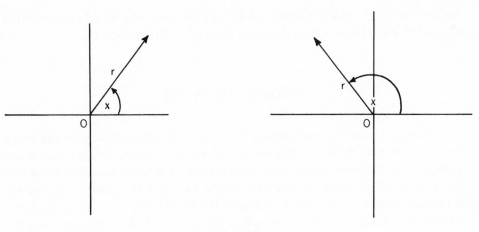

Figure 20-6

nometric functions defined in terms of this newly defined angle may be determined. Thus, we are no longer concerned with the limitations imposed upon
us by the fixed triangle approach of the initial study of trigonometric ratios.
While in this approach we have extended the domain of x to include values
greater than $90°$, we have developed this in a different manner from the previous discussion based upon an oscillating spring. Here, the x-values still represent angle measure, whereas the earlier discussion translated them into real
numbers.

Exploration of the values of each of the functions in the four quadrants,
graphs of the functions, operations with vectors, and the rectangular coordinate description of a vector as a complex number all result from the consideration of applications involving navigation and any other situation in which the
physical quantities require a description of both magnitude and direction.
For these the concept of vector is uniquely suited. In order to demonstrate
the use of these ideas, two sample problems and their diagrams follow:

1. Find the velocity of a boat being rowed straight across a river with a
   5 m.p.h. current, if the boy in the boat can row at 4 m.p.h. in still
   water.
2. A plane is flying on a course of $130°$ at a speed of 250 m.p.h. If a wind
   is blowing from the east with a speed of 50 m.p.h., what is the resulting speed and direction of the plane?

We have extended our earlier concept of trigonometry from ratio to
function in two very different ways. One approach required a change in the
domain from the set of angle measures to the real numbers. The other maintained the concept of angle. The Commission on Mathematics has indicated
very clearly how the transition can be made from angle measures to real
numbers by wrapping a line about a unit circle.[6] This is one way in which
the circular functions may be introduced. However one decides to proceed,

the way in which many diverse mathematical ideas run together should not be minimized. This is one of the great strengths of trigonometry.

RADIAN MEASURE

Perhaps the work emphasizing the nature of the variable x in the equation $y = \sin x$ as discussed previously will help to clarify an idea that many students find unusually difficult—the concept of radian measure. Somehow the description of angles in radians simply mystifies the student despite the apparently simple concept of a radian as the measure of a central angle intercepting an arc equal to the radius (Fig. 20-7). If we look at an angle of 180°, we see that we have intercepted a semicircle, or half the circumference: πr.

Since the radian measure of any central angle is $\frac{s}{r}$, the ratio of its arc length to the length of the radius, we get $\frac{\pi r}{r}$ or

$$180° = \pi \text{ radians}$$

We may also conclude that there are 2π radians in the entire circle. This relationship will enable us to convert from degrees to radians and back again.

A beginning for the study of the vital ideas underlying the consideration of trigonometric relationships as functions has been presented. The trigonometric formulas, the area formula for a triangle, and the solution of triangles all follow the beginnings made here. The important concepts will determine to a large degree just how the student will react to trigonometry. If we keep our beginnings immersed in the physical and build abstractions slowly, even at this level, we offer the majority of our students the greatest opportunity for success.

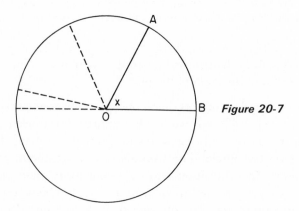

Figure 20-7

ANALYTIC GEOMETRY

It is expected that most students in high school will study trigonometry. It is becoming a common subject in the eleventh year of high school. Since more and more colleges require that entering students have completed three years of high school mathematics, we find that increasing numbers of students will be coming to college after having had some work in a full-fledged course of trigonometry. When we examine the senior year of high school, however, we find that we are no longer considering a mathematics course for everyone. The simple elective procedures of most high schools result in a rather select student population asking for a fourth year of high school mathematics. Despite the variety of offerings one may find in schools across the nation today, it is suggested here that analytic geometry and calculus would seem to be the courses of greatest value for this student.

Let us consider analytic geometry first. The study mentioned before by Lauren Woodby is concluded with the recommendation that analytic geometry is a particularly suitable course for the high school because

> (1) it increases the student's understanding of algebra and helps him to maintain algebraic skills; (2) the vector approach can be used; (3) college courses in calculus and analytic geometry tend to de-emphasize analytic geometry; and (4) a qualified high school teacher is usually available to teach the course.[7]

It does seem somewhat a shame that this course has been subordinated to the study of the calculus. The very nature of analytic geometry makes it the kind of course that students enjoy—the construction of graphs of functions of many types and the general geometric representation of the algebraic ideas encountered. But yet, it is virtually disappearing from the college curriculum as a course in its own right. Perhaps Woodby is correct when he indicates that the high school should fill in this gap. Let us explore further.

"I think, therefore I am!" With these words René Descartes undertook the writing of a major work in the field of philosophy that he believed would render him immortal. Almost as an afterthought he included a supplementary section on analytic geometry. It was this work that was to truly stamp the name Descartes upon the history of man, for it was the analytic geometry that was to have great influence upon mathematics and science and upon the society at large.

While much of the information about curves contained in analytic geometry was already known to man through the works of Euclid and Apollonius, it took the genius of Descartes (and Fermat) to bring the power of the techniques of algebra to bear upon the problems of geometry. In geometry, each problem is approached as a separate entity, requiring careful thought and the application of ingenious ideas to work to a solution. In algebra, the body of techniques that are built up offers a ready-made method

473

with which to attack problems. Descartes brought this method into the study of curves.

In her book *A Long Way From Euclid* Constance Reid demonstrates how an insolvable problem of the ancients falls apart under the methods of Descartes, i.e., the problem of doubling the cube.[8] The legend has it that the people of Athens had to double the size of the cube-shaped altar to Apollo that existed if they were to satisfy the gods and put an end to a terrible plague. Naturally this problem proved to be much more difficult than was anticipated, for when the Athenians immediately constructed a new altar whose dimensions were twice those of the original, they found that they had increased the volume eight times rather than twice. Of course, the plague eventually ran its course, but the problem remained. Greek mathematicians, looking for an exact answer but using only the traditional instruments of compass and straightedge, were unable to solve what amounted to the equation $x^3 = 2$. (Thinking of the original cube as unit size.) Reid goes on to point out that the problem is quickly resolved once the method of Descartes is available. It becomes a consideration of the intersection of two curves:

$$y = x^2 \qquad \text{and} \qquad xy = 2$$

The x-coordinate of this intersection point provides the desired length of the new temple to be built (Fig. 20-8). Suffice it to say, the newfound power offered by the method of analytic or coordinate geometry was immense.

We have already explored many of the curves that make up the field of study for this new work. In the discussion of geometry we investigated geometric properties of the conic sections. We also explored some beginning work in coordinate geometry itself and saw how some theorems were reduced to simple statements of equations in order to establish proof. Hence, this subject does not begin in the senior year. But its formal study does, and perhaps it should begin at the very beginning with the definition of a point, since this immediately serves notice that something new and wonderful is in the wind. When Euclid spoke of a point, he was referring to something he defined as follows: A point is that which has no parts and no magnitude. This certainly tells what a point is not, but it does little to help our understanding of what a point is. We do not attempt to define a point any longer, realizing that it is one of our basic and undefined terms. Still, many teachers reflect the definition of Euclid: The class is often told that a point simply shows position, that it has no dimensions at all. Compare both of these variations with the simple and direct definition that is a consequence of the work of Descartes: A point is an ordered pair of numbers of the form (x, y). Here we have the beginning of a system that reduces geometric relationships to number relationships and one that opens up possibilities never even visualized by its inventor.

The establishment of the rectangular coordinate axes and their corresponding number scales assigns to every point in the plane a unique number

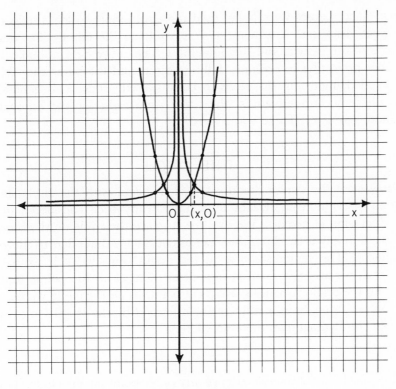

Figure 20-8

pair. Conversely every number pair has a unique point in the plane to which it refers. As we explore the special conditions that make one curve different from another and as we describe these differences in terms of some relationship in x and y, we begin to investigate the infinite varieties of curves that make up the study of coordinate geometry. Indeed, if we extend our axes to include three mutually perpendicular reference lines (forcing us to leave the plane and move into three-space), we open up an entirely new universe for study. And the very act of extending the universe to a three-dimensional one points the way to further expansion of ideas until we are in a position to discuss the mathematical side of n-dimensional spaces, while we may as yet be hard put to provide some intuitive understanding of what we have before us.[9] This is the way in which ideas are extended in mathematics; this is the fountainhead of ideas opened up to mathematicians by Descartes.

Earlier we spent considerable time with examples of the interaction of mathematics and the physical world. Are these to fall by the wayside as we undertake the study of analytics? Not at all. As a matter of fact, the implications for science have been as numerous as those for mathematics. As is usually the case, the need for information about the properties of curves was one of the motivating factors that led to the development of coordinate geometry in the first place. Lenses were being used more and more to focus light coming from great distances. Astronomers were studying the curves that described the paths of the planets and their satellites. The entire field of bodies in motion, from projectiles to ordinary falling objects and the paths they followed, also included important questions to be answered. Thus, as is generally the case with important advances, the times were right for the innovation of coordinate geometry. There was a need.

THE CIRCLE

How were the curves described? Let us begin with the circle since the algebraic description of straight lines has already been considered in detail in the discussion of algebra. We are free to place the circle on the coordinate axes system in any desired position. Let us choose one that offers us the greatest convenience: The center shall be at the origin (Fig. 20-9). If we assume a radius of 4, we are now in need of a description of all the points that are 4 units from the origin. Choosing a typical point, A, on the circle whose coordinates are (x, y), we have a right triangle formed by the lengths x, y, and the radius 4. The Pythagorean theorem yields

$$x^2 + y^2 = 4^2$$

which would hold for the selection of any other point on the circle. Thus, the familiar circle of plane geometry now has an analytic description.

The Pythagorean theorem also leads to the basic distance formula for the distance between any two points in the Cartesian plane. If we choose two arbitrary points, A and B, and designate their respective coordinates as (x_1, y_1) and (x_2, y_2), the triangle formed by constructing the perpendiculars

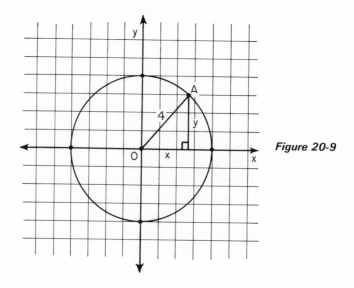

Figure 20-9

476

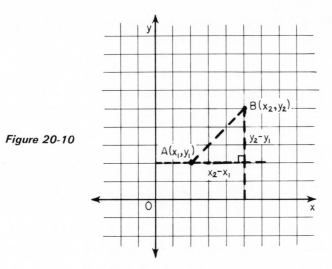

Figure 20-10

through A and B to the y- and x-axes, respectively, enables us to apply the Pythagorean theorem to determine the length AB (Fig. 20-10). This results in $AB = \sqrt{(x_2 - x_1)^2 + (y_2 - y_1)^2}$, the distance formula. Of course, this process is greatly simplified if the line segment joining the points in question is parallel to either of the axes.

Once the distance formula is available, we may explore the equation of a circle whose center is not at the origin but at some other point, say (h, k). (See Fig. 20-11.) All points a fixed distance from (h, k), say 5 units, may be

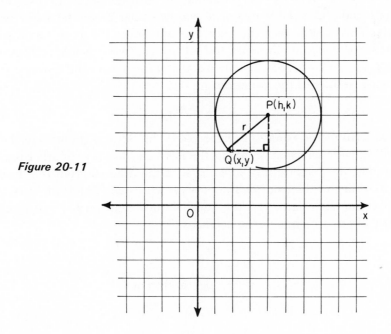

Figure 20-11

477

described by still another application of the theorem of Pythagoras. We find that the equation for this circle becomes

$$(x - h)^2 + (y - k)^2 = 5^2$$

and the general equation for all circles is

$$(x - h)^2 + (y - k)^2 = r^2$$

with the center at (h, k) and radius r.

THE PARABOLA

The same basic approach employed to find the equation of the circle will also enable us to describe other collections of points that satisfy different conditions. For example, the parabola was defined earlier to be the set of points whose distance from a fixed point was always equal to its distance from a given line. Where shall we place the parabola in relation to the axes in order to simplify the determination of a description of these points? If the students are encouraged to think of this problem for themselves, they can formulate their own hypotheses about it and observe the consequences of their ideas by setting about to derive a description of this set of points. There is more than one way to develop the desired equation. Some placements of the axes result in far less complication than others. Trial and error is a good teacher.

It is customary to place the fixed line (directrix) and the fixed point (focus) so that the vertex of the parabola will be at the origin, midway between the focus and the intersection of a perpendicular from the focus with the directrix. This would place the fixed line parallel to the x- or y-axis, however it is preferred, with the focus on the other axis. One possible arrangement is shown in Figure 20-12. Setting the distance PF equal to the distance PR, and simplifying, results in the equation

$$x^2 = 4ay$$

a simple form of the equation of the parabola. Several things may be noted that will provide information about the form and location of other parabolas, for example, the coefficient of y: $4a$ is twice the distance from the fixed point to the fixed line of the locus definition with which we began; the vertex of the parabola is at the origin, and the parabola opens upward. What happens to the parabola as we change the coefficient?

$$x^2 = 4y$$
$$x^2 = 9y$$
$$x^2 = 16y \quad \text{and so on.}$$

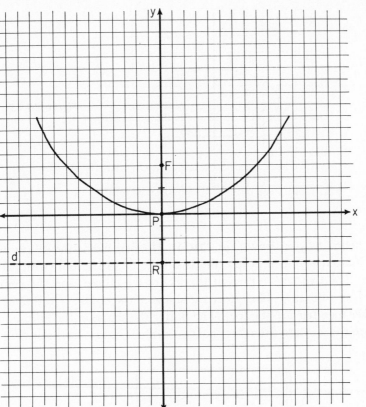

Figure 20-12

Suppose we move the vertex to another point in the plane? What is the equation of a parabola that opens downward? There are many fascinating investigations that students can undertake in this area as they seek out patterns of consequence. One result may well be the formulation of their own "tricks" for graphing and identifying curves from equations and the reverse.

THE ELLIPSE

In much the same fashion as the pattern established for the circle and the parabola, the study may be extended to include the ellipse. The locus definition, together with the most useful placement of the axes, will form the focal point of the discussion (Fig. 20-13). Earlier it was shown that you could draw the ellipse by looping string around two fixed points and pulling taut

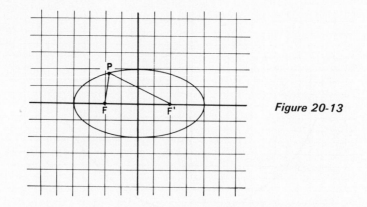

Figure 20-13

with a pencil as you draw (Fig. 20-14). Hogben likens the ellipse to a soccer ball.[10] Flattened out, it is like the two lines of string. Blown up, it is almost circular. The two pegs represent the foci of the ellipse, and the center is midway between them, 0. The closer the shape of the ellipse is to that of the circle, the closer together are the foci. The flatter the shape of the ellipse, the farther apart are the foci and the more like two straight lines is its shape (Fig. 20-15). If

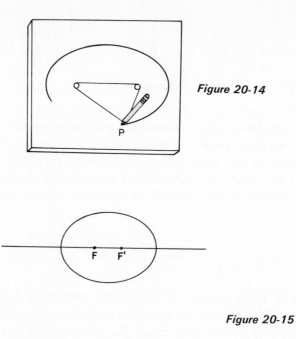

Figure 20-14

Figure 20-15

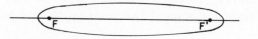

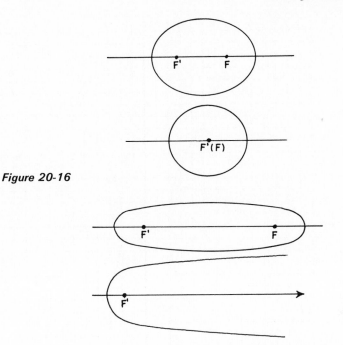

Figure 20-16

we think in terms of limiting positions, we may quickly relate the circle, the parabola, and the ellipse to each other. Starting with the ellipse, we find that if the foci are brought closer and closer together, the limiting position will be the circle. If they are moved farther and farther apart until we consider one focus to be at infinity, then the ellipse degenerates into a parabola with the other focus point as its focus.[11] Each figure may be seen as a special case of the other (Fig. 20-16).

THE HYPERBOLA

Following the pattern of this discussion, we could employ the locus definition to establish the equation of the hyperbola. The definition of this curve is the set of points satisfying the condition that the difference of each point's distances from two fixed points is a constant. Using this and placing the curve on the axes so that the center is at the origin and the foci are on one of the coordinate axes will yield the simple form of the equation of this curve (Fig. 20-17). Later, the students may once again seek a description of hyperbolas

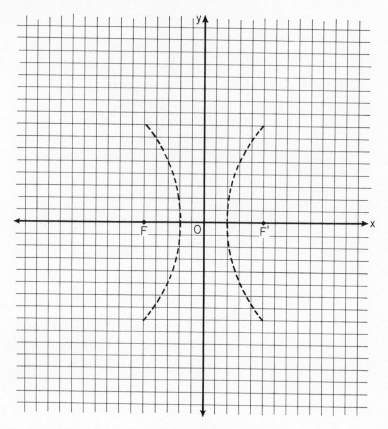

Figure 20-17

located in any position in the Cartesian plane. In addition, patterns of form and location may also be explored here as they were with the other conics.

APPLICATIONS

The previous development of the conic sections may leave the impression that we are now prepared to abandon our physical considerations and concentrate upon only the mathematics. This is not true. The curves described here are some of the more important ones to be studied in analytic geometry; and as such, they offer the students many worthwhile opportunities to conduct mathematical explorations. But the applications of these curves to science are equally important. If we wished to construct a light reflector that would send rays emanating from a given point out in the same direction (an automobile headlight is a good example), how should we shape the reflector? The reflection laws of light rays, our needs, and the properties of the situation result in the establishment of the parabola as the shape to employ.[12] (Actually it is the paraboloid formed by revolving the parabola about its axis.)

We cannot begin to consider the movement of the planets and other satellites, natural or man-made, without involving the ellipse, which also has important reflection properties, such as those mentioned in the earlier discussion of geometry.

The hyperbola is another useful shape for the reflection of light and sound rays, which is one of the reasons outdoor band shells are generally made in this shape. Many physical laws, such as Boyle's law relating the pressure and volume of gases, bring the hyperbola into use. Indeed, any law of the form $xy = k$, will involve the hyperbola.

IN CONCLUSION

There is a host of important ideas and activities that make up the study of analytic geometry. Graphic analysis involving the concepts of symmetry, range and domain, intercepts, and asymptotes; the polar coordinate description of these and other curves; the transformation of coordinates; and the tangents to the several curves are omitted here because of a lack of space, not significance. Standard textbooks on analytical geometry are an excellent source of information here. Suffice it to say that coordinate geometry forms an important beginning for the study of the calculus but is also important in its own right. The marriage of curve and equation has accelerated progress in both the mathematics and science fields. It has provided power to attack problems where it was previously lacking. We turn now to still more powerful methods for the study of the physical world: the calculus.

THE CALCULUS

Of all the many alternatives that are appropriate for study by high school seniors, it would seem that the calculus should receive the first priority. E. T. Bell points up the importance of calculus in application and theory as he states,

> The chief instrument of applied mathematics is also of the highest importance—in its modern developments—to those who cultivate mathematics for its own sake.[13]

In addition, Von Neumann, one of the greatest mathematicians of the twentieth century, adds,

> The calculus was the first achievement of modern mathematics, and it is difficult to overestimate its importance. I think it defines more

unequivocally than anything else the inception of modern mathematics, and the system of mathematical analysis, which is its logical development, and still constitutes the greatest technical advance in exact thinking.[14]

Despite the recognized importance of the calculus and the fact that it is the focus of the Advanced Placement Program, it is still not generally taught to the fourth year high school mathematics student. A serious hindrance has been the lack of an experienced teacher who is qualified to do justice to the course. Perhaps one way to resolve this problem is to be clear about the specific aims for such a course. Woodby notes that while many high schools are teaching good quality calculus courses, he detects a trend towards the offering of calculus courses that are exercises in mechanical computation.[15] He describes these as "warm-up courses" that are supposed to give students a head start in college.

This is an unfortunate point of emphasis for high school teachers to take. If we are to think in terms of offering a respectable course in the calculus, built upon a full semester course in analytic geometry (and at the same time keep in mind the notion of preparation for college work), it would seem that our concern should be the reverse of mechanical manipulation and center upon developing insight into the important ideas. In considering this same problem W. W. Sawyer states:

> First learn to use the calculus, to see what can be done with it, to feel what it is about. In the course of this you will gradually become aware of a need for more exact ideas—then is the time to study the modern treatment, usually known by the name of Analysis.[16]

Rather than to get into extensive mechanics of differentiation and integration, let us develop situations in which our students proceed using basic understandings. These attempts at rough calculations using fundamental ideas may well provide a basis in understanding that will make present work meaningful and at the same time provide a sound basis for continued study. In fact, the teacher himself may gain a great deal from such an introduction as he adds to his own background as well as to that of his students.

DIFFERENTIATION

How may we begin such a development? The focal point of much of our earlier work has been the notion of function. The students have studied a wide variety of functions that were necessary to explore the relationships found in the environment. As they worked, they were constantly giving their attention to the way a change in one variable resulted in a corresponding change in another variable. For example, a dropped object falling free was described by $v = 32t$. The longer the object fell, the faster it fell. We were always seeking to determine the value taken by one variable when the other variable assumed a specific value. In this way we were constantly dealing with changing variables and determining the resulting effect of the change. While changes are important if man is to study the physical world, it is as important, if not more so, to study how fast or slow these changes are taking place. An elevator may drop some 20 floors and you get out feeling perfectly all right—if the rate of descent is slow. However, if the drop was negotiated at the speed of free fall, a considerably different situation prevails. Bringing a car from 50 m.p.h. to a stop will have differing effects upon its occupants, depending upon how much time transpires in the process. And of course, a change in depth while underwater will be an enjoyable or troublesome experience, depending upon the speed with which it is carried out. The need to know *rates of change* is as great a need as is the quest for change itself. With this in mind we have already begun to study the calculus. Let us investigate a problem in motion.

A runner is timed over a measured 100 yard track. He starts before the starting line so that he may enter the course at top speed. Here is the time he reached different distance markers:

t (seconds)	0	1	2	3	4	5	6	. . . 10
d (feet)	0	10	20	30	40	50	60	. . . 100

We can tell at a glance where the runner is at any time, but can we tell how fast he is running? Perhaps a graph of this information will help (Fig. 20-18). The graph turns out to be a straight line. Let us find his speed when $t = 4$. The rule for the function just described is easy enough to find: $d = 10t$. Since he seems to gain 10 feet each second, his speed seems to be just that, 10 ft./sec. Does this speed change as he runs? We know the speed is constant by examining the table and observing the steady increase in distance for each second.

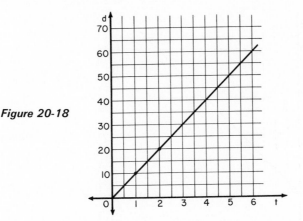

Figure 20-18

We can also tell that the speed is constant from the graph. The curve is a straight line. The formula $d = 10t$ indicates the constant speed as well. His speed at $t = 4$ will therefore be the same as at $t = 2$ or 5 or any other number of seconds. It is a constant 10 ft./sec. throughout. Could we find this speed from the distance-time graph? What is speed? We may think of it as the change in distance for a given time interval. Let us look at the graph and determine how the distance changed in the 1-second time interval from 2 to 3 seconds (Fig. 20-19). The distance changed by 10 feet in the 1-second time interval. From the graph we can see that this is also the slope of the line. Thus, we find that

$$\frac{d_2 - d_1}{t_2 - t_1} = \frac{\Delta d}{\Delta t} = \frac{30 - 20}{3 - 2} = 10$$

We know from our earlier work that the slope of a straight line is constant at each point on the line, so once again we find the speed is constant and is 10 ft./sec. Despite the fact that our graph involves distance-time, we found the speed by determining the slope or steepness of the line. Will this always work? A look at other functions will enable us to find out.

At this point the students might pursue the answers to the same questions for other simple linear functions, such as:

$$y = 3x$$
$$y = 2x + 5$$
$$y = -x - 3, \text{ etc.}$$

In each of these cases, the speed is constant and is represented by the slope of the straight line describing the function. We are concentrating on familiar information from a new point of view: We are exploring the rate of change of the distance with respect to the change in time. It is well to list the results:

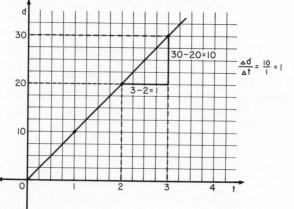

Figure 20-19

486

Formula	Speed
$y = 10x$	$v = 10$
$y = 3x$	$v = 3$
$y = 2x + 5$	$v = 2$
$y = -x - 3$	$v = -1$

The slope of the line has provided us with the speed. Let us see the effects of a more complicated function:

A boy sledding down a hill passes distance markers as follows:

t	0	1	2	3	4	5
d	0	1	4	9	16	25

Are we able to answer the same questions we faced before? That is, since we know where the boy is at any instant, say $t = 3$, can we find how fast he is going at that particular second? If our previous work held any clues, let us draw the graph and seek out the slope of the curve at the point where $t = 3$ (Fig. 20-20). Here we seem to have a bit of a problem. The line is not straight and may be recognized as a portion of the familiar parabola. The formula for this motion (looking at the table) is $d = t^2$. The speed is not constant because the boy gains speed as his sled comes down the hill. Thus, the speed will be different at each point—as the graph indicates. Indeed, the graph curls upward to show that more distance is being covered in the same amount of time; hence, the speed is increasing. At the instant where $t = 3$, the distance is 9 feet. Since it took 3 seconds to cover the 9 feet, the speed appears to be 3 ft./sec. But wait, something is wrong here. If we declare the speed to be 3 ft./sec. when $t = 3$ and if the speed is increasing continuously, in the time before $t = 3$ the speed must have been less than 3 ft./sec. But

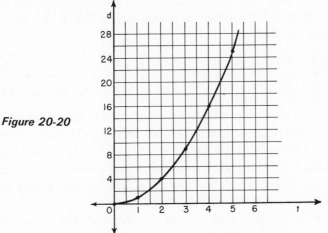

Figure 20-20

if this is so, then how could the sled have covered 9 feet in 3 seconds? Something is amiss somewhere. We are having trouble because we are confusing two different ideas: average speed over an interval and speed at an instant in time or *instantaneous speed.* The sled went 9 feet in 3 seconds. Its *average* speed is 3 ft./sec. and not its speed at that instant. Indeed, its speed at the instant of 3 seconds will undoubtedly have to be greater than 3 ft./sec. since it began at zero and gradually increased. If its average was 3, then somewhere in the interval it must have exceeded 3 to take care of the period when it was less than 3.

How shall we get at this elusive *instantaneous* speed? Let us take a smaller interval around 3 and perhaps we will better see what is happening. Here the students may embark upon the arithmetical exercises of finding the distance corresponding to $t = 2.9$ and $t = 3.1$. Our original table is expanded to include:

t	2.9	3	3.1
d	8.41	9	9.61

Computing average speed $\left(\dfrac{\Delta d}{\Delta t}\right)$ between 2.9 and 3 gives a change in distance

(Δd) of .59 for a change in time (Δt) of .1, or $\dfrac{.59}{.1}$ or 5.9 ft./sec. If we carry

out the same computation for the interval from 3 to 3.1, we get $\dfrac{.61}{.1}$ or 6.1

ft./sec. We begin to get a sense of the speed at the instant $t = 3$: It is somewhere between 5.9 and 6.1 ft./sec. The students should repeat these calculations for a shorter interval, $t = 2.99$ and 3.01, and then to $t = 2.999$ and $t = 3.001$. Eventually we seem to be fairly well convinced that the speed at 3 itself must be 6 ft./sec. The students begin a new table of instantaneous speeds and continue their investigation and calculation at the instant $t = 1$ through $t = 5$ or 6. Each time the speed is recorded in the new table so that a pattern may be observed:

t	1	2	3	4	5	6
v	2	4	6	8	10	12

It soon becomes clear that when the distance-time relationship is $d = t^2$, the speed-time counterpart is $v = 2t$. Going through the entire experience with other motion problems ($y = 2x^2$, $y = x^3$, $y = x^2 + x$, etc.) and listing the results as before leads to a general rule for answering the central problem of the calculus: Given a rule for finding where an object is at any instant in time, find how fast it is moving at that instant.

What of the graph? If we accept the fact that the reduction in the size of the interval of time eventually leads to the conclusion that the instantaneous speed at $t = 3$ is 6 ft./sec., what does this mean graphically? If we first clarify the meaning of average speed and then follow graphically the same process we carried out arithmetically, we reach the point at which we see that the slope of the tangent to a point describes the instantaneous speed at that point (Fig. 20-21). The slope of AB is 5.9, the average speed for the given interval. The same is true of BC, whose slope is 6.1. As we move point A toward point B, we reduce Δt. If we imagine this process being carried out until points A and B virtually merge, we can illustrate intuitively how the slope at the point B may be thought of as the slope of the tangent to the curve at that point. We also have begun to establish an intuitive foundation for the general description of the instantaneous speed. Using $y = x^2$, we chose a small interval about x: Δx. This change in x brings about a corresponding change in y: Δy.

$$y = x^2$$
$$y + \Delta y = (x + \Delta x)^2$$

Removing parentheses, we get $y + \Delta y = x^2 + 2x\Delta x + \Delta x^2$

We are concerned with the change, so we subtract the original equation, $y = x^2$:

$$y + \Delta y - y = x^2 + 2x\Delta x + \Delta x^2 - x^2$$
$$\Delta y = 2x\Delta x + \Delta x^2$$

The average speed is $\dfrac{\Delta y}{\Delta x}$. We divide both sides by Δx:

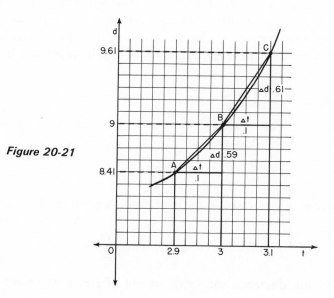

Figure 20-21

489

$$\frac{\Delta y}{\Delta x} = \frac{2x\Delta x + \Delta x^2}{\Delta x}$$

$$\frac{\Delta y}{\Delta x} = 2x + \Delta x \text{ (\textbf{average speed})}$$

Now if we move point B toward A so that $\Delta x \to 0$,

$$\lim_{x \to 0} \frac{\Delta y}{\Delta x} = \frac{dy}{dx} = 2x \text{ (\textbf{instantaneous speed})}$$

This process is not attempted until the students have calculated the results and drawn freehand tangents to curves in a vast number of cases. There is no hurry. We are struggling to build a "feel" for the process in the minds of students. If we provide sufficient examples, the general development just shown becomes an obvious "next step" rather than a mystery. But this can occur only if its formulation is at the end of the experiences described rather than at the beginning.

The notion of limit and the new symbolism are introduced *after* the rich variety of experiences has been undertaken. The important notion is that the derivative tells us the speed or steepness of the given formula at a point. We use the word "speed," but the functions to be explored need not be limited to motion. Since a function, by its nature, indicates changing values of variables, the derivative will tell us how fast changes are taking place, hence our focus upon *rates of change*. We may be concerned with spring stretch and time, area of a wound and time, pressure and height, price and time, or any other pair of variables. When we are concerned with *instantaneous rates of change*, we are concerned with the derivative. Repetition of the process takes us another step forward and indicates the rate at which *changes* are taking place. This process may be continued indefinitely. Thus, if we begin with $s = 16t^2$ we find the *instantaneous* rate of change to be $v = 32t$. Repetition of differentiation yields $a = 32$. The significance of the results may best be described as follows:

Distance: $s = 16t^2$

Speed: The change in *distance* with respect to time is the speed or velocity.

$v = 32t$ (first derivative $\frac{ds}{dt}$ or s')

Acceleration: The change in *speed* with respect to time is the acceleration.

$a = 32$ (second derivative $\frac{d^2s}{dt^2}$ or s'')

We have not discussed the vital concept of limits. We have only dealt with simple functions and assumed these functions to be continuous. We have not considered the inverse process to differentiation. These will be explored shortly. For the conclusion of this discussion, it is important to realize that our goal has been an introduction to the calculus based upon familiar functions and known processes. The remainder of work with differentiation involves working with more and more complicated functions. There are four basic principles that students must learn, in addition to what has already been discussed. Suitable problems are plentiful for the introduction of these principles of differentiation: If we let $f(x) = u$ and $g(x) = v$, then:

1. Sum and difference:

$$y = u + v \qquad\qquad y' = u' + v'$$
$$y = u - v \qquad\qquad y' = u' - v'$$

2. Product:

$$y = uv \qquad\qquad y' = u'v + uv'$$

3. Quotient:

$$y = \frac{u}{v} \qquad\qquad y' = \frac{u'v - uv'}{v^2}$$

4. Function of a function (chain rule):
   If $y = f(u)$ and $u = f(x)$,

$$\frac{dy}{dx} = \frac{dy}{du} \cdot \frac{du}{dx}$$

LIMIT

The key idea in the preceding work was the notion of limit. It was intuitively dispatched by seeing that values tended in a certain direction and toward a given value. We said that as the size of the interval was made smaller and smaller and tended toward zero, the limit of the average rate became the instantaneous rate. Does the interval ever *become* zero; and if not, how could the speed at a point ever actually *become* the value we call the instantaneous rate? For example, $y = x^2$. The instantaneous rate at $x = 3$ is 2×3 or 6. The definition we use of this rate is $\lim_{x \to 0} \frac{\Delta y}{\Delta x}$. Is the speed at the point $x = 4$ actually 8? Then does Δx ever actually take the value zero? No. If it did, we could not divide by it and all our work is fruitless. This problem plagued mathematicians for years. Indeed, the inventors of the calculus, both Newton and Leibniz, did not have an exact formulation of limits. Is it any wonder, then, that our students find this concept so difficult to understand? Only extended

491

experience with the idea will render it meaningful, and this is not likely to occur in a single semester. We have already appealed to student intuition by considered values that the variable in question approached. We may offer some additional aid in the very situation that generated the idea initially and by following the same kinds of arithmetic procedures developed before. When we say that the limit of the average speed as x approaches 3 is 6, in effect we are declaring that we can make the average speed differ from the limit (instantaneous speed) by as little as we wish. In fact, we may consider it to be a challenge. If you select as small an interval as you like about the limit, there must be an average speed that differs from the limit by less than that amount. Let us turn to the calculations. The student should form a chart listing the succeeding x-values approaching 3, the resulting y-values, and the average speeds:

$$y = x^2$$

$$\text{as } x \to 3$$

x-values	Δx	y-values	Δy	Average speed $\dfrac{\Delta y}{\Delta x}$
3.1	.1	9.61	.61	6.1
3.01	.01	9.0601	.0601	6.01
3.001	.001	9.006001	.006001	6.001
3.0001	.0001	9.00060001	.00060001	6.0001

The average speed values are heading for 6. If 6 is truly the limit, then the challenge must be met. It goes like this: You select as small an interval as you wish close to 6 and, to beat off the challenge, I must find a number sufficiently close to 3 to yield an average speed that is between 6 and your value. For example,

> Your challenge: get closer than .1 from 6
> My reply: Let $x = 3.01$, because when $x = 3.01$, the average speed $= 6.01$; this is closer to 6 than .1, your challenge.

This challenge can only be met successfully by the number we call the limit. One more thing: It must also be true that not only 3.01 satisfies the test, but all numbers between 3 and 3.01 also satisfy the test. In effect, we can say that if we think of the average speeds as a sequence of numbers (for example, 6.1, 6.01, 6.001, 6.0001, . . .), to call 6 the limit of this sequence is to indicate that as we keep taking terms we get closer and closer to 6, and we can get as close to 6 as we wish. Given the challenge in different terms, if an interval is selected (say, .1 from 6) and if 6 is the limit as described, there is a finite number of terms of the sequence outside the interval, but an *infinite* number inside! This is true despite the fact that the interval may be made as small as you desire! A remarkable idea is this notion of limit. To do more in the high school would seem to be rushing things. We have tried to provide the student with some intuitive feeling about limits. This should be our chief goal at this level. College instruction will serve to refine the ideas only introduced here.

INTEGRATION

The final concept of the calculus for high school to be examined is the integral calculus. Every operation the student has met has involved an inverse operation. Differentiation is no exception. It is rather curious to observe how the inverse operation arises through a consideration of areas under a curve. What possible connection can there be between rates of change and the summation of areas? We shall soon find out. If we are going to develop an inverse process to differentiation, since the derivative is the speed calculated by knowing the distance relationship, we evidently will reverse this process and begin with a description of the speed in an attempt to find the distance formula. This is a familiar undertaking. In an earlier chapter we saw how speed-time graphs could help us to determine the distance traveled. Perhaps an example will refresh the memory. An object falls on a strange planet as shown by the following data:

t	0	1	2	3	4	5	6
v	0	3	6	9	12	15	18

The graph is shown in Figure 20-22. How far has the object fallen in 4 seconds? In our earlier work we found that the area under the curve provided us with the required distance.[17] Briefly, the rationale for this consisted of finding the area of a rectangle equal in area to the desired triangle. Since

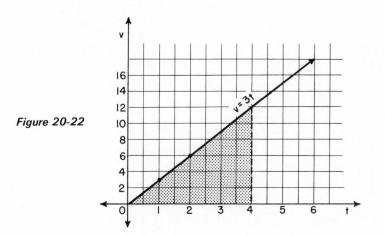

Figure 20-22

distance is defined by $d = rt$ and the rectangle area by $A = lw$, the parallel is clear. We can find the triangle area directly by use of the familiar triangle formula, $A = \frac{1}{2}bh$. In the preceding problem the solution may be arrived at as follows: $A = \frac{1}{2}(4)(12)$, where 12 is the value of $3x$ when $x = 4$. The distance traveled by the object in 4 seconds is 24 feet. Or we may use average speed over the interval again: $\dfrac{0 + 12}{2} = 6$. Then $6 \times 4 = 24$. The area under the curve and the distance traveled are indeed related. To build upon this idea and to allow time for the notion to develop, many additional problems may be solved by the students in this rudimentary way. Samples of such problems are shown in Figure 20-23. Each time the distance is calculated, the student has reversed the process of differentiation. We call this finding the anti-derivative. Perhaps we can find a general formula for the area under the curve in any interval, instead of dealing with each problem anew. Generalization can only result from a broad collection of experiences. If we investigate the curve $y = 4x$ and carry out the same ideas using a general point, what happens? (See Fig. 20-24.) The area of the enclosed triangle becomes

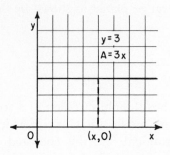

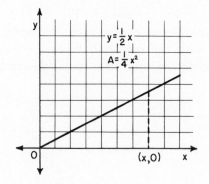

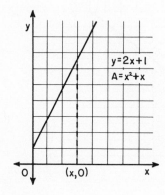

Figure 20-23

494

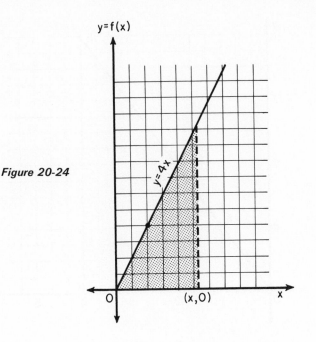

Figure 20-24

$$A = \tfrac{1}{2}(x)f(x) = \tfrac{1}{2}x(4x) = 2x^2.$$

We have our first statement of the indefinite integral. We began with the formula for speed and determined the function—distance. A quick check on our results would be to differentiate the function and match the result with the speed formula: $\dfrac{d(2x^2)}{dx} = 4x$. The pieces seem to begin to fit together. We have thus derived a general statement for finding the area bounded by the curve, the x-axis, and a perpendicular from a point on the curve to the x-axis. Will this result enable us to find the area under the curve in an interval that does not include the origin? (See Fig. 20-25.) If we apply the function we just derived, the antiderivative of $y = 4x$ (that is, $2x^2$), we find that if we make use of the right end point $x = 4$, we get

$$A = 2(4)(4) = 32$$

The area is 32 square units. But what exactly have we found? And why should we use the right end point and not the left end point? If the students are free to resolve these questions for themselves in their own way, they will have a good opportunity to make sense of the situation. Eventually they will realize that substitution of $x = 4$ into the antiderivative yields the area of $\triangle BOC$. But this contains more area than was intended. The extra piece is $\triangle AOD$, which also happens to be the area that results from substitution of the x-coordinate of the left end point. In effect we have carried out the following:

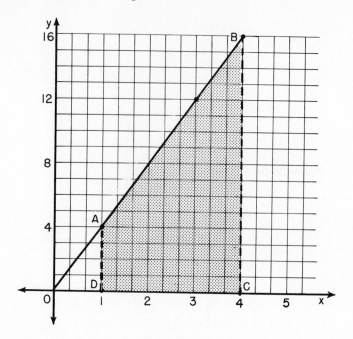

Figure 20-25

The desired area is area $\triangle BOC$ − area $\triangle AOD$.

$$2(4)^2 - 2(1)^2$$
$$32 - 2 = 30$$

The desired area is 30 square units.

The process employed here is most interesting. If we generalize to any function, assuming for the moment that the method will hold up, we find that we have done the following:

$$A = F(b) - F(a)$$

where a is the x-coordinate of the left end point, b is the x-coordinate of the right end point, and $F(x)$ is the antiderivative of $f(x)$, the formula for speed. We therefore have arrived at our first statement of the definite integral. It seems a bit premature to introduce the integral notation at this time, since the integral sign is more meaningful as the sum of areas. It may be desirable to continue to use "antiderivative" until the summation of areas is considered.

Added experience with straight line functions is necessary before the generalized form just presented is discussed. Case by case, the idea is formed until the student is virtually able to state the general form himself. Once we have progressed to this stage, we may ask: Can we use this method for finding the area under any curve, not simply straight lines? In particular,

496

Find the area under the curve $y = x^2$ between $x = 3$ and $x = 5$. (See Fig. 20-26).

To state the question another way, if the speed of an object is described by $y = x^2$, find the distance it traveled in the 2 seconds following the third second of its motion. If we assume that the process will work,

$$f(x) = x^2$$

then

$$F(x) = \frac{x^3}{3}$$

$$a = 3 \qquad b = 5$$

$$A = F(5) - F(3) = \frac{(5)^3}{3} - \frac{(3)^3}{3} = \frac{125 - 27}{3} = \frac{98}{3} = 32\tfrac{2}{3}$$

The method indicates that the area is $32\tfrac{2}{3}$ square units, but is this correct? Once again the students are faced with the problem of determining whether or not the answer is a good one. The methods used to ascertain this are as important as the particular processes we are focusing upon. The students may wish to draw straight lines approximating the curve; they may wish to sub-divide the area. Whatever the method, their results will approximate $32\tfrac{2}{3}$. Can we ever be certain? Since rectangle areas are easily computed, let us explore an approximation of the area in question by subdividing it into rec-

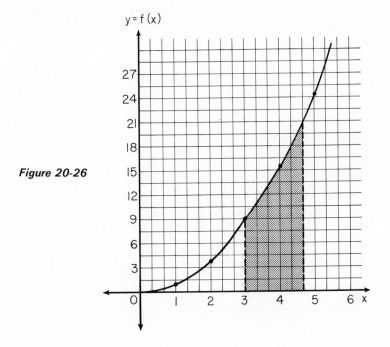

Figure 20-26

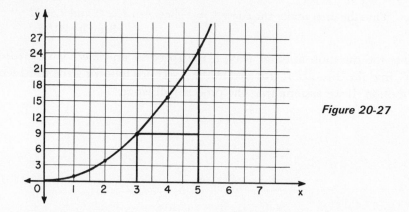

Figure 20-27

tangles. We may begin by thinking of the area as a single rectangle (Fig. 20-27). We may use either end point to determine the height. Here we have selected the left end point. The area of the rectangle formed is base × height. The height is the function value for $x = 3$, or $f(3)$. The base is the difference between the x-values of the interval end points, Δx or $5 - 3$. The calculation is:

$$A = f(3)\Delta x = (9)(2) = 18$$

This approximation yields an area of 18 square units. This is not too close to $32\frac{2}{3}$. If you look at the graph, you will see that the rectangle is indeed a good deal less in area than the region under the curve. However, if we subdivide the region into a greater number of rectangles, we can get closer to the desired area. So we divide the area into two rectangles in the same manner as before, using the left end point (Fig. 20-28). The sum of these rectangle areas forms our second approximation:

$$A = f(x_1)\Delta x + f(x_2)\Delta x = [f(x_1) + f(x_2)]\Delta x = [f(3) + f(4)](1)$$
$$= 9 + 16 = 25$$

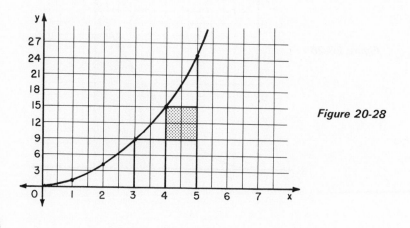

Figure 20-28

498

Now we see that we are moving closer to the expected area. A look at the curve shows just how much closer this second approximation has come. The shaded portion is included in this calculation and was not included in the earlier one. As you might expect at this point, if we continue to subdivide into more and more rectangles, gradually reducing the width of each (Δx), we get closer and closer to the actual area under the curve. Figure 20-29 shows the area subdivided into four rectangles. Once again the gap between the desired area and the area of the rectangles is narrowed:

$$
\begin{aligned}
A &= f(x_1)\,\Delta x + f(x_2)\,\Delta x + f(x_3)\,\Delta x + f(x_4)\,\Delta x \\
&= [f(x_1) + f(x_2) + f(x_3) + f(x_4)]\,\Delta x \\
&= [f(3) + f(3\tfrac{1}{2}) + f(4) + f(4\tfrac{1}{2})]\tfrac{1}{2} \\
&= (9 + \tfrac{49}{4} + 16 + \tfrac{81}{4})\tfrac{1}{2} \\
&= (57\tfrac{1}{2})(\tfrac{1}{2}) = 28\tfrac{3}{4}
\end{aligned}
$$

Breaking the region into 8 and 16 rectangles would serve to convince students that the area is indeed closing in on $32\tfrac{2}{3}$. We seem to have another instance of the use of limits, and that is the case. As we reduce the width of the rectangles and construct more of them, we find that in effect we are doing the following:

$$
\lim_{\Delta x \to 0} \sum_{i=3}^{5} f(x_i)\,\Delta x
$$

where Σ indicates that we are taking the sum of all of the heights. It is the Greek letter sigma, which represents our letter S. It is only a short step then to the integral notation

$$
\lim_{\Delta x \to 0} \sum_{i=3}^{5} f(x_i)\,\Delta x = \int_{3}^{5} f(x)\,dx
$$

which represents the limit of the sum of the areas of the rectangles as the width

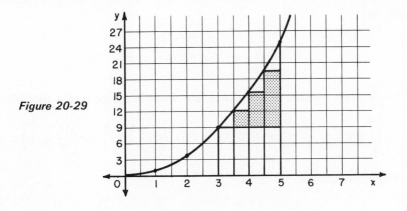

Figure 20-29

of each shrinks smaller and smaller. Since the end points are specified, this is known as the definite integral.

The method we found earlier does indeed work for all continuous functions, and we may state this in our new notation in several ways: The area under the curve $y = x^2$, from $x = 3$ to $x = 5$, is

$$A = \int_3^5 x^2 dx$$

If $f(x) = x^2$, then $F(x) = \dfrac{x^3}{3}$ (antiderivative)

$$\int_3^5 x^2 dx = F(5) - F(3)$$

$$= \frac{125}{3} - \frac{27}{3} = 32\tfrac{2}{3}$$

This may also be written in the following form:

$$\int_3^5 x^2 dx = \frac{x^3}{3}\bigg|_3^5 = \frac{5^3}{3} - \frac{3^3}{3} = 32\tfrac{2}{3}$$

Practice with many problems will help to develop student confidence with the reverse of differentiation: integration. This practice should also include problems in which the constant is of consequence. For example, differentiate the following:

$$3x^2 + 5$$
$$3x^2 + 105$$
$$3x^2 + 9000$$

In each case the derivative is $6x$. If we reverse the process, how can we be sure which of these functions is the desired one? The indefinite integral then should actually be:

$$F(x) = \int x^2 dx = \frac{x^3}{3} + c$$

In the examples we have completed, we were in effect doing the following:

$$\int_3^5 x^2 dx = \frac{x^3}{3}\bigg|_3^5 = F(5) - F(3) = \left(\frac{5^3}{3} + c\right) - \left(\frac{3^3}{3} + c\right)$$

Removing parentheses, we get

500

$$\frac{125}{3} + c - \frac{27}{3} - c = \frac{125 + 27}{3}$$

In each case $c = 0$. But this is not always the case. It will be true here because the area at the left end point is zero. Other situations will pertain as the notion of integration is applied to a variety of problems going far beyond those employed here.

The emphasis has been upon intuitive understanding. The assumption of this type of beginning is that it provides the solid foundation upon which the mechanics may be built. This would seem to be the chief contribution a high school course could hope to make. If we open up some of the past mysteries to our students and teachers, perhaps we will be surprised by the resulting progress.

OTHER ALTERNATIVES FOR SENIORS

It has been the position here that the best thing we can do for advanced students of high school mathematics is to direct them into an analytic geometry course followed by a calculus course that places heavy emphasis upon intuitive understandings and leaves the more formal, logical work for the college. There are other possibilities for these gifted mathematics students, including probability, statistics, linear algebra, and non-Euclidean geometries, to name but a few. While these are all significant topics for study, I cannot help referring once more to the often-used representation of mathematics as a tree. In the trunk of this tree are arithmetic, algebra, geometry, trigonometry, analytic geometry, and the calculus. The other topics mentioned are up in the branches. Perhaps if we build a strong, sturdy trunk, a solid foundation for each student of mathematics, we will be pleasantly surprised to find our students reaching new heights on the tree of mathematics. That is the hope and, indeed, the quest of this book.

FOOTNOTES

1. Lauren G. Woodby. *Emerging Twelfth-Grade Mathematics Programs.* U. S. Department of Health, Education and Welfare, Office of Education, No. OE 29060, U. S. Government Printing Office, 1965, pp. 5–6.
2. Edmond R. Kiely. *Surveying Instruments: Their History and Classroom Use.* National Council of Teachers of Mathematics, 19th Yearbook. The National Council of Teachers of Mathematics, 1947, pp. 194–206. See also *The Construction and Use of Homemade Instruments in Indirect Measurement* by Virgil S. Mallory. *In* National Council of Teachers of Mathematics, 18th Yearbook. The National Council of Teachers of Mathematics, 1945, pp. 182–193.
3. Morris Kline. *Mathematics and the Physical World.* Thomas Y. Crowell Company, 1959, pp. 274–315.

4. Report of the Commission on Mathematics. *Program for College Preparatory Mathematics.* College Entrance Examination Board, 1959, p. 28.

5. Report of the Commission on Mathematics. *Appendices.* College Entrance Examination Board, 1959, pp. 186–199.

6. Report of the Commission on Mathematics. *Appendices.* College Entrance Examination Board, 1959, pp. 206–207.

7. Lauren G. Woodby. *Emerging Twelfth-Grade Mathematics Programs.* U. S. Department of Health, Education and Welfare, Office of Education, No. OE 29060, U. S. Government Printing Office, 1965, pp. 36–37.

8. Constance Reid. *A Long Way from Euclid.* Thomas Y. Crowell Company, 1963, pp. 60–77.

9. I. M. Gelfand, E. G. Glagoleva, and A. A. Kirillov (translated by Leslie Cohn and David Sookne). *The Method of Coordinates,* Vol. 1. Library of School Mathematics, M. I. T. Press, 1967, pp. 41–69.

10. Lancelot Hogben. *Mathematics for the Million.* W. W. Norton & Company, 1937, p. 420.

11. For an interesting discussion of this see *Studies in Mathematics, Volume X: Applied Mathematics in the High School* by Max M. Schiffer, School Mathematics Study Group, Stanford University, 1963, pp. 99–105.

12. See Chapter 19, pages 439 to 441.

13. E. T. Bell. *Mathematics: Queen and Servant of Science.* McGraw-Hill Book Co., 1951, p. 320.

14. John Von Neumann. "The Mathematician." *In* James R. Newman (Editor): *The World of Mathematics,* Vol. 4. Simon and Schuster, Inc., 1956, pp. 2055–2056.

15. Lauren G. Woodby. *Emerging Twelfth-Grade Mathematics Programs.* U. S. Department of Health, Education and Welfare, Office of Education, No. OE 29060, U. S. Government Printing Office, 1965, p. 35.

16. W. W. Sawyer. *Mathematician's Delight.* Penguin Books, Inc., 1943, pp. 150–151.

17. See Chapter 8, pages 148 to 150.

FOR INVESTIGATION AND DISCUSSION

1. Select a topic from trigonometry and illustrate how trigonometry may be thought of as unifying the earlier work of arithmetic, algebra, and geometry.

2. Make a plan for a lesson that will take students outside the building in order to enable them to undertake the indirect measure of objects around the school. Be sure to list all necessary materials.

3. Construct the device described that will enable you to form your own trigonometry tables. Using the device, construct the sine and cosine tables for the following angles: $0°, 15°, 30°, 45°, 60°, 75°,$ and $90°$.

4. Compare the introductions of the function concept of trigonometry presented in this chapter (i.e., through vectors, using oscillating springs). State which you would prefer and explain why.

5. Investigate the life of Descartes. Emphasize the events that preceded and may shed light upon how he was led to the invention of coordinate geometry.

6. Use the methods of Descartes to solve the problem of doubling the cube.

7. Make a plan for a lesson that will encourage student exploration of the effect upon the equation as the parabola changes its position in the Cartesian plane.

8. Illustrate how you would help students realize that the slope of the straight line of a linear distance-time graph will provide the speed of an object moving at a constant rate.

9. Develop a similar lesson to help students gain insight into the concept of instantaneous speed. Show how the slope of the tangent to the curve at a point is related to this.

10. Demonstrate how the area under a curve is related to finding rates of change.

11. List the steps you would prescribe for students to enable them to find out for themselves how they may sum the areas of an infinite number of rectangles and thereby arrive at the area under a curved line.

12. Consider arguments for and against the teaching of calculus in the high school. Take a position and explain why you feel as you do.

FOR FURTHER READING

Books

C. B. Allendoerfer and C. O. Oakley. *Fundamentals of Freshman Mathematics*. McGraw-Hill Book Co., 1959, Chapters 12-16.

E. T. Bell. *Mathematics: Queen and Servant of Science*. McGraw-Hill Book Co., 1951, pp. 121–140, 320–356.

Charles H. Butler and F. Lynwood Wren. *The Teaching of Secondary Mathematics*, Ed. 4. McGraw-Hill Book Co., 1965, Chapters 19–21.

I. M. Gelfand, E. G. Glagoleva, and A. A. Kirillov (translated by Leslie Cohn and David Sookne). *The Method of Coordinates*, Vol. 1. Library of School Mathematics. M. I. T. Press, 1967.

Banesh Hoffman. *About Vectors*. Prentice-Hall, Inc., 1966.

Lancelot Hogben. *Mathematics for the Million*. W. W. Norton & Co., 1937, Chapters VI, IX, XI.

Morris Kline. *Mathematics and the Physical World*. Thomas Y. Crowell Company, 1959, Chapters 18, 19, 22, 24.

Frank Land. *The Language of Mathematics*. Doubleday & Company, Inc., 1963, Chapter 12.

National Council of Teachers of Mathematics, 17th Yearbook: *A Source Book of Mathematical Applications*. AMS Reprint Co., 1966, pp. 215–284.

National Council of Teachers of Mathematics, 23rd Yearbook: *Insights Into Modern Mathematics*. The National Council of Teachers of Mathematics, 1957, Chapters VI, VII.

Report of the Commission on Mathematics. *Appendices*. College Entrance Examination Board, 1959, pp. 176–222.

W. W. Sawyer. *What is Calculus About?* School Mathematics Study Group, New Mathematical Library, No. 2, 1961.

Stephen S. Willoughby. *Contemporary Teaching of Secondary School Mathematics*. John Wiley & Sons, Inc., 1967, Chapters 12, 14.

Periodicals

Trigonometry

Ali R. Amir-Moez. "Teaching Trigonometry Through Vectors." *Mathematics Magazine*. Vol. 32 (September-October, 1958), pp. 19–23.

John C. Biddle. "The Square Function: An Abstract System for Trigonometry." *The Mathematics Teacher*. Vol. 60 (February, 1967), pp. 121–123.

James D. Bristol. "Construction and Evaluation of Trigonometric Functions of Some Special Angles." *The Mathematics Teacher*. Vol. 54 (January, 1961), pp. 4–7.

J. Garfunkel and B. Leeds. "The Circle of Unit Diameter." *The Mathematics Teacher*. Vol. 59 (February, 1966), pp. 124–127.

R. F. Graesser. "The Direction of Sunset." *The Mathematics Teacher*. Vol. 60 (February, 1967), pp. 115–116.

Trigonometry and Other Topics

Edna E. Kramer. "The Integration of Trigonometry with the Physical Science." *The Mathematics Teacher*. Vol. 41 (December, 1948), pp. 356–361.

Herman Rosenberg. "The Changing Concept of Trigonometry as a School Subject." *The Mathematics Teacher*. Vol. 51 (April, 1958), pp. 246–252.

Robert Thomas. "A New Introduction to the Ideas and Methods of Trigonometry." *The Mathematics Teacher*. Vol. 54 (October, 1961), pp. 427–435.

Frederick H. Young. "The Addition Formulas." *The Mathematics Teacher*. Vol. 50 (January, 1957), pp. 45–48.

Analytic Geometry

Carl B. Allendoerfer. "Angles, Arcs, and Archimedes." *The Mathematics Teacher*. Vol. 58 (February, 1965), pp. 82–88.

Arthur Coxford. "Classroom Inquiry Into the Conic Sections." *The Mathematics Teacher*. Vol. 60 (April, 1967), pp. 315–322.

A. C. Crombie. "Descartes." *Scientific American*. Vol. 201 (October, 1959), pp. 160–173.

Irene Fischer. "The Shape and Size of the Earth." *The Mathematics Teacher*. Vol. 60 (May, 1967), pp. 508–516.

Ladis Kovach. "A Note on Curve Fitting With Rational Polynomials." *The Mathematics Teacher*. Vol. 60 (February, 1967), pp. 129–132.

Harry Levy. "Analytic Geometry and Calculus." *The American Mathematical Monthly*. Vol. 68 (November, 1961), pp. 925–927.

William R. Ransom. "The Ellipse From the Circle." *The Mathematics Teacher*. Vol. 42 (April, 1949), p. 186.

Charles K. Robbins. "Analytic Geometry—The Framework of Mathematics." *Mathematics Magazine*. Vol. 22 (March-April, 1949), pp. 201–210.

Calculus

Carl B. Allendoerfer. "The Case Against Calculus." *The Mathematics Teacher*. Vol. 56 (November, 1963), pp. 482–485.

Albert A. Blank. "Remarks on the Teaching of Calculus in the Secondary School." *The Mathematics Teacher*. Vol. 53 (November, 1960), pp. 537–539.

Kenneth Cummins. "A Student Experience-Discovery Approach to the Teaching of the Calculus." *The Mathematics Teacher*. Vol. 53 (March, 1960), pp. 162–170.

W. Eugene Ferguson. "Calculus in the High School." *The Mathematics Teacher*. Vol. 58 (October, 1960), pp. 451–453.

Otto Karst. "The Limit." *The Mathematics Teacher*. Vol. 51 (October, 1958), pp. 443–449.

D. E. Richmond. "Calculus—A New Look." *The American Mathematical Monthly*. Vol. 70 (April, 1963), pp. 415–423.

Dorothy V. Schrader. "The Newton-Leibnitz Controversy Concerning the Discovery of the Calculus." *The Mathematics Teacher*. Vol. 55 (May, 1962), pp. 385–396.

Angus E. Taylor. "Convention and Revolt in Mathematics." *The Mathematics Teacher*. Vol. 55 (January, 1962), pp. 2–9.

SECTION FOUR

ON HUMAN WORTH

21

INDIVIDUALIZED INSTRUCTION

INDIVIDUALIZING—A NECESSITY

Human beings are our most precious resource, although at times it certainly doesn't appear that this is true. When you read statistics of auto deaths you wonder how anyone who feels life is precious can get into a car. And if you think of the manner in which mathematics classes are generally conducted, too often it seems that mathematics is far more important than the human beings trying to learn it.

Teaching and learning are activities that involve people. One person, the teacher, is trying to help 25 to 35 other persons become proficient in mathematics. Try as we might to convince ourselves that our chief concern is mathematics and not the problems of those we are teaching, we cannot escape from the fact that we have chosen to spend our professional lives working with people—and young people at that, the future generations of society. When one person is in a position in which he must work intensively with others, he cannot avoid the fact that human relationships are going to have a sharp influence on everything that happens, or fails to happen. This is especially true of teaching.

As teachers, we live together with our students in our classrooms over an extended period of time. These are rather close confines for human beings, and many of the interactions that are known to take place in intimate relationships will occur in the classroom. If we turn our head, or rather bury it in a book, ostrich-style, we do not avoid these interactions; we merely shape them differently. Every morning before we arrive in class, we may say that we are not going to get involved with our students and their problems, that

507

our job is to teach mathematics and that is all. Let the home, the synagogue or church, and the community provide for all those other things, like ethics and morals and social skills. They are not our concern; mathematics is.

Yes, we may say this as often as we wish, and we may even struggle manfully to be sure that there are no encroachments upon us from these "life-adjustment" areas. But our protests have a rather hollow ring, for life is going on in the classroom whether we choose to recognize it or not, whether we choose to deal with it or not. Students react differently to the experiences we provide for them in class if they like us or if they do not like us. Students' class performances are affected by their personal fears, problems, and difficulties—even though these have nothing at all to do with mathematics.

The relationships that exist between students are also going to influence the success that we may have with them. And despite all the influences mentioned, we have not considered for a moment the satisfactions and desires of the teacher who is himself under the influence of a variety of forces, some of which may not relate to school at all but will nevertheless affect what will happen there. What is more, we haven't considered the past experiences of both students and teachers that have brought each to where they are. We can, and many of us certainly do, make clear that we have no interest in these "irrelevant" forces. But they are there, they are operating, and they are having more than a casual effect on all our efforts.

Does this mean then that a teacher must be a psychologist, a social worker, a priest or rabbi, a father or mother, and so on? If one person could manage to be skilled in all these areas, and in mathematics and teaching as well, he would seem to have a high probability of becoming a most effective teacher. No, it is not expected that a teacher of mathematics be a professional in every other area mentioned, but it is expected that teachers will be aware of all the factors that will affect the ultimate result of the teaching-learning process. Only if we recognize these influences can we hope to organize learning situations that will provide for these forces to operate for us and our goals, rather than against us. They are there and operant. Whether they influence for better or worse is up to each of us.

This is a far cry from asking one to become an expert in several different areas. We see a typical example of the effect of ignoring these factors in the work of most student teachers. Because they are new, fearful, and untried, they have a good deal of difficulty working in a manner that reflects an awareness of student reaction to what is going on. Student teachers in their beginning lessons will generally stay close to the desk and chalkboard, and they are all business with relationship to the subject matter. They have a tendency to complete their plan and move through mathematics at a fixed pace, regardless of what may or may not be happening to students. Some are so remote from the students that, in their anxiety to "cover" material, they will even answer their own questions without being aware of what they have done. This is perfectly natural behavior for a beginner. After all, the student teacher knows his mathematics. This is safe; this is true. There are no surprises in store for him there. He wishes the same were true of the youngsters facing him, but it is not. Here he does not know what will happen, and he does not know what to expect: "Out there" lies mystery, fear, and expectation. In mathematics lies security, reliability, and familiarity. Is it any wonder that the student teacher hides behind the subject at the start? It is to be expected. But if the student teacher remains hidden in his subject and rarely strays outside, even after he becomes a teacher, then there are difficult days ahead. This is the crux of the matter.

Don't try to be a psychologist, counselor, or social worker. This is impossible for most of us. But *do* be yourself when you are in the classroom with your students. Be a real person, not a mathematics computer programmed for action and reaction. Whether we admit it or not, most adults in our society do act out different roles, including those we may protest we cannot accept. Which of us has not played the role of psychologist in trying to help friends over difficult times ("You know, John, you keep overeating because you are unhappy in your job!")—or social worker, banker, or doctor, among others? In the classroom all that can be asked of any teacher is that he be himself and look upon his relationships with his students as those of one human being with other human beings. The variety of roles that are involved in such relationships will evolve as they ordinarily do. When expert assistance is required, the teacher can go to the appropriate source for this help—guidance counselor, school psychologist, assistant principal. Being at home in the classroom is vital for the mental health of both teacher and student. Can you imagine the strain on a person who must act out an idealized version of "teacher" for five periods a day, 200 days each year? Such pressures can only result in trouble for all. Teachers are people. Just as there are teachers who would prefer to forget that students are people, there are students who think of teachers as something unusual on the Darwinian scale. Both of these attitudes are detrimental to our goals. They do not help us to get where we would like to go. And that is the central reason why we cannot ignore all but the mathematical side of our classroom life with our students. With this in mind, let us now take a look inside the classroom.

We frequently hear arguments going on about the fact that one group of students is getting more attention than another. "Why is everybody so concerned about the 'slow learner'? Isn't it time we did something about the gifted? When are we going to stop ignoring this group and do something about helping the future mathematicians. These are the important students." Sometimes the complaint is in the reverse direction so that the failures of the less successful groups are seen to require immediate attention, rather than the gifted who seem to do well, often in spite of us. Which of these positions is the correct one? Which of these groups should receive our major attention as we build mathematics programs for the future?

These two problems are actually part of a larger, more significant problem: How can we help each student to learn as much as he can, as quickly as he can? This is the central problem in education today. It is not what we can do for the gifted or the slow or the middle or any other possible classification. Rather, it is what we can do to help each and every child realize his own potential as a student of mathematics. Every child who comes to us is different in so many ways from every other child. His life experiences, his interests, his abilities, his fears, and his expectations are all unique to him and only him. It is impossible to find two youngsters who share the same characteristics just mentioned. Even identical twins differ in so many important ways. Despite the known diversity of students, we have conducted classes on a completely opposite premise: We have assumed that it is possible to teach 25 or 35 students the same things, in the same amount of time, and in the same way. For the most part, we have proceeded to conduct our classes on this basis, although we know full well that this fundamental assumption is absurd.

Why then do highly intelligent people continue to do something that is known to be operating upon a false base? The answer is simple: What else are they to do? Can anyone conduct a class of 30 students in a manner that will enable each student to learn in a way best suited to his particular needs, interests, and abilities? Most teachers would say it is impossible. To help teachers meet the objective of enabling each child to develop, administrative devices have been constructed in an attempt to reduce the existing differences between students grouped together as a class. It is believed that grouping techniques and tracking make it possible for the teacher to reach greater numbers of students with his lessons than he could expect to reach under heterogeneous class organization. As a result, extensive tests are given to each student, his previous work in school is considered, his teacher is asked to evaluate him, and all this information is carefully analyzed as youngsters are arranged in classes that are homogeneous with regard to mathematics ability and achievement. And when all this time, energy, and money has been expended, the resulting classes still consist of some 25 to 35 students who are each different from the other in a multitude of ways that will directly influence their success in mathematics! No matter how we try, we simply cannot make all people alike and have them learn at the same rate and in the same amount of time! It is often admitted that such is the case, but grouping minimizes the differences. It removes the extreme cases. While this certainly may be true, it does not alter the fact that in all the important mathematical, and psychological, traits that most influence the learning situation, we still have a collection of completely unique individuals before us.

But this is not the whole story. Were we successful at this grouping process and were we able to select 30 students that match so in ability, interests, and learning styles that we could teach them as one, we would still be creating more problems than we could solve by homogeneous grouping. It is common knowlegde that this type of grouping has definite disadvantages.

510

The expectation level of child and teacher are directly affected by grouping. Recent studies have shown that when teachers are told that their children are superior, they achieve superior results with their students—despite the fact that the students were not superior at all. It was just that the teacher believed they were.[1] This belief alone resulted in greater student achievement. In addition, there is the stigmatizing that is also present when we arrange students in ability groups, as well as the snob element that often is found in high-ability groups.

Why then do we bother to group children? It is done because grouping is seen as the best device for helping teachers deal with the unavoidable differences. It is a device to help teachers, not students. What else can we do? Well, for one thing, it is time to cast aside the notion that being able to provide for each child in a heterogeneous setting is impossible. Nearly everyone agrees that it would be fine to teach a class of 30 heterogeneous students so that each may proceed at his own rate and learn in a way best suited to him, but this is impossible. That is why we do the next best thing: We group by ability. But this does not square with the evidence. There have been too many instances in which instruction has been organized to provide the opportunity for each child to set his own pace.

As far back as 1888, Preston Search organized the Pueblo, Colorado schools so that each child progressed at his own rate. Later, more prominent programs were developed to meet this problem, the Winnetka Plan and the Dalton Plan being perhaps the best known.[2] Despite marked successes, these plans have all but disappeared from American education, although Dalton Plan schools may be found in other countries. More recently the Nuffield Project has individualized mathematics instruction in the elementary school.[3] At the least, these programs indicate that individualizing instruction is certainly possible. But we should have known this all along. We have only to think back to the days of the one-room schoolhouse. Here, a teacher had a large number of students from grades one to twelve in a single room. Her aids consisted of textbooks along the lines of the *McGuffey Reader,* a slate chalkboard, and some chalk; yet this teacher conducted school and managed to help such diverse children work along and learn. We have now narrowed the age gap for today's teacher so that all his children are roughly the same age. We have beautiful, readable texts, pamphlets, newspapers, and booklets. We have film strips, moving pictures, loops, transparencies, automated programs, and a broad variety of manipulative devices. And with all of this some teachers say that they cannot match the achievements of the one-room schoolhouse teacher.

Perhaps we are too quick to admit that a problem cannot be solved. It is hard to believe that the modern-day teacher, who is probably better trained and of higher quality than teachers have ever been, is unable to devise creative and effective solutions to the problem of providing for each student. Perhaps fear of failure has inhibited attempts at solution. It would be of interest to see what would develop once teachers were convinced that individualizing is possible. To help dispel doubts, one such plan is presented here that has already been classroom tested. It is presented not as a model for imitation, but merely as additional evidence for the *possibility* of ordinary humans to conduct classes so as to care for each student. Once you overcome the inertia of impossibility, you will probably be able to devise more effective plans.

A PLAN FOR INDIVIDUALIZED INSTRUCTION

Individual instruction and individualized instruction may appear to be two names for the same thing. They may not be. As a matter of fact, these words have been used for so many different ideas and patterns of classroom organization that in terms of specifics these words make for little communication. It often happens that one man's individual instruction program is another man's whole-group teaching program. Greater definition is needed.

Individualized has been chosen to explain instruction here because it has reference to a style of instruction. There is no intention to isolate students one from the other, as conditions are established that somehow enable each student to proceed at his own rate. On the contrary, this kind of isolation is seen to be in opposition to our goals for the student, which include the improvement of his ability to relate to other people. We cannot help students to get along by cutting them off from their fellow students. This is exactly what is accomplished in the "you must not talk, you must not move, you must only sit still and listen" kind of classroom.

Individual instruction would seem to imply that the work is carried out by each student without contact with his classmates. That is why the term individual*ized* is employed here. And thus we have one of the basic principles upon which the program presented here will be built: The students must be free to form small groups with their classmates and to carry out their work in contact with each other. These small work groups may be formed by students in any manner they wish; i.e., they may select their friends, students with common vocational goals, or students whom they look up to and admire. Some may even wish to work alone. Those who desire to work alone should be permitted to do so, although the interaction of students in small groups is of such importance that these students should be encouraged over the course of the term to become part of one group or another. But we are getting ahead of ourselves. The plan for individualizing to be described was formulated by Dr. Gwladys Crosby and me.[4]

In addition to the importance of maximum student interaction, the plan is based upon these fundamental assumptions:

1. Learning is an individual process; i.e., people tend to learn in different ways and at different rates.

2. A democratic classroom environment is necessary to prepare students to live in a democracy.
3. Each student must take the responsibility for his learning.
4. The teacher's role is to create a classroom atmosphere in which students are free to learn and have the desire to learn.
5. Insight and understanding depend upon the freedom to discover and invent concepts and relationships.

Now that we have clarified the basis upon which this individualized program of instruction has been built, perhaps the best way to describe the method itself is to present a picture of how it functions. Upon entering an individualized tenth year geometry classroom, you might find a group of three or four students in one corner of the room working on loci. In another corner of the room a small group of students is completing a unit on triangles. Several students are at the chalkboard doing various constructions or proofs, while still others are working alone, scattered about the room. One may come upon a group of students working together and, surprisingly, find that each member of the group is working on a different topic; yet these students will insist that they constitute a group.

Looking about, you will notice that most of the students are using their textbooks, a few are using programmed learning materials, some are using visual aids, and others are making use of manipulative devices. It will also be found that in the midst of all this there are several students sprinkled about the room taking examinations. What is the teacher doing while all this is going on? The teacher is busily moving from group to group providing help wherever it is needed. If a test is completed before the end of the period, the teacher and student go to the desk and the paper is scored, corrections are discussed, and ensuing work is planned for.

How did this come about? How are assignments made? When is the test given? How does a teacher keep track of everything? These are but a few of the questions a visitor to the individualized classroom would have in mind.

GETTING STARTED

From the first day of class the teacher, conducting business as usual, involves the students in decisions regarding planning and testing. Shall there be homework today? Are you ready to be tested tomorrow? This is one small way in which students are beginning to aid in decision making. Although the teacher is conducting his class without change at this time, these small choices offered to the students begin to prepare them for the larger, more important choices that are ahead. The first time that any change is made in the class structure is after the first examination has been given to the class.

513

When the scored papers are returned and discussed, it becomes clear that some students are ready to move on to the next unit, whereas others are not and need additional study of the present unit. At this point, to require all students to follow one course or the other is to work against the obvious interests of some. This is an excellent time to introduce the individualized approach. The need for something is clear to all. Indeed, if the problem of what to do about the situation that finds some ready to go on and others not is presented to the students, they may well suggest some kind of change that would enable each student to proceed in a manner best suited to his needs. The change in class structure can now begin to be made with a minimum of student resistance. Those who are ready to go on are offered the opportunity to do so using the class textbook. They may change seats and group themselves if they so desire. It is up to them to plan what they will do, with the teacher acting as adviser. Those who need additional time for the unit just completed will be instructed by the teacher as usual, except that the lessons will involve about 15 minutes of teacher-student discussion followed by work for students to do at their seats. While this is going on, the teacher can circulate about the room and offer assistance to the students who moved on to the next unit, having successfully passed the earlier test. As each test is administered, more and more students will join or form work groups; and eventually the entire class will consist of a collection of such groups, each group working at its own pace on materials of its own choosing and on a topic of its own choice. This is one way in which a gradual transition can be made from traditional to individualized instruction. Do not think that the student works entirely on his own. He does not. Although the student plans his work within the framework of the syllabus, the teacher has not abandoned him: The teacher oversees all student work.

When the student begins his work as planned, he works primarily with his textbook. He must have the answers available to be able to determine success or failure. He also chooses the students with whom he would like to work; or, if he so desires, he works alone. Choosing the people with whom to work is carefully discussed by the class. The various criteria one may employ are enumerated and explained. The final decision, however, rests with each student. The student is aware that the formed groups are fluid and that he may change at any time, for any reason.

HOMEWORK

When work is progressing, the assignment of homework is discussed. It is brought out that there are several values that result from homework and thus students make their own assignments as they feel the need. This is simply another step toward achieving the goal they have set, that is, the completion of a specified unit within a planned length of time. These are also decisions

Table 21-1. Homework Record Sheet.

Homework Number	Assignment	Date Completed	Homework Number	Assignment	Date Completed

Table 21-2. Weekly Plan Sheet.

Name _____   Class _____

Topic(s): _____   For the week ending: _____

My group members are:

Planned	Completed
Monday	
Tuesday	
Wednesday	
Thursday	
Friday	

515

Table 21-3. Student Progress Sheet.

Name

Topic:	Constructions	Congruence	Indirect Reasoning	Parallel Lines	Angles of Polygons	Parallelograms	Inequalities
Dates (**Start** – Finish)							
Test Score(s)							
Materials Used							
Group Members							

Topic:	Concurrent Lines	Angles in a Circle	Lines and Circles	Locus	Similarity	Areas	
Dates (Start – Finish)							
Test Score(s)							
Materials Used							
Group Members							

made by the student with the aid of the teacher. Completed plans and assigned homework are recorded by students on the record sheets provided (Tables 21-1 and 21-2). These, together with a progress sheet, offer the teacher a complete account of student progress at a glance (Table 21-3).

TESTING

At the completion of a unit, the problem of evaluation arises. If students are to proceed at their own rates, they alone know when they are ready to be tested. Tests must be administered when the student so requests. With different students taking different tests at various times, the construction of tests to keep the procedure a fair one can be a problem for the teacher. This problem may be overcome to a great extent by constructing three tests at a time, rather than one. If Ditto masters are used, it is a relatively simple matter to work on three masters simultaneously, constructing one test but altering the numbers slightly on the other two so that the degree of difficulty is not radically changed. In effect, then, you will have three forms of a given unit test. If the chapters of the chosen textbook are used to determine units for test purposes, several advantages are derived. For one thing, the students can make use of the end-of-chapter review and test in order to evaluate their own test readiness. The answers must be readily available to them for this work, as well as their classwork, in order that the students can easily determine the outcome of their work. In addition, using text chapters as units enables the teacher to organize the work and construct teacher-made tests as required.

One additional word about testing: Since our chief concern in this situation is with the mastery of content, we need not record any grades on tests that the students do not pass. If a student is permitted to request a test when he is ready, he should also be permitted to say that he has erred in his judgment after sitting down to write a test; and the paper should be tossed away after it has been discussed with an eye toward establishing where the problems are and what further work has to be undertaken. The fact that the teacher will have constructed multiple tests per unit eliminates the problem of retaking tests. The student simply takes a test he did not take before. This is a most important characteristic of the program. There is no penalty for not knowing. A test is simply a device for finding out how much has been learned and determining readiness to go on to a new topic. Report card grades may consist of comparing the work completed and test scores made with the amount of work the teacher estimates the particular student can complete in a given period. How much of the potential has been realized? An individual progress sheet contains the record of the unit, date, and score.

CLASSWORK

During class time, the teacher is constantly moving from group to group or from student to student. Frequently he refers questions from students to other students. If someone (or some group) is having difficulty that cannot be easily overcome, the student may be referred to programmed learning materials, another text, a particular device, or film strips. It is important that the teacher become the last resort for learning—not the first. In some cases the teacher may take a group of students to the chalkboard and provide the more familiar type of instruction. On the occasion when circumstances so require, the entire class may work together as a single group. Throughout all that happens, the student is the master of his fate, with the teacher ever present to provide the help and suggestions that enable the student to move along as he desires. The teaching skill that develops as a teacher gains experience with this method is the skill of knowing how much freedom a student is ready to accept at a given moment. We cannot simply step back and say, "All right, each of you has a textbook. From this point on you are on your own!" Far from it. In certain instances we may have to make homework assignments for a student. We may have to tell him what unit would be best for him or what kind of material may help him over a given rough spot. We may even have to maintain a small group that will receive instruction from us in the usual manner. But our aim is to help each student to work toward the day when he is able to fully accept this responsibility for himself. The teacher is the leader of the class group. This role cannot be denied. But the student must take the responsibility for his own learning: We cannot force him to learn. This is the goal toward which we strive. If we can accomplish this with our students, they will have acquired something very valuable indeed.

PLANNING

The student planning referred to earlier is a fundamental part of this approach. The students must be free to select the unit upon which they will work (within the limitations of the syllabus) in any order they wish. Although mathematics is a highly sequential subject, we cannot be sure of the best sequence to be prescribed for each student. It is curious to watch students select units of work purely on the basis of what seems to be of interest to them. I observed a student working under this approach in an algebra class select the unit on quadratic equations before he had undertaken the study of factoring. Because he could not do what was before him, he had to turn to the factoring chapter. He learned just those ideas that he needed to proceed with the task at hand, and then he continued the study of the quadratic. If I were to have asked him if he had studied the unit on factoring, his answer would have been "No." He did not see what he had done in that light. To him, he was working on quadratics. He had read the factoring material because he had a genuine need to solve the problem before him. Later he would undertake the formal study of factoring. What a wonderful thing to observe: A student studies a topic because he needs to know in order to do what he wants to. In this way each student may well develop a sequence of topics that differs from that of his neighbor, but it will be a sequence that makes the best sense to him.

Table 21-4 summarizes the important differences between the individualized approach described here and the more generally observed single-group approach used in most mathematics classes.

The approach described here changes the entire structure of the mathematics classroom. It is a radical change from what we have known school to be, because, among other things, it is founded upon the assumption that an

Table 21-4.   A Comparison of the Individualized Method with Single-Group Instruction.

	Single-Group Instruction *(Traditional)*	*Individualized Instruction*
Goals	Set by teacher in terms of syllabus and text	Set by teacher and pupil within framework of syllabus—after group discussion and individual conferences
	Classwork	
Tasks	Assigned by teacher on basis of time, syllabus, and text	Assigned by pupil in terms of goals—after group planning and individual planning
	Homework	
	Assigned by teacher on the basis of pupil needs	Assigned by pupil on basis of felt need for practice or confidence in ability to proceed alone
Evaluation	Done by teacher on basis of classwork, tests, and other teacher-selected criteria	Done by teacher and pupil on basis of progress toward goal as determined by tests and subjective discussion
Tests	Constructed and administered by teacher Scored on basis of teacher's need for evaluation	Made by teacher Requested by pupil when he is ready Scored jointly

attempt to stand before a group of some 30 students and expect every student to get to the same place at the same time is simply not realistic in terms of what we know about people. Effective instruction should widen the gap of differences between people, not seek to narrow them. If each individual is offered the opportunity to develop in a way best suited to him, we emphasize his differences and try to make the most of them, rather than ignore differences and attempt to eliminate them. That is why a broad variety of materials must be present in an individualized classroom. Since we cannot isolate the best way for a given student to learn a particular concept, we do the next best thing and use a kind of "buckshot" approach in which the student is able to move through a variety of instructional materials until he finds one that satisfies his need.

Of course, teachers who have worked and worked well with a structure, including that of a single class group, may feel that a radical change in structure is not desirable for them. There are many things that can be done within the present familiar class organization to provide for those who have difficulties, as well as for those who are gifted in mathematics. A description of such activities is presented in the next chapter.

FOOTNOTES

1. Robert Rosenthal. "Experimenter Outcome-Orientation and the Results of the Psychological Experiment." *Psychological Bulletin*. Vol. 61 (June, 1964), pp. 405–412.
2. Helen Parkhurst. *Education on the Dalton Plan*. E. P. Dutton Co., Inc., 1922. See also *Adapting the Schools to Individual Differences* by Guy W. Whipple (Editor). National Society for the Study of Education, 24th Yearbook, Part II, University of Chicago Press, 1925.
3. Nuffield Foundation. *I Do and I Understand*. John Wiley & Sons, Inc., 1967. See also "The Nuffield Mathematics Teaching Project" by Geoffrey Matthews. In *The Arithmetic Teacher*. Vol. 15 (February, 1968), pp. 101–102.
4. Gwladys Crosby, Herbert Fremont, and Harold Mitzel. *Mathematics Individual Learning Experiment*. Research Project No. 391, Title VII, National Defense Education Act of 1958, United States Department of Health, Education and Welfare, 1962. See also *Individualized Instruction in Plane Geometry* by Herbert Fremont. Doctor's Thesis, New York University, 1963.

FOR INVESTIGATION AND DISCUSSION

1. Identify and discuss some of the factors that may influence your effectiveness with a particular child, in addition to his aptitude for mathematics and his previous achievement.

2. Discuss the reasons for the following statement: It is unrealistic to teach a group of 30 or so students and expect each to come away with the same thing.

3. Examine the research done on ability grouping in mathematics and indicate what the findings are with regard to the advantages and disadvantages of this organizational technique.

4. Discuss the implications of the Rosenthal studies for homogeneous grouping of students in mathematics.

5. Describe in detail one plan of individualized instruction offered as an alternative to ability grouping (e.g., Winnetka or Dalton).

6. Five basic assumptions are presented on pages 512 and 513 that underlie the individualized plan presented. Consider each assumption in turn and indicate whether you agree or disagree and explain why.

7. Consider briefly the implications for instruction of your responses to question 6.

8. Compare the important characteristics of the individualized plan presented in this chapter with those of the more traditional whole-class instruction approach (see Table 21-4). Evaluate these differences and support your reactions with explanation of why you think as you do.

9. Make a listing of the varieties of instructional media now available to teachers of mathematics and indicate briefly how each may help the teacher of mathematics increase the probability of reaching each of his students.

FOR FURTHER READING

Books

Gwladys Crosby, Herbert Fremont, and Harold Mitzel. *Mathematics Individual Learning Experiment*. Research Project No. 391, Title VII, National Defense Education Act of 1958, U. S. Department of Health, Education and Welfare, 1962.

Herbert Fremont. *Individualized Instruction in Plane Geometry*. Doctor's Thesis, New York University, 1963.

Nelson B. Henry (Editor). *Individualizing Instruction*. National Society for the Study of Education, 61st Yearbook, Part I, University of Chicago Press, 1962, Chapters XI–XVII.

John Jarolimek. *A Study of Current Practices of Individualizing Instruction in the Minnesota Schools*. Doctor's Thesis, University of Minnesota, 1955.

R. Stewart Jones and Robert E. Pingry. "Individual Differences." *In* National Council of Teachers of Mathematics, 25th Yearbook: *Instruction in Arithmetic*. The National Council of Teachers of Mathematics, 1960, pp. 121–148.

Ona Kraft. "Adjusting Work Within the Class to the Varying Abilities of Its Members." *In* National Council of Teachers of Mathematics, 22nd Yearbook: *Emerging Practices in Mathematics Education*. The National Council of Teachers of Mathematics, 1954, pp. 45–49.

Maria Montessori. *The Montessori Method*. Stokes, 1912.

Helen Parkhurst. *Education on the Dalton Plan*. E. P. Dutton & Co., Inc., 1932.

Rolland R. Smith. "Provisions for Individual Differences." *In* National Council of Teachers of Mathematics. 21st Yearbook: *The Learning of Mathematics: Its Theory and Practice*. The National Council of Teachers of Mathematics, 1953, pp. 271–302.

Guy W. Whipple (Editor). *Adapting the Schools to Individual Differences*. National Society for the Study of Education, 24th Yearbook, Part II, University of Chicago Press, 1925.

Periodicals

M. J. Brannon. "Individual Mathematics Study Plan." *The Mathematics Teacher*. Vol. 55 (January, 1962), pp. 52–56.

Paul Brimm and Guy Wagner. "Individualizing Instruction in the Secondary School." *Midland Schools*. Vol. 75 (December, 1960), pp. 15–16.

Gwladys Crosby and Herbert Fremont. "Individualized Algebra." *The Mathematics Teacher*. Vol. 53 (February, 1960), pp. 109–112.

Theodosius Dobzhansky. "Genetics and Equality." *Science*. Vol. 137 (July 13, 1962), pp. 112–115.

Individualized Instruction

N. K. Hamilton. "Providing for Individual Differences." *Educational Leadership.* Vol. 18 (December, 1960), pp. 177–182.

Lola May. "Individualizing Instruction in a Learning Laboratory Setting." *The Arithmetic Teacher.* Vol. 13 (February, 1966), pp. 110–112.

M. Schultz and M. M. Ohlsen. "A Comparison of Traditional Teaching and Personalized Teaching in Ninth Grade Algebra." *The Mathematics Teacher.* Vol. 42 (February, 1949), pp. 91–96.

Richard R. Skemp. "The Psychology and Mathematics Project." *Mathematics Teaching.* (Spring, 1964), pp. 5–9.

Daniel W. Snader. "A Program for Individualizing Instruction in Mathematics." *The Mathematics Teacher.* Vol. 38 (March, 1945), pp. 116–119.

Fay Wert. "Individualized Patterns of Thinking—Results the Same." *The Arithmetic Teacher.* Vol. 10 (February, 1963), pp. 93–95.

22

THE LOW ACHIEVER
AND THE GIFTED

THE LOW ACHIEVER

A good deal of time is generally spent trying to identify those students who are low achievers. Sometimes they are called slow "learners" or, at other times, "underachievers." When we get to the ghetto areas of our large cities, we run into a host of changing names from "culturally deprived" to "disadvantaged." Let us dispose of the labels quickly but efficiently for our purposes here by indicating that we are referring to those students who have failed to enjoy any consistent success in their study of mathematics, whatever the causes, wherever they attend school. This would include students from a variety of economical levels as well as a broad range of cultural groupings. These students do not seem to be able to "make it" in mathematics. They are usually found in the lower tracks or low-ability groups and in the general mathematics classes of ninth grade. What can we do to help such youngsters reverse their previous experiences in mathematics?

There are two basic paths that may be followed in attempting to render assistance. One direction calls for the development of diagnostic techniques to enable the teacher to locate disability areas and then formulate remedial-type programs to treat the disabilities. Another approach would be to try to involve the students in new experiences offering success, treating disability areas as they arise out of the work at hand. As you probably have guessed, these two paths are not necessarily mutually exclusive. It may well be possible to interweave the two as we plan a program for the youngsters. But let us take a closer look at each.

The diagnostic procedure usually requires that the student take a series of tests which would provide information about the skills and concepts that are in need of instruction. SRA has recently placed a Basic Skills Box on the market that is designed to enable a teacher to do just that.[1] In addition, this box has a collection of skill cards that the student is to use as he attempts to improve his mastery of a given area. This is an interesting attempt to provide teachers with help through a diagnostic-treatment procedure. One difficulty with such a program is that it is not uncommon to find students who are unable to do any of the examples of the diagnostic test correctly. They require help in all areas.

Another interesting attempt to help teachers with this process is a recent book by Bernstein and Wells.[2] In this book the authors have attempted to assist teachers in diagnosing exactly what student difficulties were present and then indicate how to go about offering exercises in order to remedy the situation. This is another valuable resource for the teacher who wishes to travel this route. There are, of course, many standardized tests available that are also designed to locate student weaknesses.[3] All in all, there is a good deal of ready assistance available to the teacher who feels that the "trouble-shooting" approach is a good way to improve student skills.

While there is no intent to rate one attack on this problem of helping low achievers against another, since any plan that helps is a good one, the experience approach is preferred here. After years of failure in mathematics, the primary need of these students is a series of quick successes—a series of experiences that cause the student to exclaim, "Hey, I can do these!" Beginning a new year with a collection of diagnostic tests would only seem to emphasize once again to the student the many skills and concepts that he does not know. This may effectively serve to eliminate the drive to attempt to improve. Why try to do an example when you know beforehand that the outcome will only be failure? Above all else, we must reverse this trend. We must try to thrust the student into a situation that catches his interest, that is "doable," that does not dredge up old failures, and yet one that provides enough challenge so that the success experienced is satisfying.

This is a rather large order, to say the least. Where shall we find such experiences? The collection of activities listed in the teaching sections of this book are just the kind of activities we may draw upon for youngsters with difficulties in mathematics. For example, why not begin the work in general mathematics with one of the simple experiments discussed in the algebra section? If low achievers are asked to carry out the spring-stretch experiments, they could complete the work of adding and removing weights and of measuring and recording results with a minimum of teacher assistance. If difficulties arise in using a ruler, help can be provided. The help offered in this way is not a class period devoted to "using a ruler" but is assistance provided by the teacher (or perhaps another student) to help the youngster get on with the central task—determining how the spring stretched. Let us look at what has happened. When the student completes his table of information, he has successfully completed his task; but more than that, he has been successful (as far as he is concerned) in algebra—the "hard" subject taken by the "good" students! These initial success experiences cannot be overestimated in importance. They are the first steps on the road back for many of these low achievers. They are the beginning of the development of the all-important "maybe I can do it" feeling that is basic to any improvement program. The fact that the beginning was made in algebra adds status and importance to the achievement. Other experiments, or similar activities, will serve to reinforce these successes, and bit by bit we begin to reconstruct the student's self-image relative to mathematics from "it's hopeless" to "maybe I can." Of course, progress is never as dramatic or consistent as it may sound in narrative, but the overall direction is the important consideration. The kind of activities that are real and concrete enough for low achievers are in ready supply in the teaching sections of this book. Of course, the work would proceed at a slower pace, and the need for staying with the concrete stage would be greater for these students. But many experiences are within their reach. The only requirement is careful teacher selection of action experiences without concern for grade level.

As for rebuilding skills in basic computation, this will take place as the need arises from the work described. At this point we should not give the impression of skill building for its own sake. That may well come later. For now, we teach basic skills as needed in order to help the student complete his experiment or other such work.

This is the basic pattern: Involve the student in concrete, meaningful work, requiring only enough computation to get by. Slowly build up a backlog of successes to strengthen the student's resistance to failure. Deal with skill building as the need occurs from the task at hand. The National Council of Teachers of Mathematics recently formed a committee for writing just this type of material.[4] Their finished product is now available and is most interesting. This is another approach to teaching low achievers.

No matter how you plan to proceed, there are some basic notions that relate directly to work with low achievers. First, and most importantly, the teacher's attitude is crucial. Earlier, a study was described that clearly showed that students' performance was a function of teacher expectation as much as it was of student ability.[5] If you are to have a chance of success, you must enter the classroom convinced that these students can and will learn. Though we may think of these students as slow learners, they are very quick to tune in on our expectations for them. If they feel that we give them no chance, we can expect to see a good deal of the disruptive behavior that is common to slower classes. But what is more, we owe it to them and to ourselves to approach the students with the quiet confidence that they will learn if they are given the proper circumstances, because that is indeed the situation. What teacher has not experienced the sudden reformation of an apparent "low achiever" to the status of a good student? If we have been mistaken about one, how many others may also be capable of successful work in the proper situation? The answer is of no consequence. Simply approach all the students as if this is the case, and curious things may happen.

Second, there is greater need than ever before for real, concrete experiences for these students. So much of what we do in school is of no consequence to the youngsters. We have got to help them to see that important things do indeed happen in school, things that are of value and consequence. The other chapters of this book have attempted to provide a storehouse of such activities.

Third, the importance of success is vital to these students. They need success and need it quickly. We can never be sure when the next failure may cause complete withdrawal from everything going on in the mathematics class. The success must be in an area that is not so easy as to be meaningless, but yet not too hard to complete. This is a difficult task.

Finally, a teacher cannot make use of too great a variety of materials here. This will be discussed further when the basic skills are considered separately. Suffice it to say that the probability of reaching a student varies directly with the number and variety of materials available for his use.

If these points sound familiar and if you are thinking that this is what was suggested for all students in the earlier sections, you are perceptive and quite correct. Perhaps participation in an active program of mathematics experiences is a basic need of all students.

Before we conclude our discussion of the less fortunate mathematics student, let us focus upon the problem of basic skills to explore what might be done in more specific terms.

IMPROVING BASIC SKILLS

Without mastery of the basic skills, our students are going to encounter continued difficulties with mathematics. If we are to help the low achiever at all, we must, in the final analysis, improve his ability to carry out the four basic operations with whole numbers and decimal and common fractions. The procedures outlined were designed to create the kind of atmosphere in which the student will want to do something about his abilities in this area. Once he has reached this point, how can we provide for him?

One thing must be clear about this skill rebuilding work: When a student has reached the junior high school without competency in elementary number work, he is a far different student than the youngster in the second, third, or fourth grade who is meeting these ideas for the first time. There is no question that students must be able to understand what they are learning if they are to achieve mastery, but our primary aim with low achievers in junior high school is automatic response for the basic combinations (addition and multiplication of whole numbers through the nines), plus the ability to do examples involving the four operations as described. There can be little hope of achieving this minimum goal unless the student knows the basic addition and multiplication facts as well as he knows his own name. If he has to think and perhaps "figure out" the answers to examples at this level, we will have failed him once more. If it is possible to achieve this type of automatic response with our students and at the same time have him fully understand exactly what he is doing, this would be progress indeed. But one thing must be clear; whether the learning of basics is based on understanding or not, it must be realized: By the time the student has arrived in the junior high school, if he still lacks basic skills, any technique that helps him master these skills is a good and valid technique. We have one clear task: The student must have automatic response with the fundamental addition-multiplication facts. How this is done is of secondary importance. Let us now turn to some specific suggestions.

Years ago, flash cards were one of the principal teaching tools of the elementary school arithmetic teacher (Fig. 22-1). The cards would be held up before the class; student hands would fly into the air as each student practically shook his arm off in an attempt to get the teacher to call upon him. In this way the children were "drilled" until mastery was achieved. Later these cards came under fire as a foremost example of the rote-learning experiences that were underlying so many of the difficulties of students in mathematics. This was a just criticism, but the accent was placed upon the wrong syllable, as is so often the case in mathematics teaching. The way the cards were used— there was little or no attempt to help students understand what the work was all about before drilling—was justifiably criticised. But condemning the cards themselves was an error. Very few of the materials used by teachers are either good or bad in and of themselves. This includes materials like flash cards and workbooks and words like "cancel" and "carrying." But materials and words

Figure 22-1

can help or hinder learning, depending upon how they are used. Flash cards may be helpful to low achievers in the junior high school if used properly. Perhaps it is a good idea to have the student make his own. Generally, pairing the students off and asking each to construct his own flash cards using 3×5 index cards is a helpful experience. When the student has placed the examples on one face of the index card and the answer on the other side, his cards are checked by his neighbor, while he, in turn, checks his neighbor's cards. Both students should have multiplication tables or even adding machines available to be certain of the correct answer. The teacher may also be consulted if there is doubt. The students then proceed to test each other with the cards, keeping track of the combinations that cause difficulty in order that they may be reviewed. Many variations may be built into these procedures, such as point scoring for each correct response and keeping records of results, as well as time keeping.

To develop automatic response once the combinations have been learned, stop watches or other timers may be used to build speed. The competition here must only be with one's self if it is to be a positive experience and not a destructive one. Youngsters enjoy the challenge of trying to "beat" their former time and strive manfully to do so.

Another technique that may be helpful is to try to build student confidence in the fact that they can master these combinations by demonstrating to them that the problem is really a good deal less formidable than it seems. For example, look at the multiplication facts. How many are there (zeros through nines)? One hundred seems like an awful lot, but wait. The student knows some facts. He probably will have mastered the zero table as well as the one, two, and three tables. Part of the fours are usually known as well as all of the five table. We are missing only the four, six, seven, eight, and nine tables.

Our task has been cut from 100 facts to only 50. We are halfway there and haven't started yet. The commutative law enables us to eliminate even more. Since we know the zero through the three table, we know 0×4, 1×4, 2×4, and 3×4; and the same is true for the six, seven, eight, and nine tables. We may then add some 20 more facts to our known list. This leaves us with 30 to be learned. But wait, we know the fives, so that adds 5×4, 5×6, and so on, which gives us five less to learn. Our original task of learning 100 facts is now down to 25, and that's not the end either. Once again, because of the commutative law, when we learn 6×4, we actually have mastered two facts; 4×6 is included. In the final analysis, then, the only thing standing between the student and mastery of the multiplication combinations is the need to learn 15 facts, and if we eliminate the doubles (6×6, 7×7, . . .), which most students learn quickly, we can cut this list down to 10 facts. That is a far cry from 100! Since most students do know the four table, there is actually a hard core of some half-dozen facts that are causing most of the problems. The student, however, is not aware of this. He sees an endless supply of these com-

Table 22-1. Table of Nines.

9 × 1	=	9
9 × 2	=	18
9 × 3	=	27
9 × 4	=	36
9 × 5	=	45
9 × 6	=	54
9 × 7	=	63
9 × 8	=	72
9 × 9	=	81

binations to bedevil him and so he gives up all hope of ever gaining mastery. Placing the problem in its proper perspective can sometimes reduce doubt and fear so that the student is able to function. It is well worth the try.

Many students fear the nines most of all since this is the highest number in the table. This group of facts should be the last to cause difficulties. Have the students write out this table and look at the results (Table 22-1). Do you notice any pattern in the answers and the examples? Soon enough, most students will find that all the answers have a digit sum of 9. Thus, if we know one digit of the answer, we can easily determine the other. It soon becomes apparent that the first digit of the answer is one less than the multiplier of 9. The rest is easy: If I wish to complete 7 × 9, the first digit of the answer is one less than 7 or 6. I now add to 6 to make 9 and the result is 63. This can be done for all the nines.

Still another aid for the nines is the fingers. Place your hands on the desk with your palms down and your fingers extended (Fig. 22-2). Now assign the

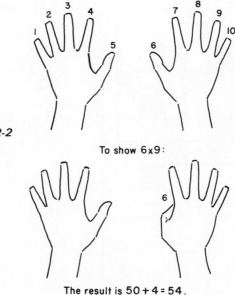

Figure 22-2

To show 6x9:

The result is 50 + 4 = 54.

529

multipliers to the fingers starting with the left-hand pinky as 1 and going across to the right-hand pinky finger, which becomes 10. For example, to multiply 6 × 9, fold under the "6" finger as illustrated and read off the answer by counting the number of fingers to the left of the folded one and to the right of it: The answer is 54. The same can be done for each combination involving 9. This also quickly narrows the number of facts to be learned.

Other practice situations can be devised involving spinners with a broad variety of numbers and operations, magic squares based upon multiplication as well as addition, cross number puzzles, and dodecahedron dice (Fig. 22-3).

The use of machines may also stimulate some students to overcome any

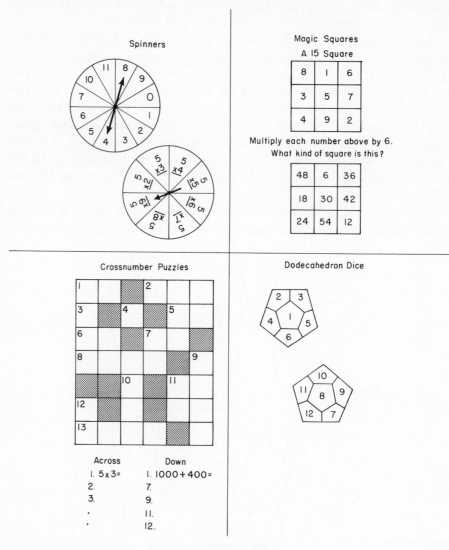

Spinners

Magic Squares

A 15 Square

8	1	6
3	5	7
4	9	2

Multiply each number above by 6.
What kind of square is this?

48	6	36
18	30	42
24	54	12

Crossnumber Puzzles

Dodecahedron Dice

Across	Down
1. 5 x 3 =	1. 1000 + 400 =
2.	7.
3.	9.
·	11.
·	12.

Figure 22-3

fears that they possess about computational skills. Desk calculators and adding machines may be just the thing to prevent learning blocks from interfering with the work at hand. In fact, each youngster may well construct his own computers by making a simple variation of Napier's rods.[6] These can be cut from Oak-tag and kept handy on the desk for frequent use (Fig. 22-4). The construction itself is highly instructional. Of course the ever-present abacus is also a fine student aid.

Sometimes a student at this level refuses to make flash cards or Napier rods because he feels that these activities are too babyish, despite the fact that mastery has not been realized. Have you ever tried to give a seventh grader a mathematics book with fifth grade marked upon it? It is virtually an insult. One nice way around this problem, which offers a helpful activity as well, is to make an arrangement with an elementary school in the area to set up a situation in which the junior high school low achiever is to "tutor" a youngster from the lower grades in helping the latter to learn his basic combinations. In order to prepare for the youngster, the rods or flash cards have to be made; and this is no longer an embarrassing activity since it is for the lower grade youngster! In addition, the simple process of helping someone else in an area

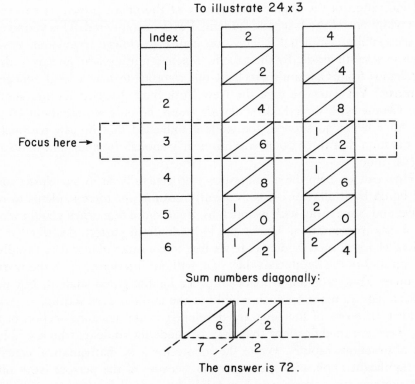

To illustrate 24 x 3

Focus here →

Sum numbers diagonally:

The answer is 72.

Figure 22-4

531

in which you have difficulty is a strongly positive experience that cannot be overestimated in value. A younger brother, sister, cousin, or neighbor can be used at home if arrangements with another school are difficult to complete.

Perhaps the ideas and suggestions presented here will help you to make a beginning with these youngsters. There are numerous other suggestions included in the references at the end of this chapter. There is no short cut that can be taken; there are no cure-alls. A healthy classroom environment, as well as interesting and challenging but "doable" activities, will help you to start youngsters on the long road back.

THE GIFTED

The other end of the ability scale concerns those students who seem to have special talents in mathematics. We could spend a good deal of time trying to carefully identify this child, but perhaps it would be sufficient to say that this is a youngster who generally finishes assigned work quickly or does this work in a way that indicates that he sees a great deal more in what is before him than most students. The nature and kind of class responses he makes give evidence of insightful thinking, and occasional outside projects demonstrate unusual understanding of a given topic. Speed alone, like grades, may not be a good indication of the degree and quality of the talent present. I can recall very vividly one of the brightest students I ever encountered. This young man had successfully completed a television course in college trigonometry when he was in seventh grade. By the time he reached ninth grade, he was studying the calculus from Courant's excellent but rigorous text at a local college on Saturdays.[7] Yet when he took the New York State Regents Examination in Plane Geometry, a three-hour statewide exam, he only scored about 80 percent. After being questioned, the student indicated that he saw so much in each question that three hours was not nearly enough time for him to do anything of value!

How can we help these youngsters who generally sit in our classes somewhat bored by it all, since it is frequently possible for these students to read the text and come away with as much as, if not more than, they could ever get from a class presentation? Under the individualized pattern described in the previous chapter, such students are set free to consume material as rapidly as they can and to the depth that they can, without interfering with the work of the others. That program is made to order for the gifted student. But what provision can we make for such a child in the familiar class setting?

First, in terms of the program developed in the teaching section of this book, there are modifications that may be made for students who are able to learn abstractions rapidly. While the involvement of mathematical concepts with significant applications is important because of the perspective it offers about mathematics, there would certainly be a need for fewer such experiences, as the student works toward the complete abstract formulation. In this way such a student would not only undertake fewer experiments (to cite an example from algebra) but would also require less time, generally, with the concrete aspects of those activities he does explore. In addition, he will probably become involved to a greater depth in the concepts themselves. Special projects or reports may well be one result of this greater in-depth study of the gifted youngster. In this way he is working in the same broad area as the other students, but he is learning a good deal more about the notions at hand. The report or project could take almost any form and might result in a sharing session between the gifted student and the rest of the class, depending, of course, upon the nature of the work he has done.

I once had a bright young man in a class of high school seniors who was fascinated by the conic sections. He went on to invent methods for graphing these second degree curves that were of such interest that he was asked to teach his methods of graphing to the other seniors. Later, he consented to visit intermediate algebra classes to do the same task. His techniques were written up and eventually appeared in The Mathematics Student Journal.[8] Thus, by pursuing his own interest in an area of common study, this student had the satisfaction and recognition that can result only from a personal creation. This is most important. If we are to whet the appetites of the bright youngsters that come to us, they require the freedom to follow through on their ideas and should receive some form of proper recognition for their accomplishments. Teaching the other class members and being published in student journals are two ways to provide recognition.

ENRICHMENT-ACCELERATION

Sometimes we hear the in-depth study of topics described as enrichment experiences. There have been many discussions held trying to determine which was the wiser course of action: enrichment or acceleration. Frequently the words *horizontal* and *vertical* are used as well, horizontal referring to the "enrichment" and vertical to "acceleration." These differences have always led to confusion. It seems like a play upon words without substance. Is there really a difference between the two? It would seem not, because by any yardstick, the point of it all seems to be that students can often learn a good deal more than they are asked to. This something more should be what we feel is most important to learn. Whether we go up or sideways is of little consequence. If given mathematical ideas are significant, that is where we should direct our students. It may well be possible to attempt to expand the horizons of our gifted students by offering them the opportunity to browse through interesting mathematical works and decide for themselves what they would like to study. For one thing, browsing generally makes them aware of all the interesting books there are for those who derive pleasure from mathematics. For another thing, it enables the student to sink his teeth into something of interest to him, rather than something of consequence to the teacher. Moreover, rummaging through a carefully stocked mathematics library gives the student an inkling of the unimaginable size of this entity called mathematics, as well as the many faces of mathematics. This is educational in more ways than one.

Providing the freedom for gifted students to follow their interests is also an educational experience for a teacher. It is amazing to see how much mathematics can be learned by these students in particular, and by most students in general. They can learn a good deal more than we require of them, but not under the usual classroom conditions. When classroom procedures are modified so as to create the environment that has been the goal of this book, our horizons open up and many surprising things happen. Students can learn more and need us a good deal less than we, as teachers, are prepared to admit.

The Dalton Plan, mentioned briefly before, has as one of its characteristics a "contract" arrangement that is made between teacher and student. This "contract" contains information about the kind and amount of work that is going to be completed in a stated amount of time. Although we must exercise care in setting time limits and in maintaining flexibility with regard to this important component, the contract may be an excellent device to use with the gifted student. While the remainder of the class is pursuing its usual work, the gifted student or students are permitted to go off by themselves to complete the work as outlined in the contract. When the work is completed, they are tested. The results are evaluated, and plans for subsequent work are made through joint student-teacher planning. In some cases students stay with their classes and turn to their contract work only when they have first completed the tasks set before the class. These kinds of assignments have been facilitated greatly by the advent of the automated program into school use, whether it be through teaching machines or the more widely used book form. Materials like these enable the student to work with his classmates as usual— the contract work always standing by, to be used as time becomes available.

There are, of course, other alternatives for using the time that accrues to the youngster who can do more. If such a student is permitted to assist those students who are in need of help, he not only reinforces his own knowledge and provides invaluable assistance to the teacher, but he is extending the knowledge of a fellow student, an experience that should be satisfying in and of itself. In addition, the projects and reports mentioned earlier may be the focal point of work done with any spare time.

All these suggestions involve the in-class experience of the student. There are out-of-class activities that may be instrumental in nurturing a gifted youngster's talents. If a check is made of the local colleges and universities, programs may be found for gifted students offered by the school. At the least, an interested professor or college student might be willing to offer such a program. The National Science Foundation sponsors many such offerings. A close tie between high school and college can benefit both institutions, as well

534

as the gifted mathematics student. A taste of the college environment is often all that is needed to turn a bright student who takes his studies rather casually into a serious-minded student of mathematics. This is a source worthy of investigation. The same may be true of local industry. Companies with sizeable computer installations may be quite willing to become a part of some kind of training program for talented high school youngsters. I can recall a situation in which two brilliant young high school students had drawn up plans for the construction of their own computer. The high school science chairman arranged for these boys to present their plan to one of the larger industrial producers of computers. The professional engineers were so surprised at the sophisticated level of the boys' plans that they gave the boys quantities of free parts with which to carry out their construction! Industry is another good source.

The teacher of today's youth has one great advantage as he tries to resolve the problem of making provision for the gifted student; it is the wealth of materials that are available for use today. Locating books, pamphlets, and monographs that will attract the interest of high school students on all levels from seventh grade through twelfth is a much simpler task than it was. Many such references will be listed in the bibliography. One particular publication is worthy of special mention here: the companion two-volume yearbook of the National Council of Teachers of Mathematics, brought out in 1963.[9] These volumes contain an invaluable collection of activities and explorations that would challenge students of any age level. The suggestions for explorations from virtually every branch of mathematics make these books invaluable source material.

As we attempt to extend the learnings of our gifted students, let us exercise one caution: shoving too much work on a student may well overload him to the point where the joy of learning is diminished and the student begins to feel that he is being punished for being bright. All too often teachers of accelerated classes have been heard to say, "Is this the best that an honors group can do?" It is an extremely destructive admonition. The concern about increased pressures upon our students was recently stated in an editorial in Science magazine, which asked, "To what extent is the current student unrest chargeable to the more stringent secondary school curricula?"[10] It is pointed out that too many gifted high school youngsters do poorly in college because they are asked to do "too much, too soon." In our desire to further the education of our gifted let us be careful not to derail the student altogether.

We have considered what might be done for students at opposite ends of the ability spectrum without destroying the class structure as it generally exists throughout schools in the United States today. On the one hand we are trying to rescue and return to the study of mathematics those students who have somehow gone astray. On the other, we are trying to open up possibilities for the unlimited growth potential in learning mathematics that seems to be present. Perhaps some of the suggestions may be of use with that vast group

535

of students that makes up the section between the extremes. In the final analysis, good teaching should reach all our students, regardless of who they are. To label certain practices as *only for gifted* or *only for low achiever* may be a fallacy in and of itself. Perhaps it is really not necessary to make this conjecture at all. Teachers are quick to seize upon good ideas from wherever they may come and then make the necessary adjustments in order to adapt these ideas to their own classes. This is one way to assure continued progress.

FOOTNOTES

1. "Computational Skills Development Kit, Grades 6–9." Science Research Associates, Chicago, Illinois.
2. Allen Bernstein and David Wells. *Trouble Shooting Mathematics Skills*. Holt, Rinehart & Winston, Inc., 1963.
3. For some of the plusses and perils of these tests see "Published Evaluation Materials" by Sheldon S. Myers. *In* National Council of Teachers of Mathematics, 26th Yearbook: *Evaluation in Mathematics*. The National Council of Teachers of Mathematics, 1961, pp. 93–103.
4. National Council of Teachers of Mathematics, *Experiences in Mathematical Discovery*, 1967. There are five independent unit booklets available: "Formulas, Graphs and Patterns"; "Properties of Operations with Numbers"; "Mathematical Sentences"; "Geometry"; "Arrangements and Selections."
5. Robert Rosenthal. "Experimenter Outcome—Orientation and the Results of the Psychological Experiment." *Psychological Bulletin*. Vol. 61 (June, 1964), pp. 405–412.
6. See the pamphlet by Donovan A. Johnson and William H. Glenn: *Computing Devices*. (Exploring Mathematics on Your Own Series), Webster Publishing, 1961, pp. 11–14.
7. Richard Courant. *Differential and Integral Calculus*, Vol. I, Rev. Ed. Wiley-Interscience, 1937.
8. Howard Waddell. "Plotting Parabolas." *The Mathematics Student Journal*. Vol. 9 (January, 1962), pp. 4–5.
9. National Council of Teachers of Mathematics, 27th Yearbook: *Enrichment Mathematics for the Grades*. The National Council of Teachers of Mathematics, 1963; and the 28th Yearbook: *Enrichment Mathematics for the High School*, 1963.
10. Philip H. Abelson. "Excessive Educational Pressures." *Science*. Vol. 156 (May 12, 1967), p. 741.

FOR INVESTIGATION AND DISCUSSION

1. Select a specific algebraic skill (e.g., solve linear equation of form $y = ax + b$, factoring a quadratic trinomial, . . .). List the possible causes for error and for each indicate remedial action that may be taken.

2. Examine a diagnostic mathematics test and inspect each item. Indicate what particular mathematical error is the focal point of each test item. Compare your analysis with that of the test manual, if available.

3. Outline the procedures you would use in teaching low achievers so that the work will satisfy the criteria of being interesting, "doable," and challenging and so that it will provide for student success.

4. Explain the logic behind teaching basic skills by apparently focusing upon everything but these skills (experiments, measuring, elementary algebra concepts, etc.).

5. Teacher expectation, concrete experiences of consequence, success experiences, and varieties of materials are all basic notions to be considered in working with slow learners. Discuss each idea and indicate how it may influence student experiences.

6. Plan a series of experiences designed to help a student in the junior high school master basic multiplication facts.

7. It has often been laughingly said that perhaps the best thing we may do for a talented mathematics student is to "get out of his way." Indicate how one such procedure may be developed in teaching a class of gifted students.

8. Select a particular topic in plane geometry. Plan a lesson in this area for a group of average tenth graders. Indicate how you would modify this plan for low achievers and for talented mathematics students.

9. Search the literature for a plan developed to meet the special needs of the talented mathematics student. Describe the plan and evaluate it in terms of its advantages and disadvantages.

10. It has been stated in the text that the labeling of practices as specifically for the slow learner or specifically for the gifted may be a fallacy. Discuss this notion and explain why you react as you do.

FOR FURTHER READING

The Low Achiever

Books

Allen L. Bernstein and David Wells. *Trouble Shooting Mathematics Skills.* Holt, Rinehart & Winston, Inc., 1963.

Leo J. Brueckner and G. L. Bond. *The Diagnosis and Treatment of Learning Difficulties.* Appleton-Century-Crofts, 1955.

Joe L. Frost and Glenn R. Hawkes (Editors). *The Disadvantaged Child.* Houghton Mifflin Company, 1966.

Donovan Johnson and Gerald R. Rising. *Guidelines for Teaching Mathematics.* Wadsworth Publishing Co. Inc., 1967, Chapter 14.

Max A. Sobel. *Teaching General Mathematics.* Prentice-Hall, Inc., 1967.

Helen F. Storen. *The Disadvantaged Early Adolescent: More Effective Teaching.* McGraw-Hill Book Co., 1968.

Hilda Taba and Deborah Elkins. *Teaching Strategies for the Culturally Disadvantaged.* Rand McNally & Co., 1966.

Staten W. Webster. *Educating the Disadvantaged Learner.* Chandler Publishing Co., 1966.

Lauren G. Woodby (Editor). *The Low Achiever in Mathematics.* Report of Conference. U. S. Office of Education and National Council of Teachers of Mathematics, Bulletin 1965, No. 31, U. S. Department of Health, Education and Welfare, 1965.

Periodicals

Peter Braunfeld and Martin Wolfe. "Fractions for Low Achievers." *The Arithmetic Teacher.* Vol. 13 (December, 1966), pp. 647–655.

Irving Allen Dodes. "Some Comments on General Mathematics." *The Mathematics Teacher.* Vol. 60 (March, 1967), pp. 246–251.

Florence Elder. "Mathematics for the Below-Average Achiever in High School." *The Mathematics Teacher.* Vol. 60 (March, 1967), pp. 235–251.

Herbert Fremont. "Some Thoughts on Teaching Mathematics to Disadvantaged Groups." *The Arithmetic Teacher.* Vol. 11 (May, 1964), pp. 319–322.

Herbert Fremont. "The Student Stockholders." *The Mathematics Teacher*. Vol. 51 (March, 1958), pp. 197–200.

Herbert Fremont and Neal Ehrenberg. "The Hidden Potential of Low Achievers." *The Mathematics Teacher*. Vol. 59 (October, 1966), pp. 551–557.

Sarah Greenholz. "Successful Practices in Teaching Mathematics to Low Achievers in Senior High School." *The Mathematics Teacher*. Vol. 60 (April, 1967), pp. 329–335.

Sarah Greenholz. "What's New in Teaching Slow Learners in Junior High School?" *The Mathematics Teacher*. Vol. 57 (December, 1964), pp. 522–528.

Helen Hammitt. "Evaluating and Reteaching Slow Learners." *The Arithmetic Teacher*. Vol. 14 (January, 1967), pp. 40–41.

Josephine Mold. "Mathematics and Fourth-Year Leavers." *Mathematics Teaching*. (Spring, 1965), pp. 49–51.

Billy J. Paschal. "Teaching the Culturally Disadvantaged Child." *The Arithmetic Teacher*. Vol. 13 (May, 1966), pp. 369–374.

Ramon Ross. "Diagnosis and Correction of Arithmetic Underachievement." *The Arithmetic Teacher*. Vol. 10 (January, 1963), pp. 22–27.

Katherine J. S. Sasse. "Mathematics for the Noncollege-Bound in Junior High School." *The Mathematics Teacher*. Vol. 58 (March, 1958), pp. 232–240.

Jane G. Stenzel. "Math for the Low, Slow, and Fidgety." *The Arithmetic Teacher*. Vol. 15 (January, 1968), pp. 30–34.

The Gifted

Books

Kenneth Brown and Philip Johnson. *Education for the Talented in Mathematics and Science*. Bulletin 1952, No. 2, U. S. Dept. of Health, Education and Welfare, 1953.

Gertrude Hildreth. *Educating Gifted Children*. Harper & Row, Publishers, 1952.

Julius H. Hlavaty. *Mathematics for the Academically Talented Student in the Secondary School*. Report of a conference sponsored by the National Education Association and the National Council of Teachers of Mathematics, The National Education Association, 1959.

Donovan Johnson and Gerald Rising. *Guidelines for Teaching Mathematics*. Wadsworth Publishing Co. Inc., 1967, Chapter 15.

National Council of Teachers of Mathematics, 27th Yearbook: *Enrichment Mathematics for the Grades*. The National Council of Teachers of Mathematics, 1963.

National Council of Teachers of Mathematics, 28th Yearbook: *Enrichment Mathematics for the High School*. The National Council of Teachers of Mathematics, 1963.

E. P. Vance. *Program Provisions for the Mathematically Gifted Student*. National Council of Teachers of Mathematics, 1957.

Periodicals

Jack W. Birch and Maynard C. Reynolds. "The Gifted." *Review of Educational Research*. Vol. 33 (February, 1963), Chapter VI, pp. 83–98.

Donovan Johnson. "Enriching Mathematics Instruction With Creative Activities." *The Mathematics Teacher*. Vol. 55 (April, 1962), pp. 238–242.

Robert D. Larsson. "A Mathematics Enrichment Program for High School Students." *American Mathematical Monthly*. Vol. 70 (November, 1963), pp. 205–206.

Joseph J. Latino. "An Algebra Program for the Bright Ninth Grader." *The Mathematics Teacher*. Vol. 49 (March, 1956), pp. 179–184.

Daniel B. Lloyd. "Ultra-Curricula Stimulation for the Superior Student." *The Mathematics Teacher*. Vol. 46 (November, 1953), pp. 487–489.

L. J. Meconi. "The Mathematically Gifted Student and Discovery Learning." *The Mathematics Teacher*. Vol. 60 (December, 1967), pp. 862–864.

National Association of Secondary School Principals. "Students Talented in Mathematics." *Bulletin of the National Association of Secondary School Principals*. Vol. 43 (May, 1959), Chapter 3, pp. 65–106 (a collection of articles).

23

EVALUATION

How can a teacher tell how effectively the goals of mathematics instruction are being achieved in his classes? How can he determine how well each student is doing in trying to accomplish all the tasks established for a given course? Indeed, how can a teacher provide for continuous improvement and growth in his own ability to succeed as a teacher of mathematics? In attempting to answer these questions, among others, the teacher must make many judgments. He is becoming involved in a process known as evaluation, a vital part of the entire teaching-learning situation.

In the early chapters, a good deal of space was devoted to the establishment of goals for mathematics instruction in general and for given mathematics courses in particular. While these objectives served as a guide for the development of a program of instruction, they also form the basis upon which criteria may be created for judging the outcomes of such instruction. And this is where evaluation must begin: with a clear statement of what is being evaluated and for what purpose. This is the basis upon which teacher judgments will be made. Only when objectives and purposes are clearly in mind, can the question of *how* to gain the desired information (what evaluative techniques and instruments shall be used) be given attention. What can a teacher do to carry out this "judging" activity in as careful and logical a manner as possible? There is a great deal.

TESTING

When teachers think of evaluation, they tend to think of testing and marking. The tests are generally paper and pencil affairs that require the students to solve a number of problems and do a number of examples. These problems and examples reflect the work that has been completed and is now being evaluated. The tests are given to determine just how much the student has been able to accomplish. In addition, it provides the teacher with evidence that will be considered when a student's mark for the grading period, term, or year must be determined. Testing and marking are activities that are fraught with danger. The one quality that should be observed when one carries out these processes is simple humility. You can estimate for yourself the importance of marks to students by carefully observing their actions the next time you return graded test papers. The feelings of elation and depression aside, watch how student interest wanes as soon as he has seen the magical number at the top of his paper and has explored every possible avenue for increasing his score. How many times have you been in a classroom in which a test is returned to students and in the process of "going over" the problems the teacher is heard to repeat, "But John, surely you should pay close attention as we examine problem 5. I believe you had it wrong!" How is it that students show little interest in what is going on? It is quite common to find the class rather noisy when time is devoted to explaining test problems one by one. It seems that once the student sees that number on the top of his paper, he loses all interest in the test. For him the show is over and the rest is anticlimactic. So powerful is the concern with the grade, that once it is known, interest vanishes.

While many deplore this emphasis upon marks, it still exists. Our students gauge themselves by these scores and formulate opinions about their abilities and potential in terms of a given school subject on the basis of them. It is not often that we find a student who says, "Yes, I am doing poorly in math, but I really love it anyway." Quite the opposite is usually the case. We tend to select as our favorites those subjects in which we do well. This may be a stronger cause and effect relationship than the converse: We tend to do well in those subjects we like most.

We can exert an important influence on the feelings of students about marks, but this is a difficult task. For now, let us understand that since grades are of such significance to our students, we must handle marks carefully and with humility. Marks may ultimately influence student career choices. We know that marking is a risky process at best. We are always open to question, but we do our best to be fair with our students. There are very definite ways in which we can reduce our margin of error, however; and we now turn our attention to some of these.

MAKING TESTS

Purpose

The chief evaluation instrument of most teachers is the teacher-made pencil and paper test. While there are many alternatives to these tests, which will be considered shortly, for now, let us focus upon the construction of an effective pencil and paper test. What can you do to enable yourself to make the best of all possible tests? Everything begins with a consideration of what you are trying to accomplish. What are you testing for? Is it mastery of given skills? Is it the ability to solve problems? Is it a test of appreciation? These questions and any others that may apply in a given situation must be clearly answered.

Content

Once our purpose is identified, we turn to the content to be covered. For most of us it is not enough to simply construct questions, exercises, and problems out of our heads with the confidence that all the important concepts and skills will have been included. The few minutes required to list all of our content to be covered results in an invaluable beginning of a plan for the test to be made.

Here is a list of content to be covered made by a teacher who is preparing a test on percent:

1. Convert percent to decimal and common fractions.
2. Convert decimal and common fractions to percent.
3. Solve proportions.
4. Find percent of a number (percentage).
5. Find what percent one number is of another (rate).
6. Given a percentage (base), find the whole.

These skills and concepts will be tested by a number of questions of different types. Some may be straight computation, others may require organization of information first. This brings us to the next step in the process: constructing the questions.

Questions Required

From our topic list we can see that some questions will have to be straight-forward computation questions, while others have to be in verbal problem

Table 23-1. Table of Topics and Types of Questions.

Topic	Type of Question		
	Straight Computation	*Verbal Problem (Familiar)*	*Verbal Problem (New Situation)*
Convert percent	4		
Convert fractions-decimals	4		
Proportion	1	1	1
Find percentage	1	1	1
Find rate	1	1	1
Find base	1	1	1

form. If we construct a table listing the kinds of questions to be constructed for each topic, we can facilitate making decisions about how many questions of what type are needed (Table 23-1). Such a table enables you to be sure that you will include all desired topics and also identifies the number and kind of items required.

Test Items

What of the test items themselves? How shall they be made up? Common sense provides some guidance: Questions should have but one correct response, should fit within the framework of your test plan, and should meet the purposes for which they were created. But what of the level of difficulty? How can we be sure before the students take the test whether or not a given item is too hard or too easy?

One interesting and effective idea is contained in a publication of the Educational Testing Service designed especially for teachers.[1] Although we cannot determine for present use the difficulty of items, over a period of time we can accumulate information to ease the construction of future tests. There must be a trial and error period when student responses are analyzed so that a teacher can build up a collection of items and a reservoir of information about the relative difficulty and effectiveness of each. Not only is the process simpler than could be hoped for, but it is a valuable learning situation for students as well. When a test has been scored and returned, the papers are arranged in order of scores from the lowest to the highest. The pile is then split into two equal halves consisting of the "highs" and the "lows." (This is an approximation method for quick results.) Assign any "middle" papers to each group at random. If there is an odd number of students, hold out the middle paper and do not count it. Distribute the papers to the class so that the right-hand side of the room gets the "high" papers and the left-hand side gets the "low." If one student is left out (the discarded middle paper when the total number of papers is odd), you might make him scorekeeper at the chalkboard. You now tally on the board by a show of hands the number of highs who got an item right, as well as the number of lows. The teacher calls for the show of hands by taking each test item in turn. When all the responses are tallied, the teacher and the students calculate two scores that the Educational Testing Service pamphlet refers to as the *success* score and the *discrimination* score, which are defined as follows:

$$H = \text{the number of highs getting the item right}$$
$$L = \text{the number of lows getting the item right}$$
$$H + L = \textit{success} \text{ (the total number getting the item right)}$$
$$H - L = \textit{discrimination} \text{ or the "high-low difference"}$$

In 10 to 20 minutes you will have completed a close approximation of what is known statistically as an item analysis. Of course, if we use standard

542

procedures to compute this or if we followed the procedures described here without student help, the required time would make the process forbidding. This approximation is quick and easy, and yet it provides good information. At the same time, the students are active participants in the entire process, adding to their understanding of how scores are arrived at and how test items can be judged. They have a better understanding of the entire grading process, as well as of how their performance fits into the overall scheme of things. But of what importance are the calculated results? A rule of thumb is provided in this same pamphlet: Divide the number of students present by 10 and round off to the nearest whole number. If the discrimination score of an item exceeds this number, it has satisfactory discrimination. For example,

> In a class of 32, 11 highs and seven lows got an item right. Hence, the *discrimination* is H − L = 11 − 7 = 4. The rule of thumb says 32 ÷ 10 = 3.2; round off to 3. This item is a good discriminator since it exceeds 3.

What does it mean for an item to be a good discriminator? One of the objectives you should have in constructing questions is to be able to make up items that will be answered correctly by those who know and incorrectly by those who do not know. Obviously a test item is telling you little about the relative achievement of students if everyone answers either correctly or incorrectly. This is not applicable to tests designed for purposes other than mastery of a unit of work and marking. If you were to design a test for the basic multiplication facts, you would have little interest in discrimination, expecting 100 percent mastery of all students. But if you are trying to determine how much has been learned about a particular unit and how well the students compare, the discriminating power of each item to "separate the men from the boys" is an index of how well the item is doing the job for which it was intended. On a single test administration, if an item should fail to discriminate, it should be discarded. However, it may be worth while to examine and possibly test the item again if it looks like a reasonable item. Results with small groups sometimes vary greatly. At any rate, you now have information about the discriminating power of each item. If an index card file is made with each item listed on a separate card, this information can be recorded on the back for reference. For example, if an item given in a test in September, 1968, has a discrimination score of 5, you would write the following on the file card:

Discrimination 5   9/68

But is the item difficult or easy? We have not as yet considered this aspect. The *success* score (H + L) that we computed enables us to make an assessment of this factor. For the sample item we have just considered, the success score was 11 + 7 = 18. If we compute what percent this is of the total class (32), we have a good gauge of the difficulty of the item—in this case about 56 percent.

If we think in terms of 90 percent as indicating items that are too easy and 30 as indicative of items that are too hard, we find 56 percent in an in-between range from which we would like most of the items to come. (This *success* score is sometimes called a "difficulty index.")[2] There is some difference of opinion among experts as to how many items there should be, of what difficulty they should be, and in what order they should appear in a given test. Many believe that you can achieve maximum reliability and dispersion of scores "if every item in the usual sort of multiple-choice test is answered correctly by somewhere between 60% and 70% of the students tested."[3]

Whatever the case, it seems that an arrangement of questions from easier to harder results in narrowing the spread of scores, since once students fail to attempt to answer the last questions, the item-analysis figures are no longer suitable. If he quits and does not reach the question, we cannot say for sure whether a student could have answered a given question or not. One way to avoid this situation might be to cycle questions as to difficulty. For example, if we employed a cycle of three, we have a question, followed by a slightly more difficult question, again followed by a slightly more difficult question. The fourth question returns to the difficulty level of the first, and the three-question cycle begins again. In this way a question that can successfully be answered is present, preventing the frustration level of the student from building to the point where he "drops out" of the test. Generally, a *success* index of 50 to 60 percent is recommended for all items.

The *success* score is also entered on the back of the item card to add to your stored information about it. In this way you have a ready-made file of items, with difficulty index and discriminating index available at a glance. After a few years of operation, you should have at your fingertips a rather large collection of tested items that will greatly facilitate the construction of future examinations.

These scores may also provide the teacher with diagnostic-type information about the class that may well influence future planning. For example, if items had generally low success scores then the question should be examined carefully in order to determine if the area in question should be retaught in class. Of course, a decision would be based upon the cause for the low success score. It may well be that the question itself is poorly constructed.

VALIDITY AND RELIABILITY

The question of whether the tests you construct are reliable and valid are basic questions to be asked of all tests. As a matter of fact, one of the important differences between standardized and teacher-made tests is that the standardized test has undergone procedures designed to evaluate its reliability and validity. This is usually accomplished by using a sample population of students and by studying how closely the test results match student performance on other criteria—grades, other tests, teacher evaluation, and so on. Does your test measure what it is supposed to measure? If it does, it is a valid test. If the students took the test again, would they come out with the same score? If they would, the test is reliable. In this instance reliability refers to consistency. Of course, these questions are seldom answered with yes or no. What we generally try to determine is the degree of validity or the degree of reliability present in the test we have before us. Although the time required and the complication of the computation of these statistics is too burdensome for most teachers, there is a good deal of information available to enable the interested teacher to carry out the calculations.[4]

There are some guidelines that may be used in trying to determine how valid and reliable standardized tests are. These will be considered later. Suffice it here to say that a careful look at the item will help you to determine if it will do its intended job. After discrimination and difficulty indexes are computed, additional information is available to ascertain the item's effectiveness. Continued refinement results in the collection of better and better items. Techniques for computing indexes of validity and reliability will be explored in the discussion of standardized tests.

CONSTRUCTION OF ITEMS

The writing of good test items is a difficult, skillful, creative task. Teachers are often heard to remark about the impossibility of writing objective questions to test some of the more complex mathematics concepts or skills, and they are not far from wrong. But professional test makers have developed many ingenious questions that appear in published examinations. As a consequence, these examinations are an excellent source of questions for the teacher as he approaches the task of making up his own tests. Whether it be to test recall of facts or to demonstrate the use of concepts learned, it is possible, albeit quite difficult, to make up questions that will do the job. There is little need here to enumerate the variety of types of objective questions. Teachers are usually quite familiar with these. There are, however, some simple guidelines that may assist the construction of questions.

It is a good idea to keep the question language simple enough for students to understand; otherwise you will find that you are testing language rather than mathematics. When you have constructed an item, ask yourself if the question may be interpreted in more than one way. If it can, it is in need of revision. Ambiguous statements foul the test purposes. These are the two most important ideas to keep before you as you make up questions. Of course, there are other cautions to be observed, such as avoiding the use of lengthy statements and double negatives and being careful that the information in one question doesn't provide the correct answer to another.

By and large, if you keep out ambiguities and maintain the use of straight-forward language without "tricks" of any kind, you will have the best chance of constructing items that will do as you intend. There are interesting collections of items and evaluative comments available to help you.[5] The use of these, together with the published tests, offers the teacher a rich source of ideas.

The use of teacher time is an important variable in the construction of tests. While an essay test requires much more time when it is being scored than does a short-answer test, the latter requires a good deal more time in the construction phase. With the various techniques that can be used to refine this test, the time question eventually resolves itself in favor of the short answer. In the long run, it may well be worth any additional initial effort. The chief consideration is how you wish to apportion your time.

SCORING

Mathematics teachers frequently assign different weights to the items that make up a given test. This is one reason for the wide disparity of grades given the same paper by different teachers of mathematics. I have often asked teachers in a graduate course to grade the same test paper as though the student were from their class. Even in small groups of 15 to 20 teachers, the range of grades given to the paper is nothing less than shocking. It will frequently exceed 30 points, with scores running from as low as 40 percent to as high as 80 percent. Some of the variation in this situation can be accounted for by the different weights teachers assign to the examples. It would seem that if test items could be constructed of equal weight, a big step would be taken toward making the teacher-made test more objective.

Objective or subjective as applied to tests is often misunderstood. It does not refer to the appearance of the test items—multiple choice as opposed to essay—but rather it is a function of the scoring process. If all people who score the test give it the same mark, the test is high in objectivity. If, on the other hand, the marking of the paper varies with the teacher doing the scoring, then that particular test is of a subjective nature. The New York State Regents Examinations are a good example of tests that are becoming more objective. The tests are scored by the local teachers and then checked by the appropriate state official. Frequently there is a disparity in the two grades. Lately, however, those constructing the tests have been creating items that are more objective, hence, most teachers will score the papers in the same way and arrive at virtually the same grade. If teachers would construct items that bear equal weights and contain only one correct response, they too would move in the direction of creating more objective tests. Essay questions may also fit this definition of objective, provided that an ideal response may be constructed with which all papers may be compared. If this results in consistency of scoring regardless of who the rater is, then we may call the essay test an objective one.

SUMMARY

We have considered teacher-tests, their construction and use. There are definite simple procedures that will help teachers to improve the effectiveness of their testing program and ease the burden of this evaluation technique. Let us now focus upon other ways to assess student behavior and teacher effectiveness. '

OTHER EVALUATION TECHNIQUES

All our attention, thus far, has been devoted to the use of pencil and paper tests. In addition to these, there are other evaluation activities open to teachers.

OBSERVATION

In a paper on evaluation, Dr. Marvin Taylor makes the point that tests are not the most widely used evaluation technique.[6] He claims that observation is probably more common. There is much to support this point. In the daily work with students, teachers are constantly acting and reacting to what is happening among their students. In fact, one of the important qualities of the successful teacher is his sensitivity to what is happening to students as the work develops. Observation is indeed a primary evaluation tool. Taylor goes on to explain that teacher observation may be assisted by making use of check lists. There are published check lists available that will enable us to accumulate valuable information about a student's behavior.[7] In addition, these check lists also minimize our tendency to allow our personal involvement to influence our observations. Thus, the information gathered may be more accurate and certainly more fair.

INTERVIEW

Disruptive behavior, lack of success, and disinterest are all common partners of the learning process in school classrooms. The interview is one of the ways in which teachers can gain important information in trying to help youngsters. It is sometimes surprising how the genuine concern of the teacher for a student as expressed in a personal interview often may be a step in the right direction for a student in trouble. There is a marked difference in the tone of an after-school interview when a student is told to "stay after school" as a means of punishment and when a student is asked to meet with a teacher after school because the teacher is concerned about apparent student diffi-

547

culties. It may well be that several brief interviews will be necessary before a student will "open up," since we cannot force him into providing information or accepting us as a helping agent.

CUMULATIVE RECORD

One of the first places to look when students are experiencing failure is the cumulative record. It is a source of constant surprise to see how many students in junior and senior high schools are working with the disadvantage of an undetected physical defect. Despite all the usual school examinations and precautions, we still find health difficulties that have remained hidden. Poor eyesight, faulty hearing, or other handicaps may well reduce the student's effectiveness in school to the danger point; and time does not seem to make a difference. The student may have been in the school for years, but somehow his medical difficulty has never been detected. Be sure that those of your students who are not achieving are not bearing the burden of some physical problem.

SOCIOGRAM

Sometimes social problems may be at the root of student difficulties. An effective, but somewhat time-consuming, device to use in this area is the sociogram.[8] The students are asked to indicate on paper or an index card the three members of the class they would most like to work with for some purpose that is germane to the work of the class. (The class will be divided into small work groups for skill work, project work, or other such activity.) The diagram and charts that result from organizing the data collected are called sociograms. They show the students' choices, as well as whether the selection was a first, second, or third choice (Fig. 23-1). These charts give the teacher quick information about the popularity of students, the isolated students, and any class cliques. Of course, the information must be used with wisdom, but the acceptance of one student for another is an important factor in the conduct of the class. The total rejection of a youngster by his classmates may well be as responsible for a lack of success in school as is partial eyesight.

QUESTIONNAIRES, RATING SCALES, AND INTEREST INVENTORIES

Questionnaires, rating scales, and interest inventories may assist the teacher in appraising factors like attitude towards mathematics, aspiration levels, and personal interests; and in general they may add information to the

SOCIOGRAMS

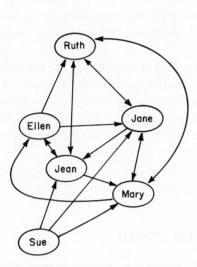 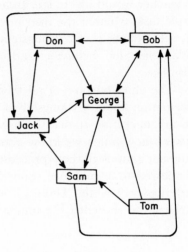

These Students Chose:	R u t h	E l l e n	J e a n	S u e	J a n e	M a r y		D o n	J a c k	S a m	G e o r g e	T o m	B o b
Ruth	╳		1		2	3							
Ellen	1	╳	2		3								
Jean	2	1	╳			3							
Sue			1	╳	3	2							
Jane	3		1		╳	2							
Mary	2	3			1	╳							
Don								╳	3		1		2
Jack								1	╳	2	3		
Sam									3	╳	2		1
George									2	1	╳		3
Tom										1	2	╳	3
Bob								2	1		3		╳

Figure 23-1

total picture of the child. These devices, more than any of the others, must be used carefully. All too often the students respond to the questions or statements on an attitude scale in the way they think the teacher would like them to respond. It is also possible for the reverse to be true; that is, students may conceal their feelings and perhaps offer as responses the opposite of what they feel the teacher would like to see. In addition, interpreting the data gathered is no simple task, whether the instrument be published or teacher-made. But clues can accumulate about youngsters that may in the long run add up to some explanation for behavior and offer a possible beginning for providing assistance.

The chief purpose of all these evaluation techniques is the collection of information about a youngster to round out the total picture we have of him. We are operating under the assumption that there is a direct relationship between how much we know about a youngster and our ability to help him. If the net gain of all these procedures is the realization that the student should be referred to a guidance counselor, or physician, then this too would have made it worth while. There is one additional area of valuable assistance for teachers and students: the standardized tests.

STANDARDIZED TESTS

A standardized test differs from the teacher-made counterpart in many ways. To begin with, published tests are usually constructed so that administration and scoring of the test are done in accordance with very specific instructions. To offer some sense of the thoroughness of the process by which the test is created, the National Council of Teachers of Mathematics yearbook on evaluation states that

> a good published test is usually the result of highly scientific construction involving advanced pretesting on appropriate populations; item analyses for discrimination and difficulty; extensive review and editing to produce terse, unambiguous phrasing; and meticulous scrutiny by mathematicians for soundness and national curricular appropriateness.[9]

Add to this the creative talents and experience of the test maker and you begin to get a notion of what is involved. In the yearbook just mentioned it is estimated that one form of a 40-minute standardized test would cost from $5000 to $10,000 to construct. Perhaps we should be a bit more careful about how quick we are to disparage the results of this type of examination. It is a rather startling paradox to find that the same teacher who belittles the effectiveness of a standardized test is somehow firmly convinced of the infallibility of a score on a test of his own. Surely a comparison of the efforts that go into the construction of each would give some indication of their relative merit!

Published tests are generally of three basic types: diagnostic, ability or aptitude, and achievement. Sometimes it is difficult to tell one from another because the content of the tests seems similar. Carefully reading the test manual (most standardized tests have an accompanying manual that contains statistical and informational data about the test and its construction), as well as examining the questions, would help in finding out just what type of test is at hand.

Standard Error

Despite the careful development of these examinations, the results must be used with great care. This is an area in which teachers have often made serious mistakes. It is only natural to want a specific number to use as a description of the achievement level or ability level of a student. How convenient it is to say that a particular student is operating at a 6.3 grade level! It truly has the ring of finality about it. Unfortunately (or perhaps fortunately), no test has yet been constructed that offers such accurate labels.

If we were to be interested in the *true score* of the child on a given achievement test, we must seek out the *standard error of the test scores*. There are a number of different standard errors that are reported in the manual, e.g., standard error of test scores, of averages, and of differences. We are now concerned with the standard error of test scores. Let us take a case in point:

> John takes an algebra achievement test. He gets 33 of 50 items correct. Bob gets 40 items correct. The standard error of the scores is 4.

What do the results show? Evidently Bob is much higher in achievement than John. He has scored seven points higher on a 50-item test; that is a considerable difference. If this were a teacher-made test and if percents were used, John would get 66 percent whereas Bob would score 80 percent. The difference is substantial, but let us look at the standard error. It tells us that John's true score lies anywhere from 29 to 37—four points above and below his test score. In fact, it tells us even more: It says that of all the possible questions available to test achievement in this area, if we continued to select samples of 50 and retest John over and over, he would score between 29 and 37 two out of three times. What's more, if we were to use two standard errors (eight points), John would score between 25 and 41 on the repeated tests 95 out of 100 times! Thus one standard error would place John's true score from 29 to 37.

Some standardized tests report scores as a band rather than as a specific number of points in order to call attention to the importance of this standard error. If we look at Bob's score and the standard error, we see that his true score is in the band from 36 to 44 (Fig. 23-2). Since his band and that of John overlap, it is recommended that teachers do not regard the scores of these

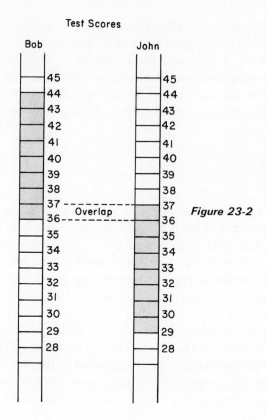

Test Scores

Bob   John

Bob		John
45		45
44		44
43		43
42		42
41		41
40		40
39		39
38		38
37	Overlap	37
36		36
35		35
34		34
33		33
32		32
31		31
30		30
29		29
28		28

Figure 23-2

boys as "really different." [10] This is true despite the large difference in percent scores!

To be clear about the implications of this we must fully understand the standard error. The only error being referred to is that of sampling—the items chosen for the test. Would the student get the same score if 50 different questions were asked about the same subject? This is the only error considered in reporting scores as a band and in discouraging attaching any importance to the difference between these two boys despite a difference of seven questions out of 50 answered correctly. We have completely ignored errors that may be introduced by bias in item selection, mistakes in scoring, the effect of weather, personal problems, and attitudes. It is rather sad to observe how some test scores have the status of a brand upon a student, especially in light of all these possible error factors. Once again we find that humility becomes an important factor in the use of these standardized test scores. When it comes to teacher-made tests, infinite wisdom is required!

One thing that enables us to use the scores of our tests to determine student success with our course is the fact that over the period of a year we administer many tests to the students. Thus, we happily do not have to rely upon a single measure. Generally, a student who is superior will consistently score

Table 23-2. Estimated Standard Error of Test Scores.*

| | | Regardless of Test Length | |
Number of Items	Standard Error	When the Score Is:	Standard Error Is:
< 24	2	0 or perfect	0
24–47	3	1 or 2 points from	
48–89	4	0 or 100%	1
90–109	5	3 to 7 points from	
110–129	6	0 or 100%	2
130–150	7	8 to 15 points from	
		0 or 100%	3

*Modified from *Short-Cut Statistics for Teacher-Made Tests,* Ed. 2. Educational Testing Service, 1964, p. 16.

higher over the year so that we are in better position to make a judgment than we would be with a single such score. If you would like to get a quick estimate of the standard error of the test scores for your own tests, you may want to use Table 23-2.

Validity-Reliability

Earlier we had considered two all-important criteria that should be applied to any test: validity (does the test measure what it is supposed to) and reliability (if a student takes the test again will he get the same score). Standardized tests are generally carefully checked for these two characteristics.

Validity is usually determined by checking against some other criterion, a criterion always open to question. Sometimes grades in the subject may be used. At other times aptitude or ability scores may form the basis for comparison. The concept of correlation is employed in order to arrive at a coefficient of validity. Thus, if the scores on the achievement test in question seem to reflect the order of the students with respect to grades, we may find the coefficient of validity to be around 0.50. If there was no relationship at all, the coefficient would be about 0.00. If those who scored high on the achievement test scored low in grades, and vice versa, the validity coefficient might turn up at −0.50. For a rule of thumb, validity coefficients that are considered satisfactory will run from about 0.40 to 0.65. It is also common to find that validity has been determined by referring the test questions to a jury of experts who examine the questions and render an opinion as to whether or not the items appear to test that which is intended. This is called *face* or *content validity* and is often used in addition to the correlation validity procedures described previously.

Reliability is concerned with the consistency of the test. Since it is easier to make a consistent test than a valid one, reliability coefficients are expected to be higher than those of validity. Most standardized test makers are not satisfied with reliabilities that are less than 0.90. Teacher-made tests may be expected to demonstrate reliability coefficients between 0.60 and 0.80. Earlier it was indicated that continued testing provides the stability required to use the test scores as indications of comparative achievement. Because of this you can increase reliability scores as you might expect simply by increasing the number of items. Once again we find that it is necessary to look beyond the statistics. A widely used formula for computing the reliability coefficient is the Kuder-Richardson Formula 21:

$$\text{reliability} = 1 - \frac{M\,(n - M)}{n\,s^2}$$

where M is the mean, n is the number of *items,* and s is the standard deviation.[11] The Educational Testing Service publication contains a table that will quickly provide approximate reliabilities.[12] This may prove a handy guide for your tests.

Marking

All of these various statistical techniques of analysis that are applied to standardized tests point up the need for the intelligent use of test results. You have seen the questions that may be asked of tests carefully standardized by experts. Were you to take the time required to approach your problems of test construction in the way that these professionals have faced the task of test making, you would improve your tests greatly, but they would probably not compare to those of experts. Hence, it seems that your tests are open to even greater question. Of course, over the period of a year you will have provided students with so many questions that they will tend to separate themselves in terms of achievement, but this is not an automatic process. It will result only from your conscientious and tireless efforts and your use of those techniques that can assist you. For example, should your test reliability fall well below 0.60, perhaps you are better off not counting the test at all. Are you prepared to eliminate it? You should be. Yet without computing the statistic, you might never be aware of the poor quality of the test.

As for figuring out marks, while teachers use classwork as a criterion, marks are dependent to a great extent upon test scores—the same test scores that we see vary greatly when different teachers score the same paper, the same test scores that are open to the serious questions just discussed: reliability, validity, standard errors, and other influences. Nevertheless, many teachers still say that they will be completely objective and average test scores and that that shall be the student's mark! Have all these other contaminating forces been considered? It is to be hoped so. The very averaging process itself is open to question. Although it may seem somewhat presumptuous in a book for mathematics teachers, let us briefly look at this example:

John takes 3 tests:

Test 1	10 items	8 correct	80%
Test 2	5 items	1 correct	20%
Test 3	15 items	12 correct	80%

What is John's average? It seems simple enough to find out:

$$
\begin{array}{r}
80 \\
20 \\
80 \\
\hline
180
\end{array}
\qquad
\begin{array}{r}
60 \\
\hline
3)\overline{180}
\end{array}
$$

His average is 60 percent.

Do you agree with this? I hope not, since it is incorrect. This student was tested on 30 items of which he got 21 correct. We therefore compute his average as follows:

$$21 \text{ out of } 30$$

$$\frac{21}{30} = \frac{7}{10}$$

His average is 70 percent.

In this one simple case we have a 10 percent discrepancy in average. Is it necessary to once again call for humility in marking?

Marks are all important to our students. Sometimes we feel they concentrate upon marks too much. It seems that they are working for the mark rather than learning, which is, after all, what school is supposed to be about. I wonder what would happen to students and teachers alike (and parents?) if all marks were suddenly banished from schools? What a beautiful thought to contemplate! Walter Mitty will forgive us. Until the day arrives when we can manage to get marks out of our way, let us make the best possible use of them. Let us put them to work for us. We know students respond better to reward than to failure; so let us be generous with marks to a fault. The notion that a student tries harder if you grade him down would seem to contradict everything psychologists would have us believe about motivation. Nothing succeeds like success. If marks are an indication of success, let's use them to advantage. One thing is sure: We will receive few complaints from parents if we grade on the high side. Since the process is a stab in the dark at best, give all students the benefit of the doubt. This is the best way to minimize unwanted side effects of marks. Perhaps then the satisfaction of achievement will center on what has been learned, rather than on some number or letter on a piece of paper.

FOOTNOTES

1. *Short-Cut Statistics for Teacher-Made Tests,* Ed. 2. Pamphlet No. 5, Evaluation and Advisory Service, Educational Testing Service, 1964, pp. 6–12.

2. Jack C. Merwin. "Constructing Achievement Tests and Interpreting Scores." *In* National Council of Teachers of Mathematics, 26th Yearbook: *Evaluation in Mathematics.* The National Council of Teachers of Mathematics, 1961, pp. 61–65.

3. *Short-Cut Statistics for Teacher-Made Tests,* Ed. 2. Pamphlet No. 5, Evaluation and Advisory Service, Educational Testing Service, 1964, p. 10.

4. *Short-Cut Statistics for Teacher-Made Tests,* Ed. 2. Pamphlet No. 5, Evaluation and Advisory Service, Educational Testing Service, 1964, pp. 30–37; and also see "Constructing Achievement Tests and Interpreting Scores" by Jack C. Merwin. *In* National Council of Teachers of Mathematics, 26th Yearbook: *Evaluation in Mathematics.* The National Council of Teachers of Mathematics, 1961, pp. 66–68.

5. See the following:

   Jack C. Merwin. "Constructing Achievement Tests and Interpreting Scores." *In* National Council of Teachers of Mathematics, 26th Yearbook: *Evaluation in Mathematics.* The National Council of Teachers of Mathematics, 1961, pp. 47–51.

   "The Evaluation of Mathematical Learning." *In* Part 5, National Council of Teachers of Mathematics, 22nd Yearbook: *Emerging Practices in Mathematics Education.* The National Council of Teachers of Mathematics, 1954, pp. 339–409.

   Making the Classroom Test. Pamphlet No. 4, Evaluation and Advisory Service, Educational Testing Service, 1959, pp. 17–23.

6. Marvin Taylor. *The Process of Evaluation.* Unpublished, Queens College of The City University of New York, 1966, p. 2.

7. Donald M. Medley and Harold E. Mitzel. "Measuring Classroom Behavior by Systematic Observation." *In* N. L. Gage (Editor): *Handbook of Research on Teaching.* Rand McNally & Co., 1963, pp. 247–328.

8. Helen Hall Jennings. *Sociometry in Group Relations,* Ed. 2. American Council on Education, 1959.

9. Sheldon S. Meyers. "Publishing Evaluation Materials." *In* National Council of Teachers of Mathematics, 26th Yearbook: *Evaluation in Mathematics.* The National Council of Teachers of Mathematics, 1961, p. 98.

10. *Short-Cut Statistics for Teacher-Made Tests,* Ed. 2. Pamphlet No. 5, Evaluation and Advisory Service, Educational Testing Service, 1964, p. 16.

11. For a quick method of calculating the standard deviation see *Short-Cut Statistics for Teacher-Made Tests,* Ed. 2. Pamphlet No. 5, Evaluation and Advisory Service, Educational Testing Service, 1964, p. 23.

12. *Short-Cut Statistics for Teacher-Made Tests,* Ed. 2. Pamphlet No. 5, Evaluation and Advisory Service, Educational Testing Service, 1964, p. 31.

For Investigation and Discussion

1. List factors that complicate the task of testing and marking. Discuss the implications of each factor for evaluation procedures.

2. Make up a pencil and paper objective test on the topic of ratio and proportion. Carry out the steps indicated in the text: identify purpose clearly, list all content to be tested, construct a table of topics and question types, and construct suitable items.

3. Describe procedures you might use to test the validity and reliability of the test you constructed for problem 2.

4. Describe evaluation procedures used by teachers other than pencil and paper tests. Explain each procedure, its purpose, and its use.

5. Your class is going to be divided into small groups in order to work on a variety of topics otherwise impossible to explore as a single group. Arrange this grouping using the sociometric device known as a sociogram. (Use a sample class of students or your own methods class.)

6. Explain the major differences that exist between teacher-made and standardized tests.

7. In the text the statement is made that although two students' scores on a standardized achievement test may differ by seven items (out of a total of 50 items), the "true ability" of the students may be equal. How is this possible?

8. Select a standardized achievement test in mathematics. (See listing in the National Council of Teachers of Mathematics, 26th Yearbook: *Evaluation in Mathematics.*) Secure a copy of the test and test manual. Describe and interpret the test validity, test reliability, and standard error of the test scores.

FOR FURTHER READING

Books

Charles H. Butler and F. Lynwood Wren. *The Teaching of Secondary Mathematics,* Ed. 4. McGraw-Hill Book Co., 1965, Chapter 8.

William D. Hedges. *Testing and Evaluation for the Sciences.* Wadsworth Publishing Co. Inc., 1966.

Donovan A. Johnson and Gerald R. Rising. *Guidelines For Teaching Mathematics.* Wadsworth Publishing Co. Inc., 1967, Chapters 23, 25.

Sheldon S. Myers. *Mathematics Tests Available in the United States.* The National Council of Teachers of Mathematics, 1959.

National Council of Teachers of Mathematics, 22nd Yearbook: *Emerging Practices in Mathematics Education,* The National Council of Teachers of Mathematics, 1954, Part 5.

National Council of Teachers of Mathematics, 26th Yearbook: *Evaluation in Mathematics,* The National Council of Teachers of Mathematics, 1961.

Edward A. Townsend and Paul J. Burke. *Statistics for the Classroom Teacher: A Self-Teaching Unit.* The Macmillan Company, 1963.

Periodicals

Marian C. Cliffe. "The Place of Evaluation in the Secondary School Program." *The Mathematics Teacher.* Vol. 49 (April, 1956), pp. 270–273.

Marion Epstein and Sheldon Meyers. "How a Mathematics Test is Born." *The Mathematics Teacher.* Vol. 51 (April, 1958), pp. 299–302.

Roland F. Gray. "An Approach to Evaluating Arithmetic Understandings." *The Arithmetic Teacher.* Vol. 13 (March, 1966), pp. 187–191.

Peter K. Gurau. "A Time For Testing." *The Mathematics Teacher.* Vol. 60 (February, 1967), pp. 133–136.

John K. Kinsella. "Evaluation of Student Learning in Secondary School." *Bulletin of The National Association of Secondary School Principals.* Vol. 43 (May, 1959), pp. 125–128.

Jack C. Merwin and Martin J. Higgins. "Assessing the Progress of Education in Mathematics." *The Mathematics Teacher.* Vol. 61 (February, 1968), pp. 130–135.

Joseph N. Payne. "Giving the Student a Part in His Evaluation." *The Mathematics Teacher.* Vol. 50 (January, 1957), pp. 77–78.

H. Taba and E. I. Swain. "A Proposed Model in Evaluation." *Educational Leadership.* Vol. 20 (October, 1962), pp. 57–71.

Pamphlets

Educational Testing Service. Evaluation and Advisory Service Series:
No. 1: *Locating Information on Educational Measurement: Sources and References.*
No. 3: *Selecting an Achievement Test: Principles and Procedures.*
No. 4: *Making the Classroom Test: A Guide for Teachers.*
No. 5: *Short-Cut Statistics for Teacher-Made Tests.*

557

24

EPILOGUE

We have come a long way. Indeed, after some 23 chapters of text, it would seem that everything of importance that had to be written was written; and this is probably the case. But perhaps there are some simple ideas that may be briefly mentioned—the kind of ideas that often elude us because of their simplicity.

For example, have fun in your mathematics classes. Make it an enjoyable place to be for both yourself and your students. We have seen the fruits of the "if-its-hard-its-good" kind of approach in the fact that so many people in our society have a deathly fear of numbers in any form. As you organize the work of your classes, maybe you should ask yourself if you are building in enough opportunities for purposeful enjoyment. There was a time when amateurs worked with mathematics strictly for the pleasure it brought them. Are we too serious about the work that goes on in mathematics classes today?

In addition, don't fuss if students misuse words or if their statements are not models of logical clarity. Try to keep in mind that teachers do business in ideas and that words and symbols are merely tools for the communication of the ideas. They are not the end product in itself. If students have some difficulty, work with what they mean instead of what they may say. We lose so many creative thoughts because the way in which students may present these is faulty. This is not their loss alone. Often we lose the student for mathematics altogether. How many times have you seen the push of a teacher for a correct statement drive an original thought from the mind of a child, with the result that the student begins to feel that what he does know is incorrect?

Finally when we feel excited about what is happening in the mathematics class, when we feel that the mathematics consideration of the moment is a most stimulating one, we should let this be reflected in our actions in the room. How catching is genuine enthusiasm! What better way to create excitement and joy about mathematics than to exhibit just these reactions as we work with our students?

Being a teacher is about the most important job you can do in our society. You will carry out all your work with the world's most precious possession: its young people. On top of that, when teaching is done in the field of mathematics, the importance is multiplied tenfold, for mathematics is itself one of man's finest creations. It is living proof of some of the wonderful things that can come from the mind of humans, as well as a most influential force in twentieth century society. In a world in which work of significance is difficult to find, those who decide to teach mathematics are to be envied. How proud they must be!

It has been the purpose of this book to help those who make mathematics teaching their career to function a little better, with an eye toward greater satisfaction for both teacher and student. If the ideas presented seem to be almost prescriptive in nature, it is not because of a desire for imitation. On the contrary, the ideas were presented in specific fashion in order to make them crystal clear to the reader. Once goals have been clarified, it is hoped that teachers will glean from the ideas enclosed here the desire to move out on their own and create more challenging and meaningful experiences for students than have found their way between these covers. In this, and in all else you may do as a teacher of mathematics, I bid you good luck!

APPENDIX*

Proof of the theorem indicating that all light rays emanating from the focus of a parabola are reflected out parallel to the axis of the parabola and each other:

The Plan

Any ray that is reflected from the focus to the parabola and out and that is parallel to the axis of the parabola will, in fact, satisfy the reflection law (angle of incidence = angle of reflection), thereby indicating that it is a light ray from the focus.

To demonstrate that these angles are indeed equal, we will show that the path from the focus to the parabola to a point on the parallel ray is the shortest such distance. Thus, we will use the converse of Heron's theorem:

> If two rays from a point A to a mirror to a second point, B, form the shortest such path, then $\angle 1 = \angle 2$ (Fig. 1).

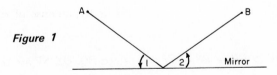

Figure 1

Preliminary (See Fig. 2)

FP strikes the tangent to the parabola at P. PV, the reflected ray, is a line through P parallel to the axis of the parabola. (V is any point on the ray.)

$FP + PV$ is the distance from the focus, F, to the tangent at P and from there to V. Let Q be any other point on the tangent. If we can establish that

$$FP + PV < FQ + QV$$

the converse of Heron's theorem enables us to conclude $\angle 1 = \angle 2$.

---

*See Chapter 19, page 443.

561

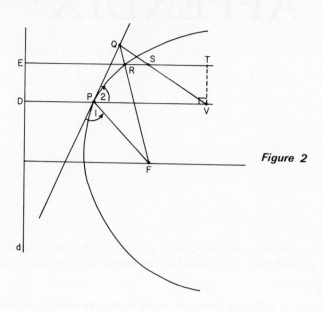

Figure 2

The Proof

The point at which FQ intersects the parabola will be called R. Draw ER through R parallel to the axis of the parabola. Let T be the point on ER at which the perpendicular from V meets ER.

(1) $FQ + QV = FR + RQ + QS + SV$

but

$\qquad RQ + QS > RS$ $\qquad\qquad$ Two sides of triangle greater than third.

and

$\qquad SV > ST$ $\qquad\qquad\qquad$ SV is hypotenuse of right triangle SVT.

Therefore

$\qquad FQ + QV > FR + RS + ST$ $\qquad$ since $RQ,\ QS,\ SV$ are replaced by smaller quantities

And since $\quad RS + ST = RT$

Then $\qquad FQ + QV > FR + RT$

Because R is a point on the parabola, $FR = RE$ (definition). Therefore

(2) $FQ + QV > RE + RT = ET$

Consider $FP + PV$. Since P is a point on the parabola, $FP = PD$. Therefore

(3) $FP + PV = PD + PV = DV$

$ET = DV$ They are perpendicular distances between parallel lines.

Thus the right-hand sides of statements (2) and (3) are equal, and

$$FQ + QV > FP + PV$$

Since P is the point on the tangent for which $FP + PV$ is shortest, using the converse of Heron's theorem, we have $\angle 1 = \angle 2$.

INDEX

565

Index

566

Index

Index